SMT359
Science: Level 3

# Electromagnetism

## Book 1

# An introduction to Maxwell's equations

John Bolton

## SMT359 Course Team

**Course Team Chair**
Stuart Freake

**Academic Editors**
John Bolton, Nicholas Braithwaite, Stuart Freake, Tom Smith

**Authors**
John Bolton, Nicholas Braithwaite, Stuart Freake, Bob Lambourne, Tom Smith, Mike Thorpe

**Consultants**
Derek Capper, Andrew Coates, Andrew Conway, Alan Durrant, Allister Forrest, David Grimes, Ian Halliday, Craig McFarlane, Robin Preston, Gillian Stansfield, Steve Swithenby, Stan Zochowski

**Course Manager**
Michael Watkins

**Course Team Assistant**
Tracey Woodcraft

**LTS, Project Manager**
Rafael Hidalgo

**Editors**
Peter Twomey, Alison Cadle, Rebecca Graham

**TeX Specialist**
Jonathan Fine

**Graphic Design Advisors**
Mandy Anton, Sarah Hofton

**Graphic Artists**
Roger Courthold, Steve Best, Sarah Hack

**Picture Researchers/Copyrights**
Lydia Eaton, Martin Keeling

**Software Designers**
Fiona Thomson, Will Rawes

**Video Producers**
Owen Horn, Martin Chiverton

**External Assessor**
Don Davis (University College, London)

This publication forms part of an Open University course SMT359 Electromagnetism. The complete list of texts which make up this course can be found at the back. Details of this and other Open University courses can be obtained from the Student Registration and Enquiry Service, The Open University, PO Box 197, Milton Keynes, MK7 6BJ, United Kingdom: tel. +44 (0)870 333 4340, email general-enquiries@open.ac.uk

Alternatively, you may visit the Open University website at http://www.open.ac.uk where you can learn more about the wide range of courses and packs offered at all levels by The Open University.

To purchase a selection of Open University course materials visit http://www.ouw.co.uk or contact Open University Worldwide, Michael Young Building, Walton Hall, Milton Keynes MK7 6AA, United Kingdom for a brochure. tel. +44 (0)1908 858785; fax +44 (0)1908 858787; email ouwenq@open.ac.uk

The Open University
Walton Hall, Milton Keynes
MK7 6AA



Edited and designed by The Open University.

Typeset at The Open University.

Printed in the United Kingdom by Latimer Trend and Company Ltd, Plymouth.

ISBN 0 7492 6985 5

**1.1**

# AN INTRODUCTION TO MAXWELL'S EQUATIONS


## Introduction 7

The founders of electromagnetism 7
Why study electromagnetism? 8
How to study this book 11

## Part I: The physics of electromagnetism 12

### Chapter 1 Electric forces and fields 12

1.1 Electric charge 12
1.2 Electromagnetic forces 14
1.3 Electric and magnetic forces 16
1.4 Coulomb's law 17
1.4.1 Adding electrostatic forces 20
1.4.2 Evidence for Coulomb's law 23
1.4.3 Limitations of Coulomb's law 24
1.5 Electric fields 25
1.5.1 Arrow maps and field lines 28
1.5.2 Symmetry arguments 30
1.5.3 Typical electric field values 33

### Chapter 2 Gauss's law 37

2.1 Charge density and electric flux 37
2.2 The road to Gauss's law 40
2.3 Putting Gauss's law to use 47
2.3.1 Spherical symmetry 48
2.3.2 Cylindrical symmetry 51
2.3.3 Planar symmetry 53
2.4 The differential version of Gauss's law 55

### Chapter 3 Magnetic forces and fields 61

3.1 Current and current density 62
3.2 The Biot–Savart force law 65
3.3 Magnetic fields due to steady currents 70
3.3.1 Splitting the Biot–Savart force law 70
3.3.2 Visualizing magnetic fields 73

| | | |
|---|---|---|
| 3.3.3 | Typical magnetic field values | 77 |
| 3.4 | The Lorentz force law | 79 |
| 3.5 | Afterword on Newton's third law | 84 |
| **Chapter 4** | **Ampère's law** | **87** |
| 4.1 | The no-monopole law | 87 |
| 4.2 | Ampère's law | 91 |
| 4.3 | Putting Ampère's law to use | 97 |
| 4.3.1 | Cylinders and tubes | 97 |
| 4.3.2 | The reflection of electric and magnetic fields | 100 |
| 4.3.3 | Solenoids and toroidal solenoids | 106 |
| 4.3.4 | A hidden consequence of Ampère's law | 109 |
| 4.4 | The differential version of Ampère's law | 110 |
| **Chapter 5** | **Electrostatic potential** | **114** |
| Introduction | | 114 |
| 5.1 | Electrostatic fields are conservative | 116 |
| 5.1.1 | Shielding in a cavity | 120 |
| 5.2 | The electrostatic potential | 122 |
| 5.2.1 | Introducing the electrostatic potential | 122 |
| 5.2.2 | The conservation of energy | 124 |
| 5.2.3 | Recovering the electrostatic field | 125 |
| 5.3 | Adding electrostatic potentials | 126 |
| 5.4 | Potential on conductors and capacitors | 131 |
| 5.4.1 | Capacitance | 133 |
| 5.4.2 | Energy in fields | 135 |
| **Chapter 6** | **Electromagnetic induction** | **138** |
| Introduction | | 138 |
| 6.1 | Current flow in circuits | 140 |
| 6.1.1 | Non-conservative electric fields | 140 |
| 6.1.2 | Voltage drop and emf | 141 |
| 6.1.3 | Ohm's law | 145 |
| 6.2 | Induction in a stationary circuit | 146 |
| 6.2.1 | Faraday's law | 146 |
| 6.2.2 | The sign in Faraday's law | 151 |
| 6.2.3 | Electromagnetic induction in action | 152 |

6.3 The differential version of Faraday's law 154
6.4 Induction in a moving circuit 157
6.4.1 Faraday's law extended to moving circuits 161
6.4.2 Einstein's radical solution 163

Chapter 7 Maxwell's triumph 165
7.1 The equation of continuity 166
7.2 The Ampère–Maxwell law 168
7.2.1 Limitations of Ampère's law 168
7.2.2 Generalizing Ampère's law 170
7.2.3 The Ampère–Maxwell law in action 171
7.3 Maxwell's equations 177
7.4 Let there be light! 179
7.4.1 Electromagnetic waves 179
7.4.2 The energy of electromagnetic waves 186

**Part II: The mathematics of electromagnetism 191**

Chapter 8 Mathematical Toolkit 191
8.1 Basic vector algebra 191
8.1.1 Scalars and vectors 191
8.1.2 The geometric picture of vectors 192
8.1.3 Vector components 194
8.2 Products of vectors 197
8.2.1 Scalar products 197
8.2.2 Vector products 199
8.2.3 Vector division? 201
8.2.4 Differentiating vectors and their products 201
8.2.5 Vector identities 202
8.3 Fields and coordinate systems 202
8.3.1 Scalar and vector fields 202
8.3.2 Spherical and cylindrical coordinates 205
8.4 Partial differentiation 212
8.4.1 First partial derivatives 212
8.4.2 Estimating small changes 214
8.4.3 Higher partial derivatives 214
8.5 Volume and surface integrals 216

| | | | |
|---|---|---|---|
| | 8.5.1 | Volume integrals | 216 |
| | 8.5.2 | Surface integrals | 220 |
| 8.6 | The divergence of a vector field | | 223 |
| | 8.6.1 | The additivity of flux | 223 |
| | 8.6.2 | The divergence theorem | 224 |
| | 8.6.3 | Divergence as a derivative | 225 |
| | 8.6.4 | Divergence in other coordinate systems | 227 |
| 8.7 | Line integrals | | 228 |
| 8.8 | The curl of a vector field | | 231 |
| | 8.8.1 | A convention for perimeters of open surfaces | 232 |
| | 8.8.2 | The additivity of circulation | 232 |
| | 8.8.3 | The curl theorem | 233 |
| | 8.8.4 | Curl as a derivative | 235 |
| | 8.8.5 | Curl in other coordinate systems | 237 |
| 8.9 | Conservative vector fields | | 238 |
| | 8.9.1 | Zero circulation and path-independence | 238 |
| | 8.9.2 | The scalar potential field | 240 |
| | 8.9.3 | The gradient of a scalar field | 241 |
| | 8.9.4 | More about the gradient | 243 |
| | 8.9.5 | Irrotational vector fields | 245 |
| | 8.9.6 | Integrating fields — a summary | 247 |
| 8.10 | Further topics in vector calculus | | 248 |
| | 8.10.1 | Del notation | 248 |
| | 8.10.2 | Vector calculus identities | 249 |
| | 8.10.3 | The Laplacian operator | 250 |

**Solutions** **251**

**Acknowledgements** **272**

**Index** **273**

# Introduction

## Founders of electromagnetism

Michael Faraday came from a poor family; at times his weekly diet consisted of no more than a loaf of bread. He was apprenticed to a bookbinder and became aware of science by reading books and attending public lectures at the Royal Institution. He secured his first job in science by taking lecture notes, binding them and presenting them to the lecturer, Humphry Davy, who took him on as an assistant. But Faraday was endlessly inquisitive and soon explored on his own initiative. By the early 1830s, he had discovered electromagnetic induction, built the first transformer, established the principle of the electric motor and produced the first continuous electrical generator. In order to account for his observations, Faraday introduced the concept of a field.

**Figure 1** Michael Faraday (1791–1867).

James Clerk Maxwell produced a unified theory of the electromagnetic field and used it to show that light is a type of electromagnetic wave. This prediction dates from the early 1860s when Maxwell was at King's College, London. Shortly afterwards Maxwell decided to retire to his family estate in Galloway in order to concentrate on research, unhindered by other duties. He was lured out of retirement in 1871, when he became the first professor of experimental physics in the Cavendish Laboratory, Cambridge. Given Maxwell's present status as one of the greatest of all physicists, it is astonishing to learn that he was the third choice for this job. Incidentally, Clerk Maxwell (without a hyphen) is a surname; Maxwell's father, John Clerk, simply appended 'Maxwell' to his own name in order to smooth a legal transaction.

**Figure 2** James Clerk Maxwell (1831–1879).

## Why study electromagnetism?

Electromagnetism was slow to get going. About a century after Newton published the law of universal gravitation, Coulomb discovered the law of electrostatic force, but it took another century before all the laws of electromagnetism were established. In retrospect, this slow development of electromagnetism is not surprising. Newton provided a mechanical world-view which worked marvellously well in the context of gravity, but which struggled to explain the more subtle effects of electricity and magnetism. It turned out that a key idea was missing — that of a *field*. Through long experience in the laboratory, Michael Faraday convinced himself that magnetic fields form part of the fabric of the world, every bit as real as particles. He explained the results of his experiments in terms of fields, drawing diagrams to help him visualize them. But the mathematics needed to describe fields was a significant hurdle, which Faraday was ill-equipped to surmount.

The full power of Faraday's field concept was revealed by James Clerk Maxwell, who deliberately chose to read Faraday's *Experimental Researches in Electricity* before applying any mathematics to the subject. In 1864, Maxwell distilled all the known properties of electric and magnetic fields into a set of four equations, known as Maxwell's equations. These equations led to one of the greatest discoveries in science — the realization that light is an electromagnetic wave. The Earth is bathed in light from the Sun. The propagation of this light, the blueness of the sky, the sparkling of ocean spray, the colours of rainbows and butterfly wings, can all be explained by Maxwell's equations. It is not every day that a whole branch of physics is merged with another, yet this is what Maxwell achieved — optics became a branch of electromagnetism. Before long, it became clear that electromagnetic waves also exist beyond the narrow band detected by our eyes. Radio waves and X-rays are other types of electromagnetic wave, important in engineering, medicine and astronomy. No wonder that Maxwell's publication of the laws of electromagnetism has been described as the most significant event of the nineteenth century. These laws are the main subject of this book.

There are many good reasons for studying electromagnetism, and therefore Maxwell's equations, in depth. Your motivation might come from a desire to understand fundamental physics, applications in science, applications in technology and medicine, or you might be interested in seeing how mathematics is used to explain physical effects. Let me say a few words about each of these motives.

**1 Fundamental physics** Electromagnetism is one of four fundamental forces of Nature — the others being gravity, the strong nuclear force and the weak nuclear force. Of these forces, electromagnetism is the one that physicists understand best. Nuclear forces are complicated and gravity is hard to reconcile with quantum mechanics, but physicists are very confident that they know how electromagnetism works. Part of the importance of electromagnetism stems from the fact that it is a theory of fields. Electromagnetism was the first, and remains the most familiar, theory of fields. Most fundamental physics is about fields of various kinds, so electromagnetism has provided a sort of template from which other, more elaborate, theories have grown.

Combining electromagnetism with a quantum theory of fields, Richard Feynman and others developed *quantum electrodynamics*. This is the most precisely confirmed physical theory ever devised; measurement and theory agree to at least 16 significant figures. The success of quantum electrodynamics has inspired the search for analogous theories of the other three forces, with the ultimate goal of obtaining a theory of everything — a super-unified theory of all four fundamental forces. Such ambitions lie beyond the scope of this book, and we will not use quantum theory at all, but it is interesting to note that classical electromagnetism has nourished all these developments. Electromagnetism has led to other profound ideas too. For example, Einstein was unconvinced by the explanations of electromagnetic induction found in the textbooks of his day. Special relativity was the fruit of this scepticism. Electromagnetism continues to suggest concepts that might be useful in other areas of physics. For example, astronomers are currently trying to detect a 'gravimagnetic' force. This is a modification of gravity that might arise when bodies move very rapidly. It can be thought of as a gravitational analogue of the magnetic force.

**2 Applications in science** The forces that bind atoms together in molecules and solids are electromagnetic in origin. This means that other sciences raise questions that require deep understanding of electromagnetism. In biology, for example, the membrane of a resting nerve cell has a negatively-charged inner surface and a positively-charged outer surface. Nerve impulses consist of localized reversals of this polarity, which sweep along the cell at speeds of up to $100\,\mathrm{m\,s^{-1}}$ (Figure 3). As you read this page, electromagnetic waves enter your eye. Even the transparent outer coating of the eye, the cornea, is a wonder of Nature. It is constructed from fibres of collagen, the same material that forms tendons, yet it is almost perfectly transparent. To understand the origin of this transparency, we need to know how electromagnetic waves propagate through media containing fibres, a topic that will be discussed in Book 3 of this series. Light focused on the back of the eye stimulates nerve impulses which propagate to the visual cortex of the brain, and in a complicated and poorly understood way, stimulate other areas of the brain. All of this activity involves electrical signals, subject to the laws of electromagnetism.

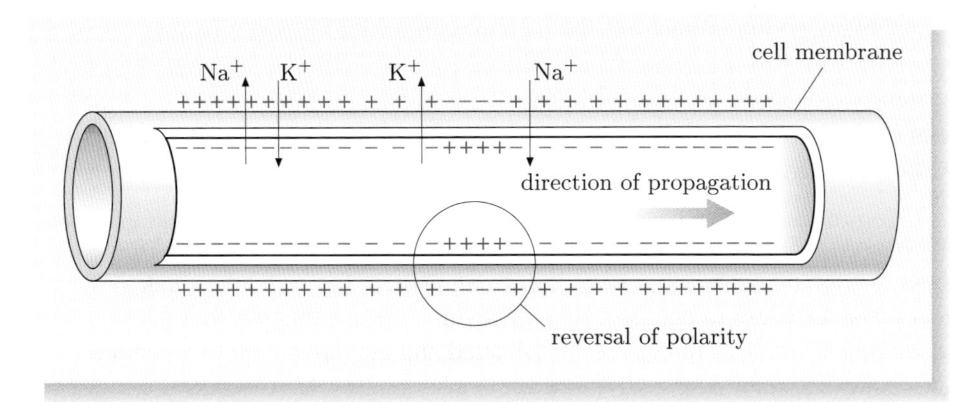


**Figure 3** A nerve impulse is a reversal of polarity across the membrane of a nerve cell. It sweeps along the cell, accompanied by a blip in the voltage difference across the membrane and sustained by flows of sodium ions ($Na^+$) and potassium ions ($K^+$) through voltage-sensitive channels in the membrane.

Step out of the house and look upwards. With clear skies you should see blue sky or stars, depending on the time of day. The blueness of the sky is due to the scattering of sunlight in the atmosphere. The stars reveal their presence by emitting electromagnetic waves, which propagate across vast distances of almost empty space. Of course, the whole subject of astronomy has progressed largely thanks to our ability to detect and analyze electromagnetic waves of various wavelengths. In polar latitudes you may see the aurora; in England you are more likely to see a rainbow (Figure 4). All these phenomena are explained by the laws of electromagnetism.

(a)

(b)

**Figure 4** (a) The aurora borealis and (b) a rainbow.

**3 Applications in technology and medicine** Modern society relies on a mastery of electromagnetic forces, currents, fields and waves. Think, for example, of electric lighting and heating, vacuum cleaners, car ignition systems, radar, mobile phones, televisions, satellite communication, body scanners, computers and the internet. Many sources of power are available to us — coal, gas, nuclear, solar, tidal or wind. In each case, there is a technology that produces electricity from the power source and distributes it across countries or even continents. It is easy to take these things for granted, but most of us would feel terribly deprived if electricity, and all its applications, were suddenly taken away from us. We are creatures of an electrical and electronic age.

**Figure 5** The experimental Japanese MAGLEV train, which has reached 360 m.p.h.

Progress shows no sign of slackening. For a few years, at least, computers will continue to improve, with faster processors, more memory and better data storage. It seems likely that electrically-driven vehicles will eventually displace our petrol-fuelled cars. Magnetically-levitated trains may become commonplace, especially if superconductors can be made to work at room temperature (Figure 5). Photonic circuits, similar to electronic circuits, but based on the propagation of electromagnetic waves rather than electrons, may be used in household devices. It is probably unwise to gaze too closely into the crystal ball, but there are certainly more surprises and delights to come, with future generations of inventors and designers continuing to exploit fundamental electromagnetic concepts and laws.

**4 Using mathematics** Lastly, you may be interested in the mathematics that underlies electromagnetism. Maxwell's equations can be described in various mathematical ways. This course uses the language of *vector calculus*, which means that you will use the ideas of divergence, curl and gradient and integrate simple functions over volumes and surfaces and along curves. If you are coming to the subject from a background in applied mathematics, you may be pleased that electromagnetism provides a concrete setting in which to practise these mathematical skills. This will be useful if you ever study other subjects, such as fluid mechanics, which are also based on vector calculus.

## How to study this book

This book is divided into two parts.

**Part I: The physics of electromagnetism** introduces Maxwell's equations in the simple context of charges and currents immersed in empty space.

**Part II: The mathematics of electromagnetism** consists of a *Mathematical Toolkit* which reviews the areas of mathematics that are needed to interpret and understand Maxwell's equations. It emphasizes the practical business of how to use vector calculus. One advantage of separating the mathematics from the physics in this way is it gives you some flexibility in studying the material, depending on your background and preferences.

- If you are confident in your mathematical preparation, or if you need some physical motivation to spark your interest in mathematics, you will prefer to begin with Part I. Following this plan, the mathematics will appear as the servant of the physics, and the motivation for each mathematical concept should be clear. At various points throughout the text you will be advised to study selected mathematical topics from Part II, and you are expected to take these detours when they appear. Watch out for the ▶ flag, which indicates a recommended detour into the *Mathematical Toolkit* MT).
- If you feel that mathematics is likely to be a major obstacle, or if you are happy to study mathematics without strong physical motivation, you may prefer to read Part II before starting Part I. In this way, you can concentrate on mastering important mathematical techniques before embarking on physical discussions.

We will refer to Section 8.X in the *Mathematical Toolkit* as MT 8.X.

The relative amounts of time you spend on physics and mathematics will depend on your background, but a typical split for this book might be 70% physics, 30% mathematics. If you plan to read the book in 11 weeks, starting with all the mathematics, you will be on schedule if you start the physics chapters at the beginning of week 4. If, like me, you prefer to study physics and mathematics together, Table 1 suggests a reasonable way of allocating your time. The study times given here allow for lengthy detours into MT. You are strongly advised to treat these detours as essential parts of your study and be prepared to spend sufficient time on them. To make precise mathematical statements, to solve problems and to pass exams, you must be familiar with the material in Part II. If you treat Part II as an optional appendix, and choose not to read it, you may only achieve an uncertain and superficial understanding of electromagnetism.

**Table 1** A study plan.

| Chapter | Time/weeks |
|---|---|
| 1 | 1.25 |
| 2 | 2.5 |
| 3 | 1.5 |
| 4 | 1.75 |
| 5 | 1.75 |
| 6 | 1.25 |
| 7 | 1.0 |

# Part I: The physics of electromagnetism

## Chapter 1 Electric forces and fields

Chapter 1 uses vector notation, unit vectors and vector addition. MT 8.1 discusses these topics. Be prepared to spend 25% of your study time for this chapter on this mathematics.

### 1.1 Electric charge

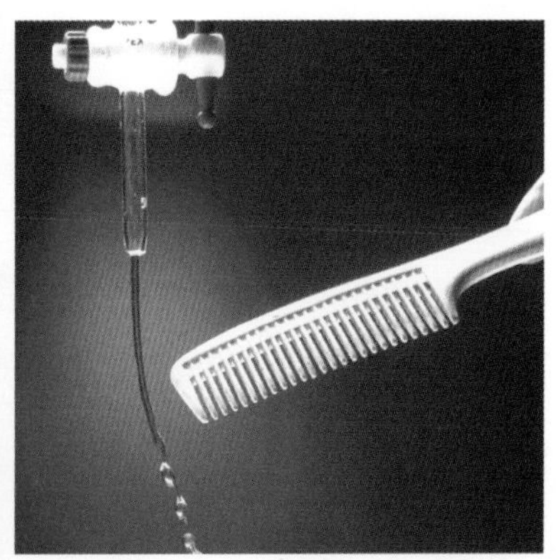

Figure 1.1 A charged comb attracts water running from a tap.

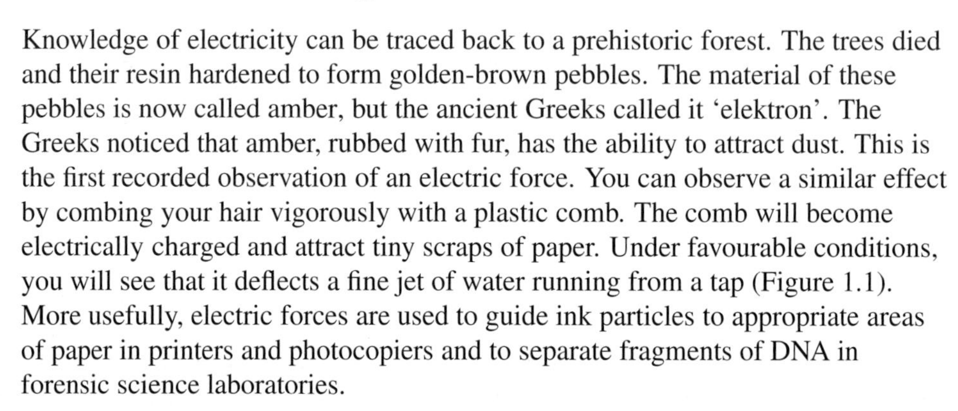

Knowledge of electricity can be traced back to a prehistoric forest. The trees died and their resin hardened to form golden-brown pebbles. The material of these pebbles is now called amber, but the ancient Greeks called it 'elektron'. The Greeks noticed that amber, rubbed with fur, has the ability to attract dust. This is the first recorded observation of an electric force. You can observe a similar effect by combing your hair vigorously with a plastic comb. The comb will become electrically charged and attract tiny scraps of paper. Under favourable conditions, you will see that it deflects a fine jet of water running from a tap (Figure 1.1). More usefully, electric forces are used to guide ink particles to appropriate areas of paper in printers and photocopiers and to separate fragments of DNA in forensic science laboratories.

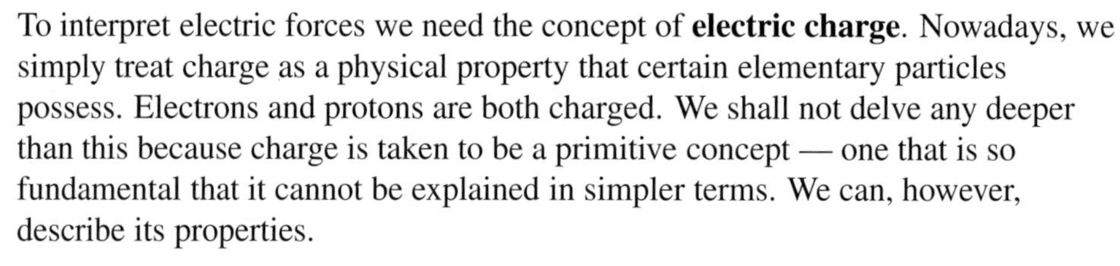

To interpret electric forces we need the concept of **electric charge**. Nowadays, we simply treat charge as a physical property that certain elementary particles possess. Electrons and protons are both charged. We shall not delve any deeper than this because charge is taken to be a primitive concept — one that is so fundamental that it cannot be explained in simpler terms. We can, however, describe its properties.

Charge is the property that allows particles to exert and experience electromagnetic forces. It comes in two types — positive and negative. For example, a proton, one of the particles in the nucleus of an atom, is positively charged, while an electron is negatively charged. Charges of the same sign repel one another while charges of opposite sign attract one another. Thus, two protons repel one another, two electrons repel one another, and an electron is attracted to a proton. The attraction between an electron and a proton is strong enough for the two particles to stay bound together, forming an atom of hydrogen. Such an atom is uncharged and is said to be electrically neutral.

Electromagnetic forces decrease with increasing separation. There is practically no attraction between an electron on the Moon and a proton on the Earth, but there is a much stronger attraction between electrons and protons in the same atom. At a given separation, it is interesting to ask how the strength of the electromagnetic force compares with that of gravity. The answer is that there is simply no contest. Electromagnetic forces are *much* stronger than gravitational forces. In a hydrogen atom, the electron is both electromagnetically and gravitationally attracted to the proton, but the electromagnetic attraction is $2 \times 10^{39}$ times greater than the gravitational attraction. Electromagnetic forces can also be compared with two other forces known to physicists — the strong and weak nuclear forces. At extremely short separations, the strong and weak nuclear forces are larger than the electromagnetic force, but these forces only act over very short ranges. At separations of more than $10^{-12}$ metres, the electromagnetic force is much stronger than either of the nuclear forces. Atoms and molecules are at least 100 times larger than this, so the electromagnetic force is the only force of any significance in chemistry and biochemistry. It is the only force needed to explain the melting point of ice, the hardness of diamond or the thoughts running through your brain.

If you are impressed by the vastness of the ratio $2 \times 10^{39}$, you might wonder why gravity is noticeable at all. Paradoxically, the answer lies in the strong attraction between opposite charges, which ensures that bulk matter is normally uncharged. For example, a positively-charged nucleus tends to pull negatively-charged electrons into its vicinity, forming a neutral atom. Large aggregates of matter tend to be made up of neutral atoms and so are themselves electrically neutral. That is why the motion of planets and stars is governed by gravity; the electromagnetic forces cancel out because planets and stars are practically uncharged.

To observe charge in detail, we need to disturb the usual neutrality of matter. This is what happens in a battery for example, or in an electron microscope which creates a stream of electrons. Fortunately, the properties of charge turn out to be remarkably simple. They can be summarized as follows:

**Charge is a scalar.** A **scalar quantity** is one that is described by a single real number together with an appropriate unit of measurement. In the case of charge, the sign of the number indicates whether the charge is positive or negative, and its magnitude (in a given system of units) tells us how much charge is present.

**Charge is additive.** The total charge within a given region is the sum of all the charges in that region. The sum is an algebraic one, with due account taken of the signs of the charges, so a system of two charges of equal magnitudes and opposite signs has a total charge of zero.

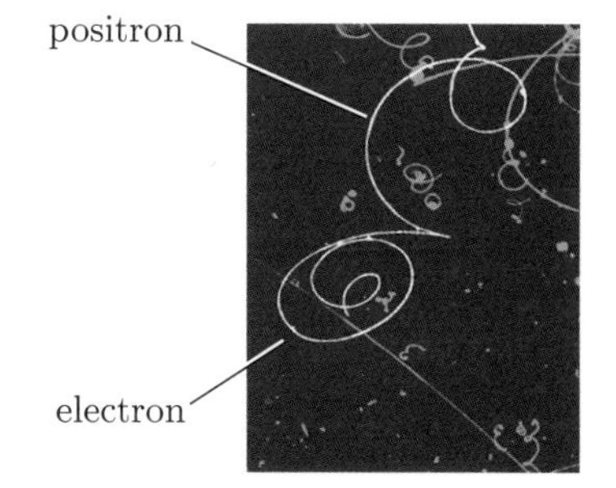


**Figure 1.2** A newly created electron–positron pair.

**Charge is conserved.** The total charge of the Universe remains constant in time. Actually, it is possible to make an even stronger statement: charge is conserved *locally*. This means that the total charge in any region of space remains constant, unless charged particles flow across the boundary of the region. If a positive charge were created at one point in space and a compensating negative charge were simultaneously created at a different point, the total charge of the Universe would remain constant. However, the *local* conservation of charge would be violated in the regions around both points, so such a process cannot happen.

Charge conservation goes beyond the idea that every particle carries a fixed charge. In modern physics, particles can be destroyed or created. It is possible for two high-energy particles to collide and annihilate one another, giving rise to completely new particles. Figure 1.2 shows tracks made in a bubble chamber following the collision of two neutral particles. These particles annihilate one another, producing a positively-charged positron and a negatively-charged electron. The newly-created particles have charges of equal magnitude but opposite sign, so the initial value of the charge (zero) is maintained locally at the site of the collision.

**Charge is invariant.** The value of a particle's charge is agreed on by all observers. It does not depend on the observer's choice of coordinate system or state of motion.

**Table 1.1** Charges of some elementary particles.

| Particle | Charge |
|---|---|
| electron | $-e$ |
| muon | $-e$ |
| tauon | $-e$ |
| proton | $+e$ |
| neutron | 0 |
| neutrino | 0 |
| photon | 0 |
| $W^+$ boson | $+e$ |
| $W^-$ boson | $-e$ |
| up quark | $+2e/3$ |
| charm quark | $+2e/3$ |
| top quark | $+2e/3$ |
| down quark | $-e/3$ |
| strange quark | $-e/3$ |
| bottom quark | $-e/3$ |

**Charge is quantized.** Charge comes in discrete lumps. Table 1.1 shows the charges of some elementary particles expressed in terms of the charge of a proton, which is given the symbol $e$. The charge on an electron is $-e$ and, so far as we know, all isolated particles have charges that are integer multiples of $e$. Quarks have charges that are integer multiples of $e/3$, but quarks have never been observed as isolated particles. They always occur as combinations with total charge $-e$, 0 or $+e$. For example, a proton consists of three quarks of charges $2e/3$, $2e/3$ and $-e/3$. By the additivity of charge, its total charge is $e$.

It is worth emphasizing that all these properties of charge are believed to be *exactly* true. I say this because strange things can happen in modern physics. In relativity, for example, mass is not additive, not conserved and not invariant. By contrast, charge is believed to be strictly additive, conserved and invariant. It is a scalar quantity, and it comes in quantized lumps. So things could hardly be more straightforward. Electromagnetism has its intricacies, but charge is not one of them. Charge is a simple concept and is always easy to deal with.

**Exercise 1.1** Why does a comb become positively charged when you run it through your hair? Is your explanation consistent with the conservation of charge? Why does a charged comb attract neutral scraps of paper? ■

## 1.2 Electromagnetic forces

Charged particles exert electromagnetic forces on one another. Before taking a closer look at these forces, let's briefly recall why force is an important concept in classical physics. The main reason is Newton's second law:

$$\mathbf{F} = \frac{\mathrm{d}\mathbf{p}}{\mathrm{d}t},$$

which describes how a force $\mathbf{F}$ influences the momentum $\mathbf{p}$ of a particle. In this book, of course, we are concerned with electromagnetic forces.

By a particle, I mean a scrap of matter which, at any instant, can be thought of as occupying a single point in space. An electron is usually thought of as a particle, for example. However, electrons have a property called *spin* which produces small magnetic effects. I therefore introduce the concept of a **point charge**. By definition, a point charge is a charged particle with *absolutely no* internal structure, internal motion or spin. The concept of a point charge will help us make precise definitions and statements without worrying about spin or magnetism. This is really a legal nicety, part of the small print. For most purposes, the distinction between charged particles and point charges is unimportant. I will sometimes use the word 'charge' as a shorthand for 'point charge'.

One of the surprising things about electromagnetic forces is that they depend on the velocities of the particles involved. For example, Figure 1.3 shows three different situations involving two negative point charges. In case (a) particle B moves uniformly along the dashed line while particle A is at rest. In case (b) both particles are held permanently at rest. In case (c) both particles move uniformly at the same velocity, perpendicular to their line of separation. These three situations are distinguished only by the motion of the particles. Just as you would expect, the charges repel one another. But you might be surprised to learn that the magnitude of the force on particle A is not the same in these three cases. It is greatest in case (a), smaller in case (b) and smaller still in case (c). In terms of symbols we can write

$$|\mathbf{F}_\mathrm{A}^{(a)}| > |\mathbf{F}_\mathrm{A}^{(b)}| > |\mathbf{F}_\mathrm{A}^{(c)}|,$$

where the subscript reminds us that we are discussing the force on particle A and the superscript refers to the case under consideration.

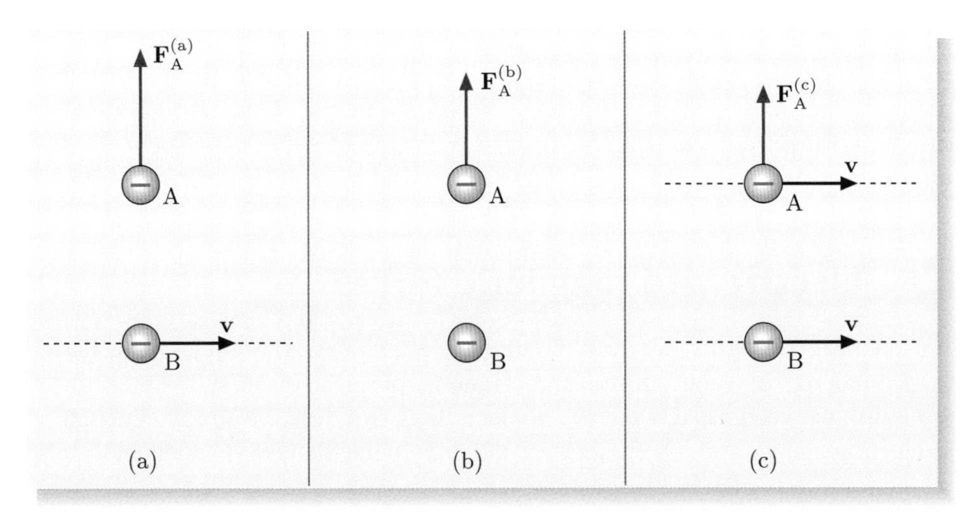


**Figure 1.3** The electromagnetic force on particle A due to particle B in three different cases.

Admittedly, the variation in $\mathbf{F}_\mathrm{A}$ is usually tiny. For it to be at all significant, the two particles must move at speeds close to that of light. However, it is not uncommon for charges to move at such high speeds. The electrons in a heavy atom travel at an appreciable fraction of the speed of light, and so do the electrons in a powerful electron microscope (Figure 1.4). In an electron microscope the reduced repulsion illustrated in Figure 1.3c has a practical consequence — the sideways spread of the electron beam is smaller than would be predicted on the basis of Figure 1.3b.

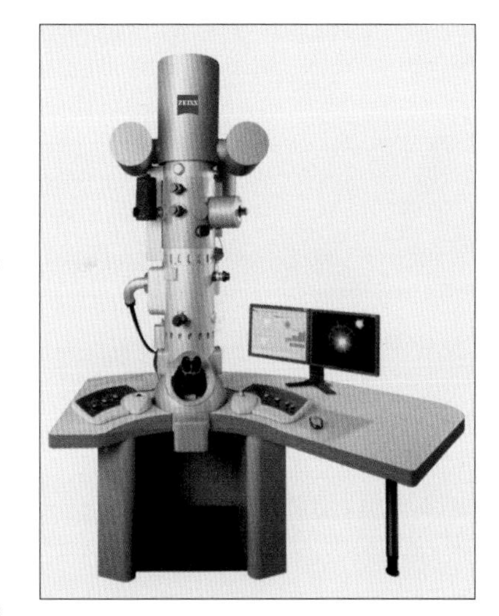

**Figure 1.4** The electrons in the beam of this electron microscope travel at 70% of the speed of light.

If many particles are involved, the variation in the force may be evident at lower speeds. Suppose that two neutral wires, A and B, are placed side-by-side. If there are no currents flowing through the wires there is no electromagnetic force between them. This is not surprising because the wires are neutral. In more detail, some electrons in the wires become detached from their atoms, leaving positive ions behind. Each metal wire can be therefore be pictured as a lattice of positive ions immersed in a sea of mobile electrons. The electrons in wire A are repelled by the electrons in wire B, but are equally attracted towards the ions in wire B. The ions in wire A are repelled by the ions in wire B, but are equally attracted towards the electrons in wire B. All the repulsions and attractions cancel out, leaving no net force between the wires.

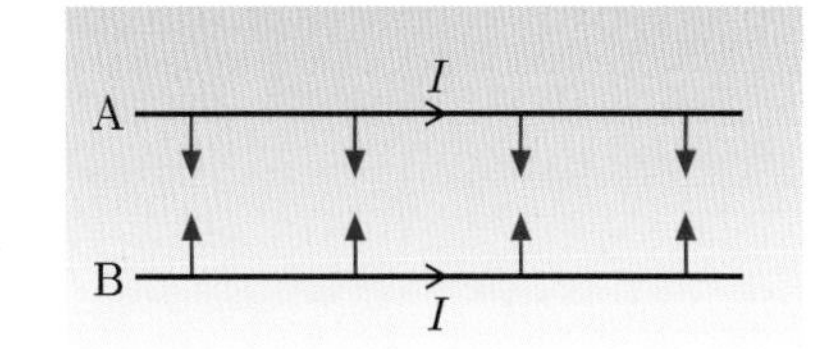


**Figure 1.5** Two parallel currents attract one another.

Now, suppose that steady parallel currents flow through the wires. In this case, the wires are observed to attract one another (Figure 1.5). This is not an exotic curiosity — it is an effect that is easily observed without any special equipment. Why does it happen? It is important to realize that an electric current in a wire is caused by a steady flow of electrons along the wire, while the positively-charged ions in the wire remain fixed. You can picture the flow of electrons as being rather like the flow of water through a pipe. The motion of the electrons disrupts the precise balance between attractive and repulsive forces mentioned above. For example, Figure 1.3c suggests that the repulsion between parallel streams of moving electrons will be less than had they been at rest. The reduction in repulsion is not matched by a compensating reduction in attraction between the electrons and the ions so, when all the forces are added together, the net effect is that the two current-carrying wires attract one another. One interesting feature of this attraction is that the electrons drift along the wire slowly, typically at a few tenths of a millimetre per second. This is 12 orders of magnitude smaller than the speed of light, so the net force on each electron will be tiny. However, a copper wire one millimetre in diameter has around $10^{21}$ mobile electrons in each centimetre of its length. This scales up the force and produces a noticeable effect.

**Figure 1.6** André-Marie Ampère (1775–1836) suggested that magnets owe their special properties to microscopic circulating currents.

## 1.3 Electric and magnetic forces

To make further progress we need to introduce force laws. These laws are usually phrased in terms of electric forces and magnetic forces, so our first task is to distinguish between these two types of electromagnetic force. Naturally enough, the electromagnetic force between two stationary point charges is called an electric force, but what is a magnetic force?

No doubt you have observed the effects of magnetic forces acting on ordinary magnets — a compass needle aligning in a South-North direction or a fridge-magnet sticking to the door of a fridge. At first sight, these magnetic forces appear to have nothing to do with the forces between charged particles, but there is actually a very deep connection. It turns out that a current-carrying coil behaves exactly like a magnet. The coil, too, aligns in a South-North direction and is attracted to a fridge door. In the 1820s, André-Marie Ampère (Figure 1.6) used this analogy to suggest that ordinary magnets owe their special properties to microscopic currents circulating within their volume. From this point of view, the essential feature of a magnetic force is that *it acts on electric currents*. Following this insight, we see that the force between parallel currents in neutral wires should be classified as a *magnetic force*. An electric current is just a flow of electric charge, so we can also say that magnetic forces act on charges that are in motion. This motivates the following definition.

### The distinction between electric and magnetic forces

The electromagnetic force on a *stationary* point charge is defined to be an **electric force**. A stationary point charge experiences no magnetic force.

The electromagnetic force on a *moving* point charge may have both electric and magnetic contributions. The electric force is defined to be the same as for a stationary point charge at the same position. The **magnetic force** is the *additional* electromagnetic force that occurs because the charge is moving, rather than at rest.

This definition effectively splits electromagnetic forces into electric and magnetic contributions. The electric force is felt by all point charges, whether they are moving or not. The magnetic force is felt only by a moving point charge. A stationary point charge experiences no magnetic force. This is a convention, rather than a deep fact about Nature, but it is a very important convention which permeates the whole subject. Let's see how it works in simple cases.

- In Figures 1.3a and b, particle A is stationary so it cannot experience a magnetic force. It experiences only an electric force. The electromagnetic repulsion is observed to be stronger in Figure 1.3a than in Figure 1.3b. This fact is interpreted by saying that particle A experiences a stronger repulsive *electric* force in Figure 1.3a than in Figure 1.3b.
- In Figure 1.3c, particle A is moving so it can experience both electric and magnetic forces. The electric force is independent of the motion of particle A, and is therefore identical to the enhanced electric repulsion of Figure 1.3a. Nevertheless, the electromagnetic repulsion is observed to be *weaker* in Figure 1.3c than in Figure 1.3b. This fact is interpreted by saying that particle A experiences an attractive *magnetic* force in Figure 1.3c which more than compensates for the enhanced electric repulsion.

One other point is worth noting. By definition, a stationary point charge experiences no magnetic force. But who should judge whether a charge is stationary or not? If you are in a jet plane and I am in an armchair, we are likely to disagree about such matters. Albert Einstein (Figure 1.7) was the first to realize that different observers are entitled to make their own judgements. If a point charge is stationary relative to you, then you must say that it experiences no magnetic force *in your reference frame*. But, if the same charge is moving relative to me, I can say that it experiences a magnetic force *in my reference frame*. We are both right, although we have different viewpoints! The separation of electromagnetic forces into electric and magnetic contributions depends on the choice of reference frame. Strictly speaking we should specify our choice of reference frame at the outset, but this is seldom done. Usually, we focus on phenomena observed in a laboratory and implicitly assume that our descriptions refer to a reference frame that is stationary in the laboratory.

Figure 1.7 Albert Einstein in 1898, when he was a 19-year old student in Zurich.

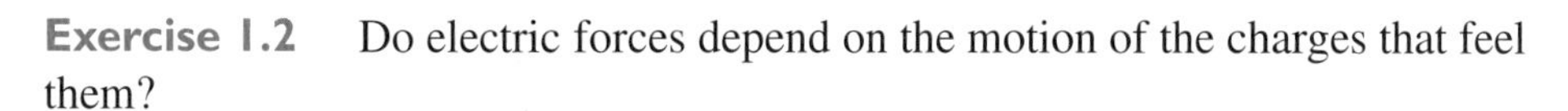

**Exercise 1.2** Do electric forces depend on the motion of the charges that feel them?

**Exercise 1.3** Do electric forces depend on the motion of the charges that exert them?

**Exercise 1.4** A stationary electron can experience a magnetic force if it is near a strong magnet. Does this invalidate our classification of electric and magnetic forces? ■

## 1.4 Coulomb's law

For the rest of this chapter we restrict attention to the forces between point charges that are at rest. Our previous discussion makes it clear that this is a special case, but it is an important one, and a good place to start. Because the charges are stationary, they cannot experience magnetic forces. Moreover, the electric forces exerted by the charges are not modified by their motion. The electric forces between stationary charges are called **electrostatic forces** and the electrostatic law of force between two stationary point charges is called **Coulomb's law**. This law can be stated as follows:

### Coulomb's law

The electrostatic force between two stationary point charges acts along their line of separation; it is repulsive for charges of the same sign and attractive for charges of opposite sign. The magnitude of the force is proportional to the product of the charges and is inversely proportional to the square of the distance between them.

Because of its dependence on distance, Coulomb's law is said to be an *inverse square* law of force. Our first task is to express this law in a suitable mathematical form. We might, for example, write

$$F_{\text{repulsive}} = k_{\text{elec}} \frac{q_1 q_2}{r_{12}^2},$$

where $q_1$ and $q_2$ are the values of the two point charges, $r_{12}$ is the distance between them and $k_{\text{elec}}$ is a positive constant of proportionality. The quantity on the left-hand side is the repulsive force experienced by a given charge in the pair. If $q_1$ and $q_2$ have the same sign, the repulsive force is positive, indicating a genuine repulsion away from the other charge. If $q_1$ and $q_2$ have opposite signs, the repulsive force is negative, which is interpreted as an attraction towards the other charge.

This equation tells no lies, but is almost useless for systems containing more than two charges. The trouble is that the direction of the force is not represented by symbols in the equation, but by the adjectives 'repulsive' or 'attractive'. But, if three charges are not in a straight line, the force experienced by one of them is a combination of forces from the other two. These forces act in different directions, in a way that the above equation cannot hope to capture. To obtain a satisfactory representation of Coulomb's law it is *essential* to use vectors, which brings us to the first mathematical detour of this book. Remember that I am assuming that you have taken such a detour *before* continuing with the rest of the text.

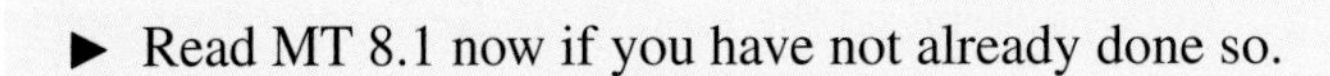

▶ Read MT 8.1 now if you have not already done so.

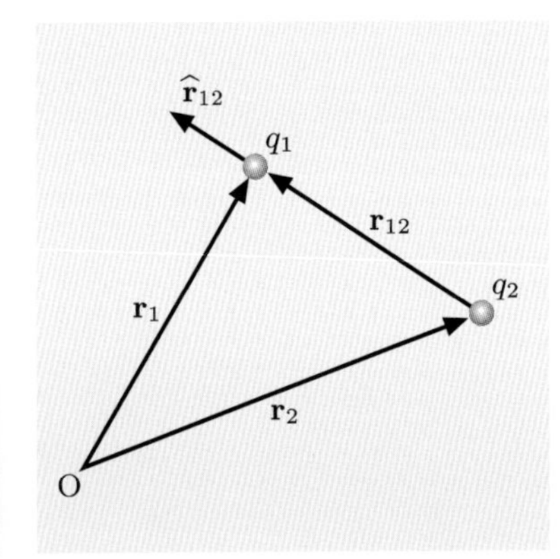


**Figure 1.8** Two stationary point charges showing the displacement vector $\mathbf{r}_{12}$ of charge 1 from charge 2 and the corresponding unit vector $\widehat{\mathbf{r}}_{12}$.

Vectors help us to define directions in space. Suppose that point charges $q_1$ and $q_2$ are at positions $\mathbf{r}_1$ and $\mathbf{r}_2$ (Figure 1.8). Then the displacement vector of charge 1 from charge 2 is

$$\mathbf{r}_{12} = \mathbf{r}_1 - \mathbf{r}_2.$$

Note that I have written $\mathbf{r}_{12}$ with its indices in the same order as those in $\mathbf{r}_1 - \mathbf{r}_2$. This is a convenient notation, but it means that the first index marks the destination of the displacement while the second index marks its start.

The displacement vector $\mathbf{r}_{12}$ has both magnitude and direction. Its magnitude is

$$r_{12} = |\mathbf{r}_1 - \mathbf{r}_2|,$$

which is the distance between the charges. Its direction is given by the unit vector

$$\widehat{\mathbf{r}}_{12} = \frac{\mathbf{r}_1 - \mathbf{r}_2}{|\mathbf{r}_1 - \mathbf{r}_2|},$$

which is a vector of magnitude 1 (with no units) pointing in the direction shown in Figure 1.8. This unit vector is useful because it is aligned with the direction of the electrostatic force. It allows us to express Coulomb's law as a vector equation:

$$\mathbf{F}_{12} = k_{\text{elec}} \frac{q_1 q_2}{r_{12}^2} \widehat{\mathbf{r}}_{12}. \tag{1.1}$$

The left-hand side of this equation is the electrostatic force *on* charge 1 *due to* charge 2. This is represented by the force vector, $\mathbf{F}_{12}$, where the first index indicates the particle experiencing the force and the second index indicates the particle responsible for the force. In this notation, the force on charge 2 due to charge 1 is written as $\mathbf{F}_{21}$. The order of indices matters here because these two forces are not the same — they point in opposite directions.

The right-hand side of Equation 1.1 is the product of the scalar factor $k_{\text{elec}} q_1 q_2 / r_{12}^2$ and the unit vector $\widehat{\mathbf{r}}_{12}$. The scalar factor ensures that the force is proportional to the product of the charges and is inversely proportional to the square of their separation. The unit vector ensures that the force points in the appropriate direction. To see how this works, consider two charges of the same sign. Since $k_{\text{elec}}$ is positive, the unit vector is multiplied by a positive quantity, and the force on charge 1 points in the direction of $+\widehat{\mathbf{r}}_{12}$, a repulsion directly away from charge 2. If the charges have opposite signs the unit vector is multiplied by a negative quantity, and the force on charge 1 points in the direction of $-\widehat{\mathbf{r}}_{12}$, an attraction directly towards charge 2. Both predictions are correct. If you are ever in doubt about the order of the indices in Coulomb's law, you should go through an analysis like this to check that everything is consistent with the rule that like charges repel one another.

It is conventional to write the proportionality constant $k_{\text{elec}}$ as $1/4\pi\varepsilon_0$, where $\varepsilon_0$ is rather grandly called the **permittivity of free space**. The reason for including a factor $1/4\pi$ at this stage is that it leads to simplifications elsewhere in the subject, especially in Maxwell's equations, as you will see later in this book. We therefore choose to write Coulomb's law in the standard form:

$$\mathbf{F}_{12} = \frac{1}{4\pi\varepsilon_0} \frac{q_1 q_2}{r_{12}^2} \widehat{\mathbf{r}}_{12}. \tag{1.2}$$

Throughout this course we will use SI units, which means that length will be measured in metres (m), mass in kilograms (kg), time in seconds (s), force in newtons (N) and charge in **coulombs** (C). In SI units, the proportionality constant in Coulomb's law has the value

$$\frac{1}{4\pi\varepsilon_0} = 8.99 \times 10^9 \,\text{N}\,\text{m}^2\,\text{C}^{-2}.$$

This means that the electrostatic force between two particles, each carrying a charge of one coulomb and separated by a distance of one metre, is $8.99 \times 10^9$ N. The large magnitude of this force tells us that one coulomb is a very large charge in the context of electrostatics. The charges on everyday objects are often measured in microcoulombs ($1\,\mu\text{C} = 1 \times 10^{-6}\,\text{C}$) and the charge on an electron is only $-1.60 \times 10^{-19}$ C.

There is another way of writing Coulomb's law which is useful for some purposes. Using the definition of the unit vector $\widehat{\mathbf{r}}_{12}$, we write

$$\mathbf{F}_{12} = \frac{1}{4\pi\varepsilon_0} \frac{q_1 q_2}{|\mathbf{r}_1 - \mathbf{r}_2|^3} (\mathbf{r}_1 - \mathbf{r}_2). \tag{1.3}$$

The extra factor of distance in the denominator ($|\mathbf{r}_1 - \mathbf{r}_2|^3$ rather than $|\mathbf{r}_1 - \mathbf{r}_2|^2$) is compensated by the factor $(\mathbf{r}_1 - \mathbf{r}_2)$ in the numerator, so the inverse-square nature of Coulomb's law is preserved, as it must be. The main advantage of Equation 1.3 is that it avoids the need to deal with unit vectors, and this can speed up some calculations, as you will see.

**Exercise 1.5** Suppose that one gram of pure electrons is separated from another gram of pure electrons by $1.5 \times 10^{11}$ m (the distance between the Earth and the Sun). Estimate the magnitude of the electrostatic force between these two concentrations of charge.

**Exercise 1.6** Is Equation 1.2 consistent with Newton's third law which states that action and reaction are equal in magnitude and opposite in direction? ■

### 1.4.1 Adding electrostatic forces

So far, we have considered two point charges, labelled 1 and 2. This situation is unusual. Normally many charges are present, and each charge exerts an electrostatic force on each of the others. Fortunately, the extension to many particles is straightforward. The total electrostatic force on a given particle can be found from the following principles.

- The total electrostatic force on a charge is the vector sum of the electrostatic forces it experiences due to all other charges.
- The electrostatic force on a given charge due to another charge is given by Coulomb's law. This depends only on the two particles under consideration and is completely unaffected by the presence of other charges.

These principles express the law of **addition of force** in the context of electrostatics. They tell us that the total electrostatic force on charge $i$ is given by the vector sum

$$\mathbf{F}_i = \sum_{j \neq i} \mathbf{F}_{ij},$$

where $\mathbf{F}_{ij}$ is the electrostatic force on particle $i$ due to particle $j$ and the sum runs over all the particles $j$ that exert an appreciable electrostatic force on particle $i$. Of course, there is no term with $j = i$ because particle $i$ cannot exert a force on itself. Since each individual electrostatic force obeys Coulomb's law, we conclude that

$$\mathbf{F}_i = \frac{1}{4\pi\varepsilon_0} \sum_{j \neq i} \frac{q_i q_j}{|\mathbf{r}_i - \mathbf{r}_j|^3} (\mathbf{r}_i - \mathbf{r}_j). \tag{1.4}$$

For any given arrangement of charges, the formal summation can be expanded to give an explicit formula for the electrostatic force on particle $i$. However, this formula can only be evaluated if particle $i$ and all the other relevant particles $j$

have known charges and positions. We will assume, for the moment, that this is the case. Note that we are dealing with a sum of *vectors*. In general, different force contributions will point in different directions, so adding or subtracting force magnitudes will not be good enough. That is why it is essential to express Coulomb's law in vector form.

Problems based on Coulomb's law can be tackled in two main ways. If the arrangement of charges is two-dimensional and highly symmetric, a method based on angles and geometry may be used.

**Essential skill**

Using the vector form of Coulomb's law

### Worked Example 1.1

Three particles, each of charge $q$, are held stationary at the corners of an equilateral triangle with sides of length $d$. Find the magnitude of the electrostatic force experienced by one of these particles due to the other two.

#### Solution

Figure 1.9 shows the arrangement of charges and a suitable choice of Cartesian axes.

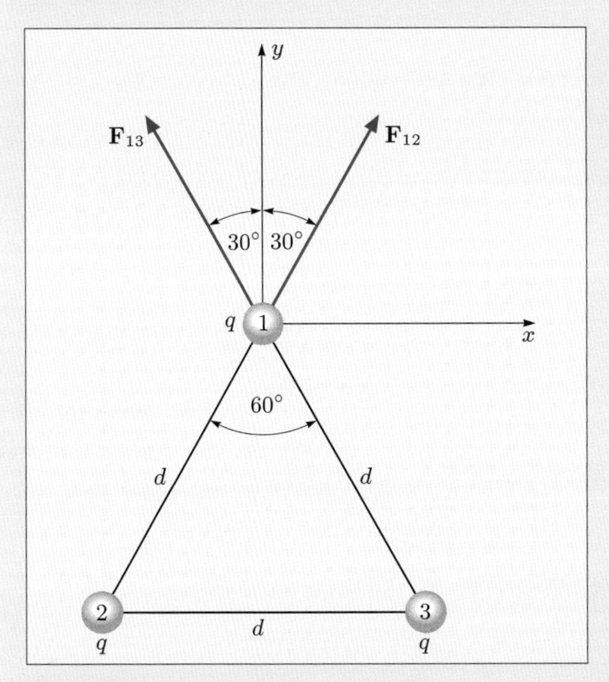


**Figure 1.9** Arrangement of charges for Worked Example 1.1.

Let's calculate the total electrostatic force on particle 1. This particle experiences forces $\mathbf{F}_{12}$ and $\mathbf{F}_{13}$ due to particles 2 and 3. By symmetry, the $x$-components of these forces cancel one another. Using Coulomb's law and some trigonometry to find the $y$-components of the forces, we see that the total force on particle 1 points along the $y$-axis and has magnitude

$$F_1 = \frac{1}{4\pi\varepsilon_0}\frac{q^2}{d^2}\cos 30° + \frac{1}{4\pi\varepsilon_0}\frac{q^2}{d^2}\cos 30° = \frac{\sqrt{3}}{4\pi\varepsilon_0}\frac{q^2}{d^2}.$$

By symmetry, particles 2 and 3 each experience forces of the same magnitude, pointing directly away from the centre of the triangle.

**Exercise 1.7** Three identical point charges, $q$, are stationary at the corners of an equilateral triangle with length of side $d$. A point charge $Q$ is placed exactly in the centre of the equilateral triangle. What value of $Q$ ensures that all four charges experience zero electrostatic force? ■

If the particles do not all lie in one plane and there is a lack of symmetry, calculations based on geometry or trigonometry become cumbersome. Fortunately, we can always represent all the vectors in component form, and use the rules of vector algebra to combine them according to the recipe given in Equation 1.4. The following example illustrates this technique.

**Essential skill**

Using the vector form of Coulomb's law

### Worked Example 1.2

Particles 1, 2 and 3, of charges $q_1 = 90\,\mu\text{C}$, $q_2 = 30\,\mu\text{C}$ and $q_3 = 20\,\mu\text{C}$, are stationary at positions $\mathbf{r}_1 = (4\mathbf{e}_x + 8\mathbf{e}_y + 5\mathbf{e}_z)\,\text{m}$, $\mathbf{r}_2 = (4\mathbf{e}_x - 4\mathbf{e}_y)\,\text{m}$ and $\mathbf{r}_3 = (1\mathbf{e}_x + 4\mathbf{e}_y + 5\mathbf{e}_z)\,\text{m}$. What is the total electrostatic force on particle 1 due to particles 2 and 3?

#### Solution

The displacement vectors of particle 1 from particles 2 and 3 are

$$\mathbf{r}_1 - \mathbf{r}_2 = [(4-4)\mathbf{e}_x + (8+4)\mathbf{e}_y + (5-0)\mathbf{e}_z]\ \text{m} = (12\mathbf{e}_y + 5\mathbf{e}_z)\,\text{m},$$

$$\mathbf{r}_1 - \mathbf{r}_3 = [(4-1)\mathbf{e}_x + (8-4)\mathbf{e}_y + (5-5)\mathbf{e}_z]\ \text{m} = (3\mathbf{e}_x + 4\mathbf{e}_y)\,\text{m},$$

and the corresponding distances are

$$r_{12} = \sqrt{(12\,\text{m})^2 + (5\,\text{m})^2} = 13\,\text{m},$$

$$r_{13} = \sqrt{(3\,\text{m})^2 + (4\,\text{m})^2} = 5\,\text{m}.$$

Consequently,

$$\begin{aligned}\mathbf{F}_{12} &= \frac{1}{4\pi\varepsilon_0}\frac{q_1 q_2}{|\mathbf{r}_1 - \mathbf{r}_2|^3}(\mathbf{r}_1 - \mathbf{r}_2)\\ &= 8.99\times10^9\,\text{N}\,\text{m}^2\,\text{C}^{-2}\times\frac{9\times10^{-5}\,\text{C}\times3\times10^{-5}\,\text{C}}{13^3\,\text{m}^3}\times(12\mathbf{e}_y + 5\mathbf{e}_z)\,\text{m}\\ &= (0.133\mathbf{e}_y + 0.055\mathbf{e}_z)\,\text{N},\end{aligned}$$

$$\begin{aligned}\mathbf{F}_{13} &= \frac{1}{4\pi\varepsilon_0}\frac{q_1 q_3}{|\mathbf{r}_1 - \mathbf{r}_3|^3}(\mathbf{r}_1 - \mathbf{r}_3)\\ &= 8.99\times10^9\,\text{N}\,\text{m}^2\,\text{C}^{-2}\times\frac{9\times10^{-5}\,\text{C}\times2\times10^{-5}\,\text{C}}{5^3\,\text{m}^3}\times(3\mathbf{e}_x + 4\mathbf{e}_y)\,\text{m}\\ &= (0.388\mathbf{e}_x + 0.518\mathbf{e}_y)\,\text{N}.\end{aligned}$$

Adding these two contributions together, we conclude that

$$\mathbf{F}_1 = (0.39\mathbf{e}_x + 0.65\mathbf{e}_y + 0.055\mathbf{e}_z)\,\text{N},$$

to two significant figures. Calculations like this are always straightforward, endangered only by lapses in concentration.

**Exercise 1.8** Particle 1, of charge $90\,\mu\text{C}$, is stationary at a point with Cartesian coordinates $(3, 2, -1)\,\text{m}$. Particle 2, of charge $-30\,\mu\text{C}$, is stationary at a point with Cartesian coordinates $(2, 4, 1)$ m. What is the electrostatic force on particle 1 due to particle 2?

**Exercise 1.9** Two charges, $-16q$ and $3q$, where $q$ is positive, are stationary at points $(2a, 0, 0)$ and $(0, a, 0)$. Find the electrostatic force on a charge $q$ placed at the origin $(0, 0, 0)$. What is the magnitude of this force and what is its direction (specified by a unit vector)? ■

## 1.4.2 Evidence for Coulomb's law

Coulomb's law is believed to be a fundamental law of Nature, but is this belief well-founded? Instead of simply accepting Coulomb's law, we had better examine the evidence. Let us assume that the magnitude of the electrostatic force decreases as $1/r^n$, where $n$ is a constant. Various laboratory experiments have measured the value of $n$. All have found that $n = 2$, to within the accuracies $\Delta n$ shown in Table 1.2. The first two measurements pre-date Coulomb's work, but were unpublished and forgotten for many years. It is the recent results that are truly impressive. We can be very confident indeed that electrostatic forces obey an inverse square law on the everyday scale of these laboratory experiments.

**Table 1.2** Testing Coulomb's law in the laboratory.

| Date | Physicist | $\Delta n$ |
|---|---|---|
| 1769 | Robison | $\pm 0.06$ |
| 1773 | Cavendish | $\pm 0.03$ |
| 1785 | Coulomb | $\pm 0.1$ |
| 1873 | Maxwell | $\pm 10^{-5}$ |
| 1936 | Plimpton | $\pm 10^{-9}$ |
| 1970 | Bartlett | $\pm 10^{-13}$ |
| 1971 | Williams | $\pm 10^{-16}$ |

As well as testing Coulomb's law on a laboratory scale, we should also test it at very short distances and at very large distances. Evidence at short distances comes from scattering experiments. A famous experiment of this type was carried out by Rutherford who fired alpha particles at metal foils and observed that a few of them bounced back in the direction from which they had come. Rutherford guessed that the atoms in the foil must contain tiny massive nuclei. Assuming that the positively-charged alpha particles and the positively-charged nuclei repel one another according to Coulomb's law, he was able to explain the angular distribution of scattered alpha particles. This is celebrated as the discovery of the atomic nucleus, but it also provided evidence that Coulomb's law works on sub-atomic length scales. Similar experiments involving electron–electron scattering confirm that Coulomb's law is accurate down to length scales of order $10^{-12}$ m.

Perhaps the most interesting challenge to Coulomb's law occurs at large distances. Here the available evidence is based on quantum field theory, which interprets electric forces in terms of an exchange of photons between charged particles. Quantum field theory shows that an inverse square law is just what is expected in a three-dimensional space, *provided that* the photon has no mass. The validity of Coulomb's law is therefore closely linked to the massless nature of the photon. Current physical theories assume that photons are massless, but it is fair to ask what would happen if the photon had a small mass. In this case, it is believed that Coulomb's law would be replaced by

$$\mathbf{F}_{12} = \frac{1}{4\pi\varepsilon_0}\frac{q_1 q_2}{r_{12}^2}\left(1 + \frac{r_{12}}{a}\right)\mathrm{e}^{-r_{12}/a}\,\widehat{\mathbf{r}}_{12},$$

where $a = h/(2\pi mc)$ has the units of length, $h$ is Planck's constant, $m$ is the photon mass and $c$ is the speed of light. For $r_{12} \ll a$, this force is essentially the same as the Coulomb force, but it becomes significantly smaller than the Coulomb force when the separation of the particles becomes comparable to, or greater than, $a$.

A non-zero mass for a photon would have measurable consequences. For example, it would imply that different colours of light travel at different speeds, even in a vacuum. These consequences can be searched for in laboratory experiments and astronomical observations. Current data show that $m < 10^{-54}$ kg, corresponding to $a > 3.5 \times 10^{11}$ m, which suggests that Coulomb's law remains valid over vast distances, comparable to the diameter of the Earth's orbit around the Sun.

### 1.4.3 Limitations of Coulomb's law

Coulomb's law can be used *provided that*:

- the charges are at rest;
- the locations of all the relevant charges are known.

Let's examine these requirements in more detail, beginning with the need for the charges to be at rest. In fact, motion of the charge that *experiences* the force is unimportant. Remember that *any* additional force that a charge experiences as a result of being in motion, rather than being at rest, is classified as a magnetic force. This means that the electric force on a given charge is unaffected by its own motion. However, the electric force does depend on the motion of other charges as illustrated in Figure 1.3. Coulomb's law gives the electric force in the special case where the source charges are permanently at rest.

At first sight, this appears to exclude Coulomb's law from many interesting phenomena. However, it is important to keep a sense of proportion. The corrections to Coulomb's law caused by the motion of charges turn out to be of order $\frac{1}{2}v^2/c^2$, where $v$ is the speed of the charges and $c$ is the speed of light ($3.00 \times 10^8\,\mathrm{m\,s^{-1}}$). So, even if the charges are moving at $100\,\mathrm{km\,s^{-1}}$, Coulomb's law is accurate to better than one part in $10^7$. For particles moving much slower than this, the accuracy is far greater. It is therefore reasonable to use Coulomb's law beyond its narrow domain of exactness. For all practical purposes, you can use Coulomb's law to calculate the electric forces between non-relativistic particles — that is, particles moving much more slowly than light.

The second restriction seems harmless and self-evident; to use Coulomb's law we need to know the locations of all the interacting charges. In fact, this requirement is far more troublesome than the speed restriction. To see why, suppose that two positive charges, A and B, are immersed in a conducting medium such as copper or silver (Figure 1.10). Electrons are free to flow through the conductor and are naturally drawn towards the two positive charges, forming clouds of negative charge around them. This phenomenon is called **screening**. Now charge A is repelled by charge B and attracted by the electron cloud around cloud B. The total force felt by two positive charges is therefore less than predicted by Equation 1.2. This is not because Coulomb's law is wrong, but because the situation inherently involves more than two charges. In principle we can use Equation 1.4 to find the total force on a positive charge, but unless we know how the electrons accumulate around the positive charges, there is not enough information to use this equation. Screening can be highly effective. Each conductor has a characteristic *screening length*, typically of order $10^{-9}$ m. If two stationary charges in a conductor are separated by a distance that is much larger than the screening length, each experiences essentially no net force.

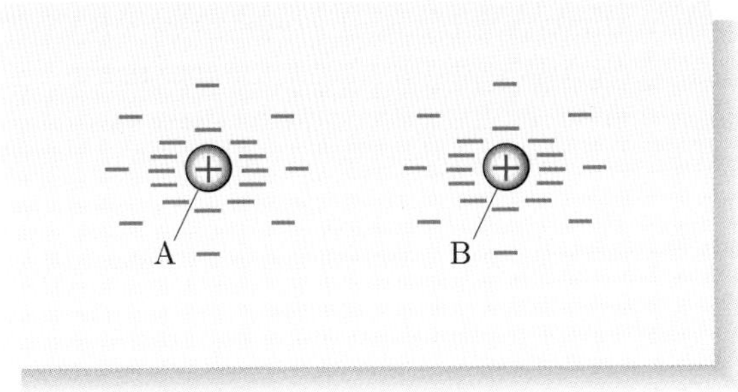

Figure 1.10 The screening of two positive charges in a metal.

Something similar, if less dramatic, occurs in non-conducting media such as water or alcohol. Electrons are not free to migrate in such materials, but the introduction of foreign charges causes small displacements of charge, either through distortions of electron clouds or re-orientations of molecules. This phenomenon is called **polarization**. These small displacements of charge, varying with the positions of molecules, produce a non-uniform charge distribution in the medium which leads to additional forces on the foreign charges. The net effect is again a reduction in the total force on each foreign charge. The effects of polarization need not be small. The net force between two stationary charges, separated by a macroscopic distance in pure water, is about $1/80$ of the force between the same charges in empty space.

In this book we restrict attention to situations where the effects of screening are simple and the effects of polarization are negligible. Polarization can certainly be ignored if the charges are surrounded by a vacuum and are far from other materials. It is also reasonable to ignore the polarization of air. The force between two charges in air is practically the same as in a vacuum, to within $0.05\%$. In general, it is possible to neglect the polarization in gases, but is unreasonable to do so in liquids or solids. The next book in this series will explain what to do when polarization really matters.

## 1.5 Electric fields

Think of two stationary charges, $Q$ and $q$, interacting via Coulomb's law in empty space. Charge $q$ seems to be aware of charge $Q$ and it is natural to suppose that information about one charge is conveyed to the other, but Coulomb's law does not describe this flow of information at all. It simply asserts that the electric force is determined by the two charges and their locations. If Coulomb's law were true for all charges, whether stationary or not, displacing a charge on Earth would have a small *but instantaneous* effect on charges on Mars. This feature is called **instantaneous action at a distance**. Faraday found this feature implausible. He believed that the ultimate laws of physics must be *local* in nature, providing relationships between quantities in each small region of space. Searching for a deeper level of understanding, he devised the concept of a field.

We now think of the space around a charge $Q$ as being subtly modified by the presence of the charge. We say that $Q$ produces an *electric field* in its surroundings. The electric field does not require the presence of a medium, and exists even in empty space. It varies from point to point, and decreases as we move away from $Q$. Now place a second charge $q$ somewhere in the region. We assume that $q$ responds to the electric field at its immediate location. Note that the charge $q$ does not need to know anything about the charge $Q$. It just responds to the electric field that it experiences. This electric field happens to be due to the charge $Q$, but that is irrelevant. If any other set of charges produced the same electric field at $q$, the response would be exactly the same. In this description, the interaction between charges is split into two steps. First, charge $Q$ produces an electric field in its surrounding space. Then charge $q$ responds locally to the electric field that it encounters.

Charge is the source of electric field.

These ideas can be made precise. In general, a **field** is a physical quantity which, at each instant, has definite values throughout a region of space. To define the value of the electric field at a given point, we place a charge at the point and measure the electric force on it. The value of the electric field is the electric force *per unit charge*. In terms of symbols, the electric field $\mathbf{E}(\mathbf{r})$ at a point $\mathbf{r}$ is defined by

$$\mathbf{E}(\mathbf{r}) = \frac{\mathbf{F}}{q}, \tag{1.5}$$

where $\mathbf{F}$ is the electric force on a charge $q$ placed at $\mathbf{r}$. This definition applies at all points in space, and the **electric field** is the function of position specified by Equation 1.5. Because its values are vectors, the electric field is a *vector field*. Our notation is very concise. In a Cartesian coordinate system it expands to

$$\mathbf{E}(\mathbf{r}) = E_x(x, y, z)\mathbf{e}_x + E_y(x, y, z)\mathbf{e}_y + E_z(x, y, z)\mathbf{e}_z,$$

where $E_x$, $E_y$ and $E_z$ are the Cartesian components of the electric field and $x$, $y$ and $z$ are the Cartesian coordinates of the point. The magnitude $E$ of the electric field is called the **electric field strength** and is given in Cartesian coordinates by

$$E = |\mathbf{E}| = \sqrt{E_x^2 + E_y^2 + E_z^2}.$$

The charge $q$ in Equation 1.5 is sometimes called a **test charge** because it tests the value of the electric field. Measurements of electric fields can be tricky because the test charge may distort the charge distribution whose field we wish to measure. This difficulty is usually avoided by taking the test charge to be small enough to create a negligible disturbance. However, the quantization of charge limits our ability to select an arbitrarily small test charge, so some disturbance may be unavoidable. This is only a practical difficulty, not a theoretical one. When we calculate an electric field from theory (using Coulomb's law or ultimately Maxwell's equations) we simply imagine that the source charges have fixed positions. Such is the power of thought!

**Exercise 1.10** What is the SI unit of electric field?

**Exercise 1.11** An isolated point charge $q_0$ is stationary at a point $\mathbf{r}_0$. Show that the electric field due to this charge is

$$\mathbf{E}(\mathbf{r}) = \frac{1}{4\pi\varepsilon_0} \frac{q_0}{|\mathbf{r} - \mathbf{r}_0|^3} (\mathbf{r} - \mathbf{r}_0). \tag{1.6}$$

Describe the nature of this electric field in words. ■

We can use Coulomb's law to find the electric field due to any arrangement of stationary charges. Suppose that charges $q_1, q_2, \ldots, q_n$ are stationary at points

$\mathbf{r}_1, \mathbf{r}_2, \ldots, \mathbf{r}_n$. If we introduce a test charge $q$ at point $\mathbf{r}$, not coincident with any of the stationary charges, Equation 1.4 shows that the electric force on this test charge is

$$\mathbf{F} = \frac{1}{4\pi\varepsilon_0} \sum_j \frac{qq_j}{|\mathbf{r} - \mathbf{r}_j|^3} (\mathbf{r} - \mathbf{r}_j).$$

Using Equation 1.5 we conclude that

$$\mathbf{E}(\mathbf{r}) = \frac{1}{4\pi\varepsilon_0} \sum_j \frac{q_j}{|\mathbf{r} - \mathbf{r}_j|^3} (\mathbf{r} - \mathbf{r}_j), \qquad (1.7)$$

where the sum is over all the charges $q_1, q_2, \ldots, q_n$. Notice that all traces of the test charge, $q$, have disappeared from Equation 1.7. The electric field is created by its sources, the stationary charges $q_1, q_2, \ldots, q_n$, and Equation 1.7 tells us how the charges and positions of these sources determine the electric field. The field is defined at any point $\mathbf{r}$ that is not coincident with one of the source charges; at the source charges themselves, it is undefined.

Notice, too, that Equation 1.7 is a sum of terms similar to the right-hand side of Equation 1.6. In other words, the electric field due to an arrangement of charges is the vector sum of the electric fields due to the individual charges in the arrangement. This is an example of a general principle, valid for all electric fields. The **principle of superposition** states that, when there is more than one source of electric field, the total electric field at any point is the vector sum of the electric fields contributed by each of the sources.

You might be tempted to think that Equation 1.7 provides an alternative definition for the electric field. Please resist this temptation. Equation 1.7 is based on Coulomb's law, so it applies only in electrostatic situations. By contrast, Equation 1.5 defines the electric field under all conditions, whether electrostatic or not. It is *the* definition of the electric field.

If we know the electric field at a given point $\mathbf{r}$, we can find the force acting on any charge $q$ placed at that point:

$$\mathbf{F} = q\mathbf{E}(\mathbf{r}). \qquad (1.8)$$

As stressed earlier, this is a *local* description. If the electric field is known at the position of a charge, the electric force on the charge can be found without further enquiry — *without knowing what is happening far away*. However, we still need to use Equation 1.7 to find the electric field. Being based on Coulomb's law, this is certainly not a local description. So our attempt to avoid action at a distance is only partially successful. The language of fields seems appropriate, but our equations still bear the non-local stamp of Coulomb's law. Nevertheless we have made a start and it is clear what should be done next. We need to find out more about the electric field in different situations. If we can understand how the values of the field in one region are related to the values in a neighbouring region we can hope to obtain a truly local theory. This will be the task of the next chapter.

**Exercise 1.12** How long does it take a proton to accelerate from rest to a speed of $1.0 \times 10^7\,\mathrm{m\,s^{-1}}$ in a constant electric field of magnitude $100\,\mathrm{N\,C^{-1}}$? ■

### 1.5.1 Arrow maps and field lines

It is useful to have a way of visualizing electric fields. The electric field at a given point can be represented by an arrow whose tail is at the point in question. The direction of the arrow is the direction of the electric field, and the length of the arrow is proportional to the magnitude of the field. The electric field throughout a region of space is then represented by an **arrow map**, which is a collection of arrows displayed at a selection of points in the region. Figure 1.11a is an arrow map for the electric field generated by an isolated positive charge, and Figure 1.11b is the corresponding arrow map for an isolated negative charge.

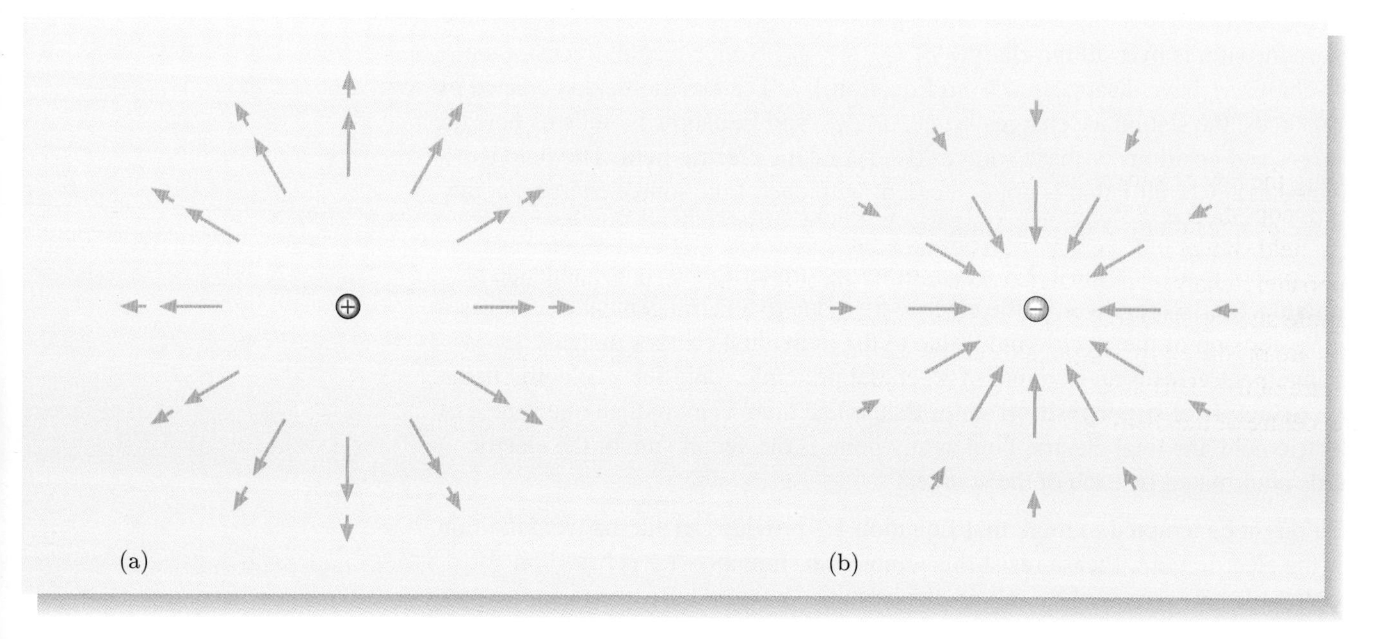


**Figure 1.11** Arrow maps for (a) an isolated positive charge and (b) an isolated negative charge. The lengths of the arrows decrease with distance according to Coulomb's inverse square law.

An alternative way of representing fields is often used. We draw continuous lines in such a way that the direction of each line is the same as the direction of the electric field at each point along its path. These lines are known as **electric field lines** and a collection of field lines is called a **field line pattern**. Figures 1.12a and 1.12b show the field line patterns generated by an isolated positive charge and by an isolated negative charge. The field lines tend to be closer together in regions where the field is strong and further apart in regions where the field in weak, but quantitative information about the strength of the field is better represented using an arrow map.

Both arrow maps and field line patterns are restricted to the two dimensions of a flat sheet of paper. In reality the field lines of Figure 1.12 occupy three-dimensional space, pointing radially outwards like the spines of a spherical hedgehog, rather than like the spokes of a wheel. In general, you will need to use some imagination to visualize how field line patterns sketched on paper extend into three dimensions.

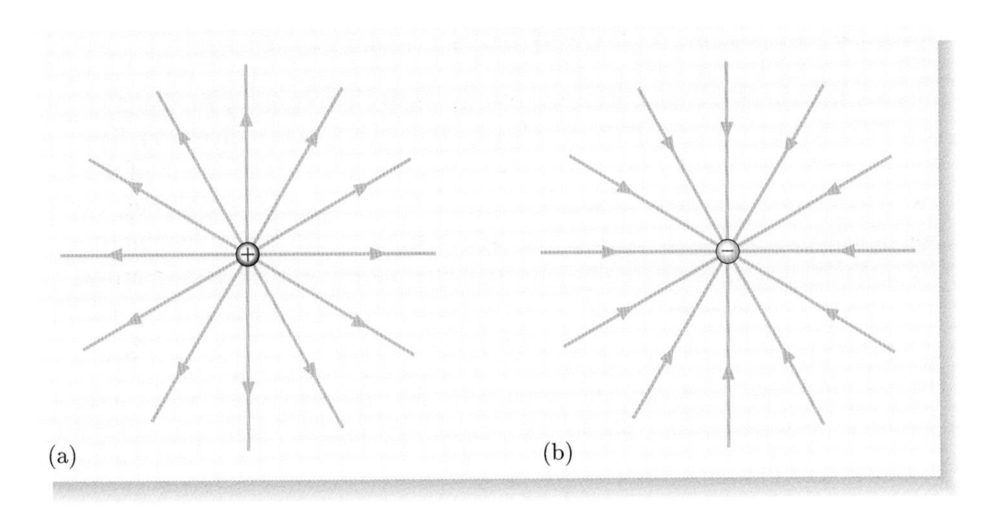


**Figure 1.12** Electric field line patterns for (a) an isolated positive charge and (b) an isolated negative charge.

Using the law of superposition, we can work out the electric fields produced by more complicated arrangements of charge, such as those shown in Figure 1.13. The field shown in Figure 1.13b is especially important. A stationary pair of oppositely-charged particles, separated by a short distance, is called an **electric dipole** and the field that it produces is called a **dipolar electric field**. Fields like this are produced by simple molecules such as hydrogen chloride, where the centre of the distribution of negatively-charged electrons does not coincide with the centre of the distribution of positively-charged nuclei.

**Figure 1.13** Electric field line patterns for: (a) a pair of positive charges; (b) a pair of opposite charges; (c) a uniform sheet of positive charge. The dashed black lines in (c) have been added to aid perspective.

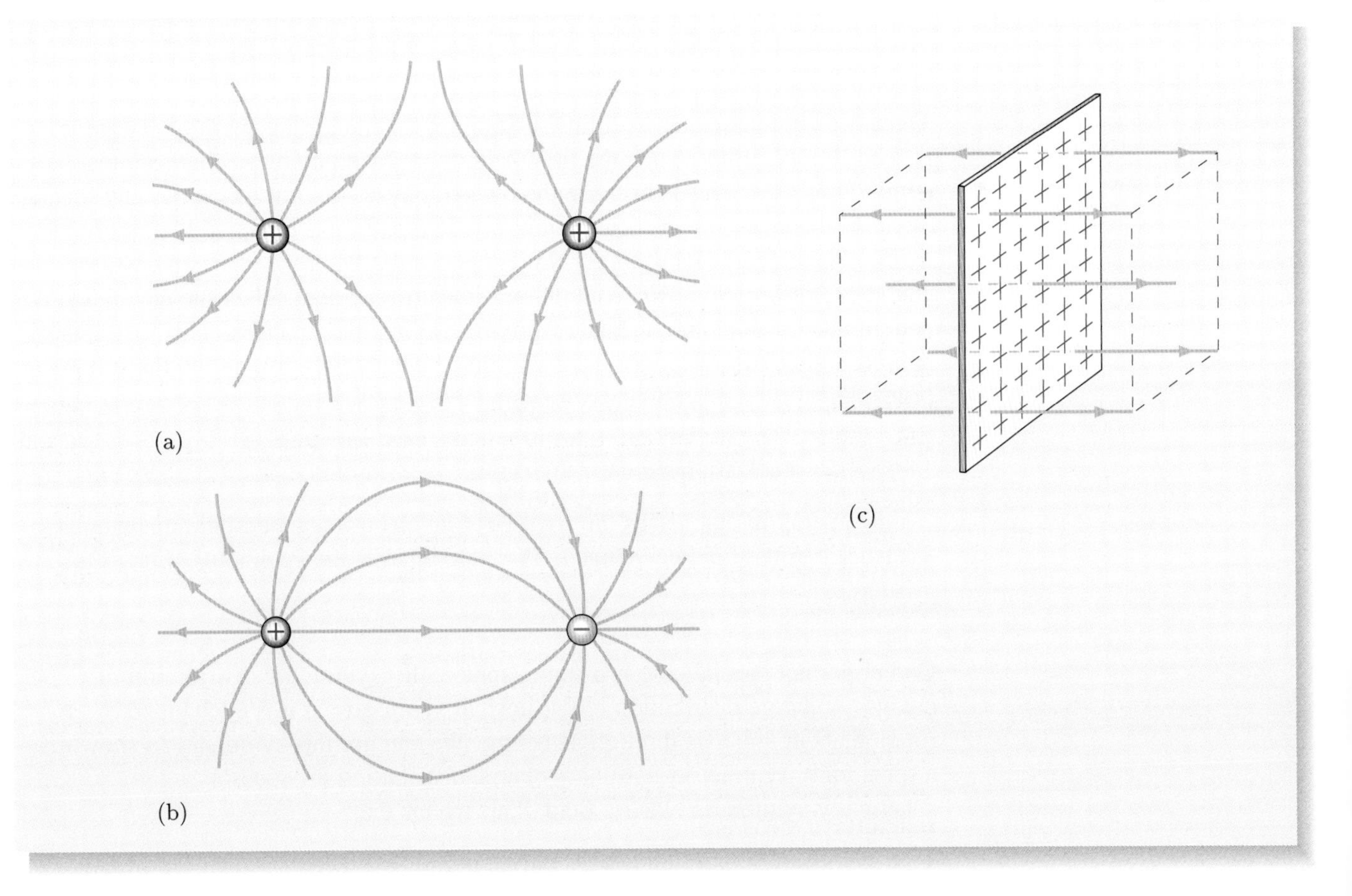

Some simple, but important points can be noted about these patterns:

- Electric field lines radiate outwards from positive charges and converge inwards towards negative charges. This captures the idea that charges are sources of electric field.
- Close enough to any point charge the electric field is similar to that for an isolated charge. Other charges have little influence in this region because they are much further away.
- Electric field lines cannot cross, except at points where the electric field vanishes. If two field lines did cross, the electric field would have two different values at the crossing point. This would give two different predictions for the acceleration of a charged particle at the crossing point, which is unreasonable.
- A situation of a given symmetry can be described by a pattern of electric field lines with the same symmetry. For example, a spherically-symmetric charge distribution generates an electric field with a spherically-symmetric pattern of electric field lines.

## 1.5.2 Symmetry arguments

When you first see an argument based on symmetry, you might wonder whether it is watertight. It might seem like intuition, guesswork or even cheating. I want to dispel such doubts. Symmetry arguments can be made completely rigorous. What is more, they are very useful in electromagnetism. Vector fields can be complicated and it helps enormously if some of this complexity can be removed at the outset.

The basic argument goes as follows. Suppose that an arrangement of charge is rotated (for example). Then the field pattern produced by these charges must be similarly rotated. This is because the laws of physics do not single out any special directions in space, so the orientation of a field pattern is completely determined by the orientation of its sources. Now, suppose that the rotated arrangement of charge is *indistinguishable* from the original arrangement. Then the new field pattern must be indistinguishable from the original field pattern. This is because a definite source must produce a definite field. We are therefore led to the following principle:

**Symmetry principle**

Any operation that leaves the sources of an electromagnetic field unchanged also leaves the field unchanged. The field inherits the symmetry of its sources.

One important special case is a static, spherically-symmetric distribution of charge. A charge distribution has **spherical symmetry** if it is unchanged by any rotation about any axis through its centre. We can use this symmetry to show that a spherically-symmetric stationary charge distribution produces a spherically-symmetric electric field. This means that:

- at any given point P the field is radial, pointing directly towards, or directly away from, the centre of the charge distribution;

- the magnitude of the field is the same at all points that are the same distance from the centre of the charge distribution.

These properties can be proved by eliminating the alternatives. Suppose, for example, that the electric field at the given point P points in some non-radial direction, as shown by the solid arrow in Figure 1.14. If we rotate the charge distribution about an axis that passes through the centre of the distribution and through the point P, the field also rotates, from the solid arrow to the dashed arrow in Figure 1.14. However, the charge distribution (being spherically symmetric) is unaffected by the rotation, so the electric field cannot change. It follows that the proposed non-radial field is impossible: the field must be radial. Similarly, let's consider the electric fields at two points, P and Q, the same distance from the centre of the spherical charge distribution. Suppose that these fields have different magnitudes, as shown in Figure 1.15a. Then we can rotate the charge distribution and the fields about an axis that passes through the centre of the charge distribution and a point midway between P and Q. A rotation of 180° produces the situation shown in Figure 1.15b. Again, the charge distribution is unaffected by the rotation, so the electric field cannot change. It follows that the magnitudes of the electric fields at P and Q must be the same.

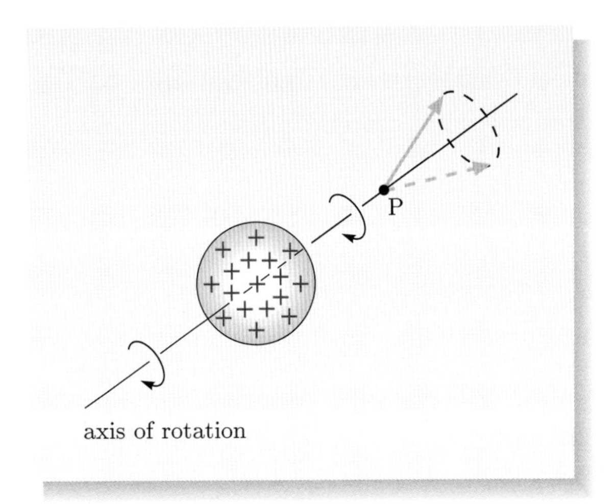


**Figure 1.14** Ruling out the possibility of a non-radial electric field at P for a spherically-symmetric charge distribution.

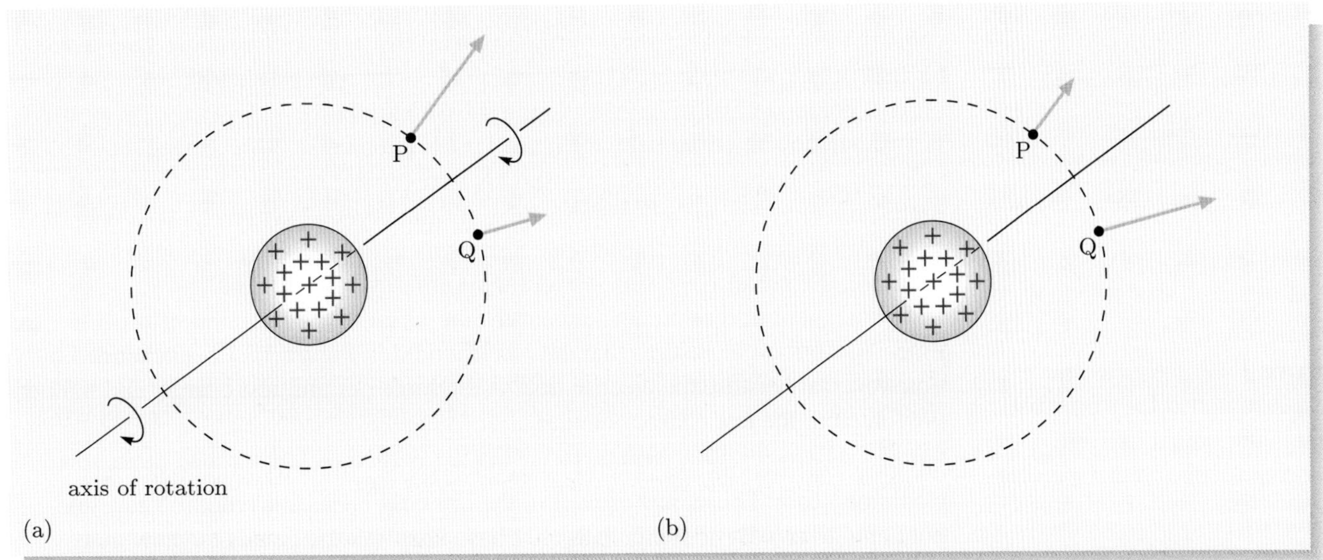


**Figure 1.15** Ruling out the possibility of an electric field with different magnitudes at P and Q for a spherically symmetric charge distribution (plan view). Situation (a) is before a 180° rotation and situation (b) is after.

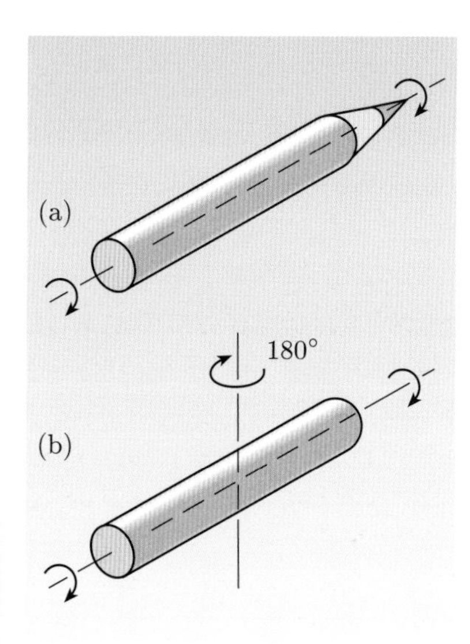


**Figure 1.16** (a) Axial symmetry and (b) cylindrical symmetry. Some books treat cylindrical symmetry as a synonym for axial symmetry. But in electromagnetism, it is helpful to distinguish between these two terms. For example, it matters that a current along a cylindrical wire has axial symmetry, but does not have cylindrical symmetry.

We are also interested in cylindrically-symmetric distributions of charge. First, note that an object is said to have **axial symmetry** if it is unchanged by any rotation about a fixed axis (the axis of symmetry). For example, a pencil with a circular cross-section has axial symmetry (Figure 1.16a). However, a pencil does not have the full symmetry of a cylinder because its sharpened end is different from its blunt end. An object is said to have **cylindrical symmetry** if, in addition to axial symmetry, it is also unchanged by a 180° rotation about any axis that passes through the midpoint, perpendicular to the axis of symmetry. Appropriately enough, a cylinder has cylindrical symmetry (Figure 1.16b). Now, consider a stationary cylinder which is infinitely-long and uniformly-charged. This distribution of charge has cylindrical symmetry. It also has **translational symmetry** because it is unchanged by any displacement along the long axis of the cylinder. These symmetries imply that:

- At any point P, not on the central axis of symmetry, the electric field is radial (pointing directly towards, or directly away from, the axis of symmetry).
- The magnitude of the electric field is the same at all points that are the same distance from the axis of symmetry.

These properties can be verified using arguments similar to those given for a sphere. In brief, the charge distribution is unchanged by a 180° rotation about an axis that passes through the given point P and meets the axis of symmetry at right angles. This implies that the electric field has no component along the axis of symmetry, and has only a radial component in the plane perpendicular to the axis of symmetry. The charge distribution is also unchanged by translations along the axis of symmetry and rotations around the axis of symmetry. This implies that the magnitude of the electric field does not vary as we move parallel to the cylinder, or around its axis, provided we stay a fixed distance from the axis.

Until now, we have considered distributions of charge that are stationary, but Figure 1.17 shows the electric field of a positive charge moving at a high steady velocity **v**. This field is *not* spherically symmetric, which is not surprising because the direction of motion of the charge singles out one direction in space from all the others. From the symmetry of the situation, one would expect the field of a uniformly-moving charge to be axially symmetric. However, the field shown in Figure 1.17 has more symmetry than this: it is *cylindrically symmetric* because it is unchanged by a 180° rotation about an axis passing through the charge, perpendicular to its line of motion. An alternative way of expressing this is to say that the electric field in Figure 1.17 is unchanged by reversing the velocity of the charge, which corresponds to reversing the direction of flow of time. This turns out to be a consequence of time-reversal symmetry — a deep symmetry which applies throughout electromagnetism. Taking charge to be invariant, the principle of **time-reversal symmetry** asserts that all electromagnetic forces are unchanged by a reversal in the direction of flow of time. This principle ensures that the electric field in Figure 1.17 is unchanged by time-reversal because the electric field is the force per unit test charge, and neither the force nor the test charge changes.

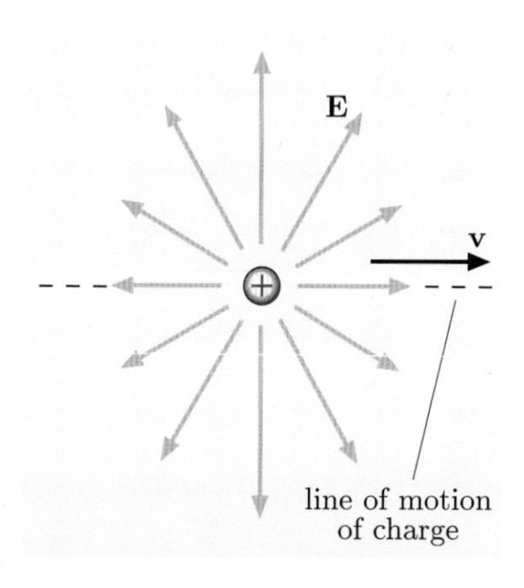


**Figure 1.17** An electric field-arrow map for a positive charge moving at uniform velocity **v** close to the speed of light.

All these conclusions are general consequences of symmetry, and do not rely on Coulomb's law. This is just as well in the last case because Coulomb's law does not apply to rapidly-moving charges. I have spelt out the details to show that symmetry arguments are respectable, but with experience you can be much more concise. Provided a question does not explicitly ask for a symmetry argument, you may simply use a suitable form for the field and briefly indicate which type of symmetry is being assumed (e.g. spherical symmetry or axial + time-reversal symmetry).

**Exercise 1.13** Use symmetry to discuss the direction of the electric field near a stationary uniformly-charged plane sheet.

**Essential skill**
Making symmetry arguments.

**Exercise 1.14** Describe the direction of the electric field on the central axis of a short cylinder carrying a uniform positive charge. Sketch a set of arrows indicating roughly how you would expect the electric field to vary in direction and magnitude along the central axis of the cylinder. ■

### 1.5.3 Typical electric field values

It is worth noting some typical values of electric fields encountered in various circumstances (Table 1.3). Some of the fields listed in this table are rapidly oscillating and cannot be discussed in the context of electrostatics. Nevertheless, a broad feeling for typical values may help you spot gross errors in calculations and appreciate the range of fields that are needed for different purposes.

**Table 1.3** Some typical electric fields.

| Context | $E/\text{N}\,\text{C}^{-1}$ |
|---|---|
| strong TV or radio signal | 0.01 |
| inside copper wire of diameter 1 mm, carrying 1 A | 0.02 |
| time-averaged field near transmitting mobile phone | 40 |
| safety guideline at radio frequencies | 60 |
| 30 cm from a hair dryer | 80 |
| average static field at Earth's surface | 100 |
| on an electric blanket | $2 \times 10^3$ |
| 30 m from a 220 kV power line | $3 \times 10^3$ |
| in DNA fingerprinting procedure | $5 \times 10^3$ |
| static field at Earth's surface below a thundercloud | $5 \times 10^3$ |
| safety guideline at mains frequency | $5 \times 10^4$ |
| just outside a charged photocopier drum | $1 \times 10^5$ |
| breakdown field in dry air | $3 \times 10^6$ |
| breakdown field in PVC insulating tape | $2 \times 10^7$ |
| in a powerful particle accelerator | $3 \times 10^7$ |
| in a hydrogen atom | $5 \times 10^{11}$ |
| in the most intensely focused laser beams | $6 \times 10^{13}$ |
| quantum electrodynamic critical field | $1.3 \times 10^{18}$ |

Several items in Table 1.3 refer to the electric fields around electrical equipment. It is reassuring to note that these fields are generally within safety guidelines. When assessing any risk, the frequency of the electric field is an important factor, for example, radio-frequency fields are far more hazardous than low-frequency or static fields. This explains why the safety of mobile phones has been investigated in depth. The issues are complex because mobile phones reduce their signals to

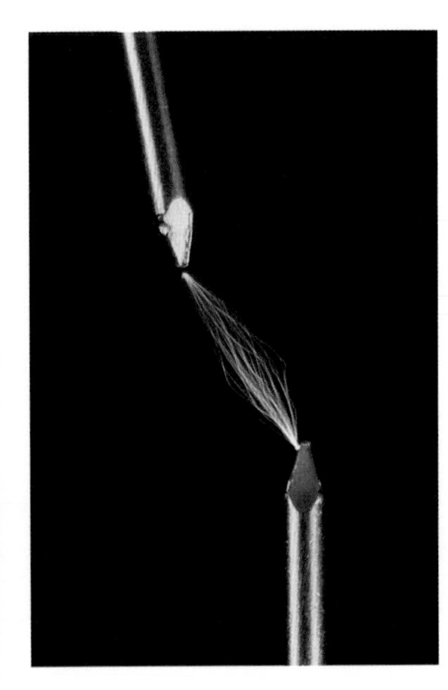

**Figure 1.18** Sparks flying between two nails.

the minimum needed to communicate with the network and do not transmit at all unless the user is speaking. Also, to increase the number of simultaneous users on the network, each phone transmits in brief sub-millisecond bursts interspersed by much longer intervals of radio silence. The result is that, while the peak electric field may exceed the radio-frequency guideline, the field averaged over 1 s does not.

Table 1.3 also gives values for breakdown fields. Any insulator becomes a conductor in a sufficiently high electric field. The minimum field needed to cause this transformation is called the **breakdown field** of the insulator. The breakdown field of dry air is about $3 \times 10^6\,\mathrm{N\,C^{-1}}$, but that of moist air is only about $1 \times 10^6\,\mathrm{N\,C^{-1}}$. Air always contains a few electrons and ionized molecules. Breakdown of air occurs when the electric field accelerates these charged particles rapidly enough, so that their collisions with other molecules produce more electrons and ionized molecules. An avalanche of charged particles then cuts a conducting path through the air and sparks fly (Figure 1.18). If you have ever felt the snap of static electricity, you must have been briefly exposed to an electric field of at least a million newtons per coulomb.

Everyone has heard of the Earth's magnetic field, but the **Earth's electric field** is less well known. Nevertheless, the Earth does have an electric field which, on average, points vertically downwards and has a magnitude of about $100\,\mathrm{N\,C^{-1}}$. This field exists because the planet's surface carries a negative charge of $-5 \times 10^5\,\mathrm{C}$ while the upper atmosphere carries a compensating positive charge. The atmosphere is not a perfect insulator so the Earth's electric field drives a small current downwards. This would neutralize the Earth's negative charge and remove the Earth's electric field within minutes were it not for the effects of lightning (Figure 1.19). Below a thundercloud the electric field points vertically upwards and is roughly 50 times stronger than normal — even higher in places, enough to make your hair stand on end. Lightning conducts currents upwards, from the ground to the cloud. Over the entire Earth, around 40 000 thunderstorms per day keep our planet negatively charged, maintaining a relatively constant downward electric field.

**Figure 1.19** Lightning keeps planet Earth negatively charged.

Finally, the last row of the table takes us beyond classical electromagnetism, into the domain of quantum electrodynamics. In rough terms, quantum electrodynamics tells us that electrons (of charge $-e$) and positrons (of charge $e$) are continuously created and destroyed in a vacuum. These particles have a rather shadowy existence — they come and go very rapidly and do not have the masses of real electrons and positrons. For this reason, they are called *virtual particles*. To conserve charge, the electrons and positrons appear and disappear in pairs. The virtual pairs exert forces on other charges so the vacuum behaves rather like a tenuous insulating medium. This leads to a number of barely measurable effects. For example, the repulsive forces felt by two closely-spaced electrons deviate very slightly from Coulomb's law at separations below $10^{-12}$ m. Such effects are ignored throughout this course. However, something much more spectacular is predicted to occur in the presence of an enormous electric field. If a static electric field exceeds a critical value throughout a region whose linear dimensions are much larger than $10^{-12}$ m, the electron and positron in a virtual pair should be able to gain enough energy from the field to transform into a real electron and a real positron. These charged particles separate rapidly in the field and the insulating nature of the vacuum is predicted to break down at the **quantum electrodynamic critical field**, $1.3 \times 10^{18}\,\mathrm{N\,C^{-1}}$, just as the insulating nature of moist air breaks down at $10^{6}\,\mathrm{N\,C^{-1}}$ in a lightning flash. Nobody has observed this effect because of the enormity of the required electric field, but recent advances in lasers raise hopes for a definitive test.

By *real* electrons, we mean of course the stable particles found in atoms.

## Summary of Chapter 1

**Section 1.1** Electric charge is the property that allows particles to exert and experience electromagnetic forces. Electric charge is a scalar quantity which is additive, quantized, locally conserved and invariant.

**Section 1.2** Electromagnetic forces are velocity-dependent. This is important for particles moving at speeds comparable to that of light and is also significant in neutral systems containing a large number of slowly-moving particles (e.g. current-carrying wires).

**Section 1.3** It is customary to split electromagnetic forces into electric and magnetic contributions. A stationary point charge experiences only the electric force. A moving charge experiences the same electric force as a stationary charge; any additional electromagnetic force that it experiences by virtue of being in motion, rather than being at rest, is classified as a magnetic force.

**Section 1.4** Electric forces between stationary charges are called electrostatic forces. The electrostatic force between two charges is given by Coulomb's law:

$$\mathbf{F}_{12} = \frac{1}{4\pi\varepsilon_0}\frac{q_1 q_2}{r_{12}^2}\,\widehat{\mathbf{r}}_{12},$$

where $\mathbf{F}_{12}$ is the force on particle 1 due to particle 2 and $\widehat{\mathbf{r}}_{12}$ is a unit vector pointing towards particle 1 from particle 2. The electrostatic force due to a number of stationary sources is found by vector addition, using Coulomb's law and the law of addition of force.

Coulomb's law has been experimentally tested over a wide range of length scales. It works well enough for slowly-moving particles and for charges in gaseous media but it is not valid for very rapidly moving particles and its implications can be obscured by the effects of screening or polarization in liquid or solid media.

**Section 1.5** The electric field $\mathbf{E}(\mathbf{r})$ is a vector field defined throughout a region of space. Its spatial variation can be visualized using an arrow map or a field line pattern. At any given point the value of the electric field is given by

$$\mathbf{E}(\mathbf{r}) = \frac{\mathbf{F}}{q},$$

where $\mathbf{F}$ is the force that would be experienced by a charge $q$ placed at the point $\mathbf{r}$. Electric fields obey the principle of superposition: the electric field due to a set of sources is the vector sum of the individual electric fields due to each source. An electric field inherits the symmetry of its sources: any operation that leaves the sources unchanged also leaves the electric field unchanged.

## Achievements from Chapter 1

*After studying this chapter you should be able to:*

**1.1** Explain the meaning of the newly defined (emboldened) terms and symbols, and use them appropriately.

**1.2** Distinguish between electric, electrostatic and magnetic forces.

**1.3** State Coulomb's law in vector form and use it to find the total electrostatic force due to a small number of point charges.

**1.4** Define the electric field.

**1.5** State the principle of superposition for electric fields and use it to find the total electric field due to a small number of point charges.

**1.6** Use symmetry principles to deduce some properties of electric fields.

*After studying MT 8.1 you should also be able to:*

**1.7** Use vector notation consistently.

**1.8** Carry out basic calculations in vector algebra involving components, magnitudes, unit vectors, multiplication of vectors by scalars and vector addition.

# Chapter 2 Gauss's law

## Introduction

This chapter has a simple aim. It takes Coulomb's law and expresses it in the language of vector calculus — that is, in terms of volume integrals, surface integrals and partial derivatives. There are many reasons to make this transition. Some problems that are difficult to solve using Coulomb's law become much easier when expressed in terms of vector calculus. More importantly, vector calculus is the natural language for fields. It allows us to construct a truly local theory of electromagnetism, expressed entirely in terms of relationships between physical quantities at individual points in space, and avoiding the troublesome idea of action at a distance. Finally, there is a marvellous gift from the gods. You will remember that Coulomb's law is an electrostatic result — it only covers situations in which the source charges are at rest. Using vector calculus, we will derive a consequence of Coulomb's law, known as Gauss's law. But we get more than we bargain for. Gauss's law turns out to be true in all situations, whether the charges are stationary or not. So vector calculus gives us a way of escaping the shackles of electrostatics. This is the path that Maxwell took. Although his notation was more cumbersome than ours, he had the basic concepts of vector calculus and set out to express all the known laws of electromagnetism (and any additional laws that he might discover) in terms of these concepts.

This chapter uses the mathematical concepts of fields, partial differentiation, volume integration, surface integration and divergence, which are covered in MT 8.3–8.6. Some of this material may be revision. Even so, you should be prepared to spend at least as much time on the mathematics as on the physics, doubling your study-time on this chapter.

## 2.1 Charge density and electric flux

Before developing Gauss's law, it is useful to get some preliminaries out of the way. One of the tasks we need to perform is that of finding the total charge within a given region. In principle, this is easy. Electric charge resides on particles such as electrons or protons. For macroscopic purposes, these particles can be treated as point-like objects, which are either inside or outside the region. According to the law of addition of charge, the total charge within a given region is then given by

► Read MT 8.3–8.5 now. This will be a lengthy detour, but is all essential material.

$$Q = \sum_i q_i, \qquad (2.1)$$

where $q_i$ is the charge on particle $i$, and the sum extends over all the particles within the region. Although adding charges is a perfectly well-defined task, it is not always a very enviable one as huge numbers of particles might be involved. For most purposes it is better to treat charge as if it were spread out continuously through space, like a fluid. A continuous distribution of charge is characterized by a charge density, which is the charge per unit volume.

The **charge density** $\rho(\mathbf{r})$ at a point $\mathbf{r}$ is defined by taking a small volume element centred on the point, adding up the charge $\Delta Q$ within the volume element, and then dividing by the volume $\Delta V$ of the element. That is,

$$\rho(\mathbf{r}) = \frac{\Delta Q}{\Delta V}.$$

For small volumes, the value of $\Delta Q/\Delta V$ will be almost independent of the shape and size of the volume $\Delta V$. However, the volume element must not be too small. If we are interested in the charge distribution throughout a battery, for example, we would not choose a volume element on the scale of an atomic nucleus. Such a volume element would give a large charge density if it contained a nucleus and a small charge density if it did not. The charge density would then vary wildly and rapidly in space (and also in time, if the nuclei move). Such detail is usually unnecessary and unhelpful. We assume that the volume elements are large enough to smooth out such variations, but still small enough to characterize the charge density in any small part of the system. With an appropriate choice, the charge density is a smoothly-varying function, except possibly at material boundaries where it may change abruptly.

Given a smoothly-varying charge density, we can find the total charge within a region $V$ by *integrating* the charge density over the volume. The sum in Equation 2.1 can then be replaced by the volume integral

$$Q = \int_V \rho(\mathbf{r})\, \mathrm{d}V, \tag{2.2}$$

where $V$ is the volume of interest. In some cases, integrating a charge density is more fundamental than adding point charges. For example, a single electron in an atom behaves like a continuous cloud of negative charge. To find the total charge within a small region of an atom we therefore rely on Equation 2.2 rather than Equation 2.1.

**Essential skill**

Exploiting symmetry to evaluate volume integrals.

**Worked Example 2.1**

A spherically-symmetric charge distribution has charge density

$$\rho(r) = Ar \quad \text{for} \quad r \leq R,$$

where $r$ is the distance from the origin and $A$ is a constant. For $r > R$ the charge density is zero. What is the total charge of this charge distribution?

**Solution**

Because the charge distribution is spherically symmetric, we subdivide it into a set of thin spherical shells, rather like the layers of an onion (Figure 2.1). The surface area of a sphere of radius $r$ is $4\pi r^2$, so a thin spherical shell with inner radius $r$ and outer radius $r + \delta r$ has thickness $\delta r$ and volume $4\pi r^2\, \delta r$. The charge density in this shell is $Ar$, so the shell contributes a charge

$$\delta Q = Ar \times 4\pi r^2\, \delta r = 4\pi A r^3\, \delta r.$$

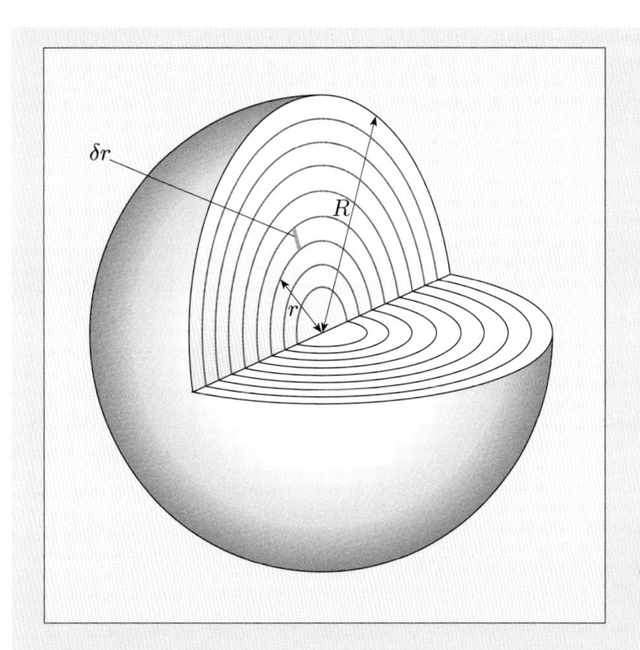


**Figure 2.1** A sphere of radius $R$ is split into thin spherical shells.

The total charge is obtained by integrating over all the shells from $r = 0$ to $r = R$, giving

$$Q = \int_0^R 4\pi A r^3 \, \mathrm{d}r = 4\pi A \left[ \frac{r^4}{4} \right]_0^R = \pi A R^4.$$

The other concept we need is that of the **electric flux** over a surface. Flux is discussed in MT 8.5.2; here, we just summarize the main ideas. The simplest surface to consider is a plane element. We consider a plane element located at $\mathbf{r}$, with area $\Delta S$ and unit normal $\widehat{\mathbf{n}}$ (Figure 2.2).

There are two possible unit normals to choose from, so our specification of a plane element involves the selection of one of these. The element is taken to be so small that the electric field is constant all over it. Then we define

$$\text{electric flux over element} = E_n \, \Delta S,$$

where $E_n$ is the normal component of the electric field on the element (that is, the electric field in the direction of the unit normal, $\widehat{\mathbf{n}}$). Writing $E_n = \mathbf{E} \cdot \widehat{\mathbf{n}}$, we have

$$\text{electric flux over element} = (\mathbf{E} \cdot \widehat{\mathbf{n}}) \, \Delta S = \mathbf{E} \cdot \Delta\mathbf{S},$$

where $\Delta\mathbf{S} = \widehat{\mathbf{n}} \, \Delta S$ is the **oriented area** of the plane element — a vector whose magnitude is the area of the element and whose direction is that of the unit normal of the element. We are generally interested in extended surfaces. To find the electric flux over an extended surface, we divide the surface into many tiny patches, each of which can be approximated by a plane element. The unit normals of neighbouring elements are chosen to be almost parallel (rather than almost antiparallel). Then the total flux over the surface is approximated by the sum of the fluxes over all the surface elements. In the limit of vanishingly small patches this approximation becomes exact and the sum is replaced by a surface integral:

$$\text{electric flux over an extended surface } S = \int_S \mathbf{E} \cdot \mathrm{d}\mathbf{S}.$$

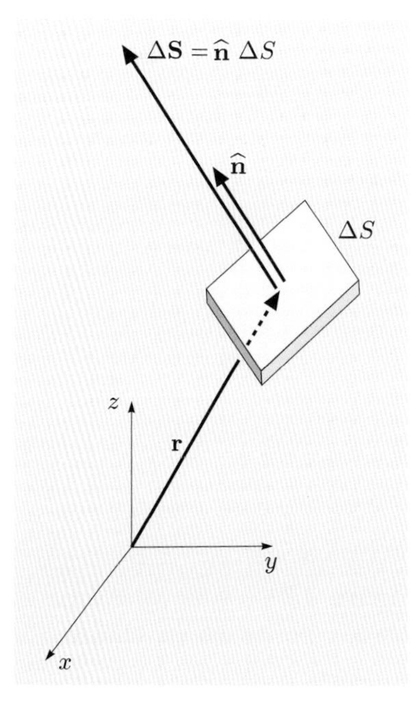


**Figure 2.2** A plane element.

One special case is very important. If the normal component of the electric field is constant all over a surface, the electric flux is just the normal component of the electric field on the surface times the surface area of the surface.

This chapter will concentrate on closed surfaces. A **closed surface** is one that forms a complete barrier between its interior and exterior regions. It is conventional to take all the unit normals on a closed surface to point outwards into the exterior region. This means that the electric flux over a closed surface is an *outward* flux. It is positive for a closed surface containing an isolated positive charge and negative for a closed surface containing an isolated negative charge.

**Exercise 2.1** An electric field is constant throughout a region of space which contains a cube. Show that the electric flux over the surface of the cube is equal to zero. ■

## 2.2 The road to Gauss's law

Coulomb's law tells us that the electric field of a stationary charge is radially directed, spherically symmetrical and falls off as the inverse square of the distance from the charge. We can express this behaviour in a striking geometric way.

Consider a sphere of radius $R$, centred on a point charge $q$ that is stationary at the origin. No other charges are anywhere near the sphere. We will calculate the electric flux produced by $q$ over the surface of the sphere. The sphere is a *closed* surface and we adopt the standard convention of taking its unit normals to point *outwards* into the exterior space. Then, at any point on the surface of the sphere, the normal component of the field is $q/4\pi\varepsilon_0 R^2$, a result which follows from Coulomb's law.

Because the normal component of the field is constant over the surface of the sphere, the required surface integral is obtained by multiplying the normal component by the surface area $4\pi R^2$ of the sphere. That is,

$$\int_{\text{sphere}} \mathbf{E} \cdot \mathrm{d}\mathbf{S} = \frac{q}{4\pi\varepsilon_0 R^2} \times 4\pi R^2 = \frac{q}{\varepsilon_0}. \tag{2.3}$$

This is positive for $q > 0$ and negative for $q < 0$, as expected from Figure 2.3.

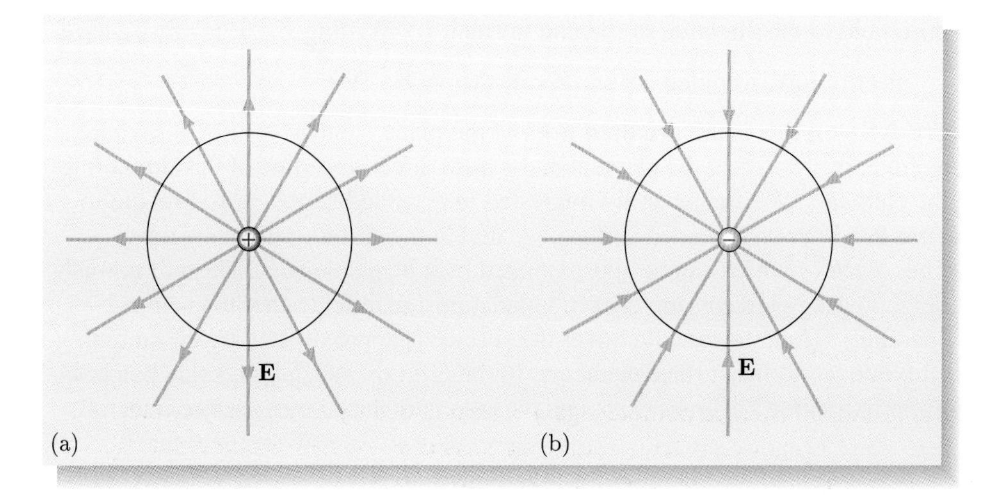


**Figure 2.3** (a) Positive flux due to a positive point charge; (b) negative flux due to a negative point charge.

Although the electric flux depends on the charge at the centre of the sphere *it does not depend on the radius of the sphere*. It is easy to see why. The electric field obeys an inverse square law, decreasing as $1/R^2$, while the surface area of the sphere grows as $R^2$. These two factors cancel out in Equation 2.3, leaving the electric flux independent of the radius of the sphere.

Equation 2.3 is the simplest example of a very powerful result. **Gauss's law** states that the electric flux over *any* closed surface $S$ is equal to the total charge enclosed by the surface, divided by $\varepsilon_0$. Moreover, any charge outside the surface makes no contribution to the electric flux over the surface, so

$$\text{electric flux over } S = \int_S \mathbf{E} \cdot \mathrm{d}\mathbf{S} = \frac{Q}{\varepsilon_0}, \tag{2.4}$$

where $Q$ is the total charge *enclosed* by $S$. You have seen that this is true for a spherical surface centred on an isolated stationary charge, but Gauss's law impressively extends this result to all closed surfaces and all distributions of charge. Gauss's law is the major subject of this chapter. I shall now explain why it is true.

**Figure 2.4** Carl Friedrich Gauss discovered Gauss's law in 1835 but did not publish it, probably because he regarded it as only one step towards a complete theory of electromagnetism, which he hoped to develop. Gauss's discovery was published posthumously in 1867 but by this time, it had been rediscovered by Lord Kelvin and identified as a fundamental law of electromagnetism by Maxwell.

For the sake of intellectual honesty you should follow the derivation through, but bear in mind that the final result is much more important than the supporting argument. The proof ends on page 45.

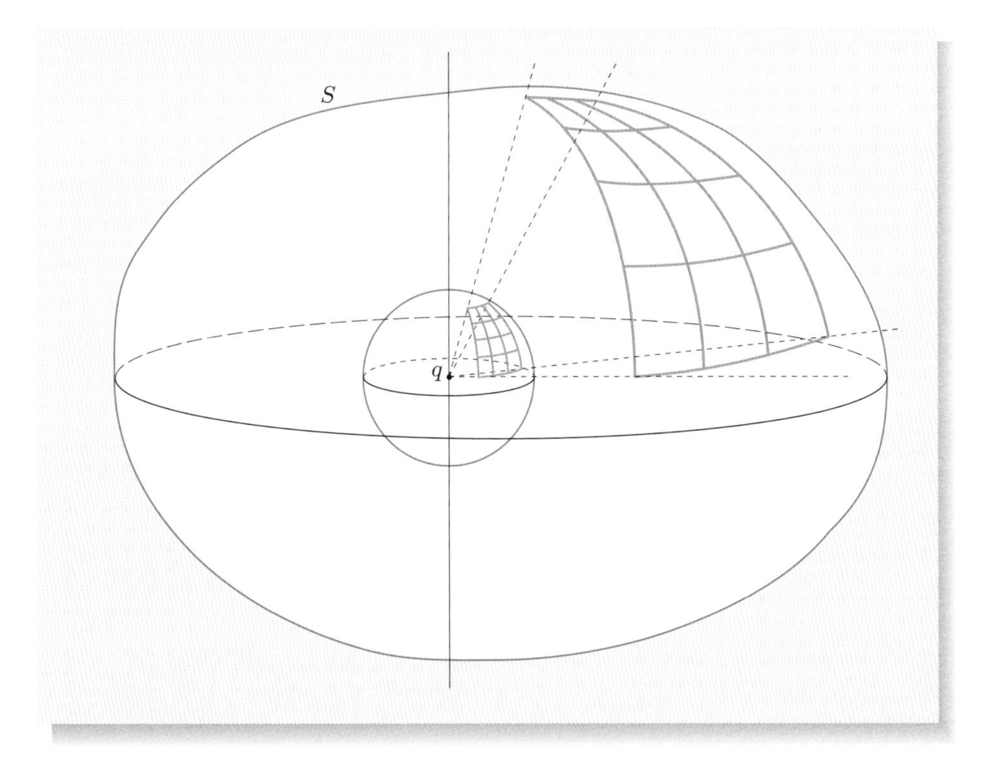


**Figure 2.5** Projecting a mesh from an inner sphere to an outer surface $S$.

**Start of proof**

Suppose that an isolated point charge $q$ is surrounded by an arbitrary closed surface $S$. To begin with, let's assume that $S$ is **convex**, which means that it bulges outwards like a rugby ball so that, viewed from the outside, there are no hollows. We imagine a small sphere, centred on the charge and contained entirely within $S$. This sphere is covered by a fine mesh which is projected from the position of the charge onto the outer surface (Figure 2.5). What is interesting is that the flux over any patch on the sphere is equal to the flux over the corresponding projected patch on the surface $S$.

To see why, let's initially look at the simplest case, in which the outer surface is a sphere. Consider a projected patch $\Delta S_{\text{sph}}$ that is part of the surface of a large sphere centred on the charge (Figure 2.6). Such a patch is an enlargement of a patch $\Delta S_0$ on the inner sphere, similar in shape but with each of its linear dimensions enlarged by a factor $R/R_0$, where $R$ and $R_0$ are the distances of the outer and inner patches from the charge. It follows that the area of the outer patch is greater than that of the inner patch by a factor $(R/R_0)^2$. The unit normals of both patches point radially away from the charge, so the normal component of the electric field over each patch is equal to the radial component of the field. Because the field obeys an inverse square law, this is smaller over the outer patch by a factor $(R_0/R)^2$. The two factors, $(R/R_0)^2$ and $(R_0/R)^2$ cancel out, confirming that the electric fluxes over the two patches are the same.

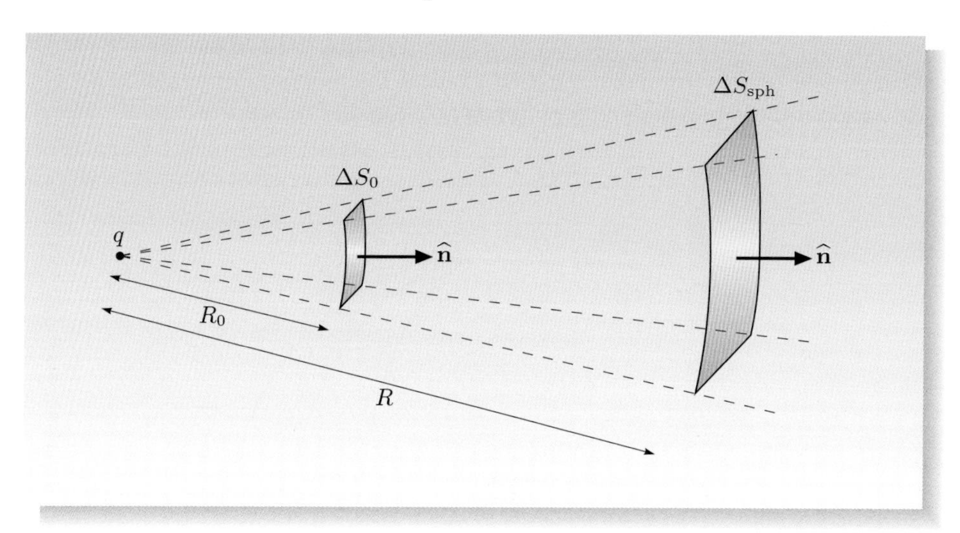


**Figure 2.6** A patch $\Delta S_0$ on an inner sphere is projected onto a patch $\Delta S_{\text{sph}}$ on an outer sphere. Both spheres are centred on the charge $q$.

Now let's look at the general case, in which the outer surface is *not* a sphere (Figure 2.7a). A patch $\Delta S_0$ on the inner sphere is projected onto a patch $\Delta S$ of the outer surface. This patch is not perpendicular to the radial direction from the charge, and it is not an enlargement of $\Delta S_0$, but is stretched more in some directions than others. To see whether this affects our conclusion, it is helpful to imagine a sphere, centred on the charge, whose surface passes through $\Delta S$. We then project $\Delta S_0$ onto this spherical surface, producing a patch $\Delta S_{\text{sph}}$. The two patches, $\Delta S$ and $\Delta S_{\text{sph}}$ are both projected from $\Delta S_0$ and are both the same distance from the charge, but they are inclined at different angles: $\Delta S_{\text{sph}}$ is perpendicular to the radial direction but $\Delta S$ is not. Bear in mind that these patches have been drawn large enough to see, but that our analysis will assume that they are arbitrarily small. This allows us to approximate each patch by a plane element, with negligible variation of electric field over the element, and for the dotted projection lines to be effectively parallel in the vicinity of the element. These approximations are illustrated in the enlarged view shown in Figure 2.7b.

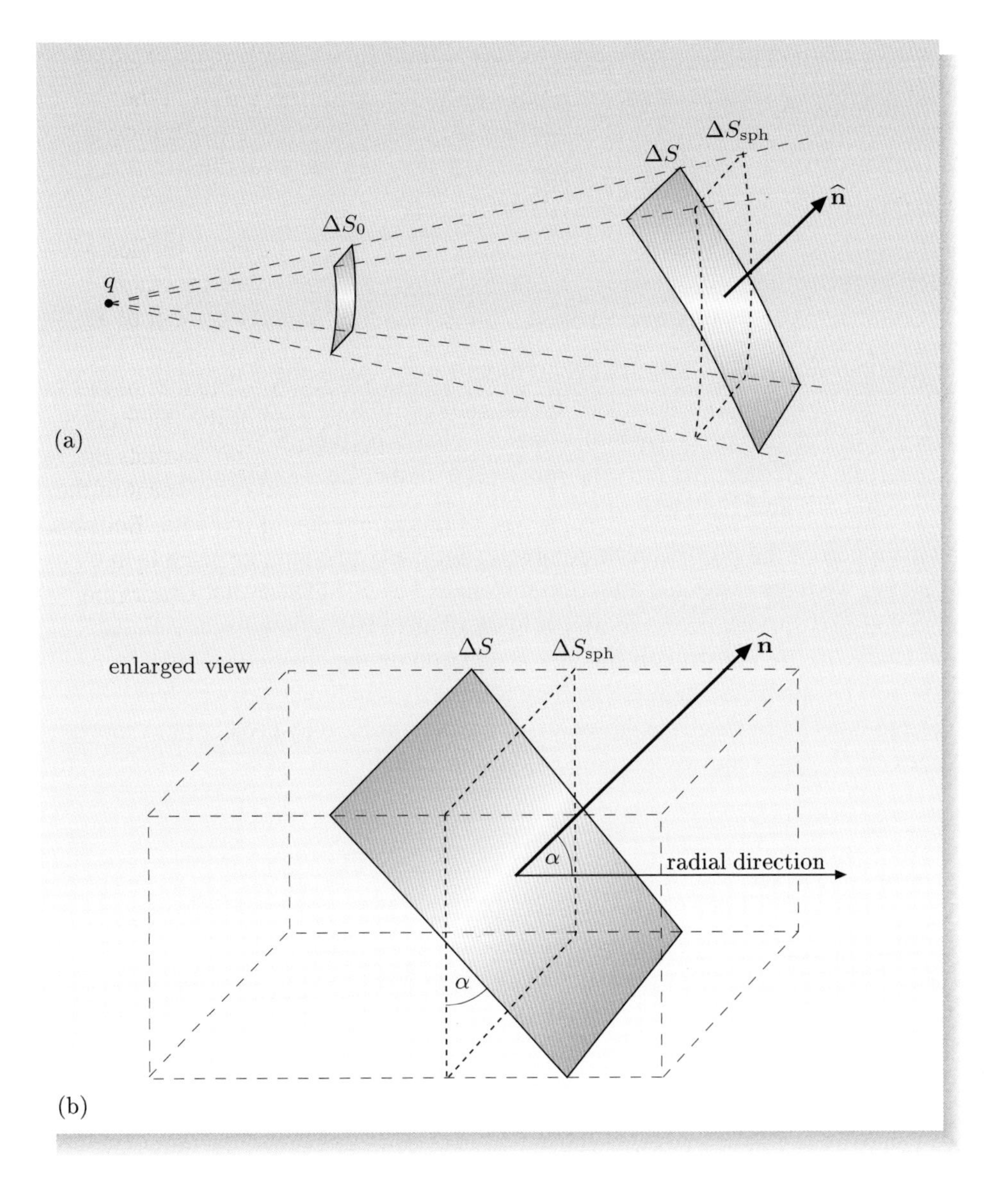


**Figure 2.7** (a) A patch $\Delta S_0$ on an inner sphere is projected onto a patch $\Delta S$ on a non-spherical surface. This is compared with the patch $\Delta S_{\mathrm{sph}}$, obtained by projecting $\Delta S_0$ onto the surface of a sphere.
(b) Enlarged view used to show that the fluxes over $\Delta S$ and $\Delta S_{\mathrm{sph}}$ are the same.

We now compare the electric fluxes over $\Delta S$ and $\Delta S_{\mathrm{sph}}$. First note that the normal component of the electric field over $\Delta S_{\mathrm{sph}}$ is $E_r$, the radial component of the electric field due to $q$, while the normal component of the electric field over $\Delta S$ is

$$E_n = E_r \cos\alpha,$$

where $\alpha$ is the angle between the normals of $\Delta S$ and $\Delta S_{\mathrm{sph}}$. Because the surface $S$ bulges outwards, $\alpha$ is an acute angle, so $E_n$ has the same sign as $E_r$ but is smaller. On the other hand, the area of $\Delta S$ is greater than that of $\Delta S_{\mathrm{sph}}$. Elementary trigonometry in Figure 2.7b shows that

$$\Delta S = \frac{\Delta S_{\mathrm{sph}}}{\cos\alpha}.$$

The flux over a plane element is the product of the normal component of the field times the area of the element so, when we compare the two fluxes, the factors of

$\cos\alpha$ cancel out. That is,

$$\begin{aligned}\text{flux over } \Delta S &= E_n\,\Delta S\\ &= E_r\cos\alpha\,\frac{\Delta S_{\text{sph}}}{\cos\alpha}\\ &= E_r\,\Delta S_{\text{sph}}\\ &= \text{flux over } \Delta S_{\text{sph}}.\end{aligned}$$

Our previous argument showed that the flux over $\Delta S_{\text{sph}}$ is the same as that over $\Delta S_0$, so the flux over $\Delta S$ must also be the same as that over $\Delta S_0$. Because the surface $S$ bulges outwards, each of its patches has a partner in $S_0$, and vice versa. We therefore conclude that the total flux over $S$ is the same as the total flux over $S_0$, and this, we already know, is $q/\varepsilon_0$.

The main part of the proof is now complete, but there are some loose ends to tidy up. So far, we have restricted attention to convex closed surfaces but Figure 2.8 shows a closed surface $S$ of a more complex shape which contains an isolated point charge $q$. We construct a sphere, $S_0$, centred on the charge and entirely inside $S$. The sphere is again covered by arbitrarily small patches which are projected onto $S$. In this case, however, one patch on $S_0$ may project onto several patches on $S$. This requires a modification of our argument.

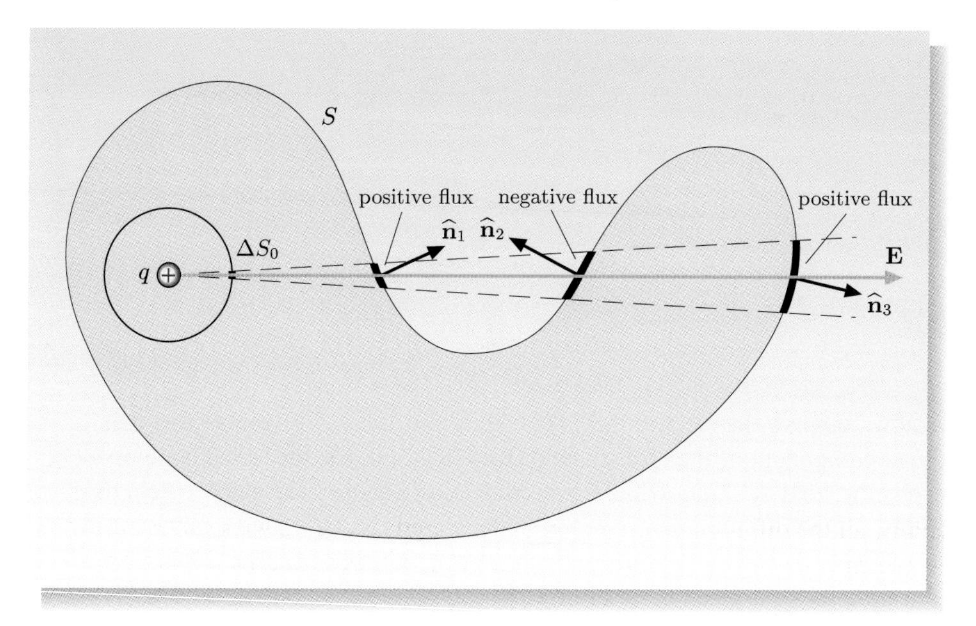


**Figure 2.8** Cross-sectional view of a general closed surface $S$. Successive projected patches have fluxes of alternating sign.

Consider all the patches that are produced when a given patch $\Delta S_0$ of the inner mesh is projected onto $S$. For reasons described earlier, the magnitude of the flux is the same over all these patches. However, we need to think carefully about the sign of the flux in each case. In the case of a spherical or rugby-ball shaped surface all the patches contribute fluxes of the same sign (positive for $q > 0$ and negative for $q < 0$), but this is not true for the surface in Figure 2.8. The electric field lines can enter or leave this surface, depending on the orientation of a given patch. Because the unit normals of a closed surface always point outwards, the flux is positive in regions where the field lines leave $S$ and negative in regions where they enter it. Consequently, as we step radially outwards from the charge, the fluxes contributed by successive projected patches cancel out in pairs. The outward journey away from the charge towards infinity must always involve an odd number of crossings of the surface, so $\Delta S_0$ projects onto an odd number of patches on $S$. Because of the cancellations, the total flux contributed by all these patches reduces to the flux over the last patch in the set. Our argument then goes through as before: the flux over this last patch is equal to the flux over $\Delta S_0$. So, summing over all the patches on $S$, the total flux over $S$ is equal to the total flux over $S_0$, namely $q/\varepsilon_0$.

We should also consider the flux produced by an isolated point charge $q$ *outside* a closed surface, $S$ (Figure 2.9). To do this we again project outwards from the charge onto $S$. Our previous argument goes through almost as before. The only important difference is that, as we step radially outwards from the charge towards infinity, we cross $S$ an *even* number of times, so projecting in a given direction produces an even number of patches on $S$. The flux contributions from these patches again cancel out in pairs so, summing over all the patches on $S$, we obtain a total flux of zero. Charges *outside* a closed surface do not contribute to the flux over that surface.

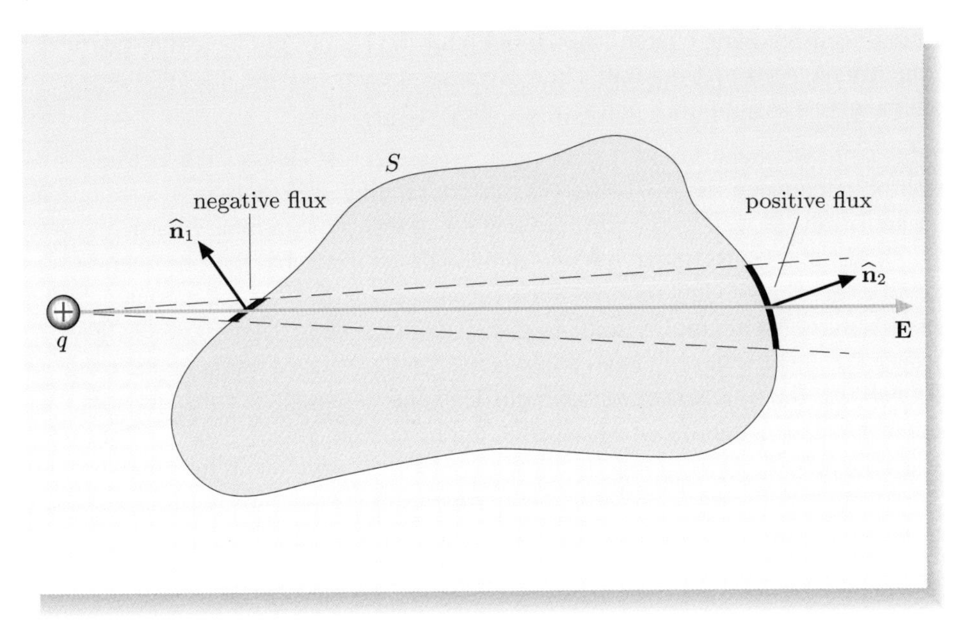


**Figure 2.9** Cross-sectional view of a charge $q$ outside a closed surface $S$.

Finally, all the different cases we have considered can be drawn together, using the principle of superposition and the law of additivity of charge. Suppose we have a number of point charges $q_1, q_2, \ldots, q_n$ producing electric fields $\mathbf{E}_1(\mathbf{r})$, $\mathbf{E}_2(\mathbf{r}), \ldots, \mathbf{E}_n(\mathbf{r})$. Then the total electric field at any point is given by the vector sum $\mathbf{E}_1(\mathbf{r}) + \mathbf{E}_2(\mathbf{r}) + \ldots + \mathbf{E}_n(\mathbf{r})$. It follows that the total electric flux over a closed surface is the sum of the individual electric fluxes due to the charges $q_1, q_2, \ldots, q_n$. We know that each charge outside the surface makes no contribution to the electric flux whereas each charge inside the surface contributes a flux equal to the value of the charge divided by $\varepsilon_0$. The total flux over the closed surface is therefore the sum of all the charges inside the surface, divided by $\varepsilon_0$. By the additivity of charge, this is just the total enclosed charge, $Q$, divided by $\varepsilon_0$, which is the general statement of Gauss's law, established now for *all* closed surfaces and *all* stationary distributions of charge.

This concludes the proof of Gauss's law.

### The scope and status of Gauss's law

Gauss's law is a gem, combining simplicity with impressive generality. The proof outlined above was based on three physical assumptions — Coulomb's law, the law of addition of charge and the principle of superposition of electric fields. These assumptions were combined with some elementary geometry in three dimensions and Gauss's law emerged as a result.

Taking the geometry, addition of charge and superposition of fields on trust, Gauss's law is sometimes said to provide an alternative expression of Coulomb's law. However, this is a very loose description. In fact, our proof of Gauss's law did not use every aspect of Coulomb's law. It only assumed that:

- *In any given direction*, the electric field of a point charge is radial and dies off according to an inverse square law.
- The electric flux over the surface of a sphere centred on an isolated point charge $q$ is $q/\varepsilon_0$.

These assumptions certainly follow from Coulomb's law, but they can also be true in situations where Coulomb's law does not apply. For example, the electric field of a uniformly-moving charge (shown in Figure 1.17) does not have the spherical symmetry required by Coulomb's law. Even so, it turns out that this field obeys both the above assumptions and so *does* obey Gauss's law.

At this point we make a bold leap of faith. We assert that Gauss's law is true under all circumstances — for charges that are moving uniformly or non-uniformly, as well as for particles that are at rest. For stationary particles, we have shown that Gauss's law follows from Coulomb's law, but the final step of asserting that Gauss's law remains valid for moving particles is taken to be a basic fact of Nature. No attempt is made to justify this fact using deeper knowledge because the universality of Gauss's law is itself regarded as a fundamental truth. Maxwell was the first person to make this leap and to pursue its consequences, and Gauss's law is the first of Maxwell's four celebrated equations of electromagnetism. The ultimate justification of Gauss's law in all its generality comes from experiment — not direct experiments that probe this particular law, but from the triumphant predictions of the whole of Maxwell's theory.

Gauss's law is the part of Coulomb's law that is universally valid — it is true for charges in motion, as well as for charges at rest. This generality is made possible by the fact that Gauss's law is less specific than Coulomb's law; it gives the surface integral of the electric field over a closed surface, not the value of the field at any point in space. The surface integral turns out to be independent of the motion of charges, even though the electric field itself depends on this motion (compare Figures 1.12 and 1.17, for example).

Any information that is left out of Gauss's law is contained in the rest of Maxwell's equations, which you will meet later in this book. In favourable circumstances, however, the missing information can be deduced from the symmetry of the situation. For example, suppose we have a point charge $q$ at rest at the origin. Because charge is a scalar quantity with no directional character, a stationary point charge singles out no special direction in space. This implies that the electric field of a stationary point charge is spherically symmetrical, pointing away from, or towards, the charge, with a magnitude that depends only on the distance from the charge. If we now suppose that the charge is at the centre of a sphere of radius $R$, the electric flux over the surface of this sphere is $E_r \times 4\pi R^2$, where $E_r$ is the radial component of the field on the spherical surface. Using Gauss's law we conclude that

$$E_r \times 4\pi R^2 = \frac{q}{\varepsilon_0},$$

$$\text{so} \quad E_r = \frac{q}{4\pi\varepsilon_0 R^2}, \qquad \text{and} \qquad \mathbf{E}_r = \frac{q}{4\pi\varepsilon_0 R^2}\,\mathbf{e}_r$$

which is essentially Coulomb's law, expressed in terms of the electric field. So Gauss's law, *supplemented by spherical symmetry*, leads to Coulomb's law. The assumption of a spherically-symmetric field is obvious for a stationary charge, but not for one that is moving, which explains why Coulomb's law is restricted to the static case.

**Exercise 2.2** An isolated point charge is placed at the centre of a sphere. Is the total electric flux over the closed surface of the sphere changed by: (a) moving the charge off-centre inside the sphere; (b) moving the charge just outside the sphere; (c) splitting the charge into two fragments, both of which remain inside the sphere; (d) allowing the charge to oscillate to and fro within the sphere; (e) adding an extra charge just inside the sphere; (f) adding an extra charge just outside the sphere; (g) increasing the radius of the sphere or (h) deforming the sphere slightly?

**Exercise 2.3** If the photon had a non-zero mass, would Gauss's law be exactly true? (*Hint*: see Section 1.4.2.) ■

## 2.3 Putting Gauss's law to use

At the risk of repetition, here is a definitive statement of Gauss's law:

**Gauss's law**

The electric flux over any closed surface $S$ is equal to the total charge $Q$ enclosed by the surface, divided by $\varepsilon_0$. That is,

$$\int_S \mathbf{E} \cdot \mathrm{d}\mathbf{S} = \frac{Q}{\varepsilon_0}. \tag{2.5}$$

This law is true for all closed surfaces, no matter what their shape, and for all distributions of charge, whether they are stationary or not. In particular, any charges outside the surface make no contribution to the electric flux over the surface. Gauss's law cannot be extended to open surfaces because the concept of the total enclosed charge only makes sense for a surface that is closed.

The total charge inside the closed surface can be expressed as a volume integral of the charge density, so Gauss's law can also be written as

$$\int_S \mathbf{E} \cdot \mathrm{d}\mathbf{S} = \frac{1}{\varepsilon_0} \int_V \rho(\mathbf{r})\,\mathrm{d}V, \tag{2.6}$$

where $S$ is any closed surface and $V$ is the region inside this surface. Because this statement involves surface and volume integrals, it is called the **integral version of Gauss's law**.

As emphasized earlier, knowledge of the electric flux does not usually reveal the value of the electric field at individual points in space. To have any chance of finding the electric field from Gauss's law, the situation must be highly symmetric. In practice, Gauss's law is most valuable when the sources of the electric field have spherical symmetry, cylindrical symmetry or planar symmetry. Ideally, the direction of the electric field should be perpendicular to, or parallel to, the chosen closed surface and the magnitude of the electric field should be constant over the surface. We are free to choose whichever surface we like, but the choice had better be made wisely, with symmetry in mind. A choice of surface made for a particular application of Gauss's law is called a **Gaussian surface**.

### 2.3.1 Spherical symmetry

**Essential skill**

Applying Gauss's law in cases of spherical symmetry.

**Worked Example 2.2**

A static uniform distribution of total charge $Q$ occupies a sphere of radius $R$, centred on the origin. Find the electric field at all points (a) outside and (b) inside this distribution of charge.

**Solution**

The static uniform charge distribution has spherical symmetry, so the electric field must also have spherical symmetry. At each point it is directed towards, or away from, the centre of the sphere and has a radial component that depends only on the distance from the centre of the sphere. So

$$\mathbf{E}(\mathbf{r}) = E_r(r)\,\mathbf{e}_r,$$

where $E_r(r)$ is the radial component at radius $r$ and $\mathbf{e}_r$ is the radial unit vector at the point $\mathbf{r}$. (Symmetry arguments like this are legitimate, safe and invaluable, as explained in Chapter 1.)

(a) Consider the field *outside* the sphere of charge. We exploit the spherical symmetry by choosing a spherical Gaussian surface, centred on the origin, with radius $r > R$. This closed surface contains the whole charge distribution, and therefore encloses charge $Q$. The electric field due to the charge distribution is perpendicular to the surface and has a constant normal component, $E_r(r)$, on this surface. Applying Gauss's law, we obtain

$$E_r(r) \times 4\pi r^2 = \frac{Q}{\varepsilon_0}$$

so

$$E_r(r) = \frac{Q}{4\pi\varepsilon_0 r^2} \quad \text{and} \quad \mathbf{E}(\mathbf{r}) = \frac{Q}{4\pi\varepsilon_0 r^2}\,\mathbf{e}_r \quad (\text{for } r \geq R).$$

*Viewed from the outside*, the sphere behaves as if all its charge were concentrated at its centre. Looking back at the derivation, it is easy to see that this result does not rely on a uniform charge density; it is true for *any* spherically-symmetric distribution of charge.

(b) Inside the sphere we choose a spherical Gaussian surface, centred on the origin, with $r < R$. This closed surface does not contain the whole charge

$Q$, but encloses a charge

$$Q_{\text{enc}} = \int_0^r \rho \times 4\pi s^2 \, \mathrm{d}s,$$

where I have written the variable of integration as $s$ to avoid any confusion with the upper limit, $r$. The symbol used for a variable of integration has no physical significance, so this is a legitimate step.

In our case the charge density is uniform so

$$\rho = \frac{\text{charge}}{\text{volume}} = \frac{Q}{4\pi R^3/3}$$

and the enclosed charge is

$$Q_{\text{enc}} = \frac{Q}{4\pi R^3/3} \int_0^r 4\pi s^2 \, \mathrm{d}s = Q \times \frac{r^3}{R^3}.$$

This is just the total charge $Q$, multiplied by the ratio of the volumes of the Gaussian sphere and the whole sphere — just as you would expect for a *uniform* charge density. Finally, Gauss's law gives

$$E_r(r) \times 4\pi r^2 = \frac{Q}{\varepsilon_0} \times \frac{r^3}{R^3}$$

so

$$E_r(r) = \frac{Q\,r}{4\pi\varepsilon_0 R^3} \quad \text{and} \quad \mathbf{E}(\mathbf{r}) = \frac{Q\,r}{4\pi\varepsilon_0 R^3}\,\mathbf{e}_r \quad (\text{for } r \leq R).$$

The question has now been fully answered, but it is always worth checking your answers. Even the most reliable computers have error-detecting codes built into their software and you should also develop the routine of checking that your answers are reasonable. In the present case, a number of points can be confirmed:

- The units are correct. This is obvious outside the sphere, where the answer is the electric field of a point charge. It is also true inside the sphere because $r/R^3$ has the same units as $1/R^2$.
- The electric field is zero at the origin. A non-zero field at the origin would be inexplicable, given the spherical symmetry of the charge distribution.
- The interior field becomes equal to the exterior field at $r = R$. A discontinuity would imply an infinite charge density at the surface of the sphere, which is physically unreasonable.

Of course, these checks do not guarantee that our answer is right, but they certainly help to boost our confidence in it. Figure 2.10 is a graph of $E_r$ versus $r$ for all $r$.

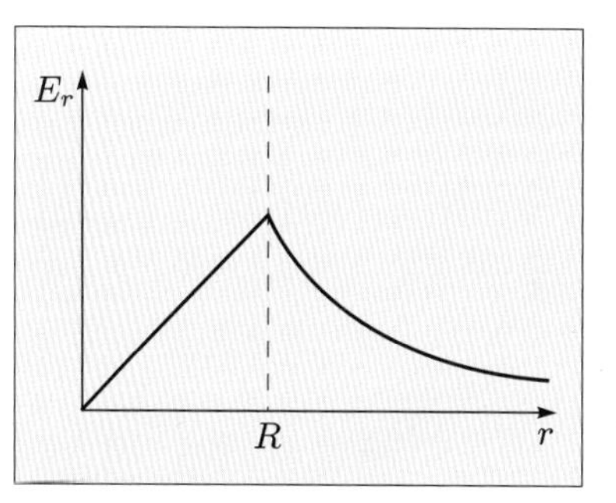


**Figure 2.10** A graph of $E_r$ versus $r$ for use in Worked Example 2.2.

**Exercise 2.4** A static spherically-symmetric distribution of charge is centred on the origin and vanishes outside a sphere of radius $R$. Inside the sphere, the charge density at distance $r$ from the origin is

$$\rho(r) = Ar,$$

where $A$ is a constant. Find the electric field at all points (a) outside and (b) inside the distribution of charge.

**Exercise 2.5** If the electric field in air becomes too great, the air undergoes breakdown, becoming a good conductor and allowing charge to leak away from objects. Show that the magnitude of static charge carried by a spherical hailstone of radius $3.0\,\mathrm{mm}$ cannot exceed one nanocoulomb ($1\,\mathrm{nC} = 10^{-9}\,\mathrm{C}$). You may assume that the charge is distributed in a spherically symmetric way in the hailstone and that the breakdown field of damp air is $1.0 \times 10^{6}\,\mathrm{N\,C^{-1}}$.

**Exercise 2.6** In fine weather there is a weak electric field pointing vertically downwards at the Earth's surface. A typical value, averaged over the surface of the Earth, is $100\,\mathrm{N\,C^{-1}}$. Estimate the total charge on planet Earth (that is the total charge within its solid or liquid surface). You may take the Earth to be a perfect sphere of radius $6.6 \times 10^{6}\,\mathrm{m}$, with a spherically-symmetric charge distribution. ■

Our next application of Gauss's law forms the basis of a famous experiment. An isolated spherical shell of radius $R$ is centred on the origin. The shell is constructed from a conducting material such as copper and given a net charge. Charge flows easily in the copper so the mutual repulsion of like charges causes the charge to spread out over the shell. Very soon, a state of equilibrium is reached in which the charge is spread out uniformly and the shell provides a static, spherically-symmetric distribution of charge. The spherical cavity inside the shell is empty and contains no charge. Under these circumstances we can show that there is no electric field inside the cavity.

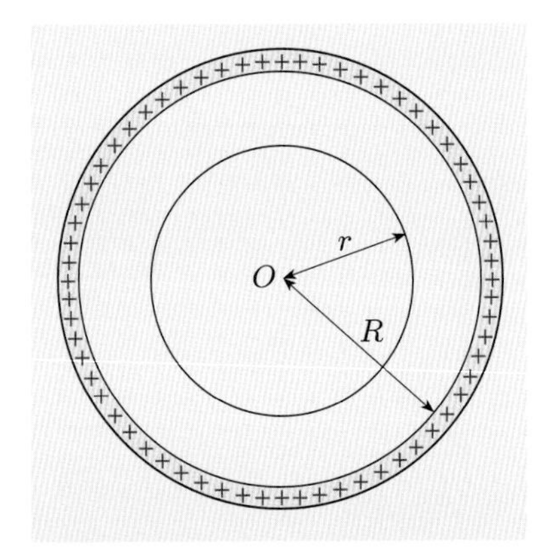

**Figure 2.11** A uniformly charged spherical shell of radius $R$ surrounds a spherical Gaussian surface of radius $r$.

We choose a spherical Gaussian surface (of radius $r < R$) inside the spherical cavity, with the same centre as the shell (Figure 2.11). There is no flux over this Gaussian surface because there is no charge inside it. We then make use of symmetry. By spherical symmetry, the magnitude of the electric field is the same at all points on the Gaussian surface. Spherical symmetry also shows that, if there is an electric field, it must be radial. No other direction is compatible with the spherical symmetry of the charge distribution. This leaves only one way of explaining the zero flux — the electric field must be zero at all points on the Gaussian surface. This argument works for all spherical Gaussian surfaces with $0 < r < R$. The point at the centre of the cavity is exempt from the argument, but spherical symmetry guarantees that the field vanishes here as well. So the electric field is predicted to be zero throughout the cavity. In 1773, Henry Cavendish tested this prediction by direct experiment and later physicists, including Maxwell himself, refined the sensitivity of this measurement. The electric field inside a hollow spherical conductor has always been below the limits of detection, providing good evidence for the validity of Gauss's law and for the underlying inverse square law of electrostatic force.

### 2.3.2 Cylindrical symmetry

We now turn to situations with cylindrical symmetry. Consider first a long cylinder of radius $R$ and length $L$ with a charge $Q$ that is spread out uniformly throughout the cylinder. The charge per unit length is $\lambda = Q/L$. Close to the axis of the cylinder and far from its ends, the electric field is well-approximated by the field of an infinitely long cylinder with the same radius and the same charge density. The approximation of taking a cylinder to be infinitely long avoids the need to discuss end effects — the modifications in the field that occur near the ends of the cylinder. We will therefore restrict attention to infinitely-long cylinders. In the context of problems in electromagnetism, you may take the description of a cylinder as being *long* as a coded invitation to regard it as being infinitely long and hence to ignore the end effects. The electric field around an infinitely-long cylinder is cylindrically symmetric around the axis of the cylinder and does not vary along the axis of the cylinder. As shown in Figure 2.12, the field is perpendicular to the axis of the cylinder. Moreover, the radial component of the field depends only on the distance from the axis. We therefore have

$$\mathbf{E}(\mathbf{r}) = E_r(r)\,\mathbf{e}_r,$$

where $E_r(r)$ is the radial component of the electric field at distance $r$ from the axis of the cylinder and $\mathbf{e}_r$ is the unit radial vector at point $\mathbf{r}$. Note that these quantities refer to cylindrical coordinates, not spherical coordinates. So $r$ is the distance from the central axis; it is not the distance from the origin. And $\mathbf{e}_r$ is a unit vector which is perpendicular to the central axis and points directly away from it; it does not point away from the origin. There is never any ambiguity about whether we are dealing with cylinders or spheres, so the intended meaning of our symbols, and of words like radius or radial, will be clear from the context.

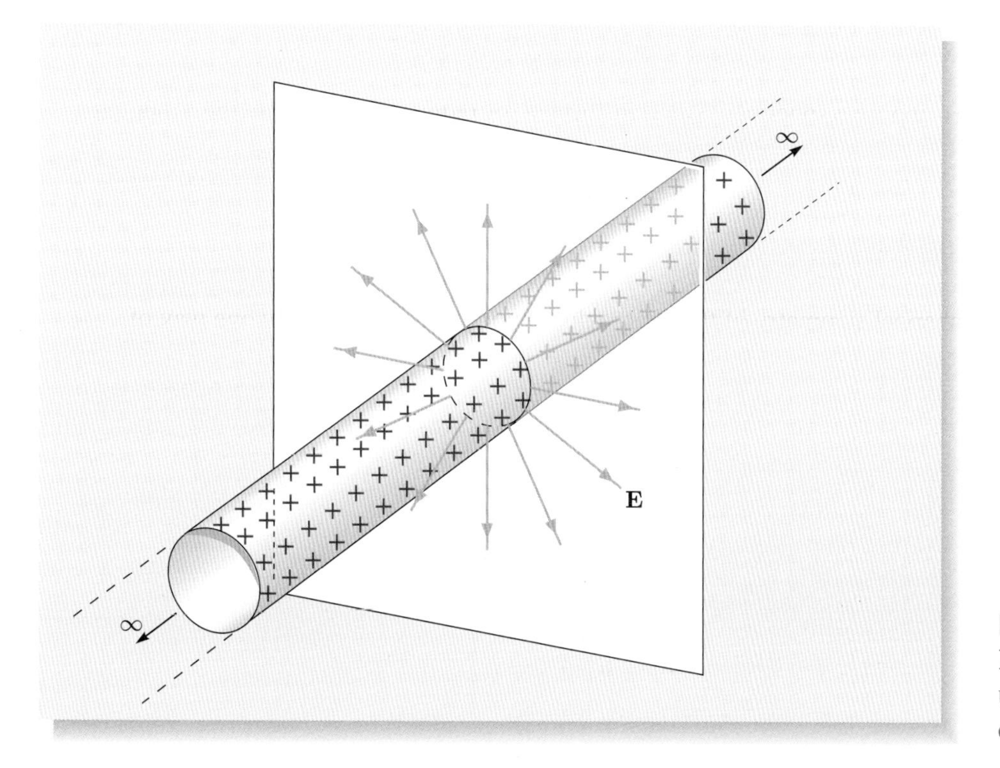


**Figure 2.12** The electric field $\mathbf{E}$ in a plane perpendicular to a uniformly-charged infinite cylinder.

**Essential skill**

Applying Gauss's law in cases of cylindrical symmetry.

### Worked Example 2.3

Find the electric field outside a stationary uniformly-charged infinite cylinder with a charge per unit length of $\lambda$.

**Solution**

This situation is cylindrically symmetric around the axis of the cylinder so the appropriate choice of Gaussian surface is a cylinder of radius $r > R$ and length $\Delta l$, with the same axis as the charged cylinder (Figure 2.13). The Gaussian surface must be closed, so it includes the two end-faces.

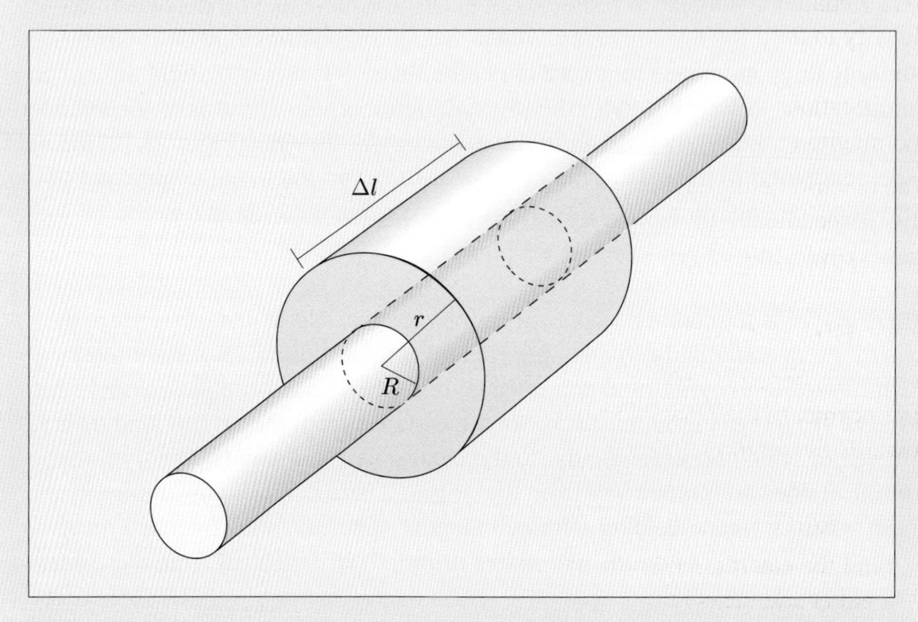


**Figure 2.13** Gaussian surface for Worked Example 2.3.

The electric field is parallel to the end-faces of the cylinder so they contribute no flux. The curved surface of the cylinder has area $2\pi r\,\Delta l$. The electric field is perpendicular to this surface and has a constant normal component over it, so the flux contributed by the curved surface is $E_r(r) \times 2\pi r\,\Delta l$. The total charge enclosed by the Gaussian surface is $\lambda\,\Delta l$ so Gauss's law gives

$$E_r(r) \times 2\pi r\,\Delta l = \frac{\lambda\,\Delta l}{\varepsilon_0}.$$

Remember that the radius $r$ and unit radial vector $\mathbf{e}_r$ refer to quantities measured outwards from the axis of the cylinder.

Hence

$$E_r(r) = \frac{\lambda}{2\pi\varepsilon_0 r} \quad \text{and} \quad \mathbf{E}(\mathbf{r}) = \frac{\lambda}{2\pi\varepsilon_0 r}\,\mathbf{e}_r. \tag{2.7}$$

One way of checking this answer is to show that its dimensions (or units) are correct. This is easily done since $\lambda$ is a *charge per unit length*, so the expressions in Equation 2.7 have the same dimensions as $Q/4\pi\varepsilon_0 r^2$, which can be recognized as the electric field of a point charge.

**Exercise 2.7** Would Equation 2.7 still be valid if the cylinder were moving at constant velocity in the direction of its own axis?

**Exercise 2.8** (a) Is the electric field outside a uniformly-charged infinite cylinder the same as the field of a uniform infinite line of charge, with the same charge per unit length, lying along the central axis of the cylinder?

(b) Is a similar statement true for the electric field *inside* a uniformly-charged infinite cylinder? ■

### 2.3.3 Planar symmetry

Finally we discuss situations with planar symmetry. Consider a plane of area $A$ with a charge $Q$ spread uniformly over its surface. We use the term **areal charge density** to describe the charge per unit area. This areal charge density has the constant value $\sigma = Q/A$ all over the plane. For simplicity, we ignore any modifications in the field that occur near the edges of the plane. This is achieved by imagining the plane to be infinite in extent, without any edges.

The electric field of a uniform infinite plane of charge has considerable symmetry. It is perpendicular to the plane, does not vary in any direction parallel to the plane and is reversed by a reflection in the plane. These symmetry properties allow us to write

$$\mathbf{E}(\mathbf{r}) = E_n\,\mathbf{e}_n,$$

where $E_n$ depends only on the distance of the point $\mathbf{r}$ from the plane and $\mathbf{e}_n$ is a unit normal to the plane, conventionally chosen to point away from the plane, towards the point $\mathbf{r}$.

**Worked Example 2.4**

Find the electric field near a uniformly-charged infinite insulating plate with areal charge density $\sigma$.

**Essential skill**

Applying Gauss's law in cases of planar symmetry.

**Solution**

An appropriate Gaussian surface is shown in Figure 2.14. This is a squat cylinder (sometimes called a pillbox) with end-faces of area $\Delta A$. The axis of the cylinder is perpendicular to the plate and straddles it symmetrically, so half of it is in front of the plate (solid lines) and half is behind (dashed lines).

The electric field is parallel to the curved surface of the cylinder so this surface makes no contribution to the flux. However, the electric field is perpendicular to the flat ends of the cylinder and has a constant normal component $E_n$ over each end-face, so the total flux contributed by the two end-faces is $2E_n\,\Delta A$. The total charge enclosed by the cylinder is $\sigma\,\Delta A$ so Gauss's law gives

$$2E_n\,\Delta A = \frac{\sigma\,\Delta A}{\varepsilon_0},$$

and

$$\mathbf{E}(\mathbf{r}) = \frac{\sigma}{2\varepsilon_0}\,\mathbf{e}_n, \tag{2.8}$$

where $\mathbf{e}_n$ is a unit vector pointing perpendicularly away from the plate towards $\mathbf{r}$. This correctly gives a field pointing away from the plate for $\sigma > 0$ and a field pointing towards the plate for $\sigma < 0$.

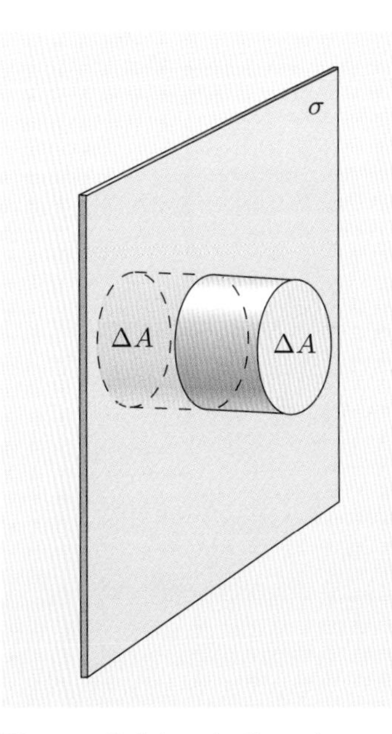


**Figure 2.14** A Gaussian surface for a plate of charge.

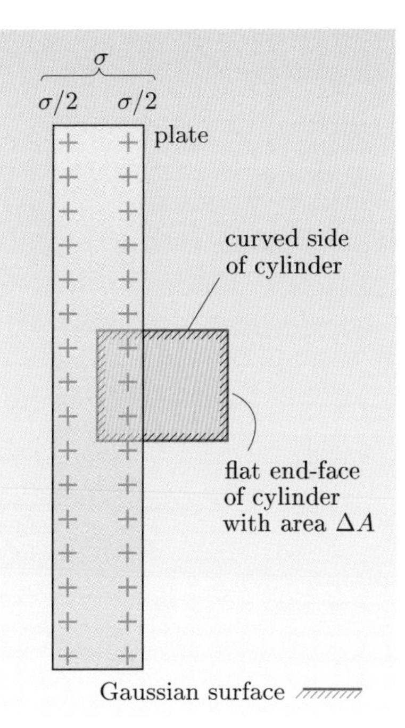


**Figure 2.15** An isolated charged conducting plate.

It is interesting to note that Equation 2.8 does not depend on the distance from the plate, even though such a dependence would be consistent with planar symmetry. The lack of dependence on distance is a consequence of Gauss's law or, equivalently, the inverse square law of force. It is only exactly true for an infinite plate of charge. Nevertheless, for a finite square plate of charge, the field is almost independent of distance provided that we keep far from the edges of the plate and the distance from the plate is small compared to the plate's lateral dimensions.

Next, we consider an isolated charged *conducting* plate. If the plate is large enough in its lateral dimensions, the charge distributes itself almost uniformly in the plane of the plate with areal charge density $\sigma$. However, the charge is not distributed uniformly through the thickness of the plate. Mutual repulsion causes charge separation and produces two similar sheets of charge on opposite surfaces of the plate. In equilibrium, each of the two charge sheets has the same areal charge density, $\sigma/2$. This is usually called a **surface charge density** because it is associated with a given surface. Of course, there is a distinction between the surface charge density $\sigma/2$ and the areal charge density of the plate, $\sigma$. The electric fields due to the two charge sheets cancel out inside the conducting plate. This is not surprising. In equilibrium, there can be no electric field inside a conductor. This is because any electric field in a conductor would drive a current, and there are no currents in a state of true equilibrium.

There are two alternative ways of applying Gauss's law in this situation. First, we can use a pillbox that straddles the whole plate. The calculation then repeats that given in Worked Example 2.4. Alternatively, we can use the Gaussian surface shown in Figure 2.15 — a squat cylinder with end-faces of area $\Delta A$, one of which is inside the plate. The flux over this end-face vanishes because there is no electric field inside the plate, while the flux over the external end-face is $E_n\,\Delta A$. The pillbox contains only one of the two surface charge sheets, so it encloses a charge $\sigma/2 \times \Delta A$. Thus, Gauss's law gives

$$E_n\,\Delta A = \frac{\sigma\,\Delta A}{2\varepsilon_0},$$

which rearranges to give the same field as before.

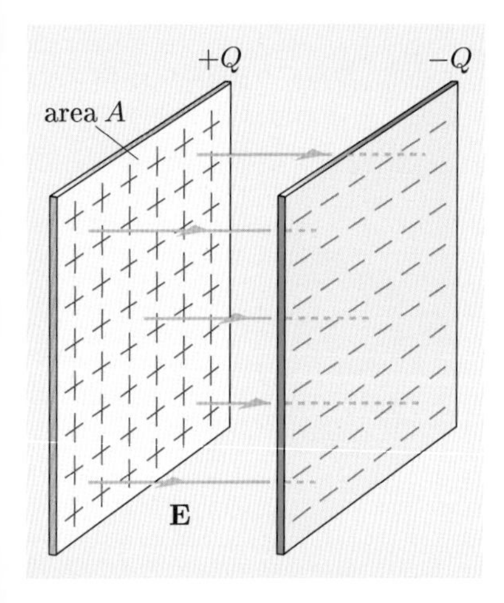


**Figure 2.16** A parallel plate capacitor with plates of area $A$ carrying charges $+Q$ and $-Q$.

Finally, let's consider a case of practical importance — a capacitor. A **capacitor** is a device used to store electrical energy by keeping positive and negative charges separated. Capacitors are used in defibrillators that save the lives of heart-attack victims and in circuits that tune radios and televisions. The membrane of a nerve cell also acts like a capacitor whose properties affect the speed of transmission of nerve impulses. To take the simplest possible case, we will consider an empty **parallel plate capacitor** (Figure 2.16). This consists of a pair of parallel conducting plates, each of area $A$, separated by a narrow gap which is empty. The plates carry opposite charges, $+Q$ and $-Q$, and their areal charge densities are $\sigma = +Q/A$ and $-\sigma = -Q/A$. We wish to know the electric field inside and just outside the capacitor.

If we keep away from the edges of the plates and are either in the narrow gap between the plates, or outside the gap but close to the plates, any edge effects can be neglected. This means that the capacitor can be modelled as having infinite plates with uniform areal charge densities $\sigma$ and $-\sigma$. In this situation, the electric field can be found using Equation 2.8, together with the principle of superposition. The electric field of an *infinite* plane of charge does not decrease with distance. Hence the two infinite planes of charge produce fields of the same magnitude. Outside the capacitor, these fields have opposite directions and cancel out. So the field outside the capacitor vanishes. In the gap between the plates, the fields have the same direction and add together. So the field in the gap is

$$\mathbf{E} = \frac{\sigma}{\varepsilon_0}\,\mathbf{e}_n,$$

where $\mathbf{e}_n$ is a unit normal, pointing from the plate with charge $+Q$ towards the plate with charge $-Q$. The field in the gap is therefore uniform and perpendicular to the plates.

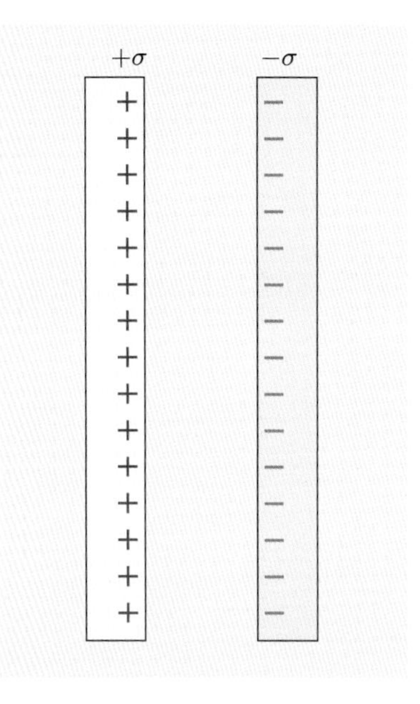


**Figure 2.17** Charge migrates to the inner surfaces of the capacitor plates.

It is instructive to take a fresh look at this problem, deriving the results more directly from Gauss's law. Remember that, in equilibrium, there is no electric field inside either plate. Inside plate 1, the field due to charges on the surface of plate 1 must cancel the field due to plate 2. To achieve this cancellation, all the charge on plate 1 migrates to its inner surface, leaving no charge on its outer surface. The same happens on plate 2, so the charge accumulates on the inner surfaces of the plates, as shown in Figure 2.17. The distribution of charge on each plate is totally unlike that on an isolated charged plate (Figure 2.15) because the two plates in a capacitor are not isolated, but interact strongly with one another. To apply Gauss's law in this situation, we can choose the cylindrical pillbox Gaussian surfaces of Figure 2.18. Each of these pillboxes has an end-face inside the plate, where the electric field vanishes. The total flux over the surface of each pillbox is therefore $E_n\,\Delta A$, where $E_n$ is the normal component of the electric field over the external end-face and $\Delta A$ is the cross-sectional area of the cylinder. Pillbox (a) contains no charge, so Gauss's law shows that $E_n = 0$ outside the capacitor. Pillbox (b) contains charge $\sigma\,\Delta A$ so Gauss's law gives

$$E_n = \frac{\sigma}{\varepsilon_0},$$

between the plates, in agreement with results obtained earlier.

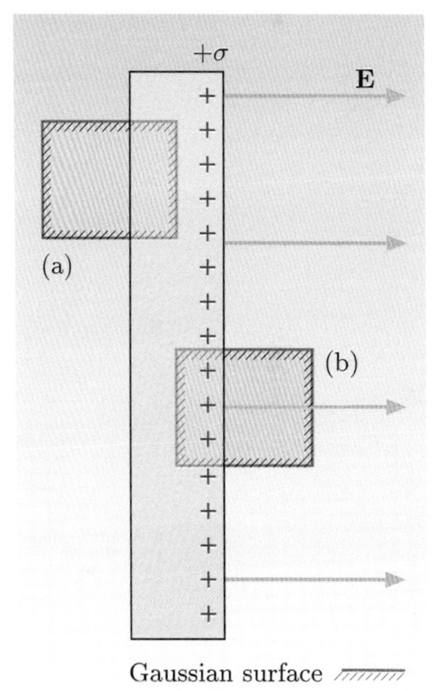


**Figure 2.18** Two Gaussian surfaces for a capacitor plate.

**Exercise 2.9** An infinite parallel plate capacitor has uniformly-charged plates. Plate 1 has areal charge density $\sigma_1$ and plate 2 has areal charge density $\sigma_2$. (Normally a capacitor has oppositely-charged plates so $\sigma_1 + \sigma_2 = 0$, but this need not be the case.) What is the electric field in the gap between the plates in general? ■

## 2.4 The differential version of Gauss's law

Gauss's law, as described so far, involves integrals; the electric flux is a surface integral and the total charge enclosed by a surface is often calculated as a volume integral. This form of Gauss's law is called the *integral* version of Gauss's law. In this section you will see that Gauss's law can be re-expressed using derivatives rather than integrals, giving a *differential* version of Gauss's law.

► Read MT 8.6 now if you have not already done so. This is essential material, and the following text will assume that you have read it.

You are familiar with the idea that mass is additive. If we divide an object into many parts, the mass of the object is the sum of the masses of its parts. This allows us to express the mass of the object as a volume integral of its density (the mass per unit volume), taken over the volume of the object.

Now, following MT 8.6, something very similar can be done for electric flux. Recall that the flux of any vector field is additive. In particular, electric flux is additive. So, if we divide a volume into many parts, the electric flux over the surface of the volume is the sum of the electric fluxes over the surfaces of its parts. This allows us to express the electric flux over the surface of a region as the volume integral of the electric flux per unit volume, taken over the volume of the region. The electric flux per unit volume is called the **divergence** of the electric field and given the symbol $\operatorname{div}\mathbf{E}$. This is a scalar field defined at each point in space. The electric flux over any closed surface $S$ can therefore be expressed as a volume integral of $\operatorname{div}\mathbf{E}$. We write

$$\int_S \mathbf{E}\cdot d\mathbf{S} = \int_V \operatorname{div}\mathbf{E}\,dV, \qquad \text{(Eqn 8.34)}$$

where $V$ is the volume enclosed by $S$. This is the content of the **divergence theorem**, as applied to the electric field.

To obtain the differential version of Gauss's law, we combine the divergence theorem with the integral version of Gauss's law (Equation 2.6) to give

$$\int_V \operatorname{div}\mathbf{E}\,dV = \int_V \frac{\rho(\mathbf{r})}{\varepsilon_0}\,dV, \qquad (2.9)$$

where both integrals extend over the same volume $V$ with boundary $S$. The key step is then to notice that Equation 2.9 applies to any volume whatsoever. In particular, it applies to volumes that are arbitrarily small. Under these circumstances, the only way to satisfy Equation 2.9 is to insist that the *integrands* are identical on both sides. We therefore conclude that

$$\operatorname{div}\mathbf{E} = \frac{\rho(\mathbf{r})}{\varepsilon_0}. \qquad (2.10)$$

Finally, as you saw in the MT 8.6.3, the divergence of a field can be expressed in terms of partial derivatives of the field. In Cartesian coordinates, there is a simple and symmetrical expression for the divergence of $\mathbf{E}$. It is

$$\operatorname{div}\mathbf{E} = \frac{\partial E_x}{\partial x} + \frac{\partial E_y}{\partial y} + \frac{\partial E_z}{\partial z}.$$

So we conclude that

$$\frac{\partial E_x}{\partial x} + \frac{\partial E_y}{\partial y} + \frac{\partial E_z}{\partial z} = \frac{\rho(\mathbf{r})}{\varepsilon_0}. \qquad (2.11)$$

Equations 2.10 and 2.11 both express the **differential version of Gauss's law**. Just like the integral version, the differential version of Gauss's law is a fundamental law of electromagnetism, valid for all charge distributions, whether they are stationary or moving. Both versions of Gauss's law are cornerstones of Maxwell's theory of electromagnetism.

The differential version of Gauss's law is a major step forward. It is a *local* description relating the charge density at a given point and time to the divergence of the electric field *at the same point and time*. There is no mention of distant charges so the concept of action at a distance is avoided. This is in the true spirit of a field theory and is a great advance on Coulomb's law. However, Gauss's law does not by itself give a complete description of the electromagnetic field. For example, we might expect that jiggling a charge in one region will cause disturbances in the field that propagate outwards, just as jiggling a stick in water causes water waves to spread out over a pond. Such effects are not described by Gauss's law because it does not include derivatives with respect to time. Gauss himself thought this was a defect, so he failed to publish his law. However, Maxwell guessed (correctly) that there is nothing wrong with Gauss's law, but Gauss's law is only part of a complete theory of electromagnetism, which contains other equations as well. These other equations are contained in the rest of Maxwell's theory, which will be developed in the rest of this book.

**Essential skill**

Applying the differential version of Gauss's law.

### Worked Example 2.5

A non-conducting slab lies between $z = -d/2$ and $z = +d/2$, and extends to infinity in the $x$- and $y$-directions. Throughout its volume this slab has a uniform charge density, $\rho_0$. The slab is isolated from all other influences, and the electric field for $z > 0$ is the reverse of the field for $z < 0$. Use the differential version of Gauss's law to find the electric field inside the slab.

**Solution**

The planar symmetry means that the electric field of the slab only has a $z$-component, and this depends only on $z$. So

$$\mathbf{E} = E_z(z)\,\mathbf{e}_z.$$

According to Gauss's law

$$\frac{\partial E_x}{\partial x} + \frac{\partial E_y}{\partial y} + \frac{\partial E_z}{\partial z} = \frac{\rho_0}{\varepsilon_0},$$

inside the slab. The partial derivatives $\partial E_x/\partial x$ and $\partial E_y/\partial y$ are equal to zero because the field has no $x$- or $y$-components. The partial derivative $\partial E_z/\partial z$ can be written as an ordinary derivative because $E_z$ depends only on $z$. Hence Gauss's law becomes

$$\frac{\mathrm{d}E_z}{\mathrm{d}z} = \frac{\rho_0}{\varepsilon_0}.$$

Integrating both sides with respect to $z$ gives

$$E_z(z) = \frac{\rho_0\, z}{\varepsilon_0} + C,$$

where $C$ is an arbitrary constant of integration.

The charge distribution, and hence the electric field, has a reflection symmetry in the plane $z = 0$ so that $E_z(z) = -E_z(-z)$. This implies that

$$\frac{\rho_0\, z}{\varepsilon_0} + C = -\left(\frac{-\rho_0\, z}{\varepsilon_0} + C\right).$$

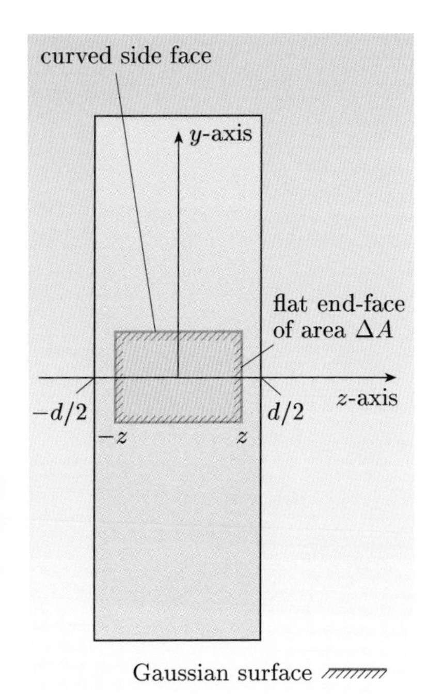


**Figure 2.19** A cylindrical Gaussian surface.

Hence $C = 0$, and

$$E_z(z) = \frac{\rho_0\, z}{\varepsilon_0}.$$

It is interesting to check the answer using the integral version of Gauss's law. We choose the cylindrical Gaussian surface shown in Figure 2.19, of cross-sectional area $\Delta A$ and with end-faces located at $z$ and $-z$, where $0 < z < d/2$. The integral version of Gauss's law then gives

$$\big(E_z(z) - E_z(-z)\big)\,\Delta A = \frac{\rho_0 \times 2z\,\Delta A}{\varepsilon_0}.$$

Then, since $E_z(z) = -E_z(-z)$, we recover our previous result.

It is not always appropriate to work in Cartesian coordinates. If the electric field has spherical or cylindrical symmetry, it is much more sensible to use spherical or cylindrical coordinates. Expressions for divergence in these coordinate systems (too long to remember) are listed inside the back cover of the book, but simplifications can often be made.

If an electric field $\mathbf{E}(\mathbf{r}) = E_r(r)\,\mathbf{e}_r$ is radial with respect to the origin, with $E_r(r)$ depending only on the distance $r$ from the origin, the divergence simplifies to

$$\operatorname{div}\mathbf{E} = \frac{1}{r^2}\frac{\mathrm{d}}{\mathrm{d}r}(r^2 E_r) \quad \text{in spherical coordinates.} \tag{2.12}$$

If an electric field $\mathbf{E}(\mathbf{r}) = E_r(r)\,\mathbf{e}_r$ is radial with respect to the $z$-axis, with $E_r(r)$ depending only on the distance $r$ from the $z$-axis, the divergence simplifies to

$$\operatorname{div}\mathbf{E} = \frac{1}{r}\frac{\mathrm{d}}{\mathrm{d}r}(rE_r) \quad \text{in cylindrical coordinates.} \tag{2.13}$$

**Exercise 2.10** Use the differential version of Gauss's law to find the electric field inside a spherical distribution of charge with charge density $\rho(r) = Ar$, where $A$ is a constant. ■

The above successes are special cases. Symmetry arguments allowed us to convert Equation 2.10 (a partial differential equation in three variables) into an ordinary differential equation in one variable. Symmetry was also used to fix the value of the constant of integration. However, a *lack* of symmetry generally blocks any such simplifications. This difficulty is related to the existence of **divergence-free fields** — that is, vector fields whose divergence vanishes everywhere. An example of such a field is

$$\mathbf{G}(\mathbf{r}) = G_x(y,z)\,\mathbf{e}_x + G_y(x,z)\,\mathbf{e}_y + G_z(x,y)\,\mathbf{e}_z,$$

which obviously satisfies $\operatorname{div}\mathbf{G} = 0$, because the partial derivatives $\partial G_x/\partial x$, $\partial G_y/\partial y$ and $\partial G_z/\partial z$ all vanish. Suppose that we find a vector field $\mathbf{E}(\mathbf{r})$ that satisfies Gauss's law,

$$\operatorname{div}\mathbf{E} = \frac{\rho(\mathbf{r})}{\varepsilon_0},$$

for a given charge density. Then

$$\operatorname{div}(\mathbf{E}+\mathbf{G}) = \operatorname{div}\mathbf{E} + \operatorname{div}\mathbf{G} = \frac{\rho(\mathbf{r})}{\varepsilon_0} + 0 = \frac{\rho(\mathbf{r})}{\varepsilon_0},$$

so $\mathbf{E}(\mathbf{r}) + \mathbf{G}(\mathbf{r})$ is another vector field that satisfies Gauss's law for this charge density. Which solution is correct? By itself, Gauss's law cannot tell us. We need further information — either supplied by symmetry or by other principles. Remember, there are more Maxwell equations to come in later chapters!

Although it is not always possible to use Gauss's law to deduce an electric field from a known charge density, it is always possible to do the reverse. If we know the electric field throughout a region, we can find the charge density in that region. According to Equation 2.10, the charge density is found by taking the divergence of the electric field and multiplying by $\varepsilon_0$.

**Exercise 2.11** Throughout a spherical region centred on the origin, the electric field is

$$\mathbf{E} = A(x^3\mathbf{e}_x + y^3\mathbf{e}_y - z^3\mathbf{e}_z),$$

where $A$ is a positive constant. What is the charge density throughout this region? Does the region contain only positive charges, only negative charges or a mixture of the two? ■

A software package on the DVD allows you to explore the integral and differential versions of Gauss's law. This package is best studied some time after completing this chapter. The DVD also contains a video of a tutorial which uses Gauss's law to solve a typical problem.

## Summary of Chapter 2

**Section 2.1** Charge density is the charge per unit volume. The total charge in a region is the volume integral of the charge density over the region. Electric flux is the surface integral of the electric field over a given surface.

**Section 2.2** The integral version of Gauss's law states that the electric flux over a closed surface $S$ is equal to the total charge enclosed by the surface, divided by $\varepsilon_0$. That is,

$$\int_S \mathbf{E} \cdot \mathrm{d}\mathbf{S} = \frac{Q}{\varepsilon_0} = \frac{1}{\varepsilon_0}\int_V \rho(\mathbf{r})\,\mathrm{d}V,$$

where $Q$ is the charge enclosed by $S$ and $V$ is the volume enclosed by $S$. This law applies to all distributions of charge (whether stationary or moving) and to all closed surfaces (no matter what their shape). It is unaffected by the presence of charges outside the closed surface. For the special case of stationary charges, Gauss's law can be derived from Coulomb's law, the principle of superposition and the additivity of charge.

**Section 2.3** To apply Gauss's law, we exploit the symmetry of the charges to constrain the possible form of the electric field, and choose a suitable closed surface (a Gaussian surface). Ideally, the field has a constant normal component over this surface, or over easily identified faces of the surface. In cases of spherical, cylindrical or planar symmetry it is possible to deduce the electric field from Gauss's law.

**Section 2.4** The divergence of the electric field is the electric flux per unit volume. This is a scalar field, represented in Cartesian coordinates by

$$\operatorname{div}\mathbf{E} = \frac{\partial E_x}{\partial x} + \frac{\partial E_y}{\partial y} + \frac{\partial E_z}{\partial z}.$$

The divergence theorem tells us that the surface integral of a vector field over a closed surface $S$ is the volume integral of the divergence of the field over the region $V$ inside $S$. That is,

$$\int_S \mathbf{E}\cdot \mathrm{d}\mathbf{S} = \int_V \operatorname{div}\mathbf{E}\,\mathrm{d}V.$$

Using this theorem, together with the integral version of Gauss's law, we obtain the differential version of Gauss's law:

$$\operatorname{div}\mathbf{E} = \frac{\rho(\mathbf{r})}{\varepsilon_0}.$$

This applies to all distributions of charge (whether stationary or moving). In highly symmetrical situations it leads to a differential equation which can be solved for the electric field.

## Achievements from Chapter 2

*After studying this chapter you should be able to do the following:*

**2.1** Explain the meaning of the newly defined (emboldened) terms and symbols, and use them appropriately.

**2.2** Find the total charge in a volume by integrating a charge density.

**2.3** State the integral version of Gauss's law and use it in simple cases involving spherical, cylindrical and planar symmetry.

**2.4** State the differential version of Gauss's law and explain how it follows from the integral version. Use the differential version of Gauss's law in simple cases.

**2.5** Recognize that Gauss's law is one of Maxwell's equations, with universal validity.

*After studying MT 8.3 — 8.5 you should also be able to:*

**2.6** Recognize the distinction between closed and open surfaces.

**2.7** Select and use appropriate coordinate systems for situations with planar, cylindrical or spherical symmetry.

**2.8** Evaluate simple volume and surface integrals.

**2.9** Use the divergence theorem to link volume integrals and surface integrals.

**2.10** Express divergence in terms of partial derivatives and evaluate the divergence of a vector field.

# Chapter 3 Magnetic forces and fields

## Introduction

An ancient Greek legend tells of the shepherd Magnes who became stuck fast when his hobnail boots were attracted by a magnetized rock. An exaggeration perhaps, but magnetic rocks are found in Greece, in a region called Magnesia. These rocks contain oxides of iron, and they became magnetized when struck by lightning. Although magnetism was observed in many ancient civilizations, little practical use was made of it at first. The earliest recorded use of a magnetic compass for sea navigation dates from the twelfth century AD. Before long, sailors were forbidden to eat garlic or onions in case their breath should interfere with the compass needle. On land, the mysterious power of magnets had other uses: it was said that 'a magnet, placed on the pillow of a guilty wife, would make her confess her iniquities as she slept'. Gradually, the study of magnets became more scientific. In 1600 William Gilbert published a book on magnetism, the first work of any kind to be firmly based on the experimental method. However, what lay unsuspected for many years was the link between magnetism and electricity.

The breakthrough came in 1819, when Hans Oersted gave a spectacular demonstration (Figure 3.1). He took a wire, aligned along a South–North line, and suspended it above a compass needle. When he passed a current through the wire, from South to North, the compass needle was deflected. Instead of pointing North, it pointed somewhere between North and West.

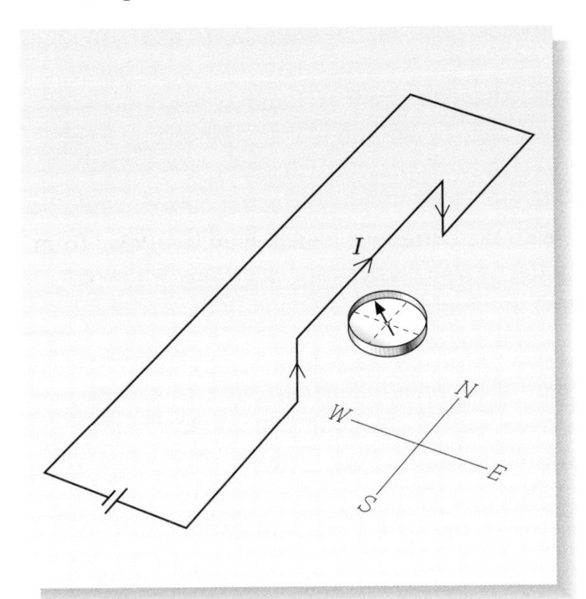


**Figure 3.1** Oersted's demonstration of the connection between electricity and magnetism.

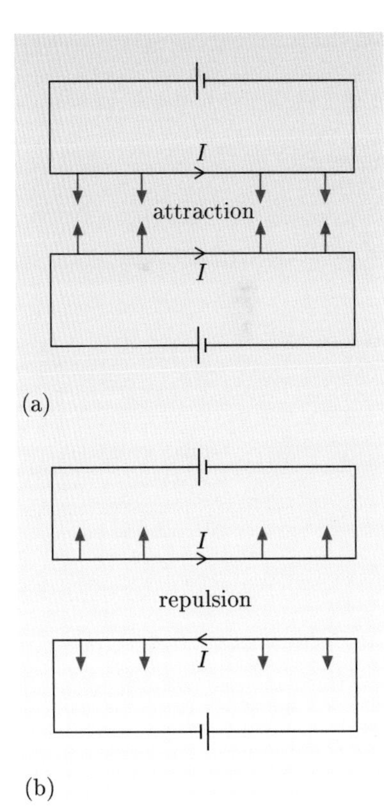


**Figure 3.2** Magnetic forces between current-carrying wires: (a) parallel currents attract one another; (b) antiparallel currents repel one another.

News of Oersted's observation spread rapidly through Europe. It was soon found that two current-carrying wires exert forces on each other (Figure 3.2). The wires attract one another if the currents are parallel and repel one another if the currents are antiparallel. Moreover current-carrying coils were observed to behave just like bar magnets, interacting with one another and aligning with external magnetic fields. All these phenomena showed that electricity and magnetism are intimately connected. They also gave physicists convenient tools for investigating magnetic effects. There is no switch or dial on a permanent magnet that allows you to change its strength, but electric currents can be adjusted with ease. Before describing the magnetic effects of electric currents, we need to explore the concept of electric current in more detail.

This chapter uses the mathematics of vector products, which are discussed in MT 8.2.2.

## 3.1 Current and current density

An **electric current** is a flow of charge. It usually refers to the one-dimensional flow of charge along a thin wire. If we choose a fixed point P on the wire and select a sense of progression along the wire as our reference direction, the current at P is

$$I = \frac{\Delta Q}{\Delta t},$$

where $\Delta Q$ is the net charge passing P in the reference direction in a small time interval $\Delta t$. Strictly speaking, we should consider a vanishingly small time interval and allow the ratio to become a derivative:

$$I = \frac{\mathrm{d}Q}{\mathrm{d}t}. \tag{3.1}$$

Thus, current is the rate of flow of charge in the reference direction. It is a scalar quantity which can be positive, negative or zero. The SI unit of current is the **ampere** or amp (A). When a current of 1 A flows along a wire for 1 s, a charge of 1 C passes any fixed point on the wire. Since a current of 1 amp is not remarkably large by everyday standards, this shows that 1 coulomb is a modest charge to be transferred by a current although, as you saw in previous chapters, it is a very large charge from the viewpoint of electrostatics. A given electric current could be carried by positive charges moving with the current or by negative charges moving against it. In a typical metal the charge carriers are electrons, which are negatively-charged and therefore drift in the opposite direction to the current, but this detail does not affect our macroscopic description.

The above definition of current is fine for the one-dimensional flow of charge along a wire, but it does not describe the flow of charge in three-dimensional space. To describe the flow of charge in the Earth's core or in the solar wind we need a more general definition that works beyond the narrow conduits provided by wires. Consider a surface, possibly curved, but with all its unit normals aligned consistently, so that unit normals at neighbouring points are almost parallel. The current flowing through this surface is defined to be the rate at which charge crosses the surface in the sense defined by the unit normals. So, Equation 3.1 still applies, but $\Delta Q$ now refers to the charge crossing a given surface rather than the charge passing a given point. We can recover our previous idea of the current in a wire by taking the surface to be one that (figuratively) cuts the wire in two.

Note carefully that, because current is defined in terms of charge crossing an extended surface, it makes no sense to talk about the current *at a single point*. Current is not a field. However, we can introduce the **current density** which is a vector field denoted by the symbol $\mathbf{J}(\mathbf{r})$. At each point in space, the direction of the current density is the direction in which charge flows, and the magnitude of current density is the magnitude of the current flowing through a tiny plane element perpendicular to the current flow, divided by the area of the element. Current density therefore has units of current per unit area ($\mathrm{A\,m^{-2}}$). For a wire with a uniform current distribution we have

$$\mathbf{J} = \frac{I}{A}\widehat{\mathbf{u}},$$

where $\widehat{\mathbf{u}}$ is a unit vector pointing along the wire in the chosen reference direction, $I$ is the current in this direction and $A$ is the cross-sectional area of the wire.

- A wire of diameter $1.0\,\mathrm{mm}$ has a uniform current density and carries a current of $1.0\,\mathrm{A}$. What is the magnitude of the current density inside the wire?

- The magnitude of the current density is the magnitude of the current divided by the cross-sectional area of the wire:

$$J = \frac{|I|}{\pi R^2} = \frac{1.0\,\mathrm{A}}{\pi \times (5.0\times 10^{-4}\,\mathrm{m})^2} = 1.3\times 10^6\,\mathrm{A\,m^{-2}}.$$

If we know the current density throughout a region, we can find the current through any surface in the region. Figure 3.3 shows a small plane element of area $\Delta S$, with unit normal $\widehat{\mathbf{n}}$. In the vicinity of this plane element, the current density $\mathbf{J}$ can be split into a sum of two vector contributions: one parallel to the element and the other normal to it. The normal contribution $\mathbf{J}_{\mathrm{normal}}$ causes charge to cross the plane element but the parallel contribution $\mathbf{J}_{\mathrm{parallel}}$ does not. From the definition of current density we see that the total rate of flow of charge across the surface is

$$\frac{\mathrm{d}Q}{\mathrm{d}t} = J_{\mathrm{normal}}\,\Delta S = \mathbf{J}\cdot\widehat{\mathbf{n}}\,\Delta S = \mathbf{J}\cdot\Delta\mathbf{S},$$

where $J_{\mathrm{normal}}$ is the component of the current density in the direction of the unit normal to the plane element and $\Delta\mathbf{S}$ is the oriented area of the plane element. An extended surface can be approximated by a patchwork of tiny plane elements. The charge crossing the whole surface is the sum of the charges crossing all the plane elements. In the limit of an infinite number of infinitesimal plane elements we conclude that

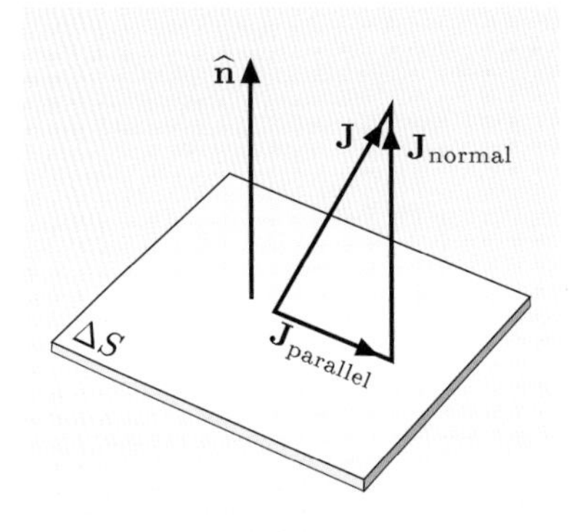


**Figure 3.3** Current flow through a plane element.

$$I = \frac{\mathrm{d}Q}{\mathrm{d}t} = \int_S \mathbf{J}\cdot\mathrm{d}\mathbf{S}. \tag{3.2}$$

In other words, the current through any surface is the surface integral (or flux) of the current density over the surface.

This chapter will concentrate on steady currents, with current densities that are independent of time. In this case it is interesting to consider a closed surface $S$. Under steady-state conditions, the current through this surface must vanish — a positive or negative current would lead to a relentless accumulation of charge within the surface, which is not sustainable. We therefore have

$$\int_S \mathbf{J}\cdot\mathrm{d}\mathbf{S} = 0.$$

Using the divergence theorem, it follows that

$$\int_V \mathrm{div}\,\mathbf{J}\,\mathrm{d}V = 0,$$

where $V$ is the volume bounded by the closed surface $S$. Since $V$ can be arbitrarily small, the integrand of the volume integral must vanish everywhere. So

$$\operatorname{div}\mathbf{J} = 0 \quad \text{for a steady current density.}$$

Any current density that is independent of time must be divergence-free. Such a current density allows charge to flow in continuous closed loops, thereby avoiding any accumulation of charge at any point.

**Exercise 3.1** In a business meeting, a region of my brain contains the current density

$$\mathbf{J} = Ax(y-z)\mathbf{e}_x + Ay(z-x)\mathbf{e}_y + Az(x-y)\mathbf{e}_z,$$

where $A$ is a constant. Can this current density remain constant without any build-up of charge? ■

We can also consider currents from a microscopic perspective. In a metal, some electrons become detached from their atoms and are able to roam freely throughout the metal. These electrons are responsible for electric currents and are called **conduction electrons**. Let's suppose that there are $N$ conduction electrons in a volume $V$. Then the **number density** of conduction electrons (the number per unit volume) is $n = N/V$. The electrons collide with vibrating ions and move erratically, but they have a small average velocity $\mathbf{v}$ along the wire. This average velocity is called the **drift velocity** and its magnitude is the **drift speed** of the electrons.

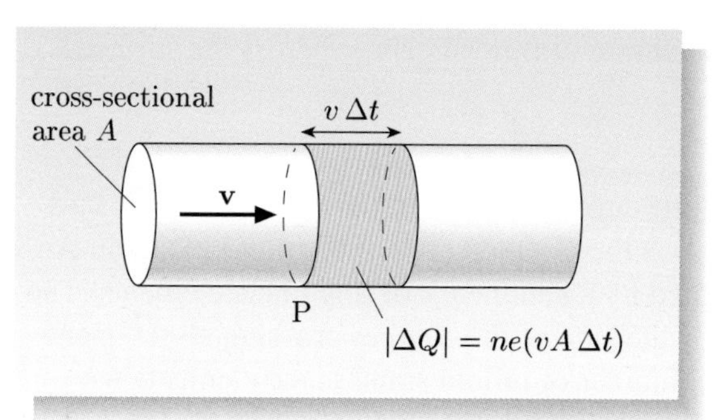


**Figure 3.4** The charge in the shaded volume passes point P on the wire in time $\Delta t$.

Referring to Figure 3.4, the electrons passing a fixed point P on the wire, in a time interval $\Delta t$, are contained in a volume $v\,\Delta t \times A$, where $v$ is the drift speed and $A$ is the cross-sectional area of the wire. The shaded volume contains $n\,vA\,\Delta t$ conduction electrons, each with charge $q = -e$, so the magnitude of the charge passing a fixed point is

$$|\Delta Q| = nevA\,\Delta t.$$

The magnitude of the current is therefore

$$|I| = nevA,$$

and the magnitude of the current density is

$$J = nev.$$

Since the current is in the opposite direction to the flow of negatively-charged electrons, the current density is

$$\mathbf{J} = -ne\mathbf{v}.$$

More generally, for charge carriers of charge $q$,

$$\mathbf{J} = nq\mathbf{v}. \qquad (3.3)$$

**Exercise 3.2** A copper wire, 1.0 mm in diameter with a uniform current density, carries a current of 1.0 A. What is the drift speed of the conduction electrons in this current? The number density of conduction electrons in copper is $8.5 \times 10^{28}\,\mathrm{m^{-3}}$. ■

## 3.2 The Biot–Savart force law

We will now explore magnetic forces, focusing in this chapter on the magnetic forces between steady (time-independent) currents. These are called **magnetostatic forces**. A simple case is shown in Figure 3.2 — two long straight parallel wires each carry a steady current. The wires attract one another when their currents are parallel and repel one another when their currents are antiparallel. This is the reverse of Coulomb's law: like *charges* repel, but like *currents* attract. The attraction between parallel currents is usually small but becomes obvious in strong electromagnets, where the coils visibly squeeze together. It is observed that the force disappears when the currents are switched off, so it is certainly not an electric force. It is a *magnetic* force associated with the motion of the conduction electrons in the wires.

The distinction between electric and magnetic forces was explained in Section 1.3.

Experiments show that the magnetic force per unit length of wire is proportional to the product of the two currents and inversely proportional to their separation:

$$\frac{F_{\text{mag}}}{L} \propto \frac{I_1 I_2}{d}. \qquad (3.4)$$

where $F_{\text{mag}}/L$ is the magnetic force per unit length of either wire, $I_1$ and $I_2$ are the currents in the wires and $d$ is the distance between them. This is remarkably similar to the electrostatic force between two long parallel rods of charge. Using the result of Worked Example 2.3, it is easy to see that the electrostatic force per unit length between two charged parallel rods is

$$\frac{F_{\text{elec}}}{L} = \frac{\lambda_1 \lambda_2}{2\pi\varepsilon_0 d}, \qquad (3.5)$$

where $\lambda_1$ and $\lambda_2$ are the charges per unit length of the rods and $d$ is the distance between them. We know, of course, that electrostatic forces are explained by Coulomb's law, which is an inverse square law. This raises an interesting question: could magnetostatic forces also obey an inverse square law? The answer to this question turns out to be yes, but the magnetostatic force law is slightly more complicated than Coulomb's law.

To formulate a magnetostatic law of force we need the concept of a **current element**. Current elements are the basic building blocks of magnetostatics, just as point charges are the basic building blocks of electrostatics. Suppose that a current density $\mathbf{J}(\mathbf{r})$ is specified in a region of space. We divide the region into many volume elements, each so small that any spatial variation of the current density within it can be neglected. For a volume element $\delta V$, centred on point $\mathbf{r}$, the current element is defined to be $\mathbf{J}(\mathbf{r})\,\delta V$, and this quantity has the SI unit ampere metre (A m). Usually, we are interested in a steady current flowing along a thin wire (Figure 3.5). In this case, we take the volume element to be a small segment of the wire of length $\delta l$, cross-sectional area $A$ and volume $\delta V = A\,\delta l$.

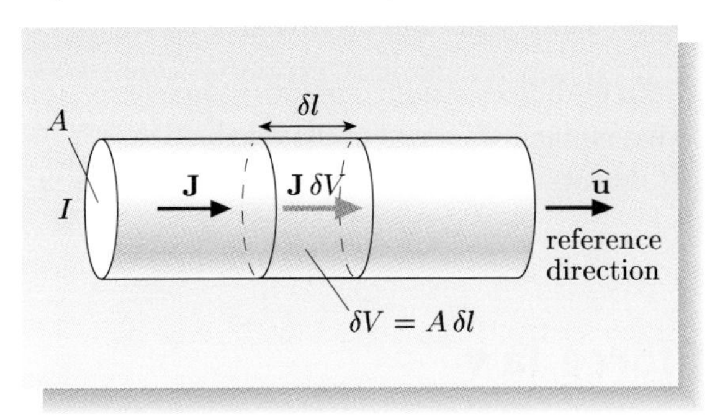


**Figure 3.5** A current element $\mathbf{J}\,\delta V$ in a wire of cross-sectional area $A$, illustrated for $I > 0$.

The current density is $\mathbf{J} = (I/A)\,\widehat{\mathbf{u}}$, where $\widehat{\mathbf{u}}$ is a unit vector pointing along the wire in the reference direction chosen to measure current flow. Combining these expressions, the current element is

$$\mathbf{J}\,\delta V = \frac{I}{A}\,\widehat{\mathbf{u}} \times A\,\delta l = I\,\delta l\,\widehat{\mathbf{u}} = I\,\delta\mathbf{l}.$$

where $\delta\mathbf{l} = \delta l\,\widehat{\mathbf{u}}$ is a directed line element of length $\delta l$ pointing along the wire in the reference direction. Usually, $I$ is positive and $\delta\mathbf{l}$ points in the direction of current flow. So, in summary, we have

$$\text{current element} = \mathbf{J}\,\delta V = I\,\delta\mathbf{l}. \tag{3.6}$$

In order to concentrate on currents carried by wires, we choose to express current elements in terms of $I\,\delta\mathbf{l}$, rather than $\mathbf{J}\,\delta V$, but this is really only a matter of notation. All the equations we derive can be extended to more general situations, beyond the guided flow of currents in wires, simply by replacing each $I\,\delta\mathbf{l}$ by $\mathbf{J}\,\delta V$.

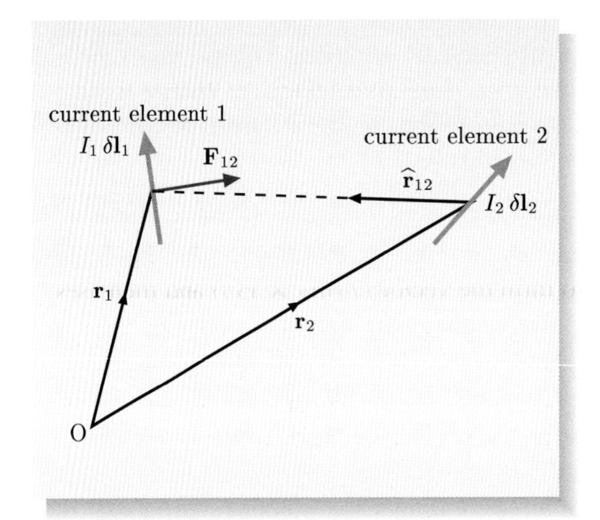


**Figure 3.6** Two steady current elements, $I_1\,\delta\mathbf{l}_1$ and $I_2\,\delta\mathbf{l}_2$, both in the plane of the page. The red arrow shows the force on current element 1 due to current element 2.

We can now ask: what is the magnetic force between two steady current elements? It is difficult to answer this question by pure experimentation. Steady current elements do not exist in isolation, but are always linked together to form complete circuits. The best we can do is to look at the forces on various circuits and try to infer the underlying law of force between individual current elements. A number of physicists looked at this problem in the nineteenth century and a consensus emerged, known today as the **Biot–Savart force law** for current elements.

### The Biot–Savart force law

Consider two steady current elements, $I_1\,\delta\mathbf{l}_1$ and $I_2\,\delta\mathbf{l}_2$ at points $\mathbf{r}_1$ and $\mathbf{r}_2$ (Figure 3.6). Then the magnetic force on current element 1 due to current element 2 is given by

$$\mathbf{F}_{12} = k_{\text{mag}} \frac{I_1\,\delta\mathbf{l}_1 \times (I_2\,\delta\mathbf{l}_2 \times \widehat{\mathbf{r}}_{12})}{r_{12}^2},$$

where $k_{\text{mag}}$ is a positive proportionality constant, the unit vector $\widehat{\mathbf{r}}_{12}$ points in the direction towards current element 1 from current element 2, and $r_{12}$ is the distance between the two current elements.

In SI units, $k_{\text{mag}} = 10^{-7}\,\text{N}\,\text{A}^{-2}$. However it is conventional to write this constant as $k_{\text{mag}} = \mu_0/4\pi$, where $\mu_0 = 4\pi \times 10^{-7}\,\text{N}\,\text{A}^{-2}$ is called the **permeability of free space**. The insertion of a factor of $4\pi$ has the same motivation as in Coulomb's law — to simplify even more important results (Maxwell's equations) that will come later. The Biot–Savart law then takes the standard form

$$\mathbf{F}_{12} = \frac{\mu_0}{4\pi} \frac{I_1\,\delta\mathbf{l}_1 \times (I_2\,\delta\mathbf{l}_2 \times \widehat{\mathbf{r}}_{12})}{r_{12}^2}. \qquad (3.7)$$

The Biot–Savart force law is an inverse square law because the factor $r_{12}^2$ appears in the denominator. However, the numerator is more complicated than the numerator $q_1\,q_2\,\widehat{\mathbf{r}}_{12}$ in Coulomb's law. There is a good reason for this. Coulomb's law is simple because charge is a scalar quantity, with no directional properties. This means that a pair of charges is symmetrical under any rotation about the line that joins them, so the electrostatic force must point along this line. The situation in magnetostatics is more complicated. Current elements are vector quantities with obvious directional character. The pair of current elements in Figure 3.6 is *not* symmetrical under rotations about the line that joins them, so there is no requirement for the magnetostatic force to point along this line. Put another way, *three* vectors play a role in determining the magnetostatic force between two current elements: $I_1\,\delta\mathbf{l}_1$, $I_2\,\delta\mathbf{l}_2$ and $\widehat{\mathbf{r}}_{12}$. The magnetostatic force is obtained by multiplying these three vectors together. Mathematics offers two ways of multiplying vectors — the scalar product and the vector product. The Biot–Savart force law uses the vector product to form the vector $(I_2\,\delta\mathbf{l}_2 \times \widehat{\mathbf{r}}_{12})$ and then uses the vector product again to form $I_1\,\delta\mathbf{l}_1 \times (I_2\,\delta\mathbf{l}_2 \times \widehat{\mathbf{r}}_{12})$.

► MT 8.2.2 reviews products of vectors. Study this section now, if you have not already done so.

Some care is needed in handling the two vector products. The order of the vectors and the placement of the brackets in Equation 3.7 matters and should not be changed carelessly. To find the direction of a magnetic force you must use the right-hand rule twice. For the situation shown in Figure 3.6, one application of the right-hand rule shows that $(I_2\,\delta\mathbf{l}_2 \times \widehat{\mathbf{r}}_{12})$ points out of the page, towards you. The magnetic force $\mathbf{F}_{12}$ on current element 1 due to current element 2 is perpendicular to this vector, so it is in the plane of the page. $\mathbf{F}_{12}$ is also perpendicular to $I_1\,\delta\mathbf{l}_1$ and a second application of the right-hand rule shows that this force is in the direction marked on the diagram. The Biot–Savart law tells us that current elements push one another sideways, with the responding current element feeling a force perpendicular to its own direction of current flow. This force acts in the plane defined by the other current element and the displacement vector between

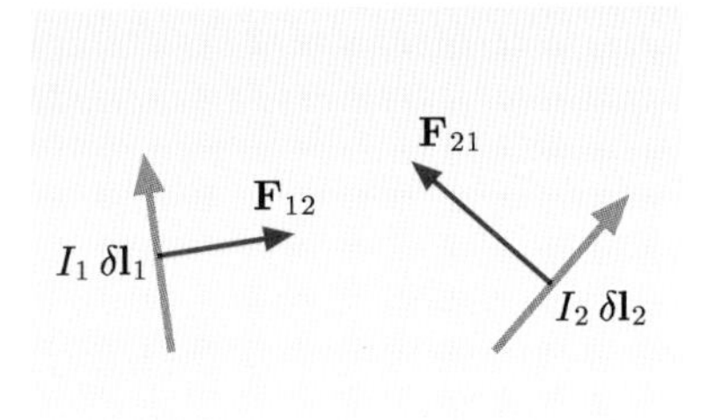


**Figure 3.7** Biot–Savart forces do not obey $\mathbf{F}_{12} = -\mathbf{F}_{21}$. These forces are neither equal in magnitude nor opposite in direction.

the two current elements.

- Is the magnetic force $\mathbf{F}_{12}$ on current element 1 due to current element 2 in the opposite direction to the magnetic force $\mathbf{F}_{21}$ on current element 2 due to current element 1?

- No, because the Biot–Savart force is perpendicular to direction of current flow in the responding current element. In the situation shown in Figure 3.7, the forces $\mathbf{F}_{12}$ and $\mathbf{F}_{21}$ are both in the plane of the page, but $\mathbf{F}_{12}$ is perpendicular to $I_1\,\delta\mathbf{l}_1$, while $\mathbf{F}_{21}$ is perpendicular to $I_2\,\delta\mathbf{l}_2$. These forces do not point in opposite directions.

This remarkable observation appears to be in conflict with Newton's third law, which states that the forces of action and reaction are equal in magnitude and opposite in direction. However, there is a loophole. In practice, a current element can only carry a steady current if it is part of a complete circuit. To find the total magnetic force on one circuit (A) due to another circuit (B), we must integrate the Biot–Savart force law over all the current elements in both circuits. When this is done, the total force on circuit A due to circuit B turns out to be equal in magnitude and opposite in direction to the total force on circuit B due to circuit A, so an uneasy truce is struck between magnetic forces and Newton's third law. I describe the resolution of the conflict in these terms because the whole idea of a current element being pushed sideways, rather than being attracted or repelled by another current element, is against the spirit of Newton's third law. We will revisit this issue at the end of the chapter and show that it is Newton's third law that has to be reassessed.

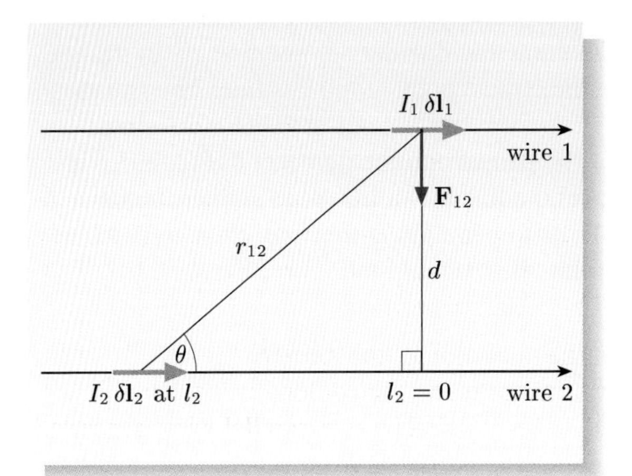


**Figure 3.8** The force $\mathbf{F}_{12}$ on current element $I_1\,\delta\mathbf{l}_1$ due to current element $I_2\,\delta\mathbf{l}_2$.

To illustrate how the Biot–Savart force law is used in practice, let's return to the case of two parallel currents. Figure 3.8 shows a current element, $I_1\,\delta\mathbf{l}_1$ in wire 1 and another current element $I_2\,\delta\mathbf{l}_2$ in wire 2. The Biot–Savart force law gives the force on current element 1 due to current element 2. The magnitude of this force is

$$F_{12} = \frac{\mu_0}{4\pi}\,\frac{I_1 I_2\,\delta l_1 \delta l_2\,\sin\theta}{r_{12}^2},$$

where $\theta$ is the angle between the direction of $I_2\,\delta\mathbf{l}_2$ and the direction towards current element 1 from current element 2. Using the right-hand rule, it is easy to see that the force acts directly towards wire 2. This is true no matter which current element is chosen in wire 2. All the current elements in wire 2 pull current element 1 in the same direction, directly towards wire 2. To find the total force $F_1$ on current element 1, we must add up contributions from all the current elements in wire 2. In other words we must integrate along wire 2. This gives

$$F_1 = \frac{\mu_0 I_1 I_2\, \delta l_1}{4\pi} \int_{-\infty}^{+\infty} \frac{\sin\theta}{r_{12}^2}\, dl_2.$$

Choosing to measure $l_2$ from the point labelled $l_2 = 0$ in Figure 3.8, and using simple trigonometry, we see that $\sin\theta = d/r_{12}$ and $r_{12} = \sqrt{d^2 + l_2^2}$, so the integral can be written as

$$\int_{-\infty}^{+\infty} \frac{\sin\theta}{r_{12}^2}\, dl_2 = \int_{-\infty}^{+\infty} \frac{d}{(d^2 + l_2^2)^{3/2}}\, dl_2 = \frac{1}{d} \int_{-\infty}^{+\infty} \frac{1}{(1 + z^2)^{3/2}}\, dz,$$

where I have changed the variable of integration from $l_2$ to $z = l_2/d$ in the last step. The only remaining integral contains no parameters, so it is just a number. Using the table of integrals inside the back cover of the book, this integral is equal to 2, so

The table of integrals inside the back cover of the book is a useful resource.

$$\int_{-\infty}^{+\infty} \frac{\sin\theta}{r_{12}^2}\, dl_2 = \frac{2}{d}. \qquad (3.8)$$

Putting everything together, and noting that the force per unit length on current element 1 is the same as the force per unit length on the whole wire, we obtain

$$\frac{F_{\text{mag}}}{L} = \frac{F_1}{\delta l_1} = \frac{\mu_0 I_1 I_2}{2\pi d}, \qquad (3.9)$$

where $F_{\text{mag}}/L$ is the attractive magnetic force per unit length of either wire. This agrees with the experimental results quoted in Equation 3.4 at the beginning of this section. Note that the $1/r_{12}^2$ in the Biot–Savart force law has been transformed into a $1/d$. This is because we have integrated along the length of wire 2. Integrating over a length produces a quantity whose units are those of the integrand times the units of length. The integrand in Equation 3.8 has the units of $1/\text{length}^2$ so the final answer must be inversely proportional to a length. The only relevant length in this problem is the separation $d$ of the wires, so it not surprising that the force between the wires is proportional to $1/d$.

Equation 3.9 provides the basis for the definition of the **ampere**. Strictly speaking, an ampere is not *defined* as a current of one coulomb per second. It is defined as that steady current which, when carried by two parallel wires separated by a metre in a vacuum, causes each wire to experience a magnetic force per unit length of $2 \times 10^{-7}\,\text{N}\,\text{m}^{-1}$. The **coulomb** is then defined as the charge transferred by a current of one ampere in one second. The niceties of which quantity is defined first are not profoundly important, but this happens to be the way SI units are set up, motivated by the fact that it is easier to prepare given steady currents than given static charges.

### Limitations of the Biot–Savart force law

The Biot–Savart force law gives the force on one current element due to another current element some distance away. If this law were true without restriction, switching off a current here would have an instantaneous effect on a current on Mars. This raises the uneasy prospect of **instantaneous action at a distance**.

How can a current on Mars respond immediately to changes made to a current on Earth? Surely time is needed for information to travel from Earth to Mars, but the Biot–Savart force law makes no mention of a time-delay. This problem is resolved by recognizing that the Biot–Savart force law is a law of magnetostatics, applying only to steady currents. This echoes the status of Coulomb's law which is a law of electrostatics, applying only to stationary charges.

A second limitation concerns the influence of media. You may recall that the electric force between two charges immersed in a medium can be modified by screening or polarization in the medium. The magnetic forces between two current elements can also be affected by media. For example, an iron rod can become magnetized when it is near a current carrying coil (this is the principle of the electromagnet). The magnetized rod then exerts magnetic forces on current elements in the coil. Fortunately, only a few materials such as iron or nickel respond strongly in this way. Throughout this book I assume that the magnetic response of media can be neglected.

**Exercise 3.3** Does one current element in a long straight wire exert a magnetic force on another current element in the same wire?

**Exercise 3.4** Consider two neutral parallel wires, each 1.0 mm in diameter and each carrying a current of 1.0 A. Find an expression for the ratio $F_{\text{mag}}/F_{\text{elec}}$ of the magnetic force between the wires to the total electric force between the conduction electrons in the two wires. Evaluate your answer numerically using the result of Exercise 3.2. ■

# 3.3 Magnetic fields due to steady currents

## 3.3.1 Splitting the Biot–Savart force law

In the case of electrostatic forces, problems arising from action at a distance motivated us to introduce the concept of an electric field. Coulomb's law was split into two parts — one describing the generation of an electric field by one charge, and the other describing the response of another charge to this field. Using the electric field we were able to formulate Gauss's law, which applies to all electric fields whether electrostatic or not.

It is natural to ask whether something similar can be achieved for magnetic forces. Can we split the Biot–Savart force law into one part describing the generation of a magnetic field by one current element, and another part describing the response of another current element to this field? This can be achieved by grouping terms in the Biot–Savart force law:

$$\mathbf{F}_{12} = I_1\,\delta\mathbf{l}_1 \times \left(\frac{\mu_0}{4\pi}\,\frac{I_2\,\delta\mathbf{l}_2 \times \widehat{\mathbf{r}}_{12}}{r_{12}^2}\right). \tag{3.10}$$

The term in brackets on the right-hand side depends on the properties of current element 2 and the position of current element 1. It is interpreted as the **magnetic field** produced by current element 2 at the position of current element 1. The **magnetic force** on current element 1 is then obtained by taking the vector product of current element 1 with this magnetic field.

It is conventional to use the symbol $\mathbf{B}$ for a magnetic field, the bold print reminding us that it is a vector field. The contribution of a single current element to the magnetic field is then denoted by $\delta\mathbf{B}$, where the $\delta$ reminds us that a circuit produces many such contributions and these must be added together to find the total magnetic field created by the whole circuit. Equation 3.10 therefore splits into two:

$$\mathbf{F}_{12} = I_1\,\delta\mathbf{l}_1 \times \delta\mathbf{B}_2, \quad \text{where} \quad \delta\mathbf{B}_2 = \frac{\mu_0}{4\pi}\frac{I_2\,\delta\mathbf{l}_2 \times \widehat{\mathbf{r}}_{12}}{r_{12}^2}.$$

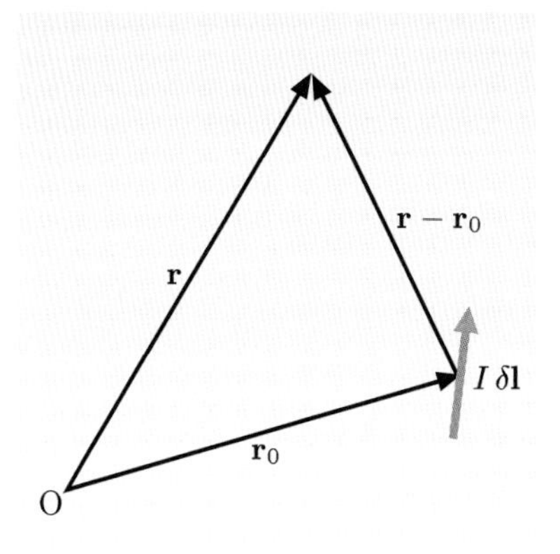


**Figure 3.9** Calculating the magnetic field at $\mathbf{r}$ due to a current element $I\,\delta\mathbf{l}$ at $\mathbf{r}_0$.

These equations refer specifically to current elements 1 and 2, but they can be expressed in more general terms. Current element 1 could be anywhere, so the formula for $\delta\mathbf{B}_2$ really tells us how to find the magnetic field at any point in space. Suppose that we wish to know the magnetic field at a point $\mathbf{r}$ due to a current element $I\,\delta\mathbf{l}$ at a point $\mathbf{r}_0$ (Figure 3.9). The distance between the current element and the point at which the field is measured is $|\mathbf{r}-\mathbf{r}_0|$ and the unit vector pointing towards $\mathbf{r}$ from $\mathbf{r}_0$ is $(\mathbf{r}-\mathbf{r}_0)/|\mathbf{r}-\mathbf{r}_0|$. Adapting our previous formula for $\delta\mathbf{B}_2$, we obtain a general expression for the magnetic field produced by a steady current element:

$$\delta\mathbf{B}(\mathbf{r}) = \frac{\mu_0}{4\pi}\frac{I\,\delta\mathbf{l} \times (\mathbf{r}-\mathbf{r}_0)}{|\mathbf{r}-\mathbf{r}_0|^3}. \qquad (3.11)$$

This is the **Biot–Savart field law** for a current element.

We can also express the equation for the magnetic force on a current element in a more general way. The whole point of a field theory is that the current element should respond locally to the magnetic field that it encounters, irrespective of how the field was generated. We can therefore consider the response of a current element $I\,\delta\mathbf{l}$ to an arbitrary magnetic field $\mathbf{B}$. Removing unwanted subscripts, we see that the current element feels a magnetic force

$$\delta\mathbf{F} = I\,\delta\mathbf{l} \times \mathbf{B}, \qquad (3.12)$$

where $\mathbf{B}$ is the magnetic field at the position of the current element. This is the **magnetic force law** for a current element. The magnetic field could be due to a complete circuit, so there is no need to include a $\delta$ in its symbol. However, I have denoted the force by $\delta\mathbf{F}$ because this is the force on a current element, which is only one contribution to the total force on a circuit. The presence of the cross-product shows that each current element is pushed sideways, perpendicular to its own direction and to the local magnetic field.

The SI unit of magnetic field is the **tesla** (abbreviated T). Equation 3.12 shows $1\,\mathrm{T} = 1\,\mathrm{N\,A^{-1}\,m^{-1}}$, so that a current element of magnitude one ampere metre experiences a force of magnitude one newton when it is perpendicular to a magnetic field of one tesla. A tesla is rather a large field by everyday standards: the magnitude of the Earth's magnetic field in London is only $5 \times 10^{-5}\,\mathrm{T}$. This is the same as the magnetic field one centimetre outside a thin wire carrying a current of 2.5 A.

When applying Equations 3.11 and 3.12 we usually have to add contributions from different current elements. The **principle of superposition** tells us that the total magnetic field at any point is the vector sum of the magnetic field contributions produced by all the current elements. The law of **addition of force** tells us that the total magnetic force on a circuit is the vector sum of the magnetic forces on its current elements. So vector addition is often a key step in tackling problems in magnetostatics.

**Essential skill**

Using the Biot–Savart field law.

### Worked Example 3.1

A circular loop of radius $a$ is centred at the origin and lies in the $xy$-plane. The loop carries a steady current $I$ is the sense shown in Figure 3.10. Find the magnetic field at a point P on the positive $z$-axis.

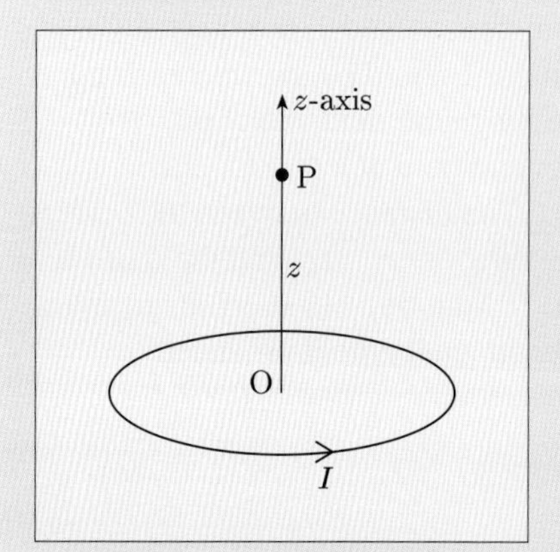


**Figure 3.10** A circular current loop lying in the $xy$-plane.

**Solution**

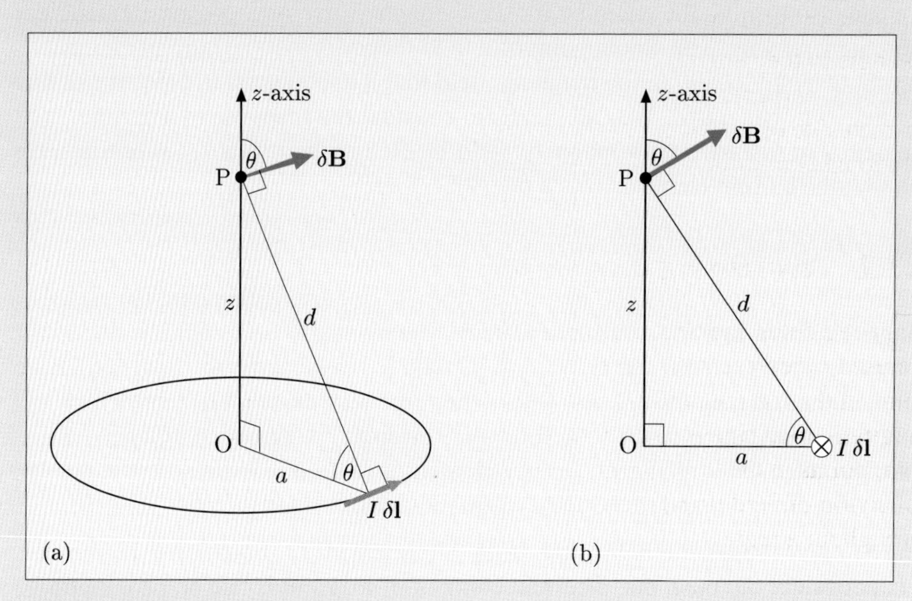


**Figure 3.11** Calculating the magnetic field at P: (a) three-dimensional view; (b) two-dimensional view. In (b) the cross in a circle indicates that the current is flowing into the plane of the paper, away from you.

Consider the current element $I\,\delta\mathbf{l}$ shown in Figure 3.11. We concentrate on a point P, with coordinates $(0, 0, z)$, which is a distance $d$ from the current element. Using Equation 3.11 and the right-hand rule, the current element produces a magnetic field at P which points in the direction shown. Taking the magnitude of Equation 3.11 and noting that $I\,\delta\mathbf{l}$ is perpendicular to the unit vector from the current element to the point P, the current element produces a magnetic field at P of magnitude

$$\delta B = \frac{\mu_0}{4\pi} \frac{I\,\delta l \times d \times \sin 90^\circ}{d^3} = \frac{\mu_0}{4\pi} \frac{I\,\delta l}{d^2}.$$

Other current elements in the loop produce magnetic fields at P with the same $z$-component, but with different components in the plane of the loop. Forming the vector sum of these contributions, the $z$-components reinforce one another, but the components in the plane of the loop cancel out. The total magnetic field is therefore

$$\mathbf{B} = \frac{\mu_0}{4\pi} \frac{I \times 2\pi a}{d^2} \times \cos\theta\,\mathbf{e}_z.$$

Using $\cos\theta = a/d$ and $d = \sqrt{a^2 + z^2}$ we conclude that

$$\mathbf{B} = \frac{\mu_0}{2} \frac{Ia^2}{(a^2 + z^2)^{3/2}}\,\mathbf{e}_z. \qquad (3.13)$$

**Exercise 3.5** A circular loop of radius $a$ carries a steady current of magnitude $I$. What is the magnitude of the field at the centre O of the loop?

**Exercise 3.6** A square loop PQRS carries a steady current as shown in Figure 3.12. Sides PQ and RS are horizontal, and sides QR and SP are inclined at an angle to the vertical. A constant uniform magnetic field acts in a horizontal direction, perpendicular to sides PQ and RS. Describe the directions of the forces on each side of the loop. How should the loop be oriented to achieve stable rotational equilibrium? ■

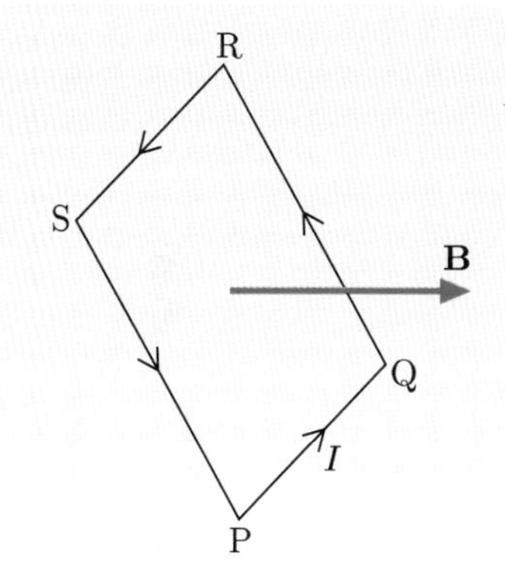


**Figure 3.12** A square current loop in a uniform magnetic field.

## 3.3.2 Visualizing magnetic fields

Magnetic fields can be visualized using arrow maps or field line patterns. Arrows are used to represent the magnitude and direction of the magnetic field at a given point, and an arrow map is a collection of arrows at a selection of points. A **magnetic field line** is a continuous directed line which, at each point along its path, points in the direction of the magnetic field. A field line pattern is a collection of field lines, showing how the direction of the magnetic field varies throughout a region.

First, consider the magnetic field produced by a single current element. The magnetic field (given by Equation 3.11) is perpendicular to both the current element and to the unit vector from the current vector to the field point. So, if you imagine the current element as being above the page, pointing perpendicularly down onto the page, the magnetic field lines in the plane of the page are concentric circles, as shown in Figure 3.13. The field lines circulate in the sense shown because the vector product in Equation 3.11 must be evaluated using the right-hand rule. A convenient way of deducing the direction of the field lines is to point the thumb of your right hand along the direction of the current element; the curled fingers of your right hand then indicate the sense of circulation of the

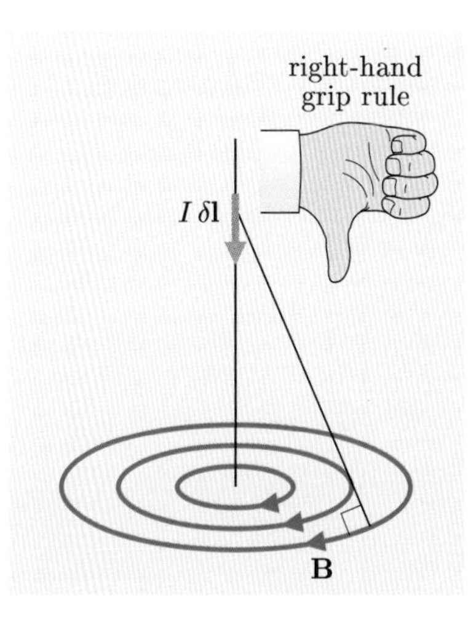


**Figure 3.13** Magnetic field lines due to a current element.

magnetic field lines. This variant of the right-hand rule is called the **right-hand grip rule**.

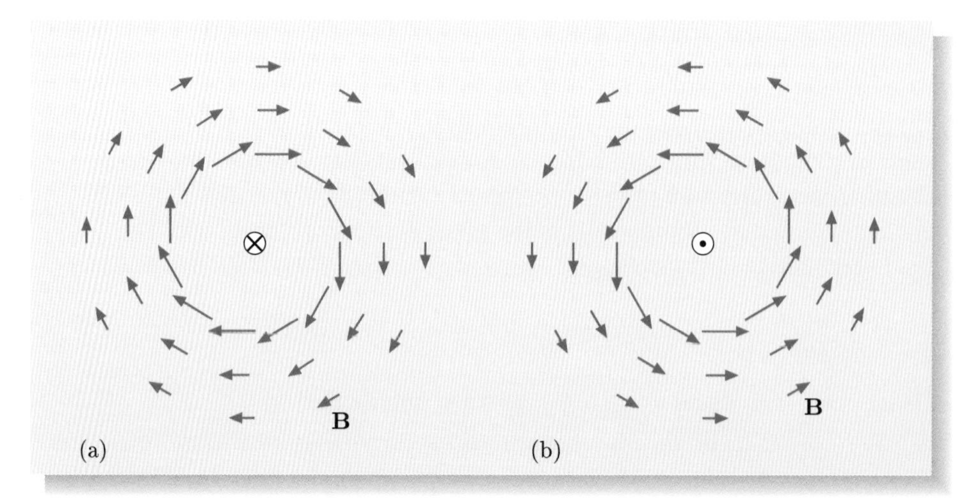


**Figure 3.14** Arrow maps for the magnetic field of a long straight wire for: (a) a current flowing away from you and (b) a current flowing towards you.

The current in a long straight wire is a series of parallel current elements placed end to end. All the current elements have circular magnetic field lines around the axis of the wire. So, using the principle of superposition, the magnetic field lines of a long straight current-carrying wire must be circles centred on the wire and perpendicular to its axis. If the wire is infinitely long, the magnetic field does not vary as we move parallel to the wire. Figure 3.14 shows arrow maps of the magnetic field in any plane perpendicular to the wire, adopting the standard convention of using a cross in a circle for a current flowing directly away from you and a dot in a circle for a current flowing directly towards you. The arrows in these maps have lengths that are inversely proportional to the distance from the wire. To see why, compare Equations 3.9 and 3.12. If two parallel wires, a distance $r$ apart, carry identical currents $I$, the magnetic force on a length $\delta l$ of one wire has magnitude

$$F_{\text{mag}} = \frac{\mu_0 I^2}{2\pi r}\,\delta l = |I|\,\delta l B,$$

so the magnetic field at distance $r$ from the other wire has magnitude

$$B(r) = \frac{\mu_0 |I|}{2\pi r}, \tag{3.14}$$

which is inversely proportional to the distance from the wire.

**Exercise 3.7** A long wire carrying a steady current is placed in a uniform magnetic field parallel to its own length. What is the shape of the magnetic field lines close to the wire? ■

Next consider a circular loop of wire, with a steady current flowing round it. The steady current might be maintained by a tiny battery built into the loop, but we will ignore such practical details here. Our main concern is the magnetic field created by the circulating current. Figure 3.15a shows the pattern of magnetic field lines in a plane that is perpendicular to the loop and passes through its centre. On a small enough scale, the wire appears almost straight so it is not surprising that, very close to the wire, the field lines are almost circular. Further from the wire, the field lines are not circular, but they still form closed loops.

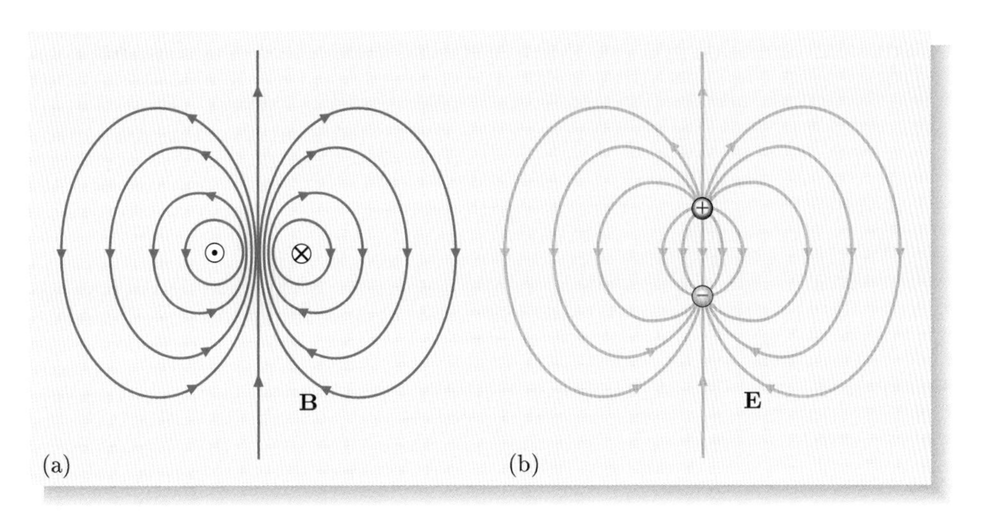


**Figure 3.15** (a) Magnetic field lines in a plane perpendicular to, and passing through the centre of, a circular current loop shown in cross section. (b) Electric field lines in the plane of an electric dipole.

This pattern of magnetic field lines is remarkably similar to the pattern of *electric* field lines produced by an electric dipole, shown in Figure 3.15b. There is one significant difference: the electric field lines always flow from the positive charge to the negative charge, so they reverse their general sense of circulation in the region between the charges, while the magnetic field lines form completely closed loops. Nevertheless, far from the current loop, the magnetic field lines look just like the electric field lines far from an electric dipole. The correspondence turns out to be precise: far from their respective sources, the field line patterns are exactly similar and the field magnitudes are proportional to one another. For this reason, a steady current round a circular loop is called a **magnetic dipole**, and the magnetic field that it produces is said to be **dipolar**.

Our previous examples — current elements and long straight wires — are really theoretical abstractions. In order for a steady current to flow in a current element, the current element must be part of a complete circuit. A straight wire, too, must have its ends joined together by other wires (which may be far enough away to have negligible magnetic influence near the straight wire). So the simplest stand-alone source of magnetic field is a magnetic dipole. Magnetic fields that are dipolar, or approximately dipolar, are found everywhere. The Earth's magnetic field is approximately dipolar, and so are those of the Sun and Jupiter. Electrons, protons and neutrons also produce dipolar magnetic fields — even when they are stationary. In classical physics this is understood by supposing that these particles contain internal current loops. In the case of a neutron, positive and negative charges (quarks) circulate in different ways, so a magnetic field is generated even though the neutron carries no net charge. When discussing the quantum world of atomic particles it is unwise to take classical pictures too literally but the notion of circulating currents persists in our language — we say that electrons, protons and neutrons have **spin**.

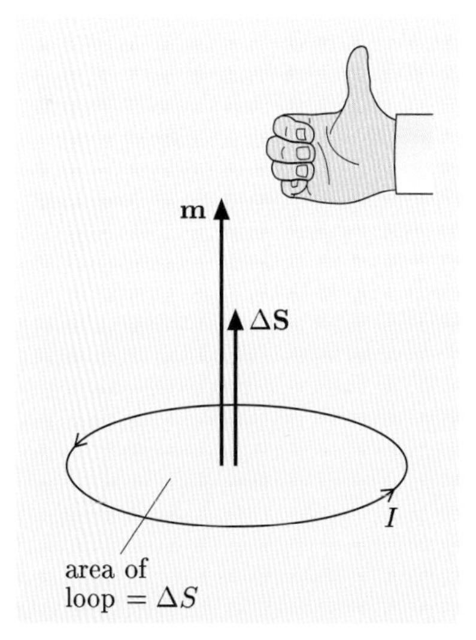


**Figure 3.16** The right-hand grip rule for a magnetic dipole moment: with the fingers of your right hand curled in the direction of current flow, your outstretched right thumb points in the direction of the magnetic moment.

Before quantifying the field of a magnetic dipole, we will introduce some terminology. For a loop of area $\Delta S$ carrying a current $I$, the **magnetic dipole moment** is defined to be a vector quantity of magnitude $|I|\,\Delta S$, whose direction is perpendicular to the loop in a sense determined by the **right-hand grip rule** of Figure 3.16. So,

$$\mathbf{m} = |I|\,\Delta\mathbf{S}, \tag{3.15}$$

where the oriented area $\Delta\mathbf{S}$ of the current loop is a vector of magnitude $\Delta S$

pointing in the direction given by the right-hand grip rule.

Now, we can relate the magnetic field of a current loop to its magnetic dipole moment. According to Worked Example 3.1, the magnetic field on the axis perpendicular to the current loop of radius $a$ has magnitude

$$B = \frac{\mu_0}{2}\frac{|I|a^2}{(a^2+z^2)^{3/2}} \simeq \frac{\mu_0}{2}\frac{|I|a^2}{z^3} \quad \text{for } z \gg a.$$

Using the fact that the area of the loop is $\Delta S = \pi a^2$ and noting the direction of the field lines in Figure 3.15a, we see that at points on the axis perpendicular to the current loop, the dipole produces a magnetic field

$$\mathbf{B} = \frac{\mu_0}{2\pi}\frac{\mathbf{m}}{r^3} \quad \text{for } r \gg a, \tag{3.16}$$

where $r$ is the distance from the loop. In other directions, the field has other values (which will not be calculated here). For example, in the plane that contains the current loop,

$$\mathbf{B} = -\frac{\mu_0}{4\pi}\frac{\mathbf{m}}{r^3} \quad \text{for } r \gg a, \tag{3.17}$$

where $r$ is the distance from the loop. The general rule is that the field of a magnetic dipole decreases as the inverse *cube* of distance, which is faster than the inverse *square* decrease of the field of a current element. This can be understood by realizing that a current loop is made up of pairs of oppositely directed current elements at opposite ends of a diameter. At points far from the current loop, the magnetic field contributions of each pair *almost* cancel out, but not quite because the current elements have different positions; this leaves a residual $1/r^3$ field.

Our repeated use of right-hand rules to find the directions of magnetic fields may lead to the impression that the laws of magnetism have an in-built tendency towards right-handedness. This is not true. By convention, the right-hand rule is used to find the direction of a magnetic field and the direction of a magnetic force. However, *two* successive applications of this rule are needed to relate a current to a measurable effect — a force. This is because the Biot–Savart force law contains *two* vector products — or, equivalently, the vector product in the Biot–Savart field law (Equation 3.11) must be combined with the vector product in the magnetic force law (Equation 3.12) to calculate a magnetic force. The key point is that all traces of the right-hand rule are lost when it is used twice. Two successive applications of a left-hand rule would give the same result as two successive applications of a right-hand rule, so the right-hand rule is a *convention*, not a law of physics. Nevertheless, it is a convention you *must* use in order to communicate effectively with other people. If you use a left-hand rule to calculate magnetic fields and forces, your magnetic field will point in the opposite direction to everyone else's, which is confusing enough to count as a mistake.

Similar remarks apply to time-reversal. If we could reverse the direction of time, the directions of currents would reverse, and so would the directions of magnetic fields (compare Figures 3.14a and b). Does the fact that a magnetic field points in a certain direction imply that the laws of magnetism select an arrow of time, distinguishing the future from the past? No, it does not. If we reverse the direction of time, the current *responding* to the magnetic field also reverses, so the magnetic force between two current elements remains unchanged. Thus magnetic forces are invariant under time-reversal, just like electric forces. This is just what is expected from the general principle of time-reversal symmetry.

**Exercise 3.8** Two magnetic dipoles are aligned along the same axis and point in the same direction. Do these dipoles attract or repel one another? Explain your answer using magnetic field lines.

**Exercise 3.9** The dipolar magnetic field of the Sun has magnitude $3.0 \times 10^{-10}$ T at the radius of the Earth's orbit ($1.5 \times 10^{11}$ m). What is the magnitude of the Sun's dipolar field at the radius of Jupiter's orbit ($8.2 \times 10^{11}$ m)? ■

### 3.3.3 Typical magnetic field values

Table 3.1 shows some typical values for magnetic fields encountered in various circumstances. I will briefly comment on some of the entries.

**Table 3.1** Some typical values of magnetic fields.

| Context | $B/\mathrm{T}$ |
|---|---|
| lowest measurable | $10^{-15}$ |
| magnetic signal from human brain | $10^{-13}$ |
| strong TV or radio signal | $3 \times 10^{-11}$ |
| galactic field | $5 \times 10^{-10}$ |
| time-averaged field near transmitting mobile phone | $10^{-7}$ |
| recommended radio frequency safety limit | $2 \times 10^{-7}$ |
| Earth's magnetic field in London | $5 \times 10^{-5}$ |
| recommended static safety limit | $4 \times 10^{-2}$ |
| in a sunspot | 0.2 |
| near an exceptionally strong permanent magnet | 1 |
| in an MRI body scanner | 1.5 |
| on proton due to electron in a hydrogen atom | 6 |
| near a strong superconducting magnet | 25 |
| instantly lethal static field | $10^{5}$ |
| at the surface of a typical neutron star | $10^{8}$ |
| at the surface of a magnetar | $10^{11}$ |
| at the surface of an atomic nucleus | $10^{12}$ |

Nerve cells carry electric currents and therefore create magnetic fields. The magnetic field of a single brain cell is below the limit of detection, but some parts of the brain contain parallel bundles of cells that fire simultaneously. These bundles produce magnetic fields that can be detected by an array of sensors just outside the head (Figure 3.17). Working backwards, scientists attempt to deduce the current density in the brain that is responsible for the measured magnetic field. This non-invasive technique, called **magnetoencephalography**, (MEG) is able to track brain activity millisecond by millisecond.

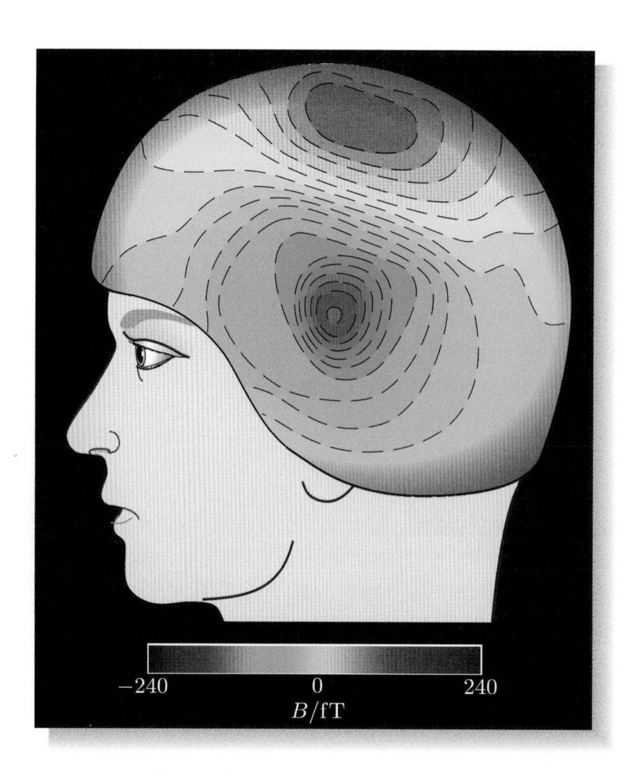


**Figure 3.17** A map of the magnetic field produced at the scalp by a typical current source in a human brain. The fields shown are tiny: $1\,\text{fT} = 1 \times 10^{-15}\,\text{T}$.

The table also includes a value for the Earth's magnetic field. In fact, this field varies over the Earth's surface, from $2.4 \times 10^{-5}\,\text{T}$ in the South Atlantic to $6.6 \times 10^{-5}\,\text{T}$ near the magnetic poles. Close to the Earth, it is dipolar with a magnetic dipole moment of $8 \times 10^{22}\,\text{A m}^2$, but beyond five Earth radii it is distorted by the solar wind, a stream of charged particles emanating from the Sun. The Earth's field deflects these harmful particles, and protects us from them. The main contribution to the dipolar field comes from electric currents in the Earth's **outer core** — a region of swirling liquid iron occupying a spherical shell with radii between 1200 km and 3500 km. The power required to keep these currents flowing, in spite of electrical resistance, is about $3 \times 10^{11}\,\text{W}$. The currents are not entirely stable: the two magnetic poles wander (independently) by as much as several kilometres a year and the magnitude of the field is declining by 6% per century. The geological record shows that the field has actually reversed hundreds of times and that another reversal is statistically overdue. In about $10^{10}$ years the outer core will solidify and the currents and magnetism will disappear. This will not trouble our descendants, however, as the Sun will have run out of fuel by then.

The Sun also has a dipolar magnetic field, with a dipole moment roughly 100 times greater than the Earth's. In addition there are **sunspots** — regions of much higher magnetic field on the Sun's surface. Sunspots are cooler and darker than the surrounding solar surface because their high magnetic fields inhibit hot gases from rising to the surface. All this magnetic activity goes through a fairly regular cycle. Every eleven years the Sun's dipolar field reverses direction and sunspot activity reaches a maximum. This cycle appears to be correlated with the Sun's variable energy output. An extended period of low sunspot activity in the late 1600s was accompanied by unusually cold temperatures throughout northern Europe marked, for example, by the Thames freezing from bank to bank.

Finally, the strongest large-scale magnetic fields are produced by special types of neutron star, called **magnetars**. These are strange, unfriendly worlds. Hydrogen atoms are distorted into cigar shapes, 200 times longer than they are wide and the speed of light depends on its state of polarization relative to the magnetic field. A sudden adjustment of the magnetic field inside a magnetar can release an immense burst of energy, equivalent to 10 000 times the Sun's annual output, but compressed into 0.2 seconds. These bursts take gamma-ray counters in satellites off-scale and also temporarily affect the Earth's ionosphere.

## 3.4 The Lorentz force law

Our expression for the magnetic force on a steady current element (Equation 3.12) can be broadened into a fundamental law which provides a general definition of a magnetic field, valid under all circumstances (not just for magnetostatics).

In microscopic terms, a current is due to a drift of charge carriers. Suppose, for simplicity that the charge carriers have number density $n$, and that each has the same charge, $q$, and the *same* velocity $\mathbf{v}$. Then the current density is $\mathbf{J} = nq\mathbf{v}$ and a current element can be expressed as

$$I\,\delta\mathbf{l} = \mathbf{J}\,\delta V = (nq\mathbf{v})\,\delta V.$$

The current element contains $n\delta V$ charge carriers. If the magnetic force on each charge carrier is $\mathbf{F}_{\text{mag}}$, the magnetic force on the whole current element is $(n\delta V)\mathbf{F}_{\text{mag}}$. So Equation 3.12 can be written in the form

$$(n\,\delta V)\,\mathbf{F}_{\text{mag}} = (nq\mathbf{v})\,\delta V \times \mathbf{B},$$

and we conclude that each charge carrier experiences a magnetic force

$$\mathbf{F}_{\text{mag}} = q\mathbf{v} \times \mathbf{B}. \qquad (3.18)$$

This is the **magnetic force law** for a point charge. The law can be traced back to the Biot–Savart force law which is a magnetostatic equation, valid only for the fields created by steady currents, but these origins are irrelevant. The responding particle does not need not know what caused the field. It just responds to its local environment. We therefore assume that Equation 3.18 is valid beyond magnetostatics. It applies to all charged particles, in all circumstances. For example, it applies in an electron microscope, where electrons travel in a vacuum and are focused by magnetic fields. It applies in mass spectrometers, where the curvature of particle tracks is used as an analytical tool. It also applies in the Earth's atmosphere, where electrons spiral in the Earth's magnetic field and produce the beautiful displays of coloured lights we call the aurora.

The universal validity of Equation 3.18 gives it a special significance. It allows us to turn the argument around to supply a general definition of the **magnetic field**:

If you can find a function $\mathbf{B}(\mathbf{r})$ which, when substituted in Equation 3.18, gives the measured magnetic force on any moving point charge, then this function is the magnetic field. The magnitude of the magnetic field is called the **magnetic field strength**.

The definition is a good one because it is completely general. It quantifies the magnetic field in circumstances where magnetostatic equations (such as

Equation 3.11) are invalid. Of course, Equation 3.18 already has much physics built into it. For example, it presupposes that the magnetic force is proportional to the particle's charge and speed and perpendicular to its velocity. These are verifiable facts. So Equation 3.18 has a mixed status — it is partly a definition and partly a law of physics.

It is worth comparing the definitions of electric and magnetic fields. Both are defined in terms of the forces experienced by electric charges. The electric field $\mathbf{E}$ is defined in such a way that the electric force on a point charge is

$$\mathbf{F}_{\text{elec}} = q\mathbf{E}. \tag{3.19}$$

A simple rearrangement gives an explicit formula for the electric field: $\mathbf{E} = \mathbf{F}_{\text{elec}}/q$. Does a similar formula exist for the magnetic field? No, it does not. This is because the magnetic force vanishes when $\mathbf{v}$ is parallel or antiparallel to $\mathbf{B}$. This means that a particle travelling in the $z$-direction is blind to the $z$-component of the magnetic field, so measuring the force on this particle will not reveal anything about $B_z$. At least two measurements, on charged particles moving in different directions, are needed to tie down all components of the magnetic field. This minor detail should not obscure the fact that Equation 3.18, together with measurements on more than one particle, provides a fundamental and unambiguous definition of the magnetic field at any point in space.

**Exercise 3.10** When a particle of charge $q$ moves through the point P its velocity is $v_z\mathbf{e}_z$ and it experiences a magnetic force $F_x\mathbf{e}_x + F_y\mathbf{e}_y$. What can be said about the magnetic field at the point P? ■

In general, charged particles move through regions where there are both electric and magnetic fields. In such cases, we must add the electric and magnetic forces. Combining Equations 3.19 and 3.18, the total electromagnetic force acting on a point charge is

$$\mathbf{F} = \mathbf{F}_{\text{elec}} + \mathbf{F}_{\text{mag}} = q\left(\mathbf{E} + \mathbf{v} \times \mathbf{B}\right). \tag{3.20}$$

This is the **Lorentz force law**. It was discovered independently by Oliver Heaviside and Hendrik Lorentz, a quarter of a century after Maxwell had written down all the other major equations of electromagnetism. The Lorentz force law incorporates three features of electric and magnetic forces that were outlined in Chapter 1:

- A stationary point charge experiences no magnetic force.
- A moving point charge experiences the same electric force, $q\mathbf{E}$, as a stationary point charge.
- Any additional electromagnetic force that a point charge experiences because it is moving is a magnetic force, $q\mathbf{v} \times \mathbf{B}$.

Another feature, also mentioned in Chapter 1, is worth emphasizing again. The velocity $\mathbf{v}$ in Equation 3.20 is measured *with respect to the reference frame of the observer*. Different observers will assign different velocities to the same motion. For example, a charge may be stationary relative to you, but moving relative to me. In order for our descriptions to be consistent, it follows that the electric and magnetic fields must depend on the choice of reference frame. This happens naturally enough because two observers moving relative to one another will disagree about the state of motion of the charges that produce the fields. However, the moral is that we should stick to one reference frame throughout any particular analysis. Usually this is a reference frame fixed in the laboratory.

The Lorentz force law tells us how to calculate electric and magnetic forces from electric and magnetic fields.

- When the magnetic field vanishes, the electromagnetic force reduces to $\mathbf{F} = q\mathbf{E}$, the *electric part* of the Lorentz force law.
- When the electric field vanishes, the electromagnetic force reduces to $\mathbf{F} = q\mathbf{v} \times \mathbf{B}$, the *magnetic part* of the Lorentz force law.

In general, both electric and magnetic fields are present and the full version $\mathbf{F} = q(\mathbf{E} + \mathbf{v} \times \mathbf{B})$ must be used. We will now show some examples of the Lorentz force law in action.

### Worked Example 3.2

**Essential skill**

Using the Lorentz force law.

An electron performs uniform circular motion in a plane perpendicular to a constant uniform magnetic field of magnitude $1.0 \times 10^{-3}$ T. There is no electric field. Calculate the angular frequency of this circular motion assuming that the usual Newtonian equations of circular motion apply.

#### Solution

A charge of magnitude $q$ and speed $v$, moving perpendicular to a magnetic field of magnitude $B$, experiences a magnetic force of magnitude

$$F = |q|vB \sin 90^\circ = |q|vB.$$

Suppose that the particle has mass $m$ and speed $v$ and that it moves in a circular orbit of radius $r$. The magnetic force must be equal to the centripetal force that keeps the particle in uniform circular motion so

$$|q|vB = \frac{mv^2}{r},$$

and

$$v = \frac{|q|Br}{m}.$$

The angular frequency of the particle's circular motion is then

$$\omega = \frac{v}{r} = \frac{|q|B}{m}.$$

For an electron in a magnetic field of magnitude $1.0 \times 10^{-3}$ T,

$$\omega = \frac{1.60 \times 10^{-19}\,\mathrm{C} \times 10^{-3}\,\mathrm{T}}{9.11 \times 10^{-31}\,\mathrm{kg}} = 1.8 \times 10^8 \mathrm{s}^{-1},$$

where the units have been combined using the unit conversions $1\,\mathrm{T} = 1\,\mathrm{kg\,A^{-1}\,s^{-2}}$ and $1\,\mathrm{A} = 1\,\mathrm{C\,s^{-1}}$, listed inside the front cover of the book. The angular frequency $\omega$ could also be expressed as $1.8 \times 10^8$ rad s$^{-1}$ since radians are dimensionless and are implicit in the definition of angular frequency.

The table of unit conversions inside the front cover of the book is a useful resource.

Note that the angular frequency does not depend on the speed of the electron or its radius of orbit; faster electrons move in larger orbits and have the same angular frequency as slower electrons moving in smaller orbits.

**Figure 3.18** A Penning trap used to compare properties of protons and antiprotons.

Circular motion in a uniform magnetic field is called **cyclotron motion** and the angular frequency at which it occurs is called the **cyclotron frequency**. The most general motion of a charged particle in a uniform magnetic field is helical, with a steady motion along the field superimposed on a uniform circular motion perpendicular to the field. One turn of the helix is completed in the **cyclotron period**, $2\pi/\omega$.

Cyclotron motion is used to trap charged particles in a vacuum. Of course, their motion is only confined perpendicular to the magnetic field; motion along the field is unhindered. In a device known as a **Penning trap**, an electric field is used to produce confinement in the third dimension. A strong magnetic field pointing in the $z$-direction is accompanied by a weak electric field with a $z$-component that changes sign at $z = 0$. The electric force draws appropriately charged particles back towards $z = 0$, so trapping is achieved in three dimensions. Penning traps are highly efficient and have been used to store particles for months and transport them across continents. One application, important in fundamental physics, is to compare the properties of matter and antimatter. Comparisons of cyclotron frequencies in the Penning trap of Figure 3.18 have shown that protons and antiprotons have charge-to-mass ratios that differ in magnitude by less than one part in $10^{10}$. Similar measurements have been carried out on molecular ions. This forms the basis of a high-precision form of mass spectroscopy which is on the verge of being able to *weigh* chemical bonds — that is, find chemical bond energies by measuring ionic masses and using Einstein's famous equation, $E = mc^2$.

Another application of the Lorentz force law follows from the obvious fact that opposite charges, $+q$ and $-q$, moving with the same velocity in the same magnetic field, feel *opposite* magnetic forces. Seawater contains both positive and negative ions. As these charged particles are carried by tidal flows through the Earth's magnetic field, they are deflected in opposite directions and separated. The separation of charge builds up a voltage which drives electric currents through surrounding regions of seawater or conducting sediments in the seafloor. These large-scale currents themselves produce magnetic fields which can be detected by sensitive instruments in satellites. The results are truly impressive (see Figure 3.19).

By contrast, opposite charges, $+q$ and $-q$, moving with opposite velocities $+\mathbf{v}$ and $-\mathbf{v}$ in the same magnetic field, feel *identical* magnetic forces. This is the basis of the **Hall effect**, illustrated in Figure 3.20. A given electric current might consist of positive charges flowing in the direction of the current or of negative charges flowing in the opposite direction. If a magnetic field is applied perpendicular to the current, the magnetic force deflects the charge carriers in a direction perpendicular to their motion and to the magnetic field. They accumulate on the sides of the conductor, producing an electric field across it. A steady state is soon established in which the electric force due to the electric field exactly balances the magnetic force due to the magnetic field. According to the Lorentz force law, the two signs of charge carrier are deflected in the *same* direction, but this means that the corresponding electric fields point in *opposite* directions. So, by observing the direction of the electric field across the conductor in a magnetic field, we can deduce the sign of its dominant charge carriers. In most metals the charge carriers are (negatively-charged) electrons but the current may be carried by positive holes in some semiconductors.

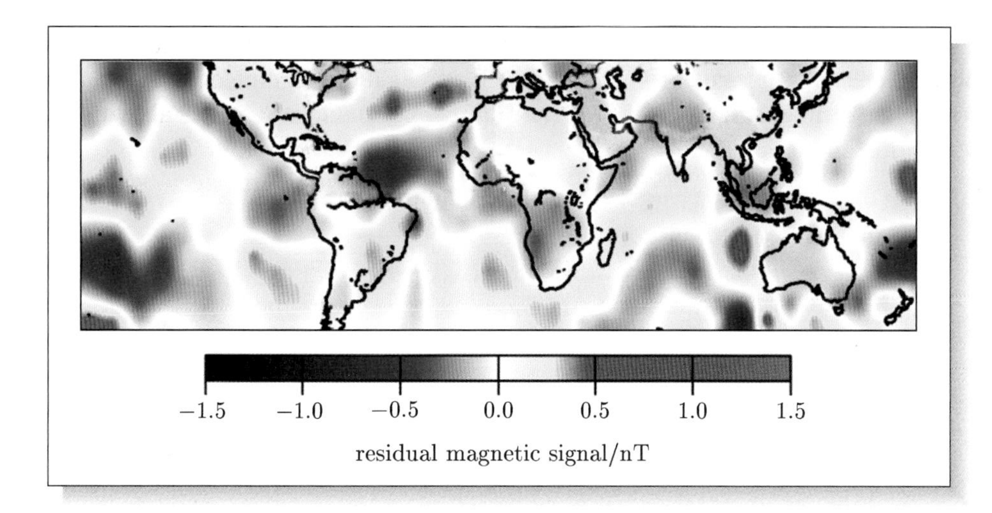


**Figure 3.19** A map of the residual magnetic signal produced by the electric currents associated with tidal flows, detected by the CHAMP satellite at an altitude of 430 km. The residual signal is extracted from a much larger background by a process of averaging and filtering to obtain a contribution in phase with the twice-daily rhythm of the ocean tides. Although this produces some artifacts, the overall pattern is remarkably close to theoretical predictions. For example, the Gulf Stream is clearly visible.

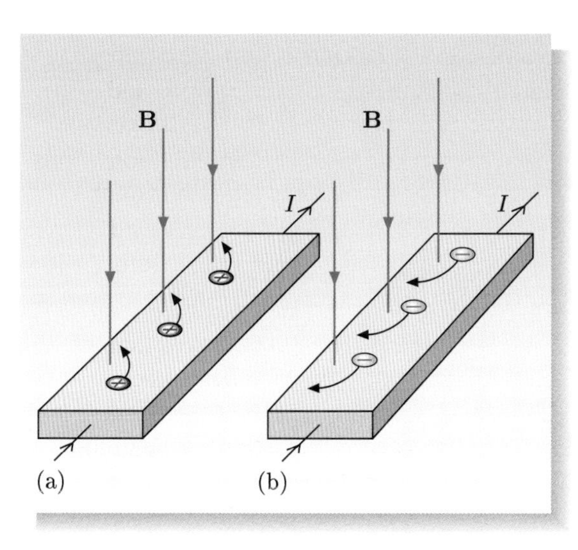


**Figure 3.20** The deflection of charge carriers in the Hall effect: (a) when the current is carried by positive charge carriers and (b) when the same current is carried by negative charge carriers.

The Hall effect gives us a way of measuring magnetic fields. A fixed current is passed through a semiconductor chip and the voltage across the chip is recorded and converted into a magnetic field reading. This idea is also exploited in various devices that detect motion. When a moving part temporarily blocks an applied magnetic field, the voltage fluctuation in a Hall effect chip gives an indication of the motion. Electronic ignition systems in cars and some computer keyboards work in this way.

**Exercise 3.11** An electron moves at speed $v$ through a region where there is a uniform electric field in the $x$-direction and a uniform magnetic field in the $y$-direction. What is the ratio of the field magnitudes if the electron travels undeflected in the $z$-direction?

**Exercise 3.12** A conductor with a rectangular cross-section of area 2.0 mm$^2$ carries a steady current of 1.5 A. With a magnetic field of magnitude $3.0 \times 10^{-2}$ T perpendicular to one pair of its faces, the Hall effect produces a constant electric field of magnitude 3.0 N C$^{-1}$ perpendicular to the other pair of faces.

(a) With the build-up of charge as shown in Figure 3.21, what is the sign of the charges carrying the current?

(b) Assuming that the current carriers each have a charge of magnitude $e$, what is their number density? ■

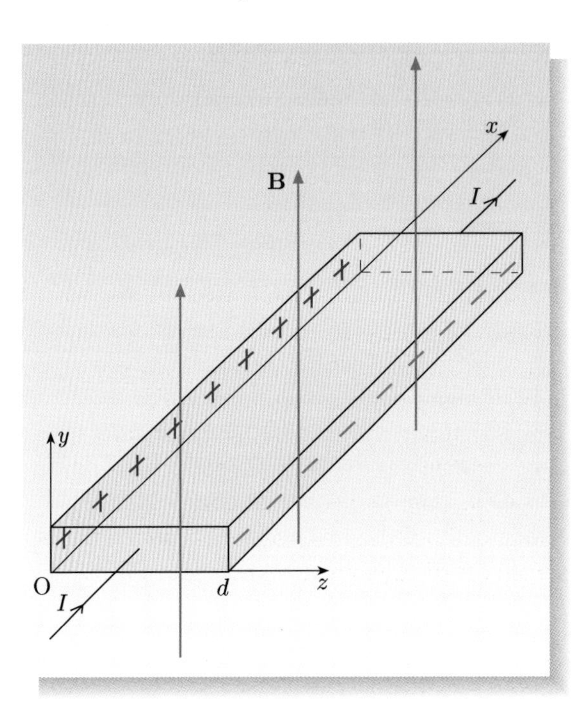


**Figure 3.21** The separation of charge in a Hall effect measurement.

## 3.5 Afterword on Newton's third law

You saw earlier that the Biot–Savart force law challenges Newton's third law. This challenge was defended by noting that the Biot–Savart force law assumes steady currents, and these can only be maintained in complete circuits. The magnetic forces between complete circuits do obey Newton's third law. However, it is less easy to deflect the challenge posed by the Lorentz force law.

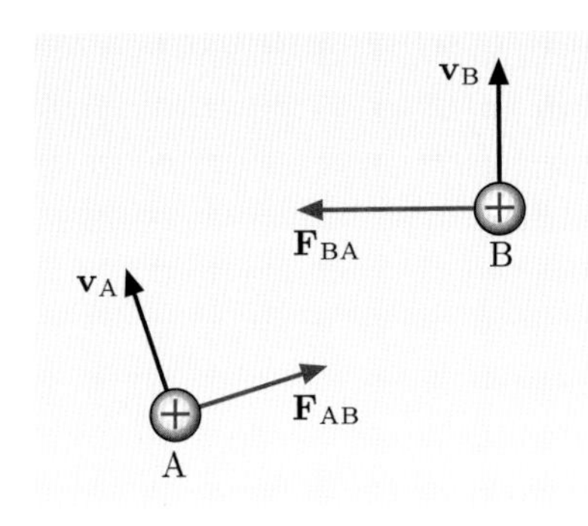


**Figure 3.22** Magnetic forces $\mathbf{F}_{AB}$ and $\mathbf{F}_{BA}$ between two uniformly-moving charges.

Figure 3.22 shows two identical positive point charges in uniform motion. Just like a current element, a uniformly-moving charge produces a magnetic field with circular field lines centred on the line of motion of the charge, directed in a sense determined by the right-hand grip rule. At the position of charge A, the magnetic field due to charge B points out of the page, towards you. At the position of charge B, the magnetic field due to charge A points into the page, away from you. So, using the Lorentz force law to determine the magnetic forces on the charges, we obtain forces $\mathbf{F}_{AB}$ and $\mathbf{F}_{BA}$ pointing in the directions shown in Figure 3.22. These forces do not obey Newton's third law. The electric forces act along the line of separation of the charges, so they do not rescue the situation. Newton's third law cannot survive the fact that the magnetic force on a charged particle is neither an attraction nor a repulsion, but is a sideways kick, perpendicular to the particle's velocity.

How should this be interpreted? The main point is that we should not seek to defend Newton's third law at all costs. In mechanics, where instantaneous action at a distance is assumed, Newton's third law is a key assumption behind two of the most cherished laws of physics — the law of conservation of momentum and the law of conservation of angular momentum. However, electromagnetism takes us beyond action at a distance by introducing electric and magnetic fields. It turns out that these fields have momenta and angular momenta of their own. Adding the momenta and angular momenta of the fields to those of the particles, the laws of conservation of momentum and angular momentum remain valid, even though Newton's third law is violated. Modern physicists are content to sacrifice Newton's third law, knowing that the conservation laws are left intact.

## Summary of Chapter 3

**Section 3.1** The current $I$ through a surface is a scalar quantity describing the rate at which charge $Q$ crosses the surface: $I = \mathrm{d}Q/\mathrm{d}t$. This is the surface integral of the current density over the surface. The current density $\mathbf{J}(\mathbf{r})$ is a vector field pointing in the direction of current flow. Its magnitude is the magnitude of the current flowing through a tiny plane element perpendicular to the current flow, divided by the area of the element. In microscopic terms, current density is given by $\mathbf{J} = nq\mathbf{v}$, where $n$ is the number density of charge carriers, $q$ is their charge and $\mathbf{v}$ is their drift velocity. To avoid an unlimited accumulation of charge, a current density that is independent of time must be divergence-free: $\operatorname{div}\mathbf{J} = 0$.

**Section 3.2** The current element associated with a volume element $\delta V$ is $\mathbf{J}\,\delta V$, where $\mathbf{J}$ is the current density at the position of the volume element. For a current in a wire, the current element is $I\,\delta\mathbf{l}$, where $\delta\mathbf{l}$ is a directed line element pointing along the wire in the reference direction for current flow.

The magnetic force between two steady current elements is given by the Biot–Savart force law:

$$\mathbf{F}_{12} = \frac{\mu_0}{4\pi}\frac{I_1\,\delta\mathbf{l}_1 \times (I_2\,\delta\mathbf{l}_2 \times \widehat{\mathbf{r}}_{12})}{r_{12}^2}.$$

This law applies only to steady currents and its use in this book assumes that the magnetic response of materials can be neglected.

**Section 3.3** The Biot–Savart law can be split into separate equations describing the production of a magnetic field by a current element and the response of a current element to a magnetic field:

$$\delta\mathbf{B}(\mathbf{r}) = \frac{\mu_0}{4\pi}\frac{I\,\delta\mathbf{l} \times (\mathbf{r} - \mathbf{r}_0)}{|\mathbf{r} - \mathbf{r}_0|^3},$$

$$\delta\mathbf{F} = I\,\delta\mathbf{l} \times \mathbf{B}.$$

**Section 3.4** The Lorentz force law states that the total electromagnetic force acting on a point charge $q$ is

$$\mathbf{F} = q\,(\mathbf{E} + \mathbf{v} \times \mathbf{B}),$$

where $\mathbf{E}$ and $\mathbf{B}$ are the electric and magnetic fields at the position of the charge. This law underpins many phenomena and devices, including the Hall effect, Penning traps and cyclotrons.

## Achievements from Chapter 3

*After studying this chapter you should be able to do the following:*

**3.1** Explain the meaning of the newly defined (emboldened) terms and symbols, and use them appropriately.

**3.2** Define current and current density. Relate the current density to the charge, number density and drift velocity of the charge carriers.

**3.3** Recognize that steady currents are divergence-free.

**3.4** State the Biot–Savart force law and use it to calculate magnetic forces in simple cases.

**3.5** State the Biot–Savart field law and use it to calculate magnetic fields in simple cases.

**3.6** Calculate the magnetic force on a current element in a given magnetic field.

**3.7** Sketch the magnetic field lines for a long straight wire and a magnetic dipole.

**3.8** State and use the Lorentz force law. Recognize that this law provides a fundamental definition of the electric and magnetic fields.

*After studying MT 8.2.2 you should also be able to:*

**3.9** Evaluate vector products and manipulate simple vector equations involving vector products.

# Chapter 4 Ampère's law

## Introduction

Chapter 2 introduced Gauss's law for electric fields, expressing it in two different forms, one involving integrals and the other involving partial derivatives. The integral version of Gauss's law relates the flux of the electric field over a closed surface to the total charge enclosed by the surface. In highly symmetric situations, this version of Gauss's law provides an efficient way of calculating electric fields, and is much easier to use than Coulomb's law. The differential version of Gauss's law relates the divergence of the electric field to the charge density. This version of Gauss's law captures the spirit of a local field theory; the divergence of the electric field tells us something about the spatial rate of change of the electric field at a given place and time, and this is determined by the charge density at the *same* place and time. There is no mention of action at a distance.

This chapter explores whether anything similar can be achieved for magnetic fields. It begins by investigating the flux of the magnetic field over a closed surface. Here, there is a significant difference between electric and magnetic fields. Electric field lines start on positive charges and end on negative charges, but magnetic field lines form closed loops. You will see in Section 4.1 that the flux of the magnetic field vanishes over any closed surface and the divergence of the magnetic field vanishes everywhere. This result is called the no-monopole law. It is the magnetic analogue of Gauss's law and is one of Maxwell's four laws of electromagnetism.

The no-monopole law expresses a basic truth about magnetic fields, but it does not make a connection between magnetic fields and their sources — electric currents. This omission is made good by Ampère's law, which will be discussed in Sections 4.2 and 4.3. In order to state Ampère's law we need some additional mathematical concepts — the line integral of a vector field along a curve and the curl of a vector field. For steady currents, you will see that the line integral of the magnetic field around a closed loop is related to the current flowing through the loop, and the curl of the magnetic field at a given place and time is determined by the current density at the *same* place and time. In highly symmetric situations, Ampère's law provides an efficient way of calculating magnetic fields, and is easier to use than the Biot–Savart law.

This chapter uses the mathematics of line integrals and curls, which are covered in MT 8.7 and 8.8. You should extend your study time on the chapter by about 50% to review this mathematics.

## 4.1 The no-monopole law

Let's recall the concept of electric flux, which is the surface integral of the electric field:

$$\text{electric flux over } S = \int_S \mathbf{E} \cdot \mathrm{d}\mathbf{S}.$$

A simple example is provided by an isolated point charge, stationary at the centre of a sphere. If the charge is positive, all the electric field lines are directed outwards, giving a positive electric flux over the surface of the sphere. If the charge is negative, all the electric field lines are directed inwards, giving a negative electric flux over the surface of the sphere.

In a similar way, we define the **magnetic flux** to be the surface integral of the magnetic field. That is,

$$\text{magnetic flux over } S = \int_S \mathbf{B} \cdot d\mathbf{S}.$$

The chosen surface $S$ can be open or closed. In this chapter we are interested mainly in closed surfaces.

Magnetic fields are quite unlike electric fields because magnetic field lines form closed loops (see Figures 3.13–3.15). Another way of expressing this is to say that **magnetic monopoles** do not exist. We can imagine a world in which positive and negative magnetic monopoles are the magnetic analogues of positive and negative charges. A positive magnetic monopole would be a starting point for magnetic field lines, and all the magnetic field lines in its immediate vicinity would diverge away from it. A negative magnetic monopole would be an ending point for magnetic field lines, and all the magnetic field lines in its immediate vicinity would converge towards it. However, no magnetic monopole has ever been detected. Recent experiments show that a superconductor contains less than one monopole per $10^{29}$ nucleons, and that any magnetic monopoles in cosmic rays pass through a detector at a rate of less than one monopole per square metre per 1000 years. These are upper limits set by experimental uncertainties, so the observations are consistent with the absence of monopoles. Classical electromagnetism assumes that magnetic monopoles do not exist.

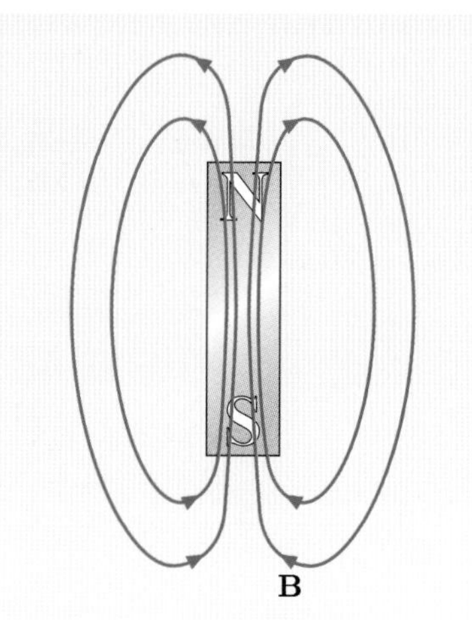


**Figure 4.1** The magnetic field lines of a bar magnet form closed loops.

You might wonder whether the poles of a north and south bar magnet are a pair of positive and negative magnetic monopoles. They are not. Outside a bar magnet, the magnetic field lines emerge from the north pole, loop around, and then disappear into the south pole, but this is not the complete picture. Inside the magnet, the magnetic field lines flow from the south pole to the north pole, joining up smoothly with the field lines from outside the magnet to form closed loops (Figure 4.1). The north and south poles are rather vague regions near the ends of the magnet, but the same number of field lines enter and leave each of these regions, so they are not magnetic monopoles. Classical electromagnetism recognizes the north and south poles of a bar magnet, but denies the existence of magnetic monopoles.

Now consider the magnetic flux over a closed surface, $S$. The closed-loop nature of magnetic field lines implies that there are patches of negative magnetic flux (where magnetic field lines enter the surface and point inwards) and patches of positive magnetic flux (where magnetic field lines leave the surface and point outwards). There must at least be partial cancellation between these two types of contribution. We will argue shortly that the cancellation is exact, so the magnetic flux over any closed surface $S$ is equal to zero:

$$\int_S \mathbf{B} \cdot d\mathbf{S} = 0. \qquad (4.1)$$

Equation 4.1 would be false if magnetic field lines were not continuous or if magnetic monopoles existed. If a magnetic monopole could be placed inside a closed surface, the magnetic flux over the surface would have the sign of the monopole, and would not vanish. We therefore call Equation 4.1 the **no-monopole law**. In fact, this is the *integral version* of the no-monopole law. Using the divergence theorem (Equation 8.34), we obtain

$$\int_V \operatorname{div} \mathbf{B} \, \mathrm{d}V = 0,$$

where $V$ is the volume inside $S$. This equation is true for all volumes, no matter how small, so the integrand must vanish everywhere. Hence,

$$\operatorname{div} \mathbf{B} = 0. \tag{4.2}$$

This is the *differential version* of the no-monopole law. It tells us that all magnetic fields are divergence-free. In Cartesian coordinates for example,

$$\frac{\partial B_x}{\partial x} + \frac{\partial B_y}{\partial y} + \frac{\partial B_z}{\partial z} = 0.$$

### Justifying the no-monopole law for a steady current

The no-monopole law can be justified for the magnetic field due to any steady current by using the Biot–Savart law (Equation 3.11). Consider a single steady current element $I \, \delta\mathbf{l}$. For simplicity, we choose our coordinate system so that the current element is at the origin and is aligned with the $z$-axis (Figure 4.2). Then at any point $\mathbf{r}$, the magnetic field $\mathbf{B}$ produced by the current element is

$$\mathbf{B} = \frac{\mu_0}{4\pi} \frac{I \, \delta\mathbf{l} \times \mathbf{r}}{r^3}.$$

In spherical coordinates, this can be expressed as

$$\mathbf{B} = \frac{\mu_0}{4\pi} \frac{I \, \delta l \sin\theta \, \mathbf{e}_\phi}{r^2}.$$

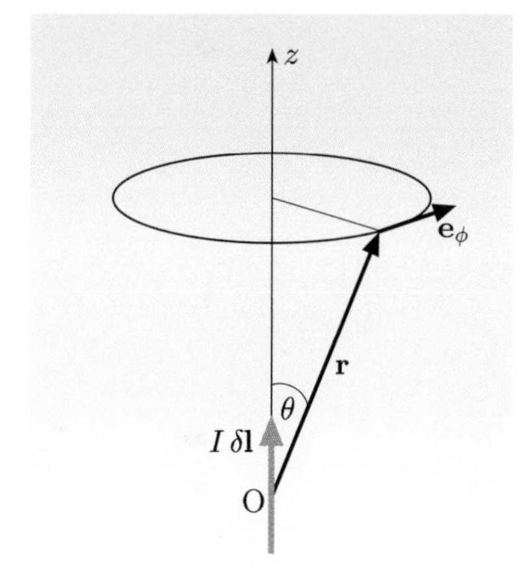


**Figure 4.2** A current element $I \, \delta\mathbf{l}$ at the origin, aligned with the $z$-axis.

Let's evaluate the divergence of this magnetic field. The formula for divergence in spherical coordinates is given inside the back cover of the book. Using this, we obtain

$$\operatorname{div} \mathbf{B} = \frac{1}{r \sin\theta} \frac{\partial}{\partial \phi} \left( \frac{\mu_0}{4\pi} \frac{I \, \delta l \sin\theta}{r^2} \right), \tag{4.3}$$

which is equal to zero because the term in brackets does not depend on $\phi$. The only possible exception is at the origin, where the current element sits; the magnetic field tends to infinity as we approach $r = 0$ and Equation 4.3 gives $0/0$ at this point, which is not well-defined. You might think that this is an uninteresting mathematical detail, but care is needed. In electrostatics, for example, the electric field of a point charge has $\operatorname{div} \mathbf{E} = 0$ everywhere, except at the point occupied by the charge. Yet this single point is hugely influential because it acts as a source of electric field lines, leading to a non-zero electric flux over any closed surface surrounding the charge.

To rule out such a possibility for magnetic fields, we calculate the magnetic flux over a sphere centred on the current element. At any point on the surface of the sphere, $\mathbf{B}$ points in the $\mathbf{e}_\phi$-direction, while the unit normal to the sphere points in the $\mathbf{e}_r$-direction. These vectors are orthogonal, so the magnetic flux over the surface of the sphere is

$$\int_{\text{sphere}} \mathbf{B} \cdot \mathrm{d}\mathbf{S} = 0. \tag{4.4}$$

The integral version of the no-monopole law can now be derived. First, consider a closed surface $S$ that does not contain the current element. In this case, $\operatorname{div} \mathbf{B} = 0$ throughout the volume $V$ inside $S$ and the divergence theorem gives

$$\int_S \mathbf{B} \cdot \mathrm{d}\mathbf{S} = \int_V \operatorname{div} \mathbf{B} \, \mathrm{d}V = 0. \tag{4.5}$$

Next, consider a closed surface $S$ that contains the current element (Figure 4.3). In this case, we split the volume inside $S$ into two pieces — a sphere $V_1$ centred on the current element and the remainder $V_2$, which has a spherical hole taken out of it. The surfaces of these two pieces are shown in blue and red in Figure 4.3b. Equation 4.4 shows that the magnetic flux over the blue surface of the sphere $V_1$ is equal to zero. Equation 4.5 shows that the magnetic flux over the red surface of the remainder $V_2$ is equal to zero. Using the additivity of flux, we conclude that the magnetic flux over $S$ is also equal to zero.

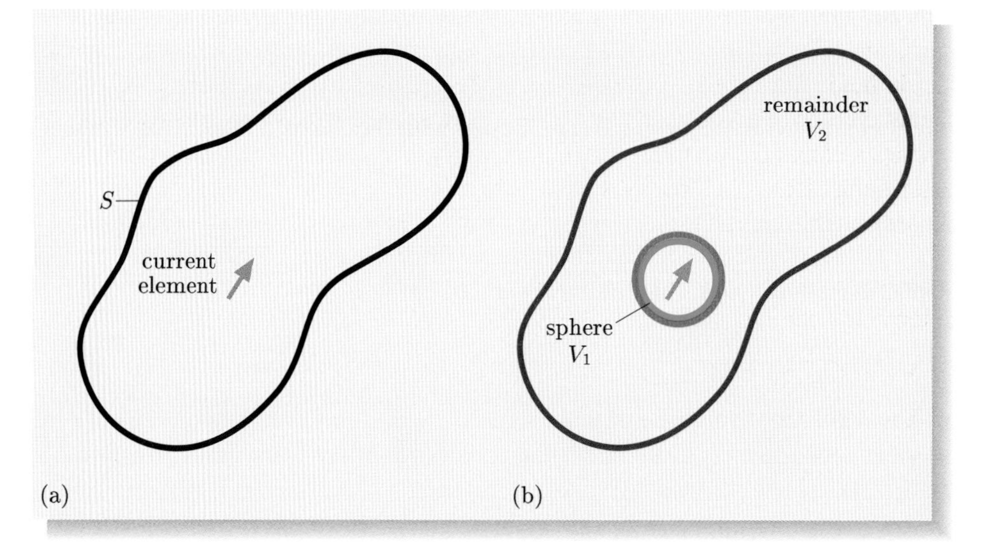


**Figure 4.3** (a) A surface $S$ that contains a current element. (b) The volume inside $S$ is decomposed into a sphere $V_1$ and a remainder $V_2$. The surface of $V_1$ is shown in blue and surface of $V_2$ is shown in red.

We have used a special coordinate system to establish this result, but the fact that the magnetic flux vanishes over any closed surface really cannot depend on our choice of coordinate system. It is true for all coordinate systems and for all current elements, no matter what their orientation or location. The magnetic field produced by any steady current can be regarded as the sum of the magnetic fields produced by many steady current elements, so the integral version of the no-monopole law is valid for any steady current. The differential version follows from the divergence theorem, assuming that the magnetic field varies smoothly. (This assumption is reasonable, provided that the magnetic field is produced by a smoothly varying current density.)

### Status and scope of the no-monopole law

Our justification of the no-monopole law is based on the Biot–Savart law, which assumes steady currents. However, we now make a bold leap of faith and assert that the no-monopole law is valid for all magnetic fields, whether magnetostatic or not. This echoes our earlier treatment of Gauss's law, which took Coulomb's law of electrostatics as its starting point, and then assumed that Gauss's law is valid for all electric fields, whether electrostatic or not. There is no logical flaw in making extensions of this kind. In fact any new law of physics, which expands the predictive power of the subject, must go beyond the certainties of proof. Instead of mathematical proof, science has the discipline of experimental tests. The no-monopole law was first suggested by Lord Kelvin in 1849, only a few years before Maxwell started to think about electromagnetism, and Maxwell incorporated it into his theory. The no-monopole law, in either of its forms, counts as one of Maxwell's four laws of electromagnetism, and the most compelling evidence for it comes from the successful predictions of the whole of Maxwell's theory.

Clearly, there is a strong analogy between the no-monopole law and Gauss's law, as both involve the divergence of electromagnetic fields. However, these equations are used in very different ways. Gauss's law provides a link between electric fields and their sources. It helps us to predict the electric field produced by a given charge distribution, or to find the charge distribution that is consistent with a given electric field. But the no-monopole law makes no mention of the sources of magnetic fields (electric currents), so it cannot be used in this way. Instead, it provides a constraint that any magnetic field must satisfy. We can think of many vector fields, $\mathbf{F}(x, y, z)$, but most cannot be magnetic fields. The only vector fields that are suitable candidates for magnetic fields are those with zero divergence.

**Exercise 4.1** If $C$ is a constant with suitable units, which of the following vector fields could be a magnetic field?

(a) $\mathbf{V}_1 = Cy^2\mathbf{e}_x$

(b) $\mathbf{V}_2 = C(x^2\mathbf{e}_x + y^2\mathbf{e}_y - z^2\mathbf{e}_z)$

(c) $\mathbf{V}_3 = C(xz\mathbf{e}_x + yz\mathbf{e}_y - z^2\mathbf{e}_z)$

**Exercise 4.2** Within a given region, a magnetic field points in the $z$-direction. Show that this magnetic field cannot depend on $z$. ■

## 4.2 Ampère's law

The no-monopole law implies that magnetic field lines form continuous closed loops, with no start-points or end-points, but it does not allow us to predict the magnetic field created by a particular arrangement of currents. This is because it specifies the magnetic flux over a closed surface, a quantity which vanishes whether currents are present or not. In order to predict magnetic fields, it is more profitable to quantify the amount by which the magnetic field circulates around a closed loop. This involves the mathematical concepts of line integrals and circulation, which are discussed in the Mathematical Toolkit. With appropriate definitions, you will see that the circulation of a magnetic field around a wire is proportional to the steady current in the wire. This is an example of Ampère's law which, in cases of high symmetry, provides a much easier way of calculating magnetic fields than the cumbersome Biot–Savart law. Ampère's law is the subject of the rest of this chapter.

▶ Read MT 8.7 now. This is essential material.

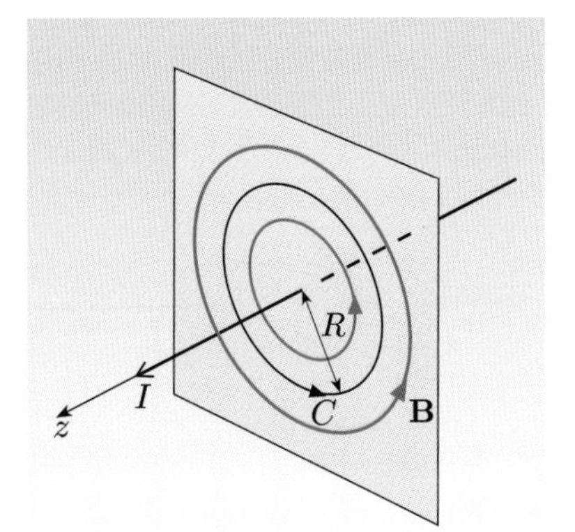


**Figure 4.4** A circular path $C$ of radius $R$ around a current carrying wire.

To establish Ampère's law, let's begin by considering the magnetic field around a long straight wire that carries a steady current $I$ along the $z$-axis. We will calculate the circulation of the magnetic field round a circular path $C$ which is centred on the wire and lies in a plane perpendicular to it (Figure 4.4). The circular path $C$ has radius $R$ and is traversed in the sense indicated so, when $I$ is positive, the magnetic field lines circulate around the wire in the same sense as the path $C$.

By definition, the **circulation** of the magnetic field around $C$ is given by the line integral

$$\text{circulation of magnetic field} = \oint_C \mathbf{B} \cdot \mathrm{d}\mathbf{l}.$$

Using Equation 3.14, the component of the magnetic field in the direction of progression around $C$ is $B_\phi = \mu_0 I/2\pi R$. This remains constant all round the path, so the line integral is simply the product of $B_\phi$ and the circumference of the circle:

$$\oint_C \mathbf{B} \cdot \mathrm{d}\mathbf{l} = \frac{\mu_0 I}{2\pi R} \times 2\pi R = \mu_0 I. \tag{4.6}$$

The circulation is positive for $I > 0$, when the magnetic field lines circulate in the same sense as $C$, and negative for $I < 0$, when the magnetic field lines circulate in the opposite sense. Although the circulation depends on the current in the wire, *it does not depend on the radius of the circular path.* It is easy to see why. The magnetic field decreases as $1/R$ as we move away from the wire, while the circumference of the circle is proportional to $R$. These two factors cancel out in Equation 4.6, leaving the circulation of the magnetic field independent of the radius of the circle.

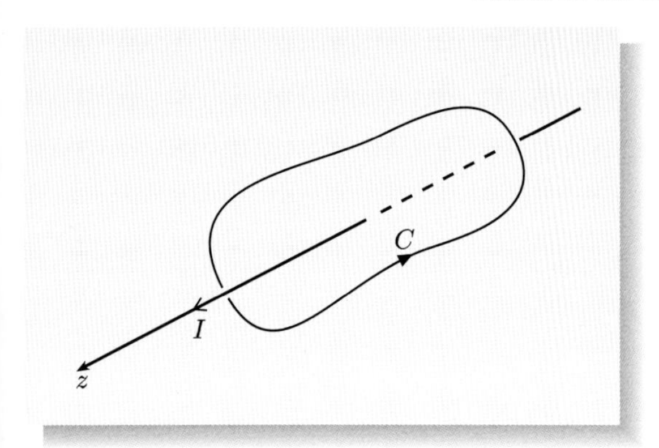


**Figure 4.5** A non-circular path $C$ around a current-carrying wire.

In fact, a much more general result can be established, valid for any closed path. We can replace the circle by an arbitrary path $C$ which laps the wire once in the same sense as the magnetic field lines (Figure 4.5).

Working in cylindrical coordinates, a small displacement along this path is represented as

$$\delta\mathbf{l} = \delta r\, \mathbf{e}_r + r\, \delta\phi\, \mathbf{e}_\phi + \delta z\, \mathbf{e}_z. \tag{4.7}$$

The magnetic field around the wire is given by

$$\mathbf{B} = \frac{\mu_0 I}{2\pi r}\, \mathbf{e}_\phi.$$

Taking the scalar product of the magnetic field $\mathbf{B}$ with the displacement $\delta\mathbf{l}$, and remembering that the unit vectors $\mathbf{e}_r$, $\mathbf{e}_\phi$ and $\mathbf{e}_z$ are mutually orthogonal gives

Remember:
$\mathbf{e}_\phi \cdot \mathbf{e}_r = \mathbf{e}_\phi \cdot \mathbf{e}_z = 0$.

$$\mathbf{B} \cdot \delta\mathbf{l} = \left(\frac{\mu_0 I}{2\pi r}\,\mathbf{e}_\phi\right) \cdot (r\,\delta\phi\,\mathbf{e}_\phi) = \frac{\mu_0 I}{2\pi}\,\delta\phi.$$

As we make one lap of the wire, $\phi$ increases from 0 to $2\pi$, so the circulation of the magnetic field around the wire is

$$\oint_C \mathbf{B} \cdot \mathrm{d}\mathbf{l} = \int_0^{2\pi} \frac{\mu_0 I}{2\pi}\,\mathrm{d}\phi = \frac{\mu_0 I}{2\pi} \times 2\pi = \mu_0 I,$$

which is exactly the same as before, but established now for *any* closed path that laps the wire once in the sense shown in Figure 4.5. If the path wrapped round the wire in the opposite sense, the circulation of the magnetic field would be $-\mu_0 I$.

We can also consider a closed path that does not wrap around the wire (Figure 4.6). The calculation of the line integral follows the same steps as before. But now, when we go once round the path, the angle $\phi$ first increases, then decreases, and finally returns to its initial value as the lap is completed. So the circulation of the magnetic field around a closed path that does *not* wrap around the wire is equal to zero:

$$\oint_C \mathbf{B} \cdot \mathrm{d}\mathbf{l} = 0.$$

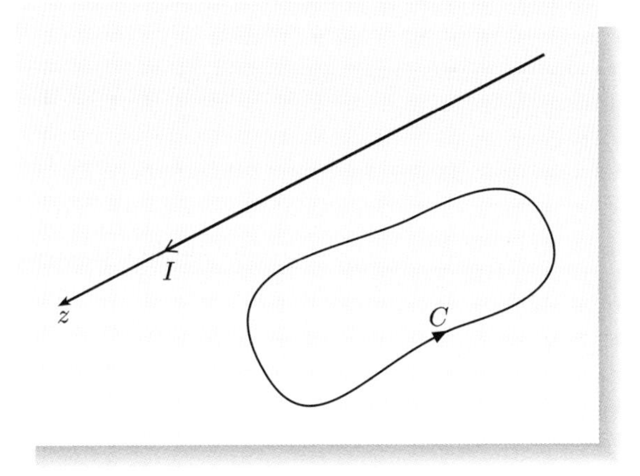


**Figure 4.6** A closed path $C$ that does not wrap around a current-carrying wire.

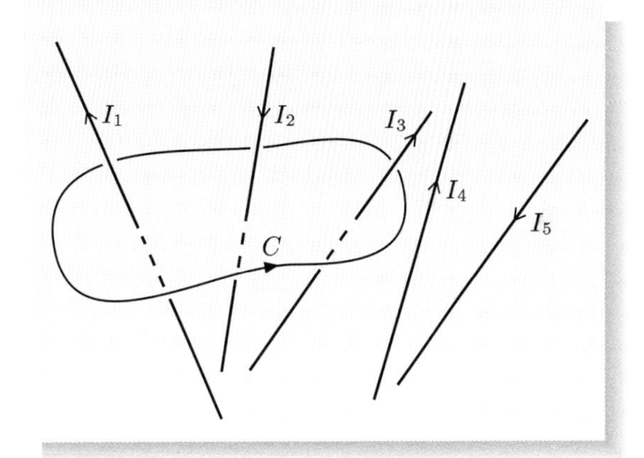


**Figure 4.7** Many straight current-carrying wires and a closed path, $C$.

Finally, consider many straight wires, inclined at various angles and carrying various steady currents (Figure 4.7). A closed path $C$, of arbitrary shape and orientation, is placed in this forest of wires. Using the above results, together with the principle of superposition, we see that the circulation of the magnetic field around $C$ is given by $\mu_0 I_{\text{tot}}$, where $I_{\text{tot}}$ is the total current carried by all the wires that thread the closed path. That is,

$$\oint_C \mathbf{B} \cdot \mathrm{d}\mathbf{l} = \mu_0 I_{\text{tot}}. \tag{4.8}$$

To calculate the total current, with the appropriate sign, the following sign convention must be used:

### Sign convention (the right-hand grip rule)

With the fingers of your right hand wrapped in the sense of positive progression round the closed path $C$, the outstretched thumb of your right hand indicates the direction of positive current flow. Currents that are more aligned with this direction than with the opposite direction are taken to be positive.

In Figure 4.7, for example, $I_1$ and $I_3$ are positive, while $I_2$ is negative, so in this case,

$$I_{\text{tot}} = I_1 - I_2 + I_3.$$

Currents $I_4$ and $I_5$ do not contribute to $I_{\text{tot}}$ because they do not pass through the closed path $C$.

The circulation of the magnetic field around the closed loop in Figure 4.7 is determined by the total current carried by wires that pass through the loop. The precise positions of the wires, their inclinations, and the precise shape and orientation of the closed loop are all irrelevant. This is a remarkable fact. It has been established above for the magnetic fields produced by steady currents in long straight wires. But it turns out to be true more generally. Bending the wires or allowing the currents to flow freely, unconstrained by wires, makes absolutely no difference, provided the currents are steady and we interpret $I_{\text{tot}}$ as the total current threading the loop — that is, the total current crossing a surface bounded by the loop. This is the content of Ampère's law:

### Ampère's law

Consider the magnetic field produced by a steady current distribution. The circulation of the magnetic field around a closed path $C$ is given by

$$\oint_C \mathbf{B} \cdot \mathrm{d}\mathbf{l} = \mu_0 I, \qquad (4.9)$$

where $\mu_0$ is the permeability of free space and $I$ is the total current flowing through an open surface $S$ that has $C$ as its perimeter. The direction of positive current through $S$ and the direction of positive circulation around $C$ are linked by the right-hand grip rule.

The total current through $S$ is the surface integral of the current density over $S$, so we also have

$$\oint_C \mathbf{B} \cdot \mathrm{d}\mathbf{l} = \mu_0 \int_S \mathbf{J} \cdot \mathrm{d}\mathbf{S}, \qquad (4.10)$$

where $S$ is any open surface and $C$ is its perimeter.

Many books give the impression that Ampère discovered the law that bears his name and that Maxwell inherited it. This is not tenable because the concept of a magnetic field did not exist in Ampère's day. In fact, Maxwell discovered the law and named it in recognition of Ampère's work on magnetic forces (summarized today by the Biot–Savart law). Like Gauss's law, Ampère's law can be expressed in terms of integrals or partial derivatives. Equations 4.9 and 4.10 express the **integral version of Ampère's law**. The differential version of Ampère's law will be discussed at the end of the chapter.

Starting from the Biot–Savart law, it is possible to prove Ampère's law for any steady current distribution. The proof is lengthy and will not be presented in this course. Instead, we have given a partial proof, valid for steady currents in long straight wires. The fact that Ampère's law applies to *any* steady current distribution must be taken on trust. However, it is prudent to make a spot check for one case that goes beyond current flow in straight wires.

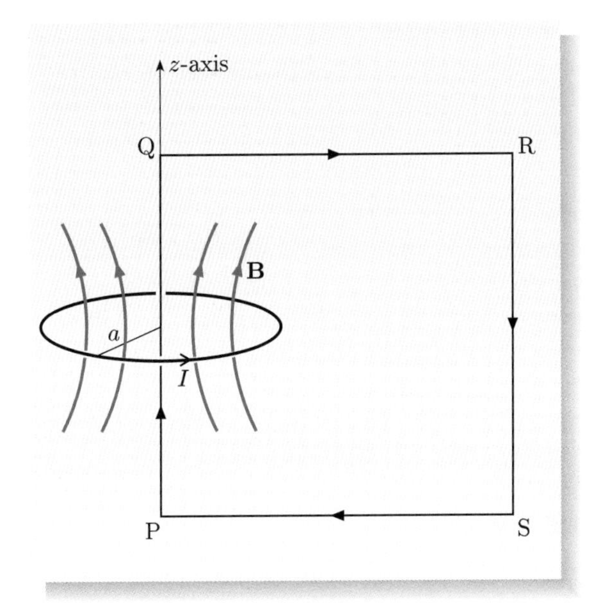


**Figure 4.8** A circular current loop threaded by a square path PQRS.

Figure 4.8 shows a circular current loop of radius $a$ carrying a steady current, $I$. We will calculate the circulation of the magnetic field around a large square PQRS, where PQ is part of the axis of symmetry perpendicular to the loop. We consider the limiting case where PQ is infinitely long, allowing the contributions from the other sides of the square path to be neglected. Then, using Equation 3.13 for the on-axis magnetic field due to the current loop, we obtain

$$\oint_C \mathbf{B} \cdot \mathrm{d}\mathbf{l} = \frac{\mu_0 I}{2} \int_{-\infty}^{\infty} \frac{a^2}{(a^2 + z^2)^{3/2}}\, \mathrm{d}z = \frac{\mu_0 I}{2} \int_{-\infty}^{\infty} \frac{1}{(1 + \xi^2)^{3/2}}\, \mathrm{d}\xi,$$

where I have changed the variable of integration to $\xi = z/a$ in the last step. The remaining integral appeared in Section 3.2, where its value was quoted as 2. We therefore conclude that

$$\oint_C \mathbf{B} \cdot \mathrm{d}\mathbf{l} = \frac{\mu_0 I}{2} \times 2 = \mu_0 I,$$

where $I$ is the current passing through the square area PQRS, in agreement with Ampère's law.

### Limitations of Ampère's law

Ampère's law is a consequence of the Biot–Savart law, and it has exactly the same domain of validity. It is a law of magnetostatics, valid for all steady current distributions, but it does not apply to time-varying currents. With Gauss's law and the no-monopole law we were lucky — results derived using electrostatics and magnetostatics turned out to be true for arbitrary electric and magnetic fields. Our luck runs out with Ampère's law, which cannot be extended in a similar way.

To see why, consider a charged particle that passes through an open surface $S$. By definition, current is the rate of flow of charge through a surface. So, before and after the particle reaches the surface, there is no current through $S$. Only while the particle is actually moving through the surface is there a brief current through $S$. If Ampère's law could be applied in this situation, the circulation of the magnetic field around the distant perimeter of $S$ would be zero, except for a sudden blip when the particle passes through the surface. This is not what is observed; as you might expect, the magnetic field, and its circulation, vary smoothly and gradually in time. The discrepancy is easily resolved — a single charged particle does not provide a steady current, so Ampère's law does not apply in this case.

The restriction to steady currents removes an apparent ambiguity in Ampère's law. To find the magnetic circulation around a closed path $C$, we need to know the current flowing through an open surface $S$ that has $C$ as its perimeter. However, many open surfaces have $C$ as their perimeter, and Ampère's law does not tell us which one to use. In some cases, there is a natural choice. If the closed path is planar, it is natural to choose $S$ to be the planar area enclosed by the path. But if the closed path twists and wiggles, there is no simple choice for $S$. Fortunately, if the currents are steady, the precise choice makes no difference. To see why, consider two surfaces, $S_1$ and $S_2$, both oriented in the same sense and both sharing the same perimeter, $C$ (Figure 4.9).

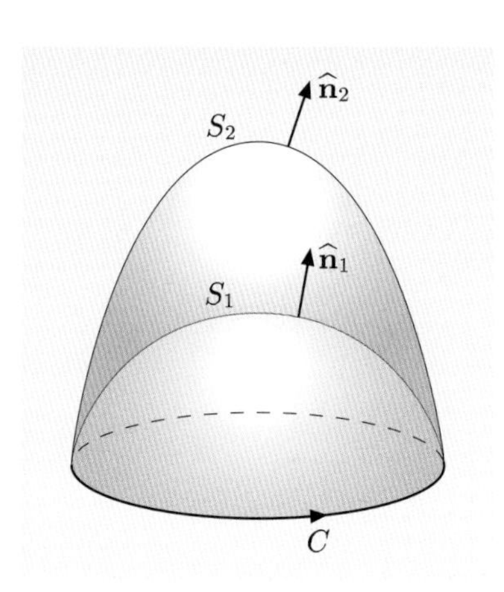


**Figure 4.9** Two open surfaces $S_1$ and $S_2$ with the same perimeter $C$. The vectors $\widehat{\mathbf{n}}_1$ and $\widehat{\mathbf{n}}_2$ are unit normals to $S_1$ and $S_2$.

If the current through $S_1$ were different from the current through $S_2$, there would be a build-up of charge in the region between these two surfaces. This cannot be tolerated in a steady-state situation, because the charge would build up relentlessly and without limit, leading to an inevitable change in the currents. Any steady current through $S_1$ must therefore be equal to the steady current through $S_2$, making the precise choice of surface irrelevant. Of course, this argument relies on steady currents. If the currents are not steady, charge may build up temporarily, and different currents may pass through $S_1$ and $S_2$. Any attempt to apply Ampère's law in this situation would lead to an ambiguous prediction for the magnetic circulation around $C$. This ambiguity is avoided by restricting Ampère's law to steady current flows.

The applications of Ampère's law described in the next section assume that all the currents are known. When materials such as iron are present there may be hidden currents associated with the magnetization of the materials, as well as the obvious currents that flow through wires. These hidden currents may not be known, leading to complications similar to those arising from screening and polarization. As usual, in this book, we ignore these effects, an approximation that is well-justified for most media, including air and copper.

**Exercise 4.3** The integral version of *Gauss's law* states that the *flux* of the *electric field*, taken *over any closed surface*, is proportional to the *total charge inside the volume* bounded by the *closed surface*. Write an analogous sentence for Ampère's law, replacing the words in italics. ■

# 4.3 Putting Ampère's law to use

## 4.3.1 Cylinders and tubes

To illustrate the use of Ampère's law, we will now apply it to a simple case — the magnetic field produced by a steady current in an infinitely-long cylindrical conductor of radius $a$. This reverses the argument that led to Ampère's law. Now we will take Ampère's law as a basic fact, and show how it is used to derive a magnetic field.

The first step is to restrict the possible form of the magnetic field. We know from the Biot–Savart law that the magnetic field produced by a current element is perpendicular to the current element. Since all the current elements point along the axis of the cylinder, the magnetic field must be perpendicular to this axis. The current distribution is unchanged by rotations around the axis of the cylinder and by translations along the length of the cylinder — it has axial and translational symmetry. Any magnetic field must inherit the symmetry of its source, so the magnetic field around the cylinder must also have axial and translational symmetry.

A vector field pointing radially outwards from the cylinder could have these symmetries, but such a field would have a non-zero flux over a closed surface surrounding the cylinder, and would therefore violate the no-monopole law. It cannot be a magnetic field. We exclude such fields from consideration by requiring that the field lines form closed loops. We then argue that the closed loops must be circles centred on the axis of the cylinder. For, consider the alternative: if the magnetic field lines were not circles, or were not centred on the axis of the cylinder, the axial symmetry of the situation would not be respected. Moreover, axial and translational symmetry require the magnetic field strength to depend only on the distance $r$ from the axis of the cylinder. In a cylindrical coordinate system, with the $z$-axis along the axis of the cylinder, in the direction of current flow, we conclude that the magnetic field takes the form

$$\mathbf{B} = B_\phi(r)\,\mathbf{e}_\phi. \tag{4.11}$$

The next step is to apply Ampère's law. To do this we need a closed path $C$ bounding an open surface $S$. Exploiting the symmetry of the situation, we choose $C$ to be a circle of radius $r > a$ centred on, and perpendicular to, the axis of the cylinder (Figure 4.10). The corresponding open surface $S$ is the disk that has $C$ as its perimeter. The unit normal to the disk is taken to be in the direction of increasing $z$. The right-hand grip rule then shows that the sense of positive progression around $C$ is in the direction of $\mathbf{e}_\phi$.

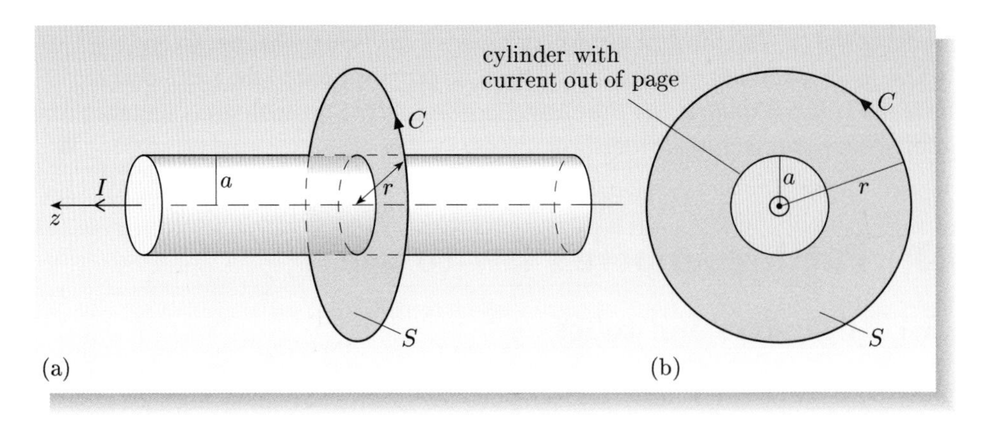


**Figure 4.10** Applying Ampère's law outside an infinitely-long cylinder: (a) perspective view and (b) plan view.

It follows that the line integral of the magnetic field around $C$ is

$$\oint_C \mathbf{B} \cdot \mathrm{d}\mathbf{l} = B_\phi(r) \times 2\pi r.$$

The current flowing through the surface $S$ is just the current $I$ carried by the conductor, so Ampère's law gives

$$B_\phi(r) \times 2\pi r = \mu_0 I.$$

Solving for $B_\phi(r)$, and using Equation 4.11, we conclude that

$$\mathbf{B}(\mathbf{r}) = \frac{\mu_0 I}{2\pi r}\,\mathbf{e}_\phi. \tag{4.12}$$

We have not mentioned the thickness of the cylindrical conductor. It could be a thin wire, with each segment of the wire constituting a single current element. In this case, Equation 4.12 is equivalent to Equation 3.14, which was derived earlier using the Biot–Savart law. However, the cylinder could also be fat, with segments that cannot be treated as single current elements. This would invalidate the argument that led to Equation 3.14, but does not affect the present argument. Equation 4.12 still applies outside a fat cylinder, provided that the current flow is axially symmetric along the cylinder. In other words, the magnetic field outside a fat cylinder is just as if all the current were flowing along the central axis. This is a new result, which would be hard to derive using the Biot–Savart law, but which emerges naturally from symmetry and Ampère's law.

**Essential skill**

Applying Ampère's law

### Worked Example 4.1

A long straight cylindrical conductor of radius $a$ carries a uniform steady current density. The total current flowing along the conductor is $I$. Find the magnetic field at all points *inside* the conductor.

#### Solution

The description of the cylindrical conductor as being long can be read as an invitation to approximate the field as being due to the current in an infinitely-long cylinder. Using cylindrical coordinates with the $z$-axis along the axis of the cylinder in the direction of current flow, and exploiting the axial and translational symmetry of the situation, the magnetic field takes the form

The answer requires no more detail than this because the question did not explicitly ask for a symmetry argument.

$$\mathbf{B} = B_\phi(r)\,\mathbf{e}_\phi. \tag{Eqn 4.11}$$

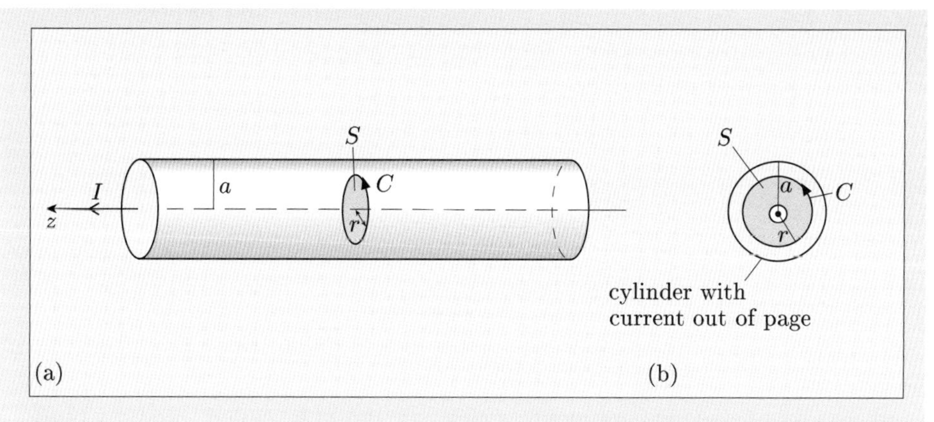


**Figure 4.11** Applying Ampère's law inside an infinitely-long cylinder of radius $a$: (a) perspective view and (b) plan view.

To find the field inside the conductor we choose a closed circular path $C$ of radius $r < a$, centred on the axis of the cylinder and perpendicular to it (Figure 4.11). The corresponding open surface $S$ is the disk which has $C$ as its perimeter. The unit normal to the disk is taken to be in the direction of increasing $z$ and the sense of positive progression around $C$ is in the direction of $\mathbf{e}_\phi$. The magnetic field is parallel to $C$ and has a constant magnitude on this path. It follows that the line integral around $C$ is

$$\oint_C \mathbf{B} \cdot \mathrm{d}\mathbf{l} = B_\phi(r) \times 2\pi r.$$

The current density throughout the conductor is $\mathbf{J} = (I/\pi a^2)\,\mathbf{e}_z$, so the total current passing through the disc $S$ is

$$\int_S \mathbf{J} \cdot \mathrm{d}\mathbf{S} = \int_0^r \left(\frac{I}{\pi a^2}\right) 2\pi s \, \mathrm{d}s = \frac{I}{\pi a^2} \times \pi r^2.$$

Not surprisingly (given that the current density is uniform) this is equal to the total current, $I$, times the fraction of the cross-sectional area of the conductor that is covered by the disc $S$.

Finally, Ampère's law (Equation 4.10) gives

$$B_\phi(r) \times 2\pi r = \mu_0 I \times \frac{\pi r^2}{\pi a^2}.$$

Hence

$$\mathbf{B}(\mathbf{r}) = \frac{\mu_0 I r}{2\pi a^2}\,\mathbf{e}_\phi \quad \text{inside the cylinder.}$$

*Comment*: There is no magnetic field on the axis of the cylinder. The magnetic field strength rises linearly as we move radially outwards and reaches its maximum value, $\mu_0 I/2\pi a$ on the surface of the cylinder. Reassuringly, this is the same as Equation 4.12, evaluated at $r = a$, so the magnetic field has no discontinuity at the surface of the cylinder.

**Exercise 4.4** An infinitely-long cylindrical conducting tube of inner radius $a$ carries a steady uniform current. Show that the magnetic field vanishes in the cylindrical space inside the tube. ■

### 4.3.2 The reflection of electric and magnetic fields

The key to exploiting Ampère's law is to use symmetry to propose a suitable form for the magnetic field. However, the symmetry argument that led to Equation 4.11 is open to criticism. We claimed that the magnetic field lines must be circles centred on the axis of the cylindrical conductor because anything else would be inconsistent with the given axial symmetry. This seems obvious but falls short of a cast-iron proof. Indeed, arguments of this type might be called 'proof by bluff' because they rely on our failure to think of suitable alternatives. In more complicated cases, they can leave us with the nagging doubt that we might have overlooked something. This section takes a closer look at symmetry arguments for electromagnetic fields. It will show that these arguments can be put on a secure basis, leaving no room for doubt.

It is interesting to compare electric and magnetic fields. Figure 4.12a shows the electric field $\mathbf{E}$ produced by a uniform charge distribution in an infinitely-long cylinder while Figure 4.12b shows the magnetic field $\mathbf{B}$ produced by a uniform current distribution in an infinitely-long cylinder. These two field patterns are completely different, although both situations have axial symmetry around the cylinder and translational symmetry along it. This section will explain this striking difference between electric and magnetic fields.

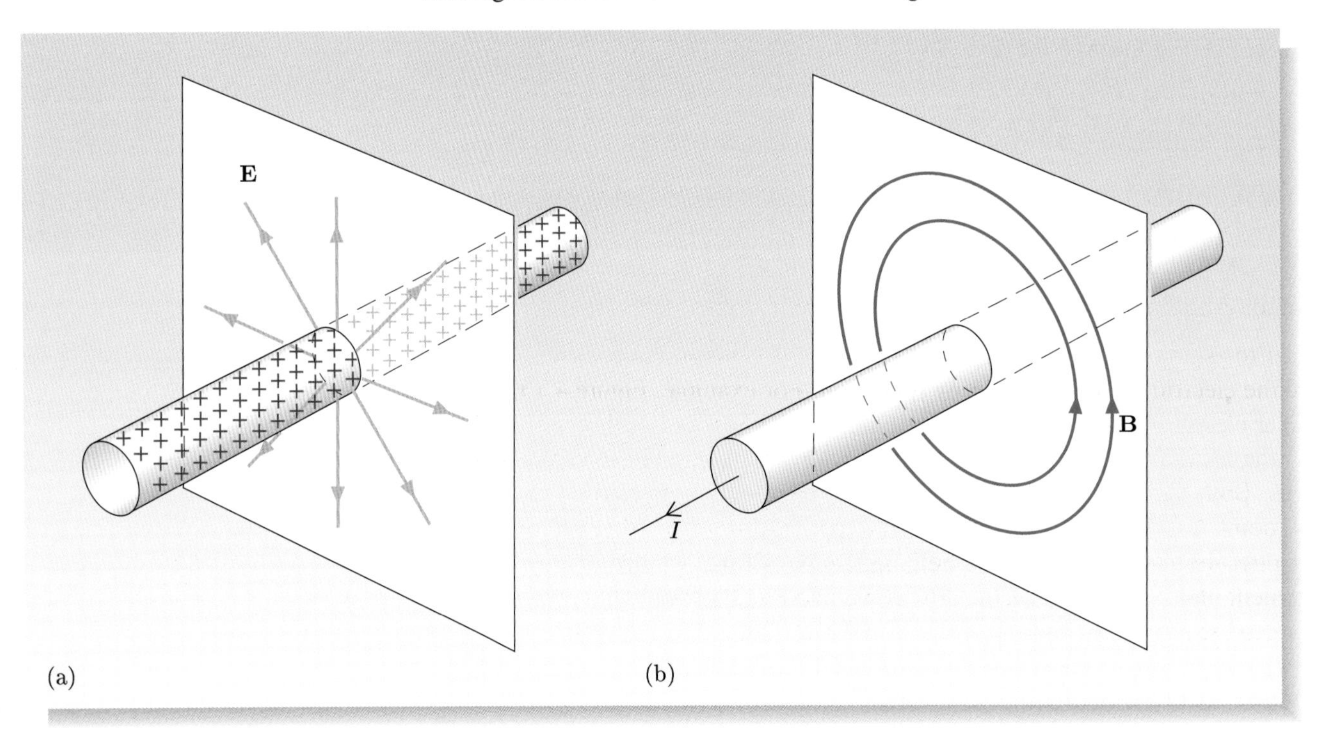


**Figure 4.12** (a) The electric field $\mathbf{E}$ due to a uniform distribution of positive charge on a cylinder. (b) The magnetic field due to a uniform distribution of current along a cylinder.

Our starting point is the following principle:

**Symmetry principle**

Any operation that leaves the source of an electromagnetic field unchanged also leaves the field unchanged.

This principle was introduced in Chapter 1, but will now be used in a more systematic way. The idea is to find a symmetry operation, such as a rotation or a reflection, that leaves the source of an electromagnetic field unchanged. We then express the field in a suitable coordinate system and apply the symmetry operation to it. The symmetry principle tells us that the new field is indistinguishable from the original field. So if, at a given point, one or more components of the field are reversed by the symmetry operation, these components must be equal to zero. Only those components that are *unchanged* by the operation survive.

To be explicit, suppose that the field at a given point is expressed as

$$\mathbf{F} = F_1\mathbf{e}_1 + F_2\mathbf{e}_2 + F_3\mathbf{e}_3,$$

where $\mathbf{e}_1$, $\mathbf{e}_2$ and $\mathbf{e}_3$ are orthogonal unit vectors, and that a symmetry operation converts the field at the same point to

$$\mathbf{F}' = F_1\mathbf{e}_1 - F_2\mathbf{e}_2 - F_3\mathbf{e}_3.$$

If the source of the field is left unchanged by the symmetry operation, the symmetry principle requires that

$$F_1\mathbf{e}_1 + F_2\mathbf{e}_2 + F_3\mathbf{e}_3 = F_1\mathbf{e}_1 - F_2\mathbf{e}_2 - F_3\mathbf{e}_3,$$

which simplifies to

$$2F_2\mathbf{e}_2 + 2F_3\mathbf{e}_3 = \mathbf{0},$$

showing that the reversed components of the field, $F_2$ and $F_3$, are both equal to zero, as we claimed. This symmetry argument will be applied repeatedly, mainly in cases where the symmetry operation is a reflection. We therefore need to know how electric and magnetic fields behave under reflections.

In order to establish the rules for reflecting fields, it is helpful to consider a case where the electric field *is* changed by reflection. For example, Figure 4.13a shows a dipolar electric field produced by a pair of opposite charges, and Figure 4.13b shows the result of reflecting this arrangement in a plane P midway between the charges. Both the charges and the electric field pattern are reflected. In more detail, point A in Figure 4.13a is reflected to point A′ in Figure 4.13b. Comparing the electric field at A with the reflected electric field at A′, we see that the component of the field perpendicular to the plane P is reversed, while components parallel to the plane are the same.

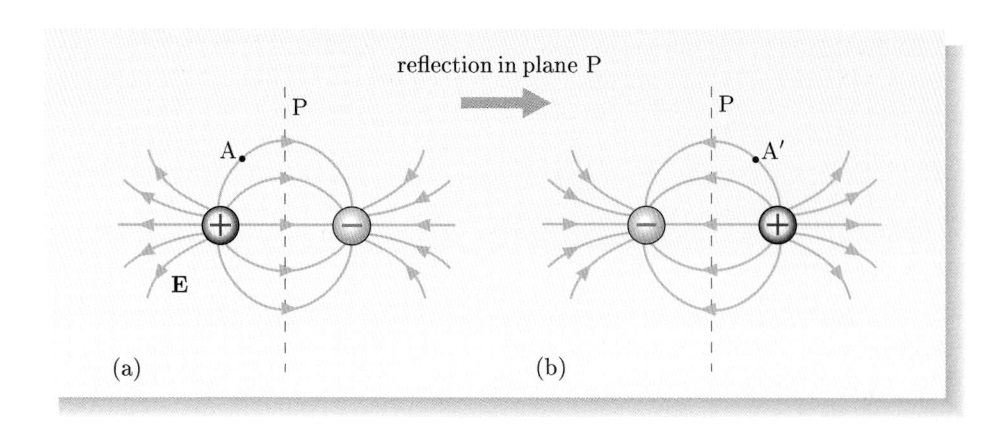


**Figure 4.13** Reflecting the electric field of a dipole in a plane P.

Now let's turn to magnetic fields. Figure 4.14a shows the magnetic field $\mathbf{B}$ produced by a current loop. Suppose we reflect this field in the plane that contains the current loop. This reflection leaves the current loop unchanged, but what does it do to the magnetic field? Figure 4.14b shows the mirror image of the magnetic field lines in Figure 4.14a. In the highly symmetric situation of Figure 4.14, the overall effect is to leave the current $I$ unchanged and to reverse the field lines. This is a serious problem. If the current is unchanged, the magnetic field should remain unchanged as well — a definite current must surely produce a definite magnetic field!

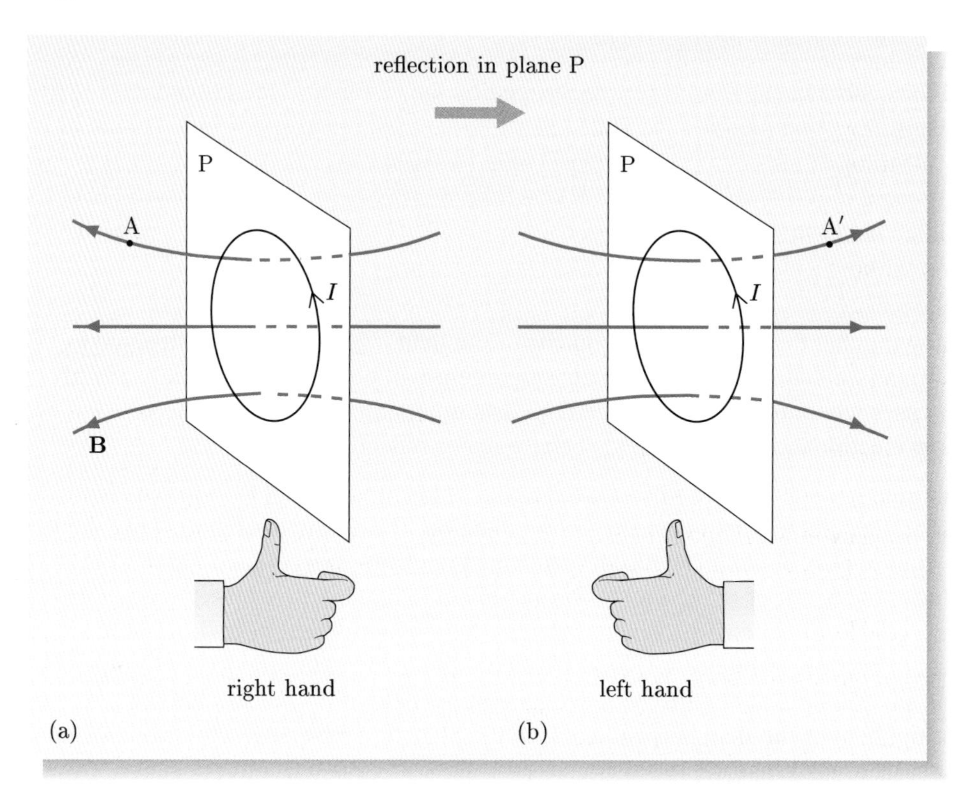


**Figure 4.14** Attempting to reflect the magnetic field $\mathbf{B}$ of a current loop in a plane P.

The resolution of this paradox is found in the hands sketched in the diagram. Figure 4.14b is the exact mirror image of Figure 4.14a, so the right hand in Figure 4.14a becomes a left hand in Figure 4.14b. This implies that the magnetic field in Figure 4.14b is defined using a *left-hand rule* rather than a right-hand rule. Of course, we are totally committed to defining magnetic fields using a right-hand rule, so the true reflected magnetic field is the *reverse* of that shown in Figure 4.14b. Reversing the magnetic field at each point in Figure 4.14b gives the same field as in Figure 4.14a, so the paradox is resolved.

For simplicity, we restrict attention to points in the plane of reflection. These points remain fixed under the reflection, so the original field and the reflected field both refer to the same point. The behaviour of electric and magnetic fields can then be summarized as follows:

**Reflection rules for electric and magnetic fields**

If an *electric field* is reflected in a plane, the reflected electric field at any point in the plane is obtained by reversing the component of the field *perpendicular* to the plane, leaving components parallel to the plane unchanged.

If a *magnetic field* is reflected in a plane, the reflected magnetic field at any point in the plane is obtained by reversing components of the field *parallel* to the plane, leaving the component perpendicular to the plane unchanged.

The reflection rule for magnetic fields may seem strange, but it is a direct consequence of the fact that magnetic fields are represented by vector products, and so have a right-hand rule built into their definition. Diagrams of magnetic field lines do not reveal this handedness, but it is present nonetheless. Taking the simple mirror image leads to magnetic fields described according to a left-handed convention, and an extra reversal is needed to retain the standard right-handed convention. This extra reversal means that the reflection rule for magnetic fields is the exact opposite of the reflection rule for electric fields. Electric fields behave more simply under reflection because they are defined without vector products and without a right-hand rule.

See also Exercise 8.9 for an example of the reflection of a vector product.

The symmetry principle and the reflection rules for electric and magnetic fields are the ingredients for the symmetry arguments in this section. As an example of the method, consider the *electric* field produced by a uniformly-charged cylinder of infinite length. We are now ready to provide a rigorous justification of the radial electric field pattern in Figure 4.12a.

Prompted by the symmetry of the situation, and without loss of generality, we choose a cylindrical coordinate system with the $z$-axis along the axis of the cylinder. In this coordinate system any electric field can be expressed as

$$\mathbf{E}(\mathbf{r}) = E_r(r, \phi, z)\,\mathbf{e}_r + E_\phi(r, \phi, z)\,\mathbf{e}_\phi + E_z(r, \phi, z)\,\mathbf{e}_z.$$

The charge distribution has axial symmetry around the $z$-axis and translational symmetry along the $z$-axis, so the components of the electric field cannot depend on $\phi$ or $z$. This leads to the simpler expression

$$\mathbf{E}(\mathbf{r}) = E_r(r)\,\mathbf{e}_r + E_\phi(r)\,\mathbf{e}_\phi + E_z(r)\,\mathbf{e}_z.$$

Now, suppose we are interested in the electric field at a point P, a distance $r$ from the axis of the cylinder. We consider a reflection in a plane that passes through P and is perpendicular to the axis of the cylinder, i.e. to the $z$-axis (Figure 4.15a). This reflection leaves the charge distribution unchanged and reverses the

$z$-component of the electric field at P. The symmetry principle then requires that $E_z(r) = 0$. We can also consider a different reflection in a plane that passes through P and contains the axis of the cylinder (Figure 4.15b). This reflection leaves the charge distribution unchanged and reverses the $\phi$-component of the electric field at P. The symmetry principle then guarantees that $E_\phi(r) = 0$.

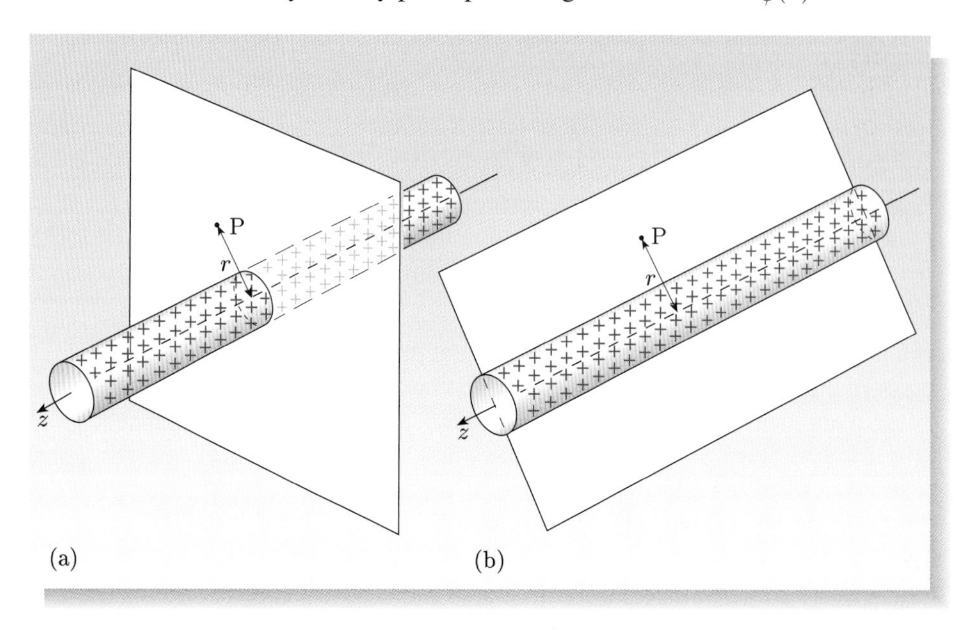


**Figure 4.15** Two planes of reflection used to investigate the electric field $\mathbf{E}$ of an infinitely long cylinder carrying a uniform positive charge.

Combining these results, we see that only the radial component of the electric field survives. Hence,

$$\mathbf{E}(\mathbf{r}) = E_r(r)\,\mathbf{e}_r,$$

as expected.

With care, this argument can be adapted to deduce the form of the magnetic field at a point P, a distance $r$ from the axis of a cylindrical conductor of infinite length. Again, we use a cylindrical coordinate system with the $z$-axis along the axis of the cylinder. The axial and translational symmetries of the situation then allow us to express the magnetic field as

$$\mathbf{B}(\mathbf{r}) = B_r(r)\,\mathbf{e}_r + B_\phi(r)\,\mathbf{e}_\phi + B_z(r)\,\mathbf{e}_z.$$

In this case, it is simplest to consider the reflection in a plane that passes through P and contains the axis of the cylinder, i.e. a plane like that shown in Figure 4.15b. This reflection does not change the current distribution. The $r$- and $z$-components of the magnetic field at P are parallel to the plane of reflection, so the reflection rule for magnetic fields tells us that these components are both reversed. Because the current distribution is unchanged, the symmetry principle requires that both these components are equal to zero, so we are left with

$$\mathbf{B}(\mathbf{r}) = B_\phi(r)\,\mathbf{e}_\phi,$$

as claimed earlier in Equation 4.11. This proof follows directly from symmetry, without using the Biot–Savart or no-monopole laws. In this sense, it is simpler than our previous intuitive argument, which used both these facts.

You might wonder what can be learnt from the reflection which passes through P and is perpendicular to the axis of the cylinder. Using the reflection rule for magnetic fields, this reflection reverses the $r$- and $\phi$-components of the magnetic field, which are parallel to the plane of reflection. Unfortunately, it also reverses the direction of the current, and this prevents us from using the symmetry principle directly. However, there is a remedy for this. If the reflection is followed by the operation of time-reversal, the current is reversed again, returning to its original direction. So the *combined* operation of reflection + time-reversal leaves the current unchanged. As explained in Chapter 3, time-reversal reverses the magnetic field. The net effect of the combined operation is therefore to leave the $r$- and $\phi$-components of the magnetic field unchanged and to reverse the $z$-component. The symmetry principle then tells us that $B_z = 0$. This is not new information, but is clearly consistent with the conclusions reached earlier.

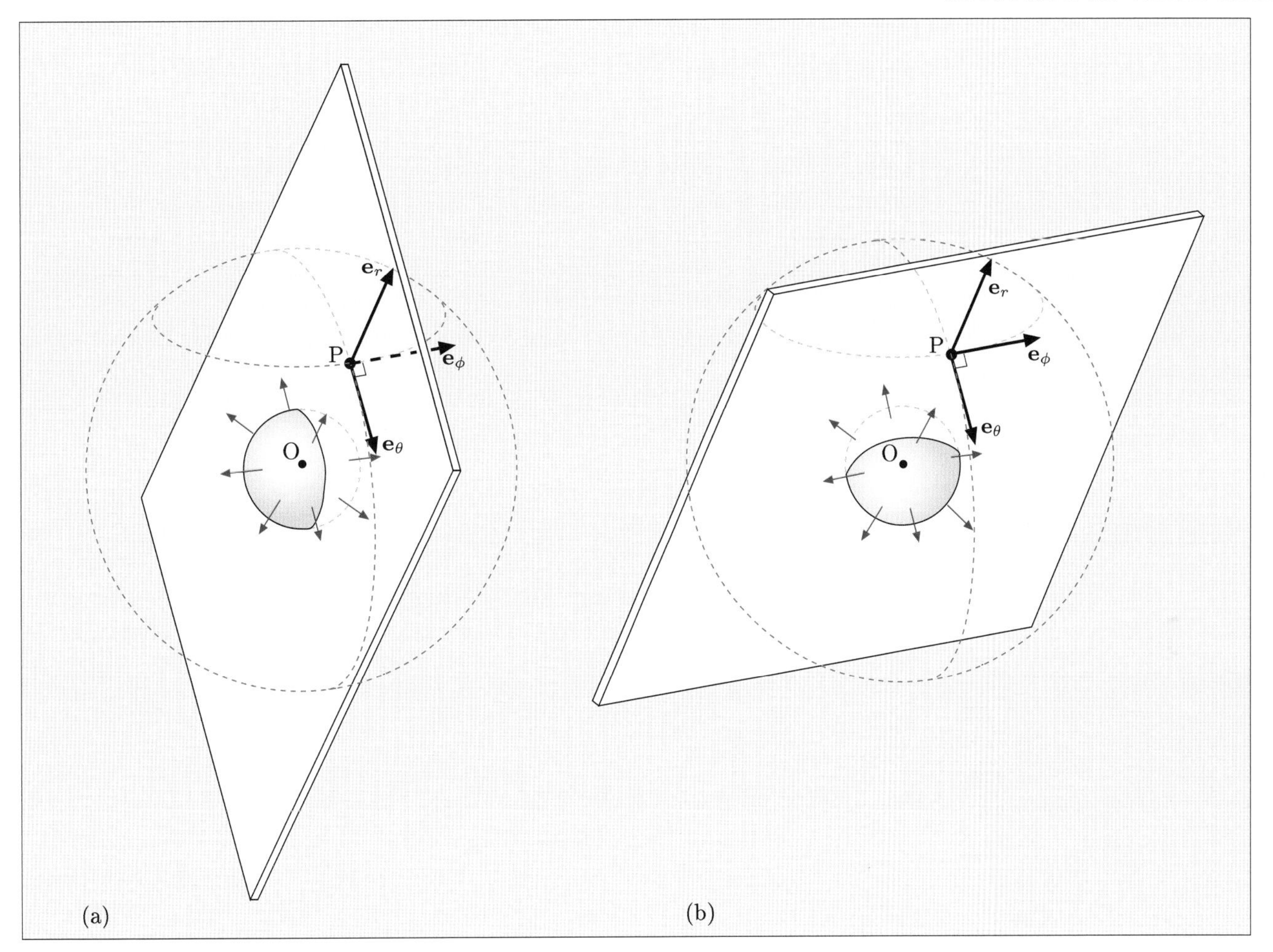


**Figure 4.16** Two planes of reflection for a spherically symmetric current. The red arrows show the current density.

**Essential skill**

Using symmetry principles for magnetic fields

**Worked Example 4.2**

A current distribution is spherically symmetric, flowing away from the origin. Figure 4.16a shows a plane that contains the $\mathbf{e}_r$ and $\mathbf{e}_\theta$ unit vectors at P, and is perpendicular to the $\mathbf{e}_\phi$ unit vector at P. Figure 4.16b shows a plane that contains the $\mathbf{e}_r$ and $\mathbf{e}_\phi$ unit vectors at P, and is perpendicular to the $\mathbf{e}_\theta$ unit vector at P. Both these planes pass through the origin O. By considering reflections in both these planes, deduce the form of the magnetic field produced by this current distribution.

**Solution**

According to the reflection rule for magnetic fields, a reflection in the plane sketched in Figure 4.16a reverses $B_r$ and $B_\theta$ at P. A reflection in the plane sketched in Figure 4.16b reverses $B_r$ and $B_\phi$ at P. Both these reflections leave the spherically-symmetric current distribution unchanged, so the symmetry principle can be used. This tells us that the reversed components, $B_r$, $B_\theta$ and $B_\phi$, are all equal to zero at P. This argument applies at any point P, so we conclude that a spherically-symmetric current distribution produces no magnetic field anywhere.

A current distribution that produces no magnetic field is said to be a **magnetically-silent source**. The existence of such sources can be troublesome. Suppose, for example, that we measure the magnetic field outside a brain and are able to show that a certain current distribution inside the brain could produce this magnetic field. We cannot be certain that this current distribution accurately describes current flows in the brain because any magnetically-silent current distribution could be added to it without affecting the detected magnetic field. The task of deducing general current flows in a brain from measurements of magnetic fields suffers from non-uniqueness. Working around this problem is a subject of active research, and involves making appropriate use of physiological constraints.

**Exercise 4.5** An infinite sheet in the $xy$-plane carries a constant uniform current density in the $y$-direction. By considering a reflection in a plane perpendicular to the $x$-axis, express the magnetic field near this current sheet in the simplest possible terms. ■

### 4.3.3 Solenoids and toroidal solenoids

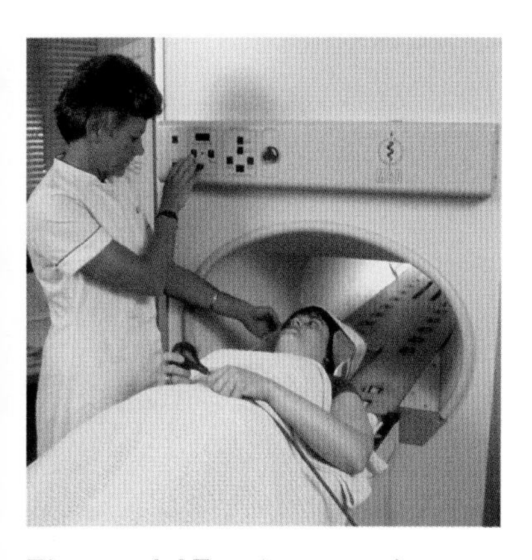

**Figure 4.17** A magnetic resonance imaging (MRI) body-scanner.

A **solenoid** is a conducting helical coil whose densely-packed turns are wrapped uniformly around the surface of a cylinder. Solenoids are used to provide strong magnetic fields in the region inside the coil. The patient in a magnetic resonance imaging body-scanner, for example, is surrounded by a set of solenoids, which produce a magnetic field of about 1.5 T (Figure 4.17).

We will use Ampère's law to find the magnetic field inside and outside a long solenoid carrying a steady current $I$. For simplicity, the solenoid is taken to be infinitely long. We also assume that the pitch of the helical coil is much smaller than its diameter, so that each turn of the solenoid is practically equivalent to a circular loop. The magnetic field produced by the solenoid is then equivalent to the magnetic field produced by a continuous stack of current loops. We restrict attention to solenoids in empty space, with no magnetic materials or other currents nearby, so the only relevant magnetic field is that produced by the current in the solenoid.

The first step, as always, is to use symmetry to restrict the form of the magnetic field. The symmetry of the situation suggests use of cylindrical coordinates with the $z$-axis along the central axis of the solenoid. Axial symmetry around the $z$-axis and translational symmetry along the $z$-axis ensure that the components of the magnetic field do not depend on $\phi$ or $z$, so the magnetic field can be expressed as

$$\mathbf{B}(\mathbf{r}) = B_r(r)\,\mathbf{e}_r + B_\phi(r)\,\mathbf{e}_\phi + B_z(r)\,\mathbf{e}_z.$$

Now consider a reflection in a plane perpendicular to the axis of the solenoid (Figure 4.18). Because we are treating the solenoid as a continuous stack of current loops, this reflection does not change the current distribution. However, the reflection rule for magnetic fields shows that $B_r$ and $B_\phi$ (the components of the magnetic field parallel to the plane of reflection) are both reversed by the reflection. The symmetry principle then tells us that $B_r$ and $B_\phi$ are both equal to zero, leaving

$$\mathbf{B}(\mathbf{r}) = B_z(r)\,\mathbf{e}_z. \tag{4.13}$$

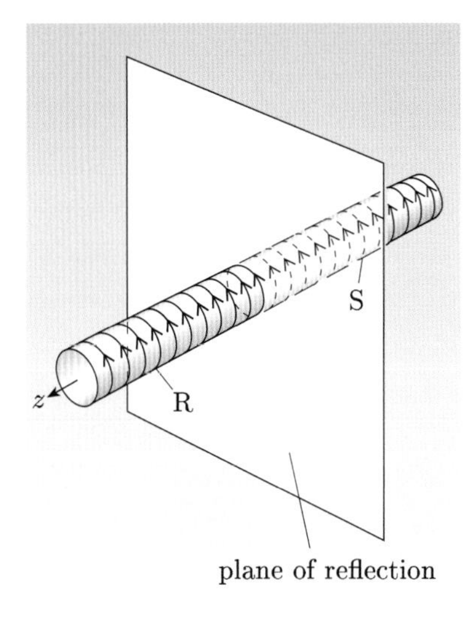


**Figure 4.18** The effect of a reflection on a solenoid. The turn at S is the mirror image of the turn at R.

Now we can use Ampère's law to find the function $B_z(r)$. First, we use the rectangular path PQRS in Figure 4.19a. Side QR is at radial coordinate $r_1$, side SP is at radial coordinate $r_2$, and both these sides have length $l$. Because $B_r = 0$, the line integral of the magnetic field around this rectangle is $B_z(r_1)l - B_z(r_2)l$. Since no current crosses the interior of the rectangle, Ampère's law gives

$$B_z(r_1)l - B_z(r_2)l = 0, \quad \text{so} \quad B_z(r_1) = B_z(r_2),$$

which shows that $B_z$ is constant outside the solenoid. We can assume that the magnetic field vanishes infinitely far away from the solenoid, so the constant value of $B_z$ outside the solenoid must be zero.

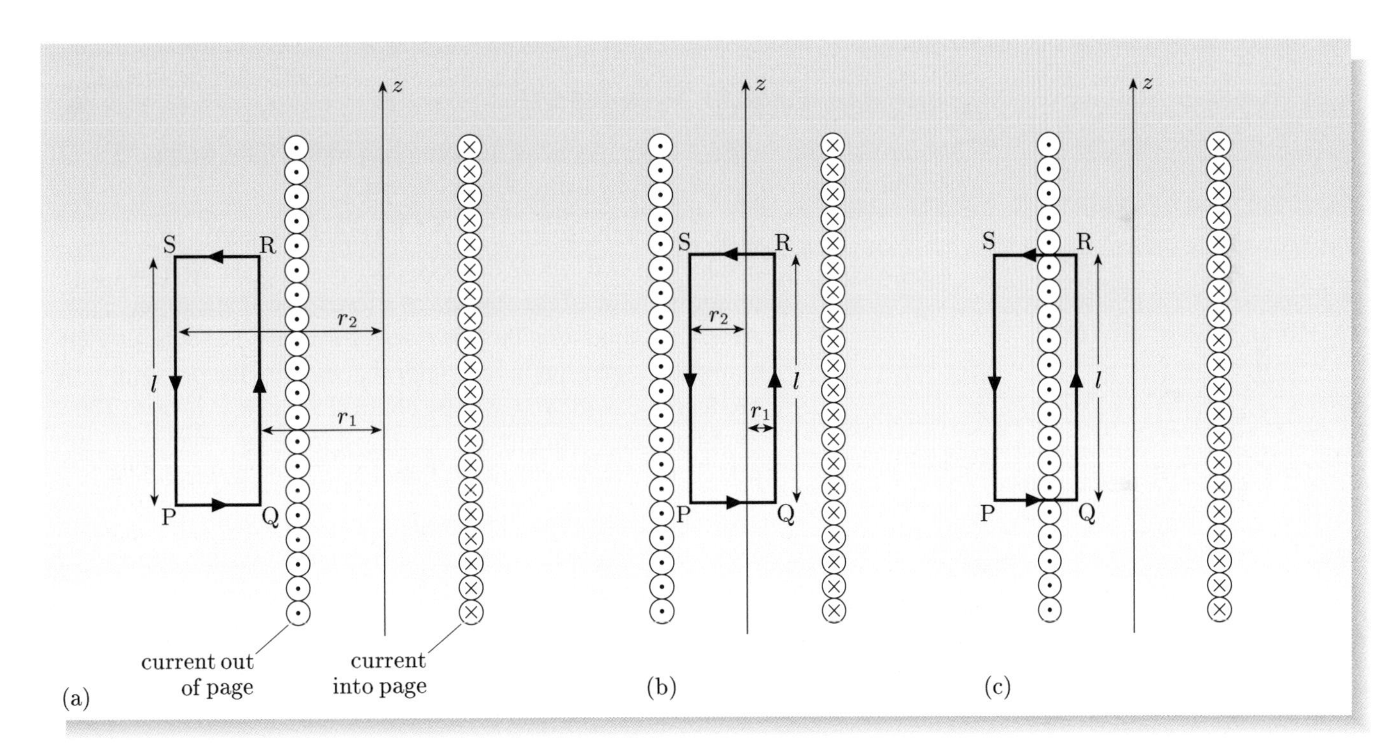


**Figure 4.19** Three paths used to apply Ampère's law to a solenoid.

This may seem strange but, remember, we are considering the limiting case of an infinitely-long solenoid. In many respects, this behaves like an infinitely-long bar magnet, and it is reasonable to expect that the field around such a magnet would be zero because the north and south poles are infinitely far away.

Similarly, applying Ampère's law to the rectangular path PQRS in Figure 4.19b shows that the magnetic field is constant inside the solenoid. The constant value of the magnetic field inside the solenoid can be found by applying Ampère's law to the rectangular path PQRS in Figure 4.19c. The interior of this loop is a rectangular surface. The turns of the solenoid enclosed by the loop carry current up through this surface. Although the current flows in the opposite direction on the far side of each turn, these downward currents flow outside the surface, and do not contribute to the current through it. The total current flowing though PQRS is therefore given by the current in each turn times the number of turns crossing the surface. That is,

$$I_{\text{tot}} = nlI,$$

where $n$ is the number of turns per unit length and $I$ is the current in each turn, which is the current carried by the solenoid. Because the magnetic field vanishes outside the solenoid, the line integral of $\mathbf{B}$ around PQRS only has a contribution from QR, and so is equal to $B_z l$, where $B_z$ is the $z$-component of the magnetic field inside the solenoid. Ampère's law therefore gives

$$B_z l = \mu_0 nlI,$$

so

$$\mathbf{B} = \mu_0 nI\,\mathbf{e}_z \quad \text{inside the solenoid.} \tag{4.14}$$

This formula shows that a large magnetic field can be produced by wrapping many turns per unit length and by using a high current.

A variant of the solenoid is the **toroidal solenoid**. This is a conducting coil whose densely-packed turns are wrapped uniformly around the surface of a torus (the shape of an American donut or a bicycle tyre). Toroidal solenoids, or their equivalent, are used in machines that explore the possibility of producing electrical power by controlled nuclear fusion. The long-term aim is to provide an almost inexhaustible source of power which does relatively little harm to the environment.

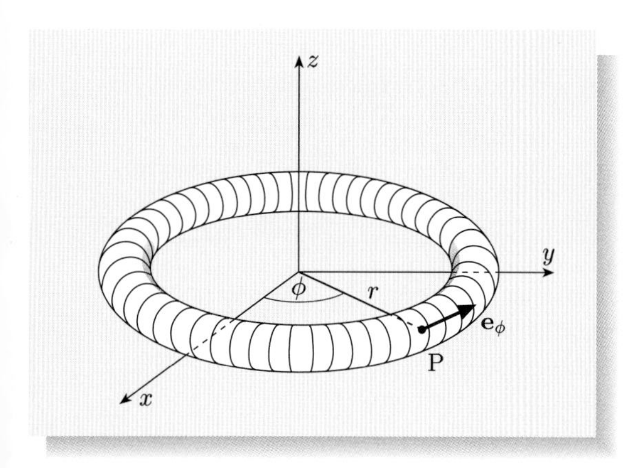


**Figure 4.20** Cylindrical coordinates $(r, \phi, z)$ for a toroidal solenoid.

To find the magnetic field inside a toroidal solenoid, it is convenient to use the cylindrical coordinate system shown in Figure 4.20, where the $z$-axis is perpendicular to the plane of the torus. This differs from the cylindrical coordinate system used to discuss a straight solenoid; now it is $\mathbf{e}_\phi$ that points along the circular central axis inside the solenoid.

As usual, we begin with a symmetry argument. At any point P, we consider a reflection in a plane that passes through P and is perpendicular to the $\mathbf{e}_\phi$ unit vector (Figure 4.20). Ignoring the detailed geometry of the helical windings, this reflection leaves the current distribution unchanged. However, the reflection rule for magnetic fields tells us that $B_r$ and $B_z$ are both reversed by the reflection. The symmetry principle then tells us that $B_r$ and $B_z$ are both equal to zero. Moreover, since the toroid is unchanged by rotations around the $z$-axis, the magnetic field is independent of $\phi$, so we conclude that

$$\mathbf{B} = B_\phi(r, z)\, \mathbf{e}_\phi.$$

This conclusion is quite intuitive. When a straight solenoid is bent round to form a torus, its magnetic field lines form circular loops, along which the magnetic field has a constant magnitude.

**Exercise 4.6** Use Ampère's law to calculate the magnetic field strength inside a toroidal solenoid. The solenoid has $N$ turns and carries a steady current $I$. ■

**Essential skill**
Applying Ampère's law

### 4.3.4 A hidden consequence of Ampère's law

This section is optional reading, but is a bonus, too good to miss!

You now know enough about electromagnetism to prove something truly wonderful. Consider two identical uniformly-charged rods. The rods are parallel, a distance $d$ apart, and are treated as being infinitely long. They each move with constant speed $v$ along their own axes. An observer stationary in the laboratory measures the charge per unit length on each rod as $\lambda > 0$. Because the rods are moving, this observer sees each rod as providing a current $I = \lambda v$. The moving charged rods feel a repulsive electric force and an attractive magnetic force. We can quantify these forces using Gauss's law and Ampère's law.

Gauss's law shows that a uniformly-charged rod produces an electric field of magnitude

$$E(r) = \frac{\lambda}{2\pi\varepsilon_0 r}, \qquad \text{(Eqn 2.7)}$$

and the answer to Exercise 2.7 verified that this remains true for a rod moving parallel to its own length.

Ampère's law shows that a moving charged rod produces a magnetic field of magnitude

$$B(r) = \frac{\mu_0 I}{2\pi r} = \frac{\mu_0 \lambda v}{2\pi r}. \qquad \text{(Eqn 4.12)}$$

These fields produce electric and magnetic forces. The total repulsive force per unit length on one of the rods is

$$\frac{F}{L} = \lambda E(d) - \lambda v B(d) = \frac{\lambda^2}{2\pi\varepsilon_0 d}\left(1 - \varepsilon_0\mu_0 v^2\right).$$

Now let's analyze the same situation from the viewpoint of an observer moving with the rods. The rods are stationary with respect to this observer, so he finds no magnetic force. He only finds an electric force, which is repulsive because the rods carry identical charges. It is impossible for one observer to see a repulsion while the other sees an attraction. For, if this happened, the observers would disagree about whether the rods collide or not, which must surely be an objective fact — we could arrange for collision of the rods to trigger an explosion, for example! Therefore the observer stationary in the laboratory also sees a repulsion. Referring back to the above expression for $F/L$, it follows that

$$v < \frac{1}{\sqrt{\varepsilon_0\mu_0}} = 3.00 \times 10^8\ \mathrm{m\,s^{-1}}.$$

This is a remarkable discovery. The laws of electromagnetism dictate that the rods cannot move faster than a certain fixed speed, $3.00 \times 10^8\ \mathrm{m\,s^{-1}}$ which is numerically equal to the speed of light in a vacuum. This would not have surprised Einstein, whose special theory of relativity makes precisely this prediction, but it is fascinating to note that the equations of electromagnetism, as established by Maxwell, anticipate this conclusion.

## 4.4 The differential version of Ampère's law

You have seen that Gauss's law and the no-monopole law have integral and differential versions. The same is true for Ampère's law, which so far has only been presented in its integral form. This section will derive and use the differential version of Ampère's law.

► Read MT 8.8 now. This is essential material.

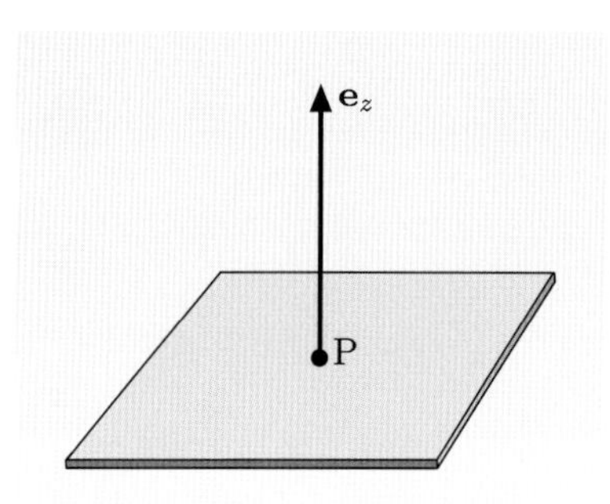


**Figure 4.21** A plane element used to define the $z$-component of $\mathrm{curl}\,\mathbf{B}$ at point P.

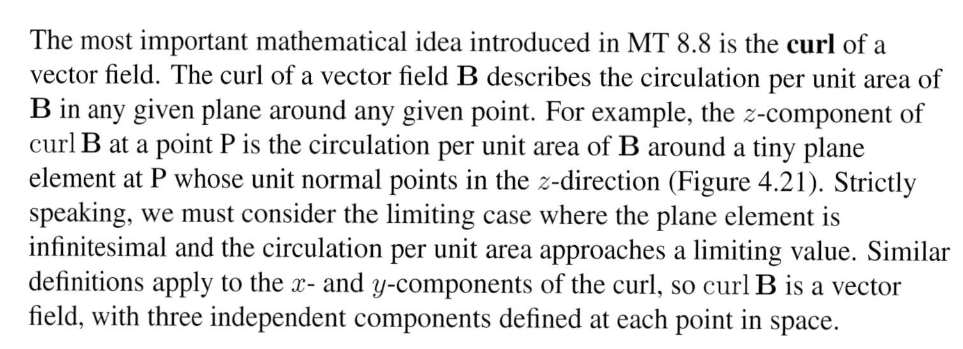

The most important mathematical idea introduced in MT 8.8 is the **curl** of a vector field. The curl of a vector field $\mathbf{B}$ describes the circulation per unit area of $\mathbf{B}$ in any given plane around any given point. For example, the $z$-component of $\mathrm{curl}\,\mathbf{B}$ at a point P is the circulation per unit area of $\mathbf{B}$ around a tiny plane element at P whose unit normal points in the $z$-direction (Figure 4.21). Strictly speaking, we must consider the limiting case where the plane element is infinitesimal and the circulation per unit area approaches a limiting value. Similar definitions apply to the $x$- and $y$-components of the curl, so $\mathrm{curl}\,\mathbf{B}$ is a vector field, with three independent components defined at each point in space.

The circulation of $\mathbf{B}$ around the perimeter of a plane element is $\mathrm{curl}\,\mathbf{B} \cdot \Delta\mathbf{S}$, where $\Delta\mathbf{S}$ is the oriented area of the plane element. Using the additivity of circulation, the circulation of $\mathbf{B}$ around any closed path $C$ is given by:

$$\oint_C \mathbf{B} \cdot \mathrm{d}\mathbf{l} = \int_S \mathrm{curl}\,\mathbf{B} \cdot \mathrm{d}\mathbf{S}, \qquad (4.15)$$

where $S$ is an open surface whose perimeter is $C$. This is the content of the **curl theorem**.

The curl theorem is also called Stokes's theorem.

To derive the differential version of Ampère's law we combine the curl theorem with the integral version of Ampère's law (Equation 4.10) to obtain

$$\int_S \mathrm{curl}\,\mathbf{B} \cdot \mathrm{d}\mathbf{S} = \int_S \mu_0 \mathbf{J} \cdot \mathrm{d}\mathbf{S}, \qquad (4.16)$$

where both integrals extend over the same surface $S$. This equation applies to any open surface. In particular, it applies to surfaces that are arbitrarily small and oriented in arbitrary directions. Under these circumstances, the only way to satisfy Equation 4.16 is to insist that the *integrands* are identical on both sides. We therefore conclude that

$$\mathrm{curl}\,\mathbf{B} = \mu_0 \mathbf{J}. \qquad (4.17)$$

This is the **differential version of Ampère's law**. Just like the integral version this equation applies only to steady currents.

Finally, as you saw in MT 8.8, the curl of a vector field can be expressed in terms of partial derivatives of the field. In Cartesian coordinates,

$$\operatorname{curl}\mathbf{B} = \begin{vmatrix} \mathbf{e}_x & \mathbf{e}_y & \mathbf{e}_z \\ \dfrac{\partial}{\partial x} & \dfrac{\partial}{\partial y} & \dfrac{\partial}{\partial z} \\ B_x & B_y & B_z \end{vmatrix}. \tag{4.18}$$

So the three components of Equation 4.17 can be expanded to give

$$\frac{\partial B_z}{\partial y} - \frac{\partial B_y}{\partial z} = \mu_0 J_x$$

$$\frac{\partial B_x}{\partial z} - \frac{\partial B_z}{\partial x} = \mu_0 J_y$$

$$\frac{\partial B_y}{\partial x} - \frac{\partial B_x}{\partial y} = \mu_0 J_z.$$

The differential version of Ampère's law relates a set of partial derivatives of the magnetic field at a given point to the current density at the *same* point. There is no mention of action at a distance.

**Exercise 4.7** The differential version of *Gauss's law* states that, at each point in space, the *divergence* of the *electric field* is proportional to the *charge density*. Write an analogous sentence for Ampère's law, replacing the words in italics.

**Exercise 4.8** Show that the divergence of $\operatorname{curl}\mathbf{B}$ always vanishes. What does this imply about the current density?

**Exercise 4.9** The magnetic field is uniform throughout a region. Prove that the current density is zero throughout this region.

**Exercise 4.10** Throughout a region of space where there are no currents, the magnetic field takes the form $\mathbf{B} = B_x(z)\,\mathbf{e}_x$. Show that $B_x(z)$ is a constant. ■

A software package on the DVD allows you to explore the integral version of the no-monopole law and the integral and differential versions of Ampère's law. This package is best studied some time after completing this chapter. The DVD also contains a video of a tutorial which uses Ampère's law to solve a typical problem and discusses the reflection of magnetic fields in a plane.

# Summary of Chapter 4

**Section 4.1** The no-monopole law states that the magnetic flux over any closed surface is equal to zero. Using the divergence theorem, it follows that the magnetic field is divergence-free:

$$\int_S \mathbf{B} \cdot d\mathbf{S} = 0 \quad \text{and} \quad \operatorname{div} \mathbf{B} = 0.$$

These equations imply that magnetic field lines have neither starting points nor ending points, but form closed loops. No magnetic monopole has been reliably detected.

**Section 4.2** The magnetic circulation around a closed path is the line integral of the magnetic field around the path. The integral version of Ampère's law states that the magnetic circulation around a closed path $C$ is equal to the total current flowing through any open surface $S$ that is bounded by $C$, multiplied by $\mu_0$, the permeability of free space:

$$\oint_C \mathbf{B} \cdot d\mathbf{l} = \mu_0 I = \mu_0 \int_S \mathbf{J} \cdot d\mathbf{S}.$$

The sense of positive progression around $C$ and the orientation of $S$ are linked by the right-hand grip rule. Ampère's law applies to all steady current distributions. It does not apply to time-varying currents.

**Section 4.3** To apply Ampère's law we use the symmetry of the sources to constrain the form of the magnetic field and choose a suitable closed path. Ideally, the field points in the direction of the closed path and has a constant magnitude around the path, or around individual sections of the path.

Any operation that leaves the source of an electromagnetic field unchanged also leaves the field unchanged. At any point in a plane of reflection, the reflected electric field is obtained by reversing the component of the field *perpendicular* to the plane, leaving the components parallel to the plane unchanged. The reflected magnetic field is obtained by reversing the components of the field *parallel* to the plane, leaving the component perpendicular to the plane unchanged.

**Section 4.4** The curl of the magnetic field is a vector field whose components are the magnetic circulation per unit area. In Cartesian coordinates,

$$\operatorname{curl} \mathbf{B} = \left(\frac{\partial B_z}{\partial y} - \frac{\partial B_y}{\partial z}\right)\mathbf{e}_x + \left(\frac{\partial B_x}{\partial z} - \frac{\partial B_z}{\partial x}\right)\mathbf{e}_y + \left(\frac{\partial B_y}{\partial x} - \frac{\partial B_x}{\partial y}\right)\mathbf{e}_z.$$

The curl theorem tells us that the line integral of a vector field around a closed path $C$ is the surface integral of the curl of the field over any surface $S$ that is bounded by $C$. So,

$$\oint_C \mathbf{B} \cdot d\mathbf{l} = \int_S \operatorname{curl} \mathbf{B} \cdot d\mathbf{S}.$$

Using this theorem, together with the integral version of Ampère's law, we obtain the differential version of Ampère's law:

$$\operatorname{curl} \mathbf{B} = \mu_0 \mathbf{J}.$$

This law applies only to steady current distributions.

# Achievements from Chapter 4

*After studying this chapter you should be able to:*

**4.1** Explain the meaning of the newly defined (emboldened) terms and symbols, and use them appropriately.

**4.2** State the integral and differential versions of the no-monopole law and use them to determine whether a given vector field is eligible to be a magnetic field.

**4.3** State the integral version of Ampère's law and use it in simple cases.

**4.4** Use symmetry arguments to deduce the form of electric and magnetic fields produced by highly-symmetric distributions of charge and current.

**4.5** State the differential version of Ampère's law and explain how it follows from the integral version. Use the differential version of Ampère's law in simple cases.

*After studying MT 8.7 and 8.8 you should also be able to:*

**4.6** Use a right-hand grip rule to relate the orientation of an open surface to the sense of progression around its perimeter.

**4.7** Evaluate simple line integrals.

**4.8** Use the curl theorem to link line integrals and surface integrals.

**4.9** Express curl in terms of partial derivatives and evaluate the curl of a vector field.

# Chapter 5 Electrostatic potential

## Introduction

You have seen that magnetostatic fields obey both the no-monopole law and Ampère's law. The no-monopole law states that the magnetic flux over any closed surface $S$ is equal to zero. This implies that magnetic fields have zero divergence:

$$\int_S \mathbf{B} \cdot \mathrm{d}\mathbf{S} = 0 \quad \text{and} \quad \operatorname{div} \mathbf{B} = 0.$$

Ampère's law states that the circulation of a magnetostatic field around a closed loop $C$ is proportional to the current $I$ through the area bounded by the loop. This implies that the curl of a magnetostatic field is proportional to the current density $\mathbf{J}$:

$$\oint_C \mathbf{B} \cdot \mathrm{d}\mathbf{l} = \mu_0 I \quad \text{and} \quad \operatorname{curl} \mathbf{B} = \mu_0 \mathbf{J}.$$

Compare this with the situation for electrostatic fields. Any electric field must obey Gauss's law, which states that the electric flux over a closed surface $S$ is proportional to the total charge $Q$ enclosed by the surface. This implies that $\operatorname{div} \mathbf{E}$ is proportional to the charge density $\rho$:

$$\int_S \mathbf{E} \cdot \mathrm{d}\mathbf{S} = \frac{Q}{\varepsilon_0} \quad \text{and} \quad \operatorname{div} \mathbf{E} = \frac{\rho}{\varepsilon_0}.$$

But, so far, we have said nothing about circulation of an electric field around a closed loop or the value of the curl of the electric field at any point. This lack of knowledge can be summarized as follows:

$$\oint_C \mathbf{E} \cdot \mathrm{d}\mathbf{l} = ? \quad \text{and} \quad \operatorname{curl} \mathbf{E} = ?$$

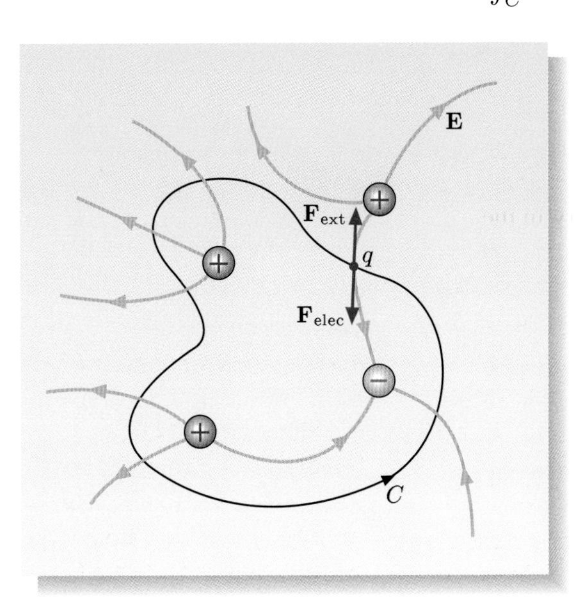


**Figure 5.1** Moving a test charge $q$ in an electrostatic field.

The next two chapters will make good this omission and replace the above question marks by something more useful. It is helpful to examine two contrasting situations.

First, consider a test charge $q$ that moves very slowly around an arbitrary closed loop, $C$, in the vicinity of an arrangement of charges that are fixed in position (Figure 5.1). At each point, the test charge feels an electrostatic force $\mathbf{F}_{\text{elec}} = q\mathbf{E}$, where $\mathbf{E}$ is the total electrostatic field at the position of the test charge. In order to guide the test charge around the loop, we must apply an external force $\mathbf{F}_{\text{ext}}$. Because the test charge moves very slowly, the external force is just sufficient to balance the electrostatic force, so $\mathbf{F}_{\text{ext}} = -\mathbf{F}_{\text{elec}} = -q\mathbf{E}$. The work done by this external force when the charge completes one lap of the closed loop $C$ is

$$W = \oint_C \mathbf{F}_{\text{ext}} \cdot \mathrm{d}\mathbf{l} = -q \oint_C \mathbf{E} \cdot \mathrm{d}\mathbf{l}.$$

We can argue that this must be equal to zero. For, if $W$ were negative, the agency supplying the external force would have work done on it, which could be used to drive an engine. After completing one lap, the test charge has returned to its initial position and none of the other charges has moved (they are held *fixed*), so we could repeat this process indefinitely and extract an unlimited amount of energy. This is clearly impossible.

On the other hand, if $W$ were positive, the external agency would do work on the test charge, involving an expenditure of energy. The law of conservation of energy demands that this energy should not be lost. However, after a complete lap, all the charges are back in their original positions and the test charge is still moving slowly, so it is difficult to see where the energy has gone. The only possibility would be for the energy to be converted into another form — perhaps the slowly-moving charge could radiate energy as it moves. We will assume that this does not happen. It then follows that $W$ is neither positive nor negative, but is equal to zero. Consequently,

$$\oint_C \mathbf{E} \cdot \mathrm{d}\mathbf{l} = 0 \qquad (5.1)$$

for any closed loop $C$ and any electrostatic field $\mathbf{E}$. An electric field that obeys this condition is said to be a **conservative electric field**.

Now consider a different situation. An electric power source continuously drives a current around a circuit containing a light bulb (Figure 5.2). As the current flows, energy is dissipated as heat and light, and this energy must be continuously supplied by the power source. Electrostatic fields are unable to satisfy this demand for energy. When a charge $q$ moves once around a closed loop, the work done by an electrostatic field $\mathbf{E}$ is the line integral of $q\mathbf{E}$ around the loop, which is equal to zero according to Equation 5.1. So an electrostatic field is unable to maintain a continuous current, even an exceedingly small one. However, in Chapter 6 you will meet **non-conservative electric fields** which have

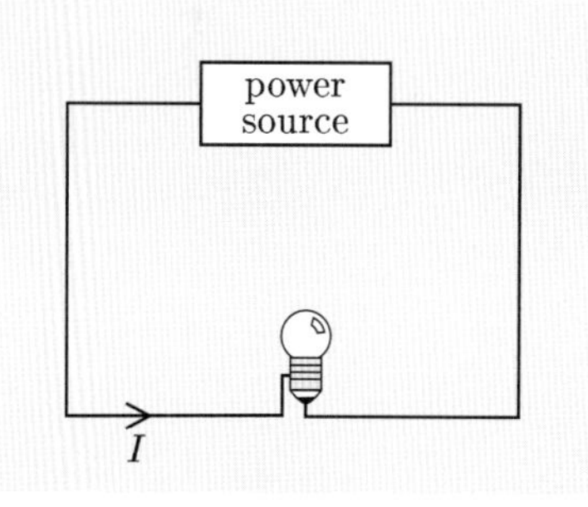


**Figure 5.2** A current $I$ driven around a stationary circuit by a power source.

$$\oint_C \mathbf{E} \cdot \mathrm{d}\mathbf{l} \neq 0 \qquad (5.2)$$

for at least one closed loop, $C$. A *non-conservative* electric field can do work on a charge that moves around a closed loop, and can therefore provide the energy needed to keep a current flowing. The distinction between conservative and non-conservative electric fields therefore marks an important boundary in the subject. In this chapter, we concentrate on electrostatic fields, which are conservative and *cannot* drive currents around circuits. The following chapter will discuss non-electrostatic, non-conservative electric fields, which *can* drive currents around circuits.

We begin by reviewing the mathematical properties of conservative vector fields. We then use the conservative nature of the electrostatic field to show why electrostatic fields are excluded from the interior of an empty conducting cage. The important concept of electrostatic potential is introduced and applied to electric dipoles and conductors. The chapter ends by discussing capacitors and capacitance, leading to the idea that electrostatic energy is stored in the electric field.

This chapter uses the mathematical properties of conservative fields, which are discussed in MT 8.9. Study of this mathematics is essential, and is likely to increase your study-time on this chapter by around 50%.

## 5.1 Electrostatic fields are conservative

Energy arguments suggest that electrostatic fields are conservative. However, these arguments are based on physical assumptions, which may be open to doubt. We will therefore proceed more carefully and show rigorously that the conservative nature of electrostatic fields follows directly from Coulomb's law and the principle of superposition.

Suppose that a point charge $q$ is stationary at the origin. According to Coulomb's law, the electric field produced by this charge has the form

$$\mathbf{E} = E_r(r)\,\mathbf{e}_r, \quad \text{where} \quad E_r(r) = \frac{q}{4\pi\varepsilon_0 r^2}, \tag{5.3}$$

and $\mathbf{e}_r$ is a radial unit vector pointing away from the origin. We wish to find the line integral of this electric field around a closed loop $C$. A small displacement around the loop can be expressed in spherical coordinates as

$$\delta\mathbf{l} = \delta r\,\mathbf{e}_r + r\,\delta\theta\,\mathbf{e}_\theta + r\sin\theta\,\mathbf{e}_\phi,$$

so

Remember, $\mathbf{e}_r \cdot \mathbf{e}_\theta = \mathbf{e}_r \cdot \mathbf{e}_\phi = 0$.

$$\mathbf{E} \cdot \delta\mathbf{l} = E_r(r)\,\delta r.$$

Suppose that the closed loop $C$ starts and ends at a point $\mathbf{r}_1$ with radial coordinate $r_1$. Then the circulation of the electric field around $C$ is

$$\oint_C \mathbf{E} \cdot \mathrm{d}\mathbf{l} = \int_{r_1}^{r_1} E_r(r)\,\mathrm{d}r = 0.$$

This circulation vanishes because the integrand depends only on $r$, and there is no net change in $r$ when we travel around a closed loop.

A minor difficulty is encountered if the loop passes through the origin. The magnitude of the electric field tends to infinity as we approach the point charge, making it impossible to define the circulation of the electric field in this case. In practice, this is not a problem. It only arises because we are dealing with the idealization of a point charge. If we think of a real charged particle, such as an electron, as being a tiny spherically symmetric distribution of charge, the electric field remains finite everywhere, and vanishes at the centre of the charge distribution. Our proof then extends over the whole of space, without any exceptions.

We have considered the electrostatic field due to a point charge that is stationary at the origin. However, the value of the circulation cannot depend on the choice of origin. It follows that the circulation vanishes for the electric field due to any stationary charge, whether at the origin or not. Finally, the principle of superposition allows us to extend this result to the electric field created by any number of stationary charges. If the fields due to the individual charges are $\mathbf{E}_1, \mathbf{E}_2, \ldots, \mathbf{E}_n$, the total field is

$$\mathbf{E} = \mathbf{E}_1 + \mathbf{E}_2 + \ldots + \mathbf{E}_n.$$

Each of the individual fields has zero circulation, so the circulation of the total field is

$$\oint_C \mathbf{E} \cdot \mathrm{d}\mathbf{l} = \oint_C \mathbf{E}_1 \cdot \mathrm{d}\mathbf{l} + \oint_C \mathbf{E}_2 \cdot \mathrm{d}\mathbf{l} + \ldots + \oint_C \mathbf{E}_n \cdot \mathrm{d}\mathbf{l} = 0,$$

in agreement with our earlier energy argument. By definition, any vector field that has zero circulation around any closed loop, is **conservative**. We therefore conclude that:

All electrostatic fields (that is, electric fields produced by stationary arrangements of charge) are conservative.

This exact result relies on the spherical symmetry of Coulomb's law and cannot be extended to moving charges. You may recall from Chapter 1 that the electric field of a uniformly-moving charge is cylindrically symmetric around the line of motion of the charge, and is *not* spherically symmetric. Figure 5.3 is an arrow map of the electric field produced by a charge that is moving uniformly at a speed close to that of light. We will consider the circulation of this electric field around the loop ABCD. The line integral along AB has a greater magnitude than the line integral along CD because the electric field is stronger along AB than along CD. The line integrals around the circular arcs BC and DA are equal to zero because the electric field is perpendicular to the displacements along these paths. Adding together the contributions from AB, BC, CD and DA, we see that $\mathbf{E}$ has a non-zero circulation around the loop ABCD. So the electric field in Figure 5.3 is certainly *not* conservative. It is important to keep a sense of proportion here. Slowly moving charges produce electric fields with negligible circulations and such fields can be reasonably approximated as being conservative. However, the principle remains that this is an *approximation*, acceptable only for particles that move slowly compared to light.

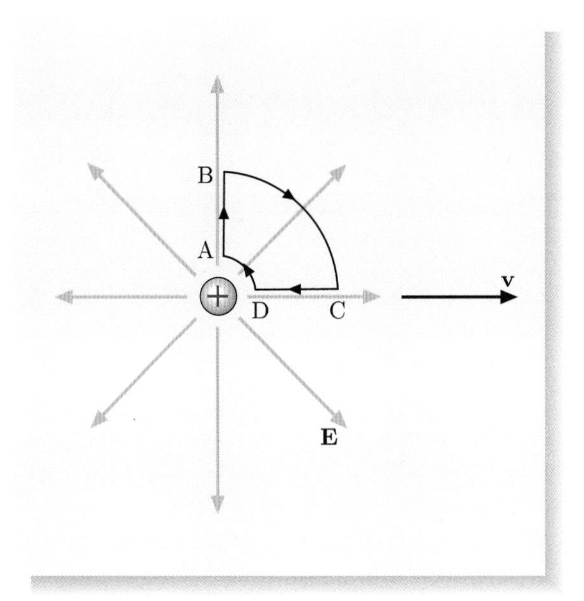


**Figure 5.3** The electric field $\mathbf{E}$ due to a positive charge moving with a uniform velocity, $\mathbf{v}$, close to the speed of light.

► Read MT 8.9 now. This is a lengthy detour, but is essential material.

As explained in the Section 8.9 of the Mathematical Toolkit, conservative fields have special properties, which are not shared by all vector fields. For convenience, these properties are summarized below:

**Properties of conservative fields**

If $\mathbf{F}$ is a conservative vector field, it follows that:

(1) The circulation of $\mathbf{F}$ around any closed loop is equal to zero.

(2) Any line integral of $\mathbf{F}$ depends on its start- and end-points, but does not depend on the path taken between these points.

(3) It is possible to define a scalar field

$$f(\mathbf{r}) = -\int_{\mathbf{r}_0}^{\mathbf{r}} \mathbf{F} \cdot \mathrm{d}\mathbf{l} + f_0,$$

where $\mathbf{r}_0$ is an arbitrarily chosen reference point at which the value of $f$ is set equal to $f_0$. This scalar field can be used to find the value of any line integral of $\mathbf{F}$:

$$\int_{\mathbf{r}_1}^{\mathbf{r}_2} \mathbf{F} \cdot \mathrm{d}\mathbf{l} = -(f(\mathbf{r}_2) - f(\mathbf{r}_1)).$$

(4) The vector field $\mathbf{F}$ is equal to minus the gradient of the scalar field $f$:

$$\mathbf{F} = -\,\mathrm{grad}\, f.$$

(5) $\mathbf{F}$ is irrotational (i.e. $\mathrm{curl}\,\mathbf{F} = \mathbf{0}$).

The last of these properties tells us that all electrostatic fields are irrotational (i.e have zero curl). This is something that can be checked directly. For example, consider the electrostatic field due to a point charge $q$ stationary at the origin. The curl of this field is most conveniently calculated in a spherical coordinate system. Selecting the appropriate formula from the list inside the back cover of the book, and using Equation 5.3, we obtain

$$\mathrm{curl}\,\mathbf{E} = \frac{1}{r^2\sin\theta}\begin{vmatrix} \mathbf{e}_r & r\,\mathbf{e}_\theta & r\sin\theta\,\mathbf{e}_\phi \\ \dfrac{\partial}{\partial r} & \dfrac{\partial}{\partial \theta} & \dfrac{\partial}{\partial \phi} \\ E_r(r) & 0 & 0 \end{vmatrix}, \quad \text{where} \quad E_r = \frac{q}{4\pi\varepsilon_0 r^2}.$$

This is equal to zero everywhere, except possibly at the origin (where $r = 0$) or along the $z$-axis (where $\sin\theta = 0$). The difficulty along the $z$-axis is an artefact of our choice of coordinate system. If we choose the $z$-axis to point in some other direction, we immediately see that $\mathrm{curl}\,\mathbf{E} = \mathbf{0}$ along the original $z$-axis. However, the difficulty at the origin cannot be removed because the electrostatic field is undefined at the point occupied by the charge. We can therefore say that the electrostatic field of a stationary point charge is irrotational everywhere (except possibly at the single point occupied by the charge).

- Does the irrotational nature of the field allow us to deduce that it is *conservative* everywhere (except possibly at the point occupied by the charge)?

- Yes, because the whole of space, with a single point removed, is simply-connected (see MT 8.9.5). Any vector field that is irrotational in a simply-connected region is also conservative in that region.

The fact that an electrostatic field must be irrotational provides a useful check, known as the **curl test** for electrostatic fields. Given a vector field, we take the curl of the field and check that it is equal to zero everywhere (except possibly at points where the curl is undefined). Fields that pass this test could be electrostatic fields. Fields that fail the test certainly cannot be electrostatic fields, though they might be electric fields produced by some source other than a static arrangement of charge.

### Worked Example 5.1

**Essential skill**

Checking whether a given vector field could be an electrostatic field.

If $C$ is a constant with suitable units, which of the following vector fields could be an electrostatic field?

$$\mathbf{F}_1 = C(yz\mathbf{e}_x + xz\mathbf{e}_y + xy\mathbf{e}_z)$$

$$\mathbf{F}_2 = Cxz\mathbf{e}_x$$

#### Solution

Taking the curl of each vector field gives

$$\operatorname{curl}\mathbf{F}_1 = \begin{vmatrix} \mathbf{e}_x & \mathbf{e}_y & \mathbf{e}_z \\ \dfrac{\partial}{\partial x} & \dfrac{\partial}{\partial y} & \dfrac{\partial}{\partial z} \\ Cyz & Cxz & Cxy \end{vmatrix}$$

$$= C\big((x-x)\mathbf{e}_x + (y-y)\mathbf{e}_y + (z-z)\mathbf{e}_z\big) = \mathbf{0},$$

$$\operatorname{curl}\mathbf{F}_2 = \begin{vmatrix} \mathbf{e}_x & \mathbf{e}_y & \mathbf{e}_z \\ \dfrac{\partial}{\partial x} & \dfrac{\partial}{\partial y} & \dfrac{\partial}{\partial z} \\ Cxz & 0 & 0 \end{vmatrix} = Cx\mathbf{e}_y \neq \mathbf{0}.$$

The curl of $\mathbf{F}_1$ is equal to zero everywhere, so $\mathbf{F}_1$ could be an electrostatic field; the curl of $\mathbf{F}_2$ is not equal to zero everywhere, so $\mathbf{F}_2$ could not be an electrostatic field.

**Exercise 5.1** Does the vector field

$$\mathbf{F} = \frac{A}{r^3}\left(x\mathbf{e}_x + y\mathbf{e}_y + z\mathbf{e}_z\right), \quad \text{where} \quad r = (x^2+y^2+z^2)^{1/2},$$

pass the curl test for an electrostatic field? ■

### 5.1.1 Shielding in a cavity

The conservative nature of electrostatic fields can be used to establish an interesting and useful result. In Chapter 2, Gauss's law was used to show that there is no electric field inside a spherical conducting shell. We will now go further and show that a similar result applies to all conducting shells, no matter what their shape. Consider a conducting shell that completely surrounds an empty cavity. There might be charges outside the shell, or the shell itself might carry a net charge. Nevertheless, in equilibrium, we will show that the electric field inside the cavity vanishes. There is no electric field inside a closed empty biscuit tin.

We exploit the fact that the walls of the cavity are conducting. In equilibrium, there is no electric field inside a conductor. This is because any electric field inside a conductor causes free charges to flow, and charge flow is not a state of equilibrium. However, charges accumulate in different parts of the conductor. A state of equilibrium is reached when the applied electric field is exactly cancelled by the electric field due to the displaced charges. The rearrangement of charge occurs very rapidly — within microseconds for a conductor 10 cm across — so it is generally safe to assume that equilibrium has been reached and the electric field inside the conductor is equal to zero. Since there is no electric field inside the conducting walls, electric field lines cannot cross from the outside of the shell to the inside. If there is an electric field inside the cavity, there are three logical possibilities, illustrated in Figure 5.4a–c.

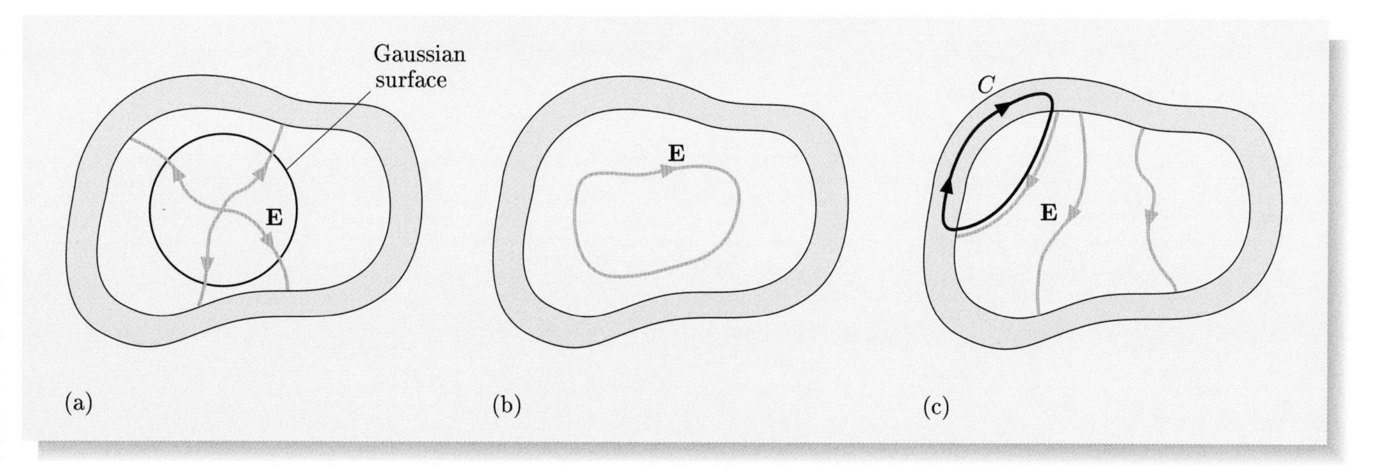


**Figure 5.4** Proposed electric field lines inside a cavity.

(a) The electric field lines start at points within the cavity and end on the cavity wall (or vice versa).

(b) The electric field lines form closed loops entirely within the cavity.

(c) The electric field lines start and end on the cavity wall.

Possibility (a) can be rejected because it is not consistent with Gauss's law. In the case shown in Figure 5.4a, the electric flux would be non-zero over the spherical Gaussian surface indicated, even though there is no charge within this surface. This is not possible for an inverse square law of force.

Possibility (b) can be rejected because it implies that the field is not conservative. In the case shown in Figure 5.4b, the circulation of **E** around a closed loop that follows the field line would be non-zero. This is not possible because electrostatic fields are conservative.

Possibility (c) can also be rejected. Suppose that we calculate the circulation of the electric field around the closed loop $C$ in Figure 5.4c. This loop travels along a field line inside the cavity and returns inside the conducting shell. The part of the loop that lies within the conducting shell makes no contribution because the electrostatic field vanishes there, so the part of the loop that lies within the cavity must also contribute nothing. This can only happen if the electric field vanishes inside the cavity.

Note that the situation is different if the cavity contains a charge. Possibility (a) outlined above is then true. Figure 5.5 shows what happens in this case. An electric field does exist in the cavity and the inner surface of the cavity wall carries a net charge, opposite to that of the charge in the cavity. This ensures that Gauss's law, applied to the Gaussian surface in Figure 5.5, gives zero electrostatic field inside the conductor, as required for equilibrium. If the conducting shell is neutral and electrically isolated, the charge on its outer surface must be opposite to the charge on its inner surface, and is therefore equal to the charge in the cavity. This charge produces an electric field outside the conducting shell. So there is a lack of symmetry here. The cavity is shielded from charges in the outside world, but the outside world is not shielded from charges in the cavity.

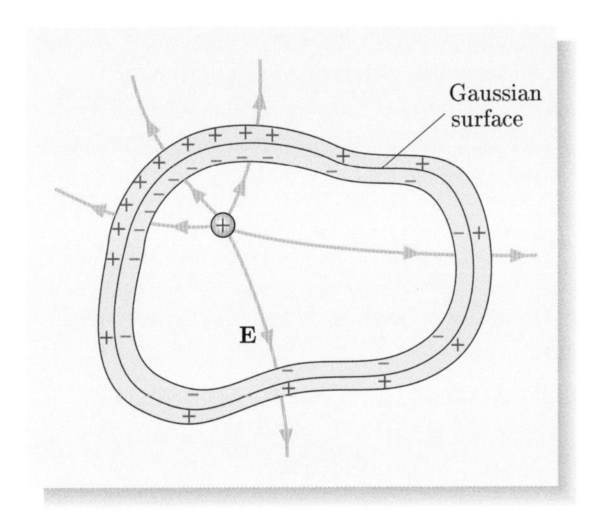


**Figure 5.5** A cavity containing a charge.

Shielding has many practical applications. A conducting shell can be used to protect sensitive electrical equipment from external electrical disturbances. For example, the logic boards in a computer are surrounded by a metal box. In principle, a complete conducting shell is needed and protection is limited to electrostatic fields. In practice, considerable protection is provided by a conducting cage (known as a **Faraday cage**), especially if the mesh size is fine enough. Moreover, time-varying electric fields are also strongly suppressed in the cavity, unless they vary extremely rapidly. The volunteer inside the Faraday cage shown in Figure 5.6 is quite safe and passengers in cars and planes are well-protected against lightning strikes.

**Figure 5.6** A trusting volunteer sits inside a Faraday cage, surrounded by powerful electrical discharges.

## 5.2 The electrostatic potential

### 5.2.1 Introducing the electrostatic potential

Because the electrostatic field is conservative, we can introduce a related scalar field. This field is called the **electrostatic potential field** (or electrostatic potential) and is denoted by the symbol $V$. We define

$$V(\mathbf{r}) = -\int_{\mathbf{r}_0}^{\mathbf{r}} \mathbf{E} \cdot \mathrm{d}\mathbf{l} + V_0, \tag{5.4}$$

where $\mathbf{E}$ is an electrostatic field, $\mathbf{r}_0$ is an arbitrarily chosen reference point and $V_0$ is the value of the electrostatic potential at this point. It does not matter which path is used to evaluate the line integral because the line integrals of a conservative field are path-independent. So, once $\mathbf{r}_0$ and $V_0$ have been fixed, Equation 5.4 gives a definite value for the electrostatic potential at $\mathbf{r}$. When it is clear that we are dealing with electrostatic problems (rather than, say, gravitational ones) we will just talk about the **potential field** or the value of the **potential** at a point.

Very often, the constant $V_0$ is set equal to zero, and the reference point is placed at infinity, but these choices are only made for convenience; they have no real physical significance. Given an electrostatic potential field, we can always add the same constant at every point without making any difference to the physical situation being described. This simply corresponds to changing the value of $V_0$ or shifting the reference point. However, if we consider the *difference* in values of the potential between two different points, we see that

$$V(\mathbf{r}_2) - V(\mathbf{r}_1) = -\int_{\mathbf{r}_1}^{\mathbf{r}_2} \mathbf{E} \cdot \mathrm{d}\mathbf{l}, \tag{5.5}$$

which does not depend on $\mathbf{r}_0$ or $V_0$. Naturally enough, we call this the **potential difference** between the points $\mathbf{r}_1$ and $\mathbf{r}_2$.

To interpret the electrostatic potential in physical terms, and to understand the reason for the minus sign in Equation 5.4, we return to the concept of the work done by a force. Suppose that a test charge $q$ is in an electrostatic field, $\mathbf{E}$, produced by an arrangement of fixed charges. The test charge experiences an electrostatic force

$$\mathbf{F}_{\text{elec}} = q\mathbf{E}(\mathbf{r})$$

which, if left unopposed, would cause it to accelerate. We will not let this happen. To prevent the acceleration, an external force, $\mathbf{F}_{\text{ext}}$, is applied which exactly cancels out the electrostatic force:

$$\mathbf{F}_{\text{ext}} = -\mathbf{F}_{\text{elec}} = -q\mathbf{E}(\mathbf{r}).$$

Now, suppose the external force is changed very slightly, so that the test charge can be guided from point $\mathbf{r}_1$ to point $\mathbf{r}_2$ along a chosen path $C$. The force is only changed infinitesimally, so the particle travels with negligible speed. This means that the journey will take a long time, but that is of no concern to us — time comes cheap in the imagination. The work done by the *external* force is then

$$\int_C \mathbf{F}_{\text{ext}} \cdot \mathrm{d}\mathbf{l} = -\int_{\mathbf{r}_1}^{\mathbf{r}_2} \mathbf{F}_{\text{elec}} \cdot \mathrm{d}\mathbf{l} = -q\int_{\mathbf{r}_1}^{\mathbf{r}_2} \mathbf{E} \cdot \mathrm{d}\mathbf{l}.$$

What becomes of this work? It cannot be converted into kinetic energy because the test charge travels with negligible speed and the other charges are fixed in position. We say that it is converted into **electrostatic potential energy**, in other words, potential energy associated with electrostatic forces. We therefore write

$$U_2 - U_1 = -q \int_{\mathbf{r}_1}^{\mathbf{r}_2} \mathbf{E} \cdot \mathrm{d}\mathbf{l},$$

where $U_1$ and $U_2$ are the electrostatic potential energies of the test charge at its initial and final positions, $\mathbf{r}_1$ and $\mathbf{r}_2$. Comparing with Equation 5.5, we see that the change in potential energy is proportional to the potential difference:

$$U_2 - U_1 = q\left(V(\mathbf{r}_2) - V(\mathbf{r}_1)\right).$$

Any arrangement of fixed charges has a potential energy of its own, acquired when it is assembled. This is not of interest here. Instead, we are focusing on the *additional* potential energy that develops when a test charge $q$ is brought to a given point with all other conditions kept the same. This is what we mean by the electrostatic potential energy *of* the test charge. It is natural to take the electrostatic potential energy of the test charge to be zero at the same point where the electrostatic potential is equal to zero. Then the electrostatic potential energy of a test charge $q$ is

$$U = qV(\mathbf{r}), \qquad (5.6)$$

and we can then state that:

> The electrostatic potential $V(\mathbf{r})$ is the electrostatic potential energy *per unit charge* of a test charge that is brought to the point $\mathbf{r}$.

In retrospect, the minus sign in Equation 5.4 was chosen to allow this simple interpretation.

Take care to distinguish between electrostatic potential and electrostatic potential energy, and avoid using the word potential as a shorthand for potential energy. These concepts are not the same and they don't even have the same units. The SI unit of electrostatic potential energy is the joule (J), while electrostatic potential is measured in joules per coulomb, a unit invariably known as the **volt** (V) .

$1\,\mathrm{V} = 1\,\mathrm{J\,C^{-1}}$.

### Worked Example 5.2

Calculate the electrostatic potential field $V(\mathbf{r})$ due to a point charge $q$, taking the zero of potential to be at infinity.

**Essential skill**

Calculating the electrostatic potential for a given conservative electric field.

#### Solution

Choose spherical coordinates with the point charge at the origin. The charge produces an electrostatic field

$$\mathbf{E} = \frac{q}{4\pi\varepsilon_0 r^2}\,\mathbf{e}_r.$$

The electrostatic potential is given by the line integral

$$V(\mathbf{r}) = -\int_{\mathbf{r}_0}^{\mathbf{r}} \mathbf{E} \cdot \mathrm{d}\mathbf{l} = -\frac{q}{4\pi\varepsilon_0} \int_{\mathbf{r}_0}^{\mathbf{r}} \frac{1}{r^2}\,\mathbf{e}_r \cdot \mathrm{d}\mathbf{l},$$

which is taken along a straight-line radial path from a point $\mathbf{r}_0$ at infinity to the point $\mathbf{r}$. We have

$$\mathbf{e}_r \cdot \delta\mathbf{l} = \delta r,$$

where $\delta r$ is a small change in radial coordinate. Therefore the line integral reduces to

$$V(\mathbf{r}) = -\frac{q}{4\pi\varepsilon_0} \int_\infty^r \frac{1}{r^2}\,\mathrm{d}r.$$

However, this is rather clumsily expressed because the variable of integration is the same as the upper limit of integration. It is therefore better to re-write the line integral using the dummy variable $s$:

$$V(\mathbf{r}) = -\frac{q}{4\pi\varepsilon_0} \int_\infty^r \frac{1}{s^2}\,\mathrm{d}s.$$

Finally, we evaluate the integral to obtain

$$V(\mathbf{r}) = -\frac{q}{4\pi\varepsilon_0} \left[-\frac{1}{s}\right]_{s=\infty}^{s=r} = \frac{q}{4\pi\varepsilon_0 r}. \qquad (5.7)$$

Although this calculation has considered a point charge at the origin, the final answer is independent of the choice of coordinate system, or the location of the charge, provided we interpret $r$ as the distance from the point charge. This is because the scalar product that appears in the line integral defining potential is itself independent of the choice of coordinate system.

*Note*: It is always worth checking the final sign in calculations of this type. If $q$ is positive, our answer shows that the potential increases as $r$ decreases, which implies that the electrostatic potential energy of a positive charge increases when it is brought closer to $q$. This agrees with experience, so we can be confident that the final sign is correct.

**Exercise 5.2** An infinite line of charge, with uniform charge per unit length $\lambda > 0$, lies along the $z$-axis. In cylindrical coordinates, the electrostatic field due to this line of charge is

$$\mathbf{E} = \frac{\lambda}{2\pi\varepsilon_0 r}\,\mathbf{e}_r.$$

Find the electrostatic potential due to the line of charge, taking the zero of potential to be zero at $r = r_0$. By how much does the electrostatic potential energy of a charge $q$ change when its distance from the line of charge is halved? ■

### 5.2.2 The conservation of energy

Another way of understanding the role of potential is to ask what happens if we place a charged particle in an electrostatic field and allow it to move freely under the sole influence of the field. We must be slightly guarded here, as motion takes us beyond the strict confines of electrostatics. It turns out that an accelerating charge emits electromagnetic radiation, and therefore loses some of its energy.

However, the radiated energy is usually a very small fraction of the energy of the particle and the energy loss is generally neglected. That is what we will do here.

We will calculate the change in the kinetic energy of a particle of mass $m$ and charge $q$ in an electrostatic field. It is helpful to use a result derived in the vectors section of the Mathematical Toolkit. Exercise 8.10 shows that

$$\frac{\mathrm{d}}{\mathrm{d}t}\left(\tfrac{1}{2}mv^2\right) = \mathbf{F}\cdot\mathbf{v},$$

where $\mathbf{F}$ is the total force acting on the particle. Integrating both sides from an initial time $t_1$ (where the particle has position $\mathbf{r}_1$ and speed $v_1$) to a final time $t_2$ (where the particle has position $\mathbf{r}_2$ and speed $v_2$) gives

$$\tfrac{1}{2}mv_2^2 - \tfrac{1}{2}mv_1^2 = \int_{t_1}^{t_2} \mathbf{F}\cdot\mathbf{v}\,\mathrm{d}t = \int_{t_1}^{t_2} \mathbf{F}\cdot\frac{\mathrm{d}\mathbf{l}}{\mathrm{d}t}\,\mathrm{d}t = \int_{\mathbf{r}_1}^{\mathbf{r}_2} \mathbf{F}\cdot\mathrm{d}\mathbf{l},$$

so the change in kinetic energy is the work done by the force. This is a well-known result in mechanics, called the **work–energy theorem**. Assuming that the only force acting on the particle is the electrostatic force $q\mathbf{E}$, and using Equation 5.5, we then have

$$\tfrac{1}{2}mv_2^2 - \tfrac{1}{2}mv_1^2 = q\int_{\mathbf{r}_1}^{\mathbf{r}_2} \mathbf{E}\cdot\mathrm{d}\mathbf{l} = -q\left(V(\mathbf{r}_2) - V(\mathbf{r}_1)\right),$$

which can be rearranged to give

$$\tfrac{1}{2}mv_2^2 + qV(\mathbf{r}_2) = \tfrac{1}{2}mv_1^2 + qV(\mathbf{r}_1). \tag{5.8}$$

This equation expresses the conservation of energy for a charged particle in an electrostatic field. The right-hand side is the total energy at the start of the particle's trajectory and the left-hand side is the total energy at the end of the trajectory. These two quantities are equal, showing us that the total energy is conserved, and confirming our interpretation of $qV(\mathbf{r})$ as the electrostatic potential energy of the particle.

**Exercise 5.3** An alpha particle of charge $3.20\times10^{-19}$ C makes a head-on collision with a gold nucleus of charge $1.26\times10^{-17}$ C. Initially, the alpha particle is far from the nucleus and has kinetic energy $1.23\times10^{-13}$ J. Assuming that the nucleus remains stationary throughout, and treating it as a point charge, find the distance of closest approach of the alpha particle. ■

### 5.2.3 Recovering the electrostatic field

At any given point, the potential field $V(\mathbf{r})$ specifies a scalar (one number) while the electrostatic field $\mathbf{E}(\mathbf{r})$ specifies a vector (three numbers). You might therefore suppose that the potential field contains less information than the electrostatic field, but this is not true. Using the general properties of conservative fields listed on page 118, we can write

$$\mathbf{E} = -\operatorname{grad} V, \tag{5.9}$$

so $\mathbf{E}(\mathbf{r})$ is completely determined by $V(\mathbf{r})$. This alchemy relies on the conservative nature of the electrostatic field, which justifies the use of

Equation 5.9. This equation also shows that the SI unit of electric field can be expressed as volts per metre ($\mathrm{V\,m^{-1}}$). This is equivalent to, and much more commonly used, than newtons per coulomb which we have used so far.

Now suppose we introduce a particle of charge $q$ into an electrostatic field. Multiplying both sides of Equation 5.9 by $q$ gives

$$q\mathbf{E} = -q\,\mathrm{grad}\,V,$$

which can be rewritten as

$$\mathbf{F}_{\mathrm{elec}} = -\,\mathrm{grad}\,U. \qquad (5.10)$$

where $\mathbf{F}_{\mathrm{elec}} = q\mathbf{E}$ is the electrostatic force acting on the particle and $U = qV$ is the electrostatic potential energy of the particle. The reason for the minus sign in Equation 5.10 is easily understood. The electrostatic force points in the direction of steepest *decrease* of electrostatic potential energy. However, the gradient of $U$ points in the direction of steepest *increase* of $U$. The minus sign on the right-hand side reverses this, ensuring that the force points downhill in the potential energy landscape, as expected.

The relationship between electrostatic fields and electrostatic potentials can be represented pictorially. We define an **equipotential surface** to be a surface on which the electrostatic potential remains constant. Using a property of gradients established in MT 8.9.4, it follows that $\mathrm{grad}\,V$ at any given point is perpendicular to the equipotential surface through the point. The electrostatic field points along the same line (but in the opposite direction) to $\mathrm{grad}\,V$ so we conclude that:

The electrostatic field at any point is perpendicular to the equipotential surface through the point.

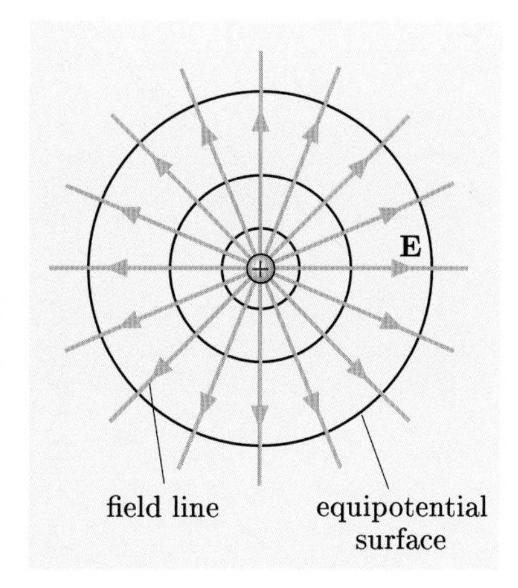


**Figure 5.7** Equipotential surfaces (in cross-section) and electrostatic field lines for a stationary point charge.

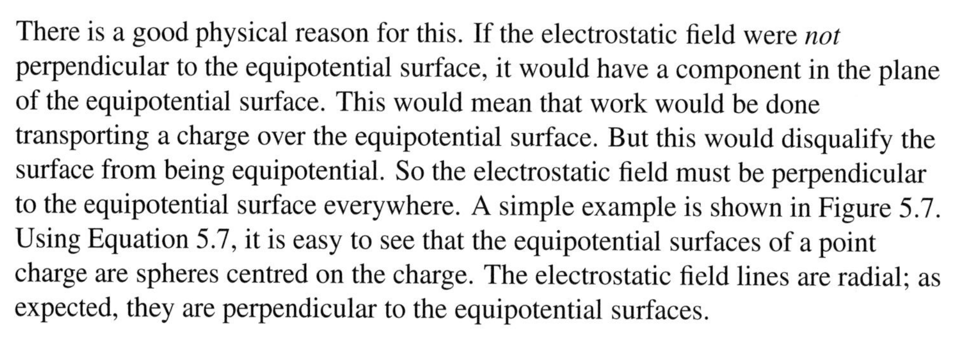

There is a good physical reason for this. If the electrostatic field were *not* perpendicular to the equipotential surface, it would have a component in the plane of the equipotential surface. This would mean that work would be done transporting a charge over the equipotential surface. But this would disqualify the surface from being equipotential. So the electrostatic field must be perpendicular to the equipotential surface everywhere. A simple example is shown in Figure 5.7. Using Equation 5.7, it is easy to see that the equipotential surfaces of a point charge are spheres centred on the charge. The electrostatic field lines are radial; as expected, they are perpendicular to the equipotential surfaces.

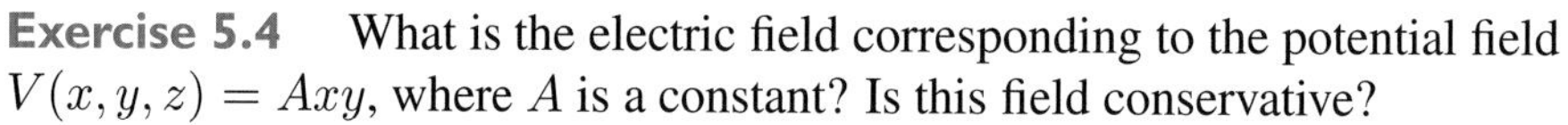

**Exercise 5.4** What is the electric field corresponding to the potential field $V(x,y,z) = Axy$, where $A$ is a constant? Is this field conservative?

**Exercise 5.5** Are electrons attracted towards regions of higher potential or regions of lower potential?

**Exercise 5.6** Is it possible for an electrostatic field line to cross the same equipotential surface more than once? ■

## 5.3 Adding electrostatic potentials

Electric fields obey a principle of superposition. In a system of many charges, the total electric field $\mathbf{E}$ is the vector sum of the electric fields due to the individual charges:

$$\mathbf{E} = \mathbf{E}_1 + \mathbf{E}_2 + \ldots + \mathbf{E}_n. \tag{5.11}$$

The total electrostatic potential is given by a line integral of the total electric field, which can be split into a sum

$$\int_{\mathbf{r}_0}^{\mathbf{r}} \mathbf{E} \cdot \mathrm{d}\mathbf{l} = \int_{\mathbf{r}_0}^{\mathbf{r}} \mathbf{E}_1 \cdot \mathrm{d}\mathbf{l} + \int_{\mathbf{r}_0}^{\mathbf{r}} \mathbf{E}_2 \cdot \mathrm{d}\mathbf{l} + \ldots + \int_{\mathbf{r}_0}^{\mathbf{r}} \mathbf{E}_n \cdot \mathrm{d}\mathbf{l}.$$

It follows that the total potential is the sum of the potentials due to the individual charges:

$$V = V_1 + V_2 + \ldots + V_n. \tag{5.12}$$

This is the **principle of superposition** for electrostatic potential.

Note that Equation 5.12 is an algebraic sum, which is simpler than the vector sum in Equation 5.11. This suggests a possible strategy for calculating the total electrostatic field:

1. Find the total potential $V$ by adding the contributions of the individual charges.
2. Find the total electrostatic field $\mathbf{E}$ by taking minus the gradient of the total potential $V$.

The strategy is a good one if the effort saved in the first step outweighs that spent in the second step, which is often the case.

### The electrostatic field of an electric dipole

We can illustrate how the method works by determining the electrostatic field of an **electric dipole** — that is, a pair of oppositely charged particles. Let's assume that the dipole is centred at the origin O with its charges on the $z$-axis; charge $+q$ at $z = d/2$ and charge $-q$ at $z = -d/2$ as shown in Figure 5.8.

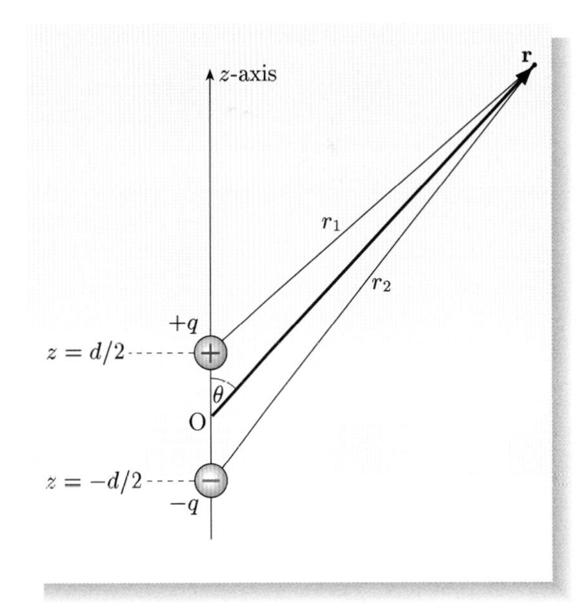


**Figure 5.8** An electric dipole.

Using Equation 5.7 and the principle of superposition we can immediately write down an expression for the total electrostatic potential:

$$V(\mathbf{r}) = \frac{q}{4\pi\varepsilon_0}\left(\frac{1}{r_1} - \frac{1}{r_2}\right). \tag{5.13}$$

Here, $r_1$ and $r_2$ are the distances from the charges $+q$ and $-q$ to the point $\mathbf{r}$ at which the potential field is measured, and the zero of potential is taken to be at infinity.

Using the cosine rule in Figure 5.8, it can be shown that

$$r_1 = \left(r^2 + \tfrac{1}{4}d^2 - rd\cos\theta\right)^{1/2}$$

$$r_2 = \left(r^2 + \tfrac{1}{4}d^2 + rd\cos\theta\right)^{1/2}.$$

Substituting these expressions in Equation 5.13 then gives an exact expression for the potential of the dipole, expressed in spherical coordinates. There is no

$\phi$-dependence because the charge distribution of the dipole is axially symmetric around the $z$-axis. Figure 5.9 shows a cross-section through the equipotential surfaces of this potential field, together with the electrostatic field lines, which always cross the equipotentials at right angles.

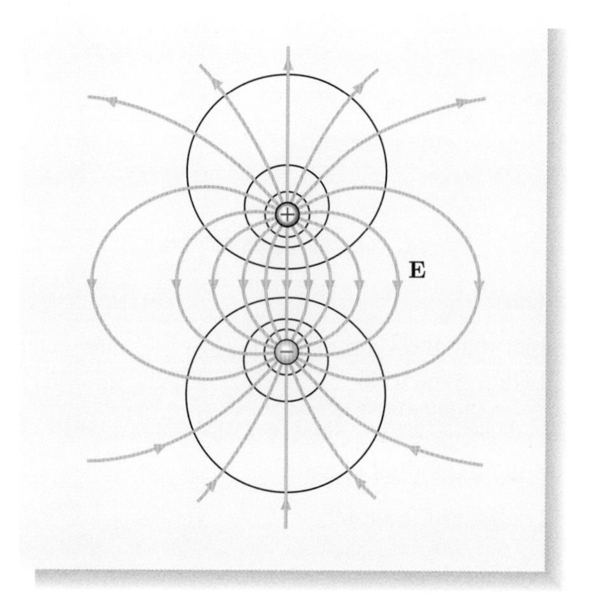


**Figure 5.9** Equipotential surfaces (black) and electrostatic field lines (orange) for an electric dipole.

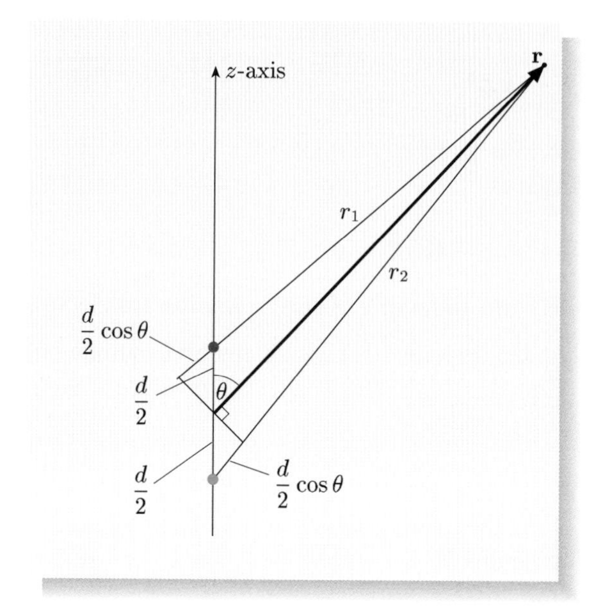


**Figure 5.10** Approximating the potential of an electric dipole. The red and blue dots show the positions of the $+q$ and $-q$ charges.

Very often, the distance from the dipole to the point at which the field is measured is much greater than the separation of the charges in the dipole ($r \gg d$). A useful approximation can then be made. We can use trigonometry in Figure 5.10 to justify the approximations

$$r_1 \simeq r - (d/2)\cos\theta, \quad \text{and} \quad r_2 \simeq r + (d/2)\cos\theta,$$

and then express the potential as

$$\begin{aligned} V(r) &= \frac{q}{4\pi\varepsilon_0}\frac{r_2 - r_1}{r_1 r_2} \\ &\simeq \frac{q}{4\pi\varepsilon_0}\frac{d\cos\theta}{r^2} \quad \text{for } r \gg d. \end{aligned}$$

Although it is an approximation, the right-hand side of this equation is usually called *the* **dipole potential**. It is sometimes expressed in terms of the **electric dipole moment** of the electric dipole. This is a vector quantity, $\mathbf{p}$, defined by

$$\mathbf{p} = q\mathbf{d}, \tag{5.14}$$

where $q$ is the charge at the positive end of the dipole and $\mathbf{d}$ is the displacement vector from the negative charge to the positive charge. Written in terms of the dipole moment, the dipole potential becomes

$$V(\mathbf{r}) = \frac{1}{4\pi\varepsilon_0}\frac{\mathbf{p}\cdot\widehat{\mathbf{r}}}{r^2} \quad \text{for } r \gg d. \tag{5.15}$$

The total electrostatic field is minus the gradient of the potential. Using the formula for gradient in spherical coordinates listed inside the back cover of the book, we obtain

$$E_r = -\frac{\partial V}{\partial r} \simeq \frac{1}{4\pi\varepsilon_0}\frac{2p\cos\theta}{r^3},$$

$$E_\theta = -\frac{1}{r}\frac{\partial V}{\partial \theta} \simeq \frac{1}{4\pi\varepsilon_0}\frac{p\sin\theta}{r^3},$$

$$E_\phi = 0,$$

$p = qd$ is the magnitude of the dipole moment.

so that

$$\mathbf{E} \simeq \frac{p}{4\pi\varepsilon_0 r^3}\left(2\cos\theta\,\mathbf{e}_r + \sin\theta\,\mathbf{e}_\theta\right), \tag{5.16}$$

where the approximations are valid for $r \gg d$. Note that the dipole potential falls off as $1/r^2$, and the corresponding electric field falls off as $1/r^3$. These are steeper than the $1/r$ decrease in potential and the $1/r^2$ decrease in electric field of a point charge. This is because the effects due to the positive and negative charges almost cancel, and the cancellation becomes more exact as we move away from the dipole.

Electric dipoles are important in many branches of science and technology. A neutral molecule behaves like a tiny dipole if the distribution of negative electrons is offset from the distribution of positive nuclei. This produces an electric field which, far from the molecule, is similar to that of an electric dipole. For example, the dipole moment of a water molecule is $6.2 \times 10^{-30}$ C m, which may seem tiny, but this is because coulombs and metres are enormous on an atomic scale. Thanks to their dipole moments, water molecules interact strongly with electric fields. If they are exposed to an oscillating electric field, they can be made to tumble back and forth in a rocking motion. This happens at gigahertz frequencies in a microwave oven. The rocking of water molecules in your food is soon dissipated as heat, warming your meal.

Some liquid crystals are composed of long molecules with electric dipole moments aligned with their axes. When exposed to an electric field, these molecules line up with the field, which can alter the transparency of the liquid crystal. This forms the basis for many display screens, from cheap pocket calculators to more expensive computer screens (Figure 5.11). Electric dipole moments are also important in the theory of atomic transitions. The electric dipole moment of an atom is zero in the ground state, but may be non-zero in certain excited states. The brightest spectral lines generally correspond to transitions in which the electric dipole moment of an atom changes.

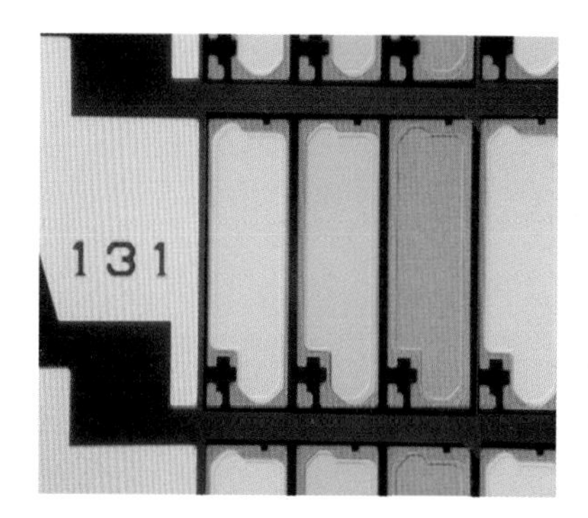


**Figure 5.11** Part of the liquid crystal display of a laptop ($\times 100$). Each triplet of green, blue and red is 1 pixel. By varying the amount of light passing through each coloured area, 16 million shades can be produced.

Finally, it is interesting to ask whether elementary particles, such as electrons, muons and neutrons have electric dipole moments. So far, none has been detected. The standard model of particle physics predicts that the electric dipole moment of an electron is less than $10^{-55}$ C m, which is too small to be measured. However several rival theories predict larger values in the range from $10^{-43}$ C m to $10^{-49}$ C m. These theories might help us to understand why the Universe seems to contain much more matter than antimatter, so very sensitive experiments are being carried out. The current limits of detection are around $3 \times 10^{-46}$ C m, in the middle of the decisive range.

**Essential skill**

Calculating an electrostatic potential and using it to derive an electric field.

### Worked Example 5.3

A uniformly charged disk of radius $R$ and total charge $Q$ is centred on the origin and lies in the $xy$-plane. Find the electrostatic potential of this disk at a point P with Cartesian coordinates $(0, 0, z)$, where $z > 0$. Hence find the electrostatic field at P.

#### Solution

Let $\sigma = Q/\pi R^2$ be the surface charge density of the disk. Consider the contribution $\delta V$ to the potential at P from the ring shown in Figure 5.12. This ring has radius $r$, thickness $\delta r$, area $2\pi r\,\delta r$ and charge $2\pi\sigma r\,\delta r$. All parts of this ring are the same distance, $\sqrt{r^2+z^2}$ from the point P, so

$$\delta V = \frac{1}{4\pi\varepsilon_0}\frac{2\pi\sigma r\,\delta r}{\sqrt{r^2+z^2}},$$

where we have used Equation 5.7, and therefore implicitly placed the zero of potential at infinity.

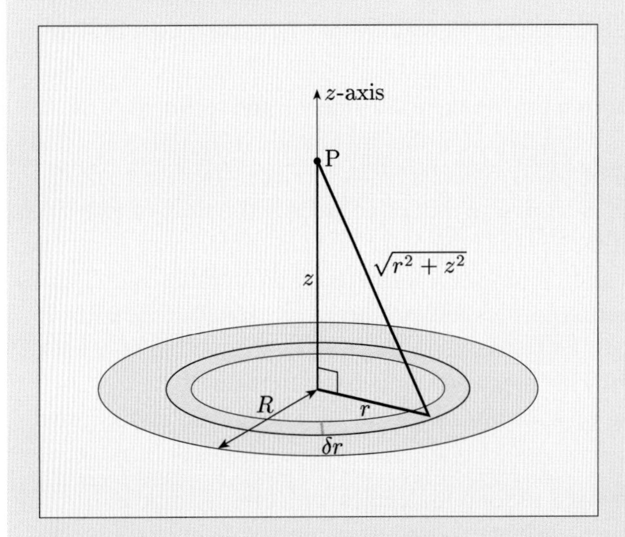


**Figure 5.12** Calculating the electrostatic potential due to a charged disk.

Integrating over the entire disk, the potential at P is

$$V = \frac{\sigma}{2\varepsilon_0}\int_0^R \frac{r}{\sqrt{r^2+z^2}}\,\mathrm{d}r = \frac{\sigma}{2\varepsilon_0}\left[\sqrt{r^2+z^2}\right]_{r=0}^{r=R}$$
$$= \frac{\sigma}{2\varepsilon_0}\left(\sqrt{R^2+z^2}-z\right).$$

The electrostatic field is found by taking the gradient of the potential. There are no $x$- or $y$-components because $V$ does not depend on $x$ or $y$, but the $z$-component is

$$E_z = -\frac{\partial V}{\partial z} = -\frac{\sigma}{2\varepsilon_0}\left(\frac{z}{\sqrt{R^2+z^2}}-1\right) = \frac{\sigma}{2\varepsilon_0}\left(1-\frac{1}{\sqrt{1+(R/z)^2}}\right).$$

This expression can be checked in two limiting cases.

(i) For $R \gg z$,

$$E_z \simeq \frac{\sigma}{2\varepsilon_0},$$

which is the electric field of an infinite plane of surface charge density $\sigma$.

(ii) For $R \ll z$, the binomial theorem gives $(1 - (R/z)^2)^{-1/2} = 1 - \frac{1}{2}(R/z)^2$, so

$$E_z \simeq \frac{\sigma}{2\varepsilon_0} \times \frac{R^2}{2z^2} = \frac{Q}{4\pi\varepsilon_0 z^2},$$

which is the electric field due a point charge $Q$ at the origin.

According to the binomial theorem, $(1 + x)^n = 1 + nx + \ldots$ where $n$ is any real number. In this case $n = -1/2$.

The only problem with calculations of this type is that they run into difficulties when we consider charge distributions that are infinite in extent. In such cases, the electric field does not tend to zero at infinity, so the zero of potential cannot be placed at infinity. It is therefore inappropriate to take the potential to be a sum of contributions that are inversely proportional to distance and vanish at infinity. For infinite charge distributions we must calculate the potential from first principles, using line integrals.

**Exercise 5.7** A line of charge extends along the $z$-axis from $z = -L$ to $z = L$ and has a uniform charge per unit length $\lambda$. Calculate the electrostatic potential due to this charge distribution at points along the $x$-axis. Does your answer make sense in the limit as $L \to \infty$. (You may need to use a standard integral listed inside the back cover of the book.) ■

## 5.4 Potential on conductors and capacitors

In equilibrium, we know that electrostatic fields vanish inside conductors . It follows from Equation 5.9 that the gradient of the electrostatic potential also vanishes inside conductors. That is,

$$\frac{\partial V}{\partial x} = \frac{\partial V}{\partial y} = \frac{\partial V}{\partial z} = 0.$$

We therefore conclude that:

In an electrostatic situation, the electrostatic potential is uniform throughout any conductor.

The word *uniform* means constant in space.

This important result allows us to talk about the potential *of* a conductor. This is a very succinct way of describing the electrical state of a conductor — useful even if we do not know exactly where the charges are located on the conductor's surface. To illustrate this concept, let's consider an isolated metal sphere of radius $R$, carrying a charge $Q$. What is the potential of this sphere?

To answer this question, we use the fact that the charge spreads out in a spherically symmetric way. You know from Gauss's law that the electric field

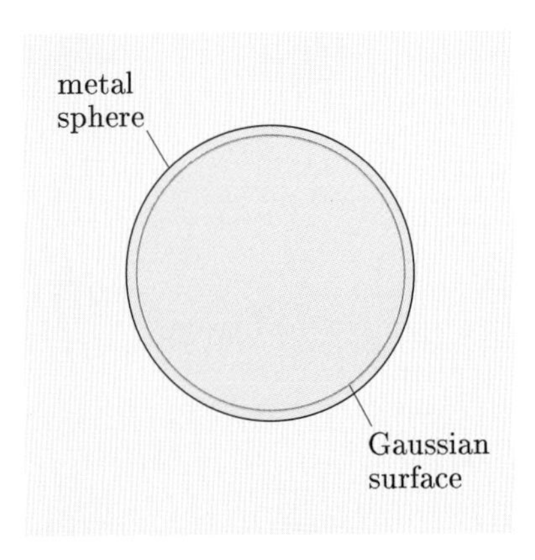


**Figure 5.13** A closed Gaussian surface just inside the surface of a sphere.

outside any spherically symmetric distribution of charge is the same as if all the charge were concentrated at the centre of the sphere. So the electric field outside the metal sphere is

$$\mathbf{E} = \frac{Q}{4\pi\varepsilon_0 r^2}\,\mathbf{e}_r \quad \text{for } r \geq R. \tag{5.17}$$

The electrostatic potential is found by carrying out a line integral of the electric field. Provided we remain outside the sphere, this line integral is exactly the same as for the electric field of a point charge, so we have

$$V(r) = \frac{Q}{4\pi\varepsilon_0 r} \quad \text{for } r \geq R. \tag{5.18}$$

The potential at the surface of the sphere is therefore

$$V = \frac{Q}{4\pi\varepsilon_0 R}. \tag{5.19}$$

This remains constant throughout the conducting sphere and is what we mean when we talk about the *potential of the sphere*. If an extra charge $q$ is brought in from infinity to the sphere, the work done by external forces is $q \times V$.

To complete the picture, we can also ask where the charge on the sphere is concentrated. The answer is that it is all on the surface of the sphere. This is easily established from Gauss's law. Figure 5.13 shows a closed Gaussian surface, just inside the sphere. We know that the electrostatic field is equal to zero inside any conductor, so the electric flux over this surface is zero. Gauss's law then tells us that there is no net charge within the closed surface. The excess charge migrates to the surface of the sphere, where it spreads uniformly, producing a spherically symmetric charge distribution.

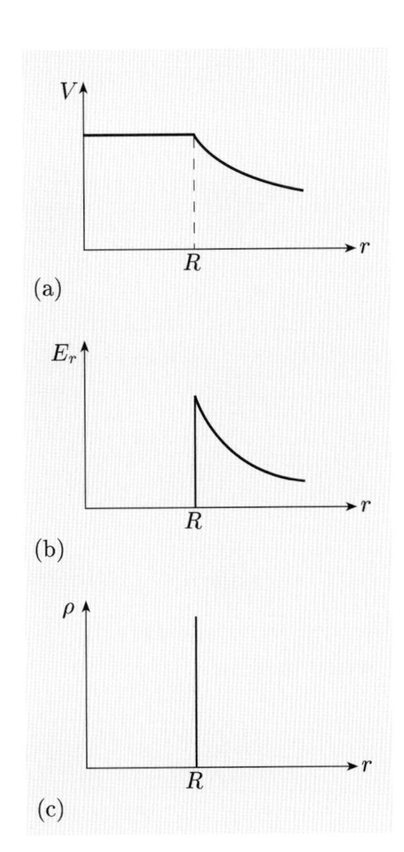


**Figure 5.14** (a) The potential, (b) the field and (c) the charge density of a charged metal sphere.

Figure 5.14 shows the electrostatic potential, electrostatic field and the charge density of a charged metal sphere. At the sphere's surface, the potential has a change in slope, the electrostatic field jumps sharply and the charge density has a spike. These relationships can be understood by remembering that the gradient of the potential is proportional to the electrostatic field and the divergence of the field is proportional to the charge density.

At the surface of the sphere, the electrostatic field is radial, and

$$E_r(R) = \frac{Q}{4\pi\varepsilon_0 R^2} = \frac{V}{R}.$$

So, if the potential $V$ is kept fixed, the electric field at the surface of the sphere is inversely proportional to the radius of the sphere. This implies that a moderate voltage, applied to a very small sphere, produces an enormous electric field. The same principle applies to all sharply-pointed metal objects. A voltage applied to a sharply-pointed metal tip can create an electric field that is large enough to suck electrons out of the metal. This effect is used to produce highly monoenergetic electron beams in some specialized electron microscopes.

**Exercise 5.8** Two widely-separated isolated spheres have radii $R_1$ and $R_2$, with $R_1 < R_2$. Initially, each sphere carries the same positive charge $Q$. The two spheres are then connected by a metal wire. Find the final charges on the spheres when equilibrium has been reached. Which sphere has the greater surface electric field? ■

### 5.4.1 Capacitance

According to Equation 5.19, the charge on a metal sphere is proportional to its potential. In general, we define the **capacitance** $C$ of an isolated conductor to be the charge $Q$ stored on the conductor, divided by the potential $V$ of the conductor, with the zero of potential at infinity. That is,

$$C = \frac{Q}{V}. \tag{5.20}$$

For example, Equation 5.19 shows that an isolated metal sphere of radius $R$ has capacitance

$$C = 4\pi\varepsilon_0 R. \tag{5.21}$$

The SI unit of capacitance is the **farad** (F), which is equal to one coulomb per volt, but a capacitance of one farad is *enormous* by everyday standards. It is the capacitance of an isolated conducting sphere of radius $9 \times 10^9$ m — more than ten times the radius of the Sun! Capacitances of nanofarad ($10^{-9}$ F) or picofarad ($10^{-12}$ F) are much more common.

$1\,\mathrm{F} = 1\,\mathrm{C\,V^{-1}}$

Conducting spheres are not generally used to store charge. A small charged sphere produces a strong electric field in its vicinity, which is undesirable for many purposes, so it is much more common to store charge in a capacitor. A **capacitor** is a pair of oppositely-charged plates separated by a small gap containing either a vacuum or an insulating medium. The plates may be parallel planes, concentric cylindrical shells or concentric spherical shells, for example. The **capacitance** of a capacitor is again defined by $C = Q/V$, but $Q$ is now the charge on the positive plate and $V$ is the potential of the positive plate relative to the negative plate (that is, the magnitude of the potential difference between the two plates).

To take a simple case, we consider a vacuum parallel plate capacitor (Figure 5.15). This consists of a pair of parallel conducting plates carrying charges $+Q$ and $-Q$. The plates each have area $A$ and they are separated by a narrow gap $d$, which is empty (that is, filled by a vacuum). If the plates are large enough, and the gap is small enough, we can ignore any edge effects. Then, according to Section 2.3.3, the field $\mathbf{E}$ in the gap is uniform, perpendicular to the plates, and has magnitude

$$E = \frac{Q}{\varepsilon_0 A}.$$

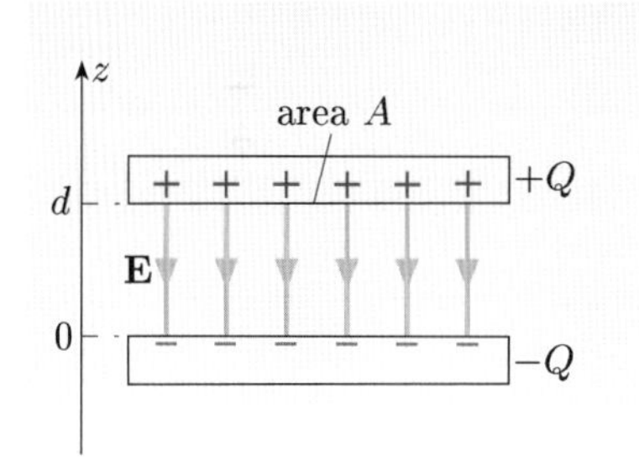


**Figure 5.15** A cross-section of a vacuum parallel plate capacitor.

The potential of the positive plate relative to the negative plate is found by using Equation 5.5, and integrating along a path parallel to the $z$-axis:

$$V = -\int_0^d (-E)\,\mathrm{d}z,$$

where the initial sign is part of the definition of potential and $-E$ appears in the integrand because the electric field points from the positive plate to the negative plate, in the negative $z$-direction. Completing the integral, we obtain

$$V = Ed = \frac{Qd}{\varepsilon_0 A}. \tag{5.22}$$

So a vacuum parallel plate capacitor has capacitance

$$C = \frac{\varepsilon_0 A}{d}. \tag{5.23}$$

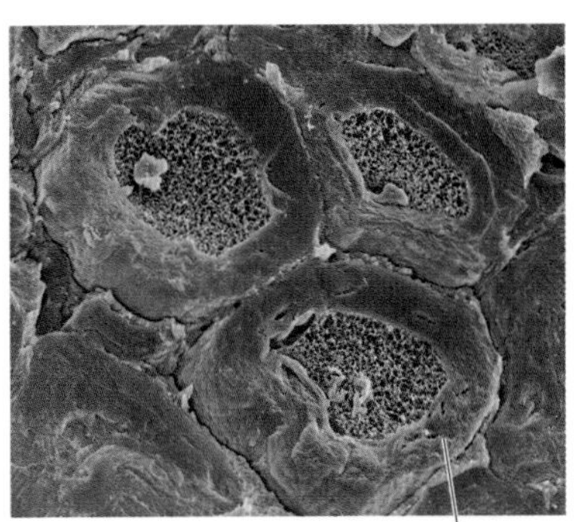


**Figure 5.16** High-speed nerve cells, surrounded by myelin sheaths.

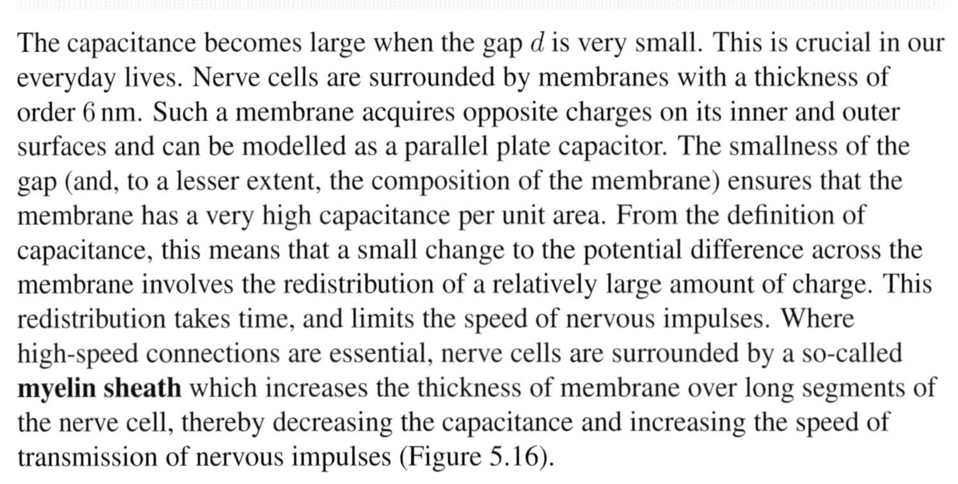

The capacitance becomes large when the gap $d$ is very small. This is crucial in our everyday lives. Nerve cells are surrounded by membranes with a thickness of order 6 nm. Such a membrane acquires opposite charges on its inner and outer surfaces and can be modelled as a parallel plate capacitor. The smallness of the gap (and, to a lesser extent, the composition of the membrane) ensures that the membrane has a very high capacitance per unit area. From the definition of capacitance, this means that a small change to the potential difference across the membrane involves the redistribution of a relatively large amount of charge. This redistribution takes time, and limits the speed of nervous impulses. Where high-speed connections are essential, nerve cells are surrounded by a so-called **myelin sheath** which increases the thickness of membrane over long segments of the nerve cell, thereby decreasing the capacitance and increasing the speed of transmission of nervous impulses (Figure 5.16).

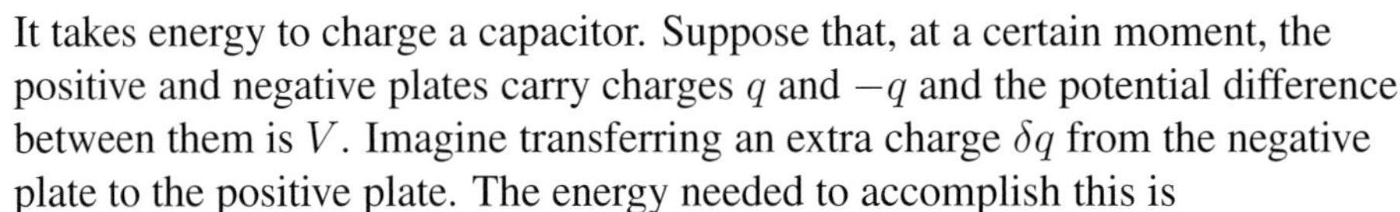

It takes energy to charge a capacitor. Suppose that, at a certain moment, the positive and negative plates carry charges $q$ and $-q$ and the potential difference between them is $V$. Imagine transferring an extra charge $\delta q$ from the negative plate to the positive plate. The energy needed to accomplish this is

$$\delta U = \delta q\, V,$$

so the total energy needed to store $Q$ on the positive plate (and $-Q$ on the negative plate) is

$$U = \int_0^Q V\,\mathrm{d}q = \int_0^Q \frac{q}{C}\,\mathrm{d}q.$$

Evaluating the integral, we obtain

$$U = \frac{1}{2}\frac{Q^2}{C} = \frac{1}{2}CV^2. \tag{5.24}$$

**Exercise 5.9** The vertical electric field between the ground and the base of a storm cloud has magnitude $5000\,\mathrm{V\,m^{-1}}$. The base of the storm cloud is horizontal at a height of $1.0\,\mathrm{km}$ and the area of the cloud base is $20.0\,\mathrm{km^2}$. Treating the storm cloud and ground as a giant parallel plate capacitor, estimate the electrical energy stored in the system.

**Exercise 5.10** The plates of a vacuum parallel plate capacitor initially have charges $Q$ and $-Q$ and potentials $V/2$ and $-V/2$. Discuss what happens to the potential difference between the plates and the electric field strength in the gap if the plates are brought closer together (a) with the plates connected to a battery and (b) with the plates disconnected from the battery. ■

### 5.4.2 Energy in fields

You have seen that energy is stored by a capacitor, but we have said nothing about the mechanism of energy storage. We will now make a bold assumption. Let us suppose that the energy stored by the capacitor is directly associated with the electric field in and around the capacitor. We will assume that it makes sense to assign an **energy density** $u$ at each point in space, and that this energy density is a function of the electric field strength. Then the energy stored by the capacitor can be represented as the energy density integrated over all space.

To identify the energy density, let's return to a vacuum parallel plate capacitor. For simplicity, we suppose that the plates are effectively infinite so that edge effects can be neglected. Combining Equations 5.22, 5.23 and 5.24, the stored energy can be then written as

$$U = \frac{1}{2}CV^2 = \frac{1}{2} \times \left(\frac{\varepsilon_0 A}{d}\right) \times (Ed)^2 = \frac{1}{2}\varepsilon_0 E^2 \times (Ad)$$

where $E$ is the magnitude of the electric field in the gap between the plates, and $Ad$ is the volume of the gap. There is no electric field outside the capacitor, so our idea of representing the stored energy as an integral of the energy density over all space can be fulfilled if we identify the energy density as

$$u = \frac{1}{2}\varepsilon_0 E^2, \tag{5.25}$$

where $E$ is the magnitude of the field. This equation was derived for a specific case, but is actually true for all electric fields in empty space.

To check that our formula for the energy density of an electric field makes sense, we now consider a situation in which the electric field varies in space. Consider a conducting sphere of radius $R$ carrying a charge $Q$. We know that there is no electric field inside the conducting sphere and that the electric field outside the sphere is just as if the total charge $Q$ were concentrated at the centre of the sphere. Integrating the energy density of the electric field over all space will give us an expression for the total energy $U$ of the electric field due to the sphere. We obtain

$$U = \int_R^\infty u \times 4\pi r^2 \, \mathrm{d}r = \int_R^\infty \frac{1}{2}\varepsilon_0 \left(\frac{Q}{4\pi\varepsilon_0 r^2}\right)^2 4\pi r^2 \, \mathrm{d}r$$

which reduces to

$$U = \frac{Q^2}{8\pi\varepsilon_0} \int_R^\infty \frac{1}{r^2} \, \mathrm{d}r = \frac{Q^2}{8\pi\varepsilon_0 R}.$$

We can compare this with the electrostatic potential energy of the sphere calculated in the usual way. This is found by adding up the work done when elements of charge are transferred from infinity to the sphere. This is equivalent to using Equation 5.24, with the capacitance of the sphere given by Equation 5.21. So we have

$$U = \frac{Q^2}{2C} = \frac{Q^2}{2 \times 4\pi\varepsilon_0 R} = \frac{Q^2}{8\pi\varepsilon_0 R},$$

as before.

It is always possible to think of the energy of a collection of charges as being stored in the electric field. The total electrostatic potential energy of the charges is equal to the energy density of the electric field integrated over all space. This is generally not the most efficient way of calculating an electrostatic potential energy, but it does shed important new light on the significance of electric fields.

When we first introduced electric fields in Chapter 1 they had an auxiliary role. It is certainly possible to use Coulomb's law and the principle of superposition without introducing the notion of an electric field. However, Gauss's law is expressed directly in terms of electric fields. The fact that Gauss's law applies more widely than Coulomb's law — to moving charges as well as to stationary charges — makes electric fields practically indispensable. Now we see that an electric field is no mere mathematical convenience. At each point in space, and at each instant in time, the electric field is directly associated with a real physical property, the energy density. We are therefore led to regard electric fields as being part of the fabric of the world, every bit as real as electrons, chairs or tables.

## Summary of Chapter 5

**Section 5.1** An electrostatic field has zero circulation around any closed loop and is therefore conservative. Conservative fields are always irrotational (i.e. have zero curl) so checking whether the curl of a vector field is equal to zero provides one way of determining whether the field could be an electrostatic field. The conservative nature of electrostatic fields (together with Gauss's law) ensures that there are no electrostatic fields inside an empty conducting cavity.

**Section 5.2** The electrostatic potential at a point $\mathbf{r}$ is defined by

$$V(\mathbf{r}) = -\int_{\mathbf{r}_0}^{\mathbf{r}} \mathbf{E} \cdot \mathrm{d}\mathbf{l} + V_0,$$

where $\mathbf{E}$ is the electrostatic field, $\mathbf{r}_0$ is an arbitrarily chosen reference point and $V_0$ is the value of the electrostatic potential at the reference point. $V(\mathbf{r})$ is the electrostatic potential energy per unit charge. The change in electrostatic potential energy when a test charge $q$ is displaced from $\mathbf{r}_1$ to $\mathbf{r}_2$ is $q(V(\mathbf{r}_2) - V(\mathbf{r}_1))$.

Any line integral of an electrostatic field can be represented as minus the difference in values of the potential between the end-point and start-point of the path. The electrostatic field corresponding to a given potential is minus the gradient of the potential.

**Section 5.3** Electrostatic potentials obey the principle of superposition. In a system of many charges, the total electrostatic potential is the algebraic sum of the electrostatic potentials due to the individual charges. This can be used to find the total electrostatic potential of a collection of charges; the total electrostatic field can then be found by taking minus the gradient of the potential. This method only works for finite distributions of charge.

An electric dipole is a pair of oppositely-charged particles. The dipole potential is an approximation to the electrostatic potential of this arrangement when the distance from the dipole is much greater than the separation of the charges. The dipole potential and the corresponding electrostatic field can be found using the principle of superposition.

**Section 5.4** In equilibrium, the electrostatic potential is uniform throughout any conductor. The capacitance of an isolated conductor is the ratio $Q/V$, where $Q$ is the charge on the conductor and $V$ is the potential of the conductor relative to a zero of potential at infinity. The capacitance of a capacitor is the ratio $Q/V$, where $Q$ is the charge on the positive plate of the capacitor and $V$ is the potential difference between the positive and negative plates.

The total electrostatic energy stored by a capacitor is

$$U = \frac{1}{2}CV^2.$$

This can be interpreted in terms of the energy stored in the electrostatic field. The energy density of an electric field is $\frac{1}{2}\varepsilon_0 E^2$, where $E$ is the electric field strength. Integrating the energy density over all space gives the total electrostatic energy.

## Achievements from Chapter 5

*After studying this chapter you should be able to:*

**5.1** Explain the meaning of the newly defined (emboldened) terms and symbols, and use them appropriately.

**5.2** Remember that any electrostatic field is conservative and deduce simple consequences of this fact.

**5.3** Define the electrostatic potential and recognize that it is a scalar field.

**5.4** Use gradients and line integrals to relate electrostatic fields to electrostatic potentials.

**5.5** Describe the relationship between electric field lines and equipotential surfaces.

**5.6** Solve simple problems involving electrostatic potential and electrostatic potential energy.

**5.7** Define electric dipole, dipole moment and dipole potential.

**5.8** Define capacitance and use it in simple problems.

**5.9** Recall that electric fields have a characteristic energy density.

*After studying MT 8.9 you should also be able to:*

**5.10** Recall the properties of a conservative vector field and determine whether a given vector field is conservative or not.

**5.11** Evaluate gradients of scalar fields.

# Chapter 6 Electromagnetic induction

## Introduction

**Figure 6.1** Two insulated circuits wound on an iron ring, used in Michael Faraday's investigations of electromagnetic induction.

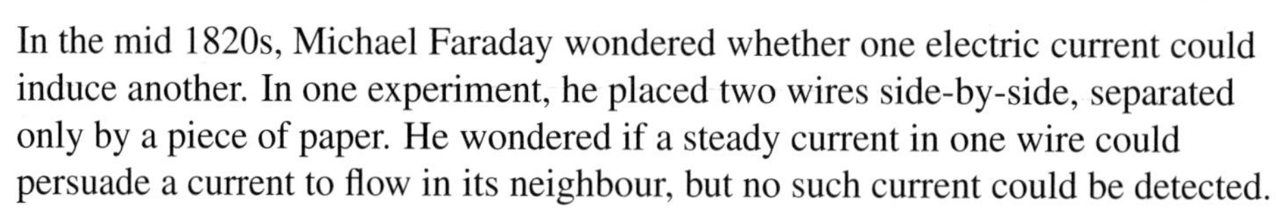

In the mid 1820s, Michael Faraday wondered whether one electric current could induce another. In one experiment, he placed two wires side-by-side, separated only by a piece of paper. He wondered if a steady current in one wire could persuade a current to flow in its neighbour, but no such current could be detected.

Several years passed before Faraday returned to this question. Then, in 1831, he wound two insulated circuits, 1 and 2, around an iron ring (Figure 6.1). Whilst switching on the current in circuit 1, he noticed a momentary blip of current in circuit 2. As soon as the current in circuit 1 had stabilized, the current in circuit 2 dropped to zero. But, whilst switching off the current in circuit 1, he noticed a second blip of current in circuit 2, this time in the opposite direction (Figure 6.2).

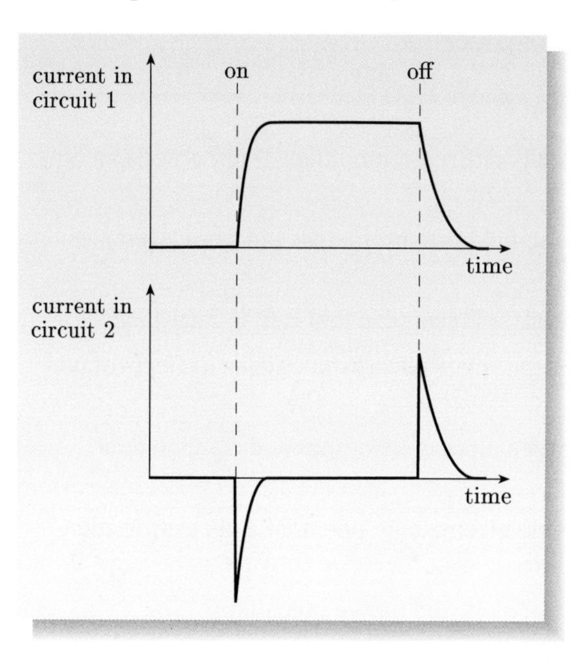


**Figure 6.2** When the current in circuit 1 is switched on and off, blips of current are observed in circuit 2.

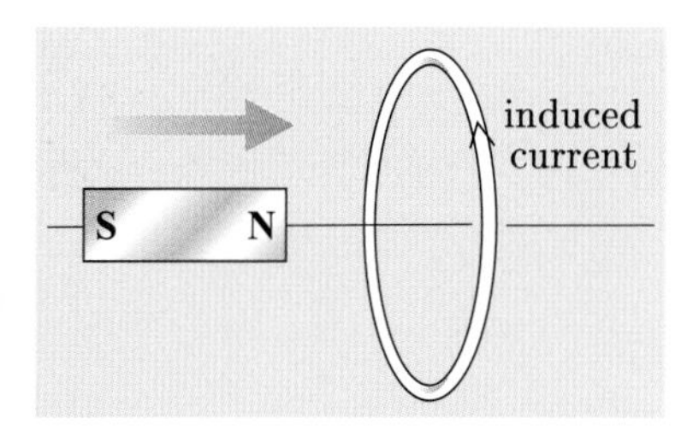


**Figure 6.3** Moving a bar magnet near a stationary wire loop drives a current around the loop.

Faraday assumed that these blips were associated with changes in the *magnetic field* in the vicinity of circuit 2. He checked this idea by moving a bar magnet near a stationary wire loop (Figure 6.3). When the bar magnet was introduced into the loop, and when it was retracted again, a current flowed around the loop. The current was small if the magnet moved slowly, but larger if the magnet moved more rapidly. So Faraday realized that a changing magnetic field can induce a electric current. This phenomenon is called **electromagnetic induction**. It is the main subject of this chapter.

Electromagnetic induction has become of immense technological importance. It underpins the operation of all the large generators that produce electricity in power stations. This is true whether the initial source of energy is in the chemical bonds of coal, gas or petrol, the binding energies of atomic nuclei, the gravitational potential energy of water in a reservoir, or the kinetic energy of winds and tides

(Figure 6.4). Electromagnetic induction is also used in the transformers that convert the voltages generated in power stations up to the very high values used in the national grid, and back down again to the voltages used in our homes. On a smaller scale, electromagnetic induction is used in microphones, radio aerials, induction hobs, metal detectors, electric guitars and brain research (Figure 6.5).

This chapter begins by introducing some concepts needed to describe the flow of a current in a circuit. It then describes Faraday's law of electromagnetic induction for a stationary circuit. Finally, it considers the phenomenon of electromagnetic induction in moving circuits. The comparison between stationary and moving circuits was of great historical importance, as it spurred Albert Einstein to create the special theory of relativity.

**Figure 6.4** Six generators in an Icelandic hydroelectric power station. Each generator produces 45 MW of electrical power.

(a)

(b)

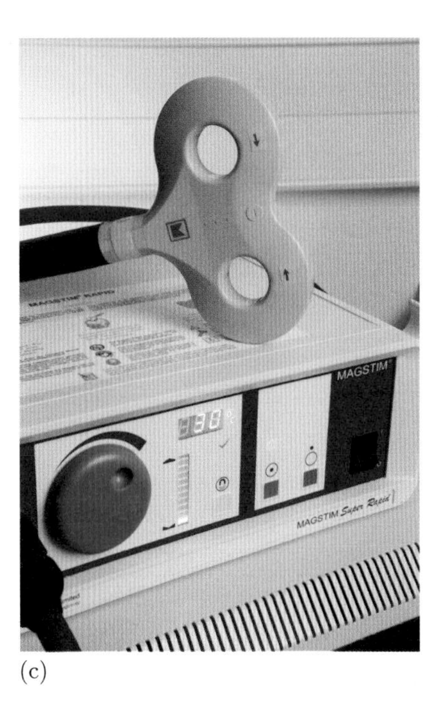


(c)

**Figure 6.5** (a) A metal detector used by a researcher looking for meteorites; (b) an electric guitar; (c) a transcranial magnetic stimulator used to induce currents in the brain.

# 6.1 Current flow in circuits

## 6.1.1 Non-conservative electric fields

Electromagnetic induction arises when a magnet moves near a stationary wire loop. It also arises when a circuit moves, or distorts, in a static magnetic field. For example, if a bar magnet is at rest, and a wire loop is moved towards the magnet, a current is induced in the loop. Changing the orientation or shape of the loop also induces a current. To structure our discussion, it is helpful to distinguish between stationary and moving circuits. To begin with, we restrict attention to circuits that remain at rest in the presence of changing magnetic fields. The extension to moving circuits will be made in the last section of the chapter.

On the face of it, Faraday's experiments show that a changing magnetic field generates an electric current in a stationary circuit. However, this fact must be understood within a wider framework. We know that an electric current consists of a stream of charged particles, so we need to understand what drives these charged particles around the circuit. Although initially observed as a transient phenomenon, the induced current lasts as long as the magnetic field is changing. We must ask what forces keep the current flowing, in spite of the dissipative effects of resistance.

There are four basic forces in physics — the strong and weak nuclear forces, the gravitational force and the electromagnetic force. It seems clear that only the electromagnetic force need be considered here. The electromagnetic force on a charge $q$ is given by the Lorentz force law:

$$\mathbf{F} = q(\mathbf{E} + \mathbf{v} \times \mathbf{B}).$$

This contains both electric and magnetic contributions, but we can show that the magnetic force cannot initiate a current in a stationary circuit. For, if there is no current to start with, the average value of $q\mathbf{v}$ is zero, so the average value of the magnetic force $q\mathbf{v} \times \mathbf{B}$ is also equal to zero. Moreover, a magnetic force cannot sustain a current in a stationary circuit: it pushes charges sideways, perpendicular to their direction of motion, but it does not push them forwards in the direction of current flow.

This can also be understood in terms of energy. When a current flows round an ordinary circuit, energy is dissipated, and an input of energy is required to maintain the current. Suppose that a small quantity of charge $q$ is transferred around a stationary circuit $C$. This transfer of charge need not involve a single particle making a lap of the circuit, but is generally accomplished by small displacements of charge all around the circuit, with the amount of charge passing any fixed point being equal to $q$. The work done by the Lorentz force during this transfer of charge is

$$W = \oint_C \mathbf{F} \cdot \mathrm{d}\mathbf{l} = q \oint_C \mathbf{E} \cdot \mathrm{d}\mathbf{l} + q \oint_C (\mathbf{v} \times \mathbf{B}) \cdot \mathrm{d}\mathbf{l}.$$

The last integral above is equal to zero because, along each small segment of $C$, the line element $\delta\mathbf{l}$ is parallel to the drift velocity $\mathbf{v}$ of the charge carriers, and is therefore perpendicular to the vector product $\mathbf{v} \times \mathbf{B}$. So we conclude that

$$W = q \oint_C \mathbf{E} \cdot \mathrm{d}\mathbf{l}.$$

This shows that the work needed to maintain the current is supplied by an *electric* field. To compensate for dissipative effects, this work must be positive. So the electric field has a non-zero circulation around the circuit — it is *non-conservative*. More generally, we are led to the following idea:

> Any magnetic field that changes in time must be accompanied by a non-conservative electric field.

The present chapter therefore requires us to consider non-conservative electric fields. It complements Chapter 5, which dealt with the conservative electric fields of electrostatics. It is important to realize that the special properties of conservative fields all stand or fall together. A *conservative* electric field $\mathbf{E}(\mathbf{r})$ has zero circulation around any closed loop, and its line integrals are independent of path. This allows us to define an electrostatic potential field $V(\mathbf{r})$.

By contrast, non-conservative fields do not have *any* of these properties. In general, they have non-zero circulations and path-dependent line integrals. This makes it impossible to define a potential for a non-conservative field. Our first task is therefore to develop terminology that is appropriate for non-conservative electric fields.

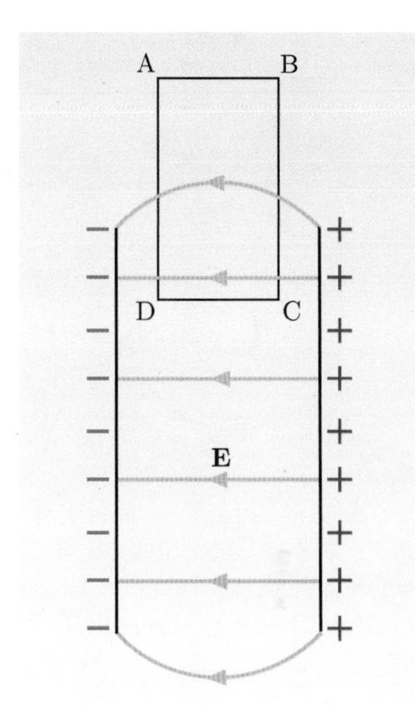


**Figure 6.6** For Exercise 6.1.

**Exercise 6.1** A conducting rectangular circuit ABCD is partially inserted between the plates of a parallel plate capacitor, as shown in Figure 6.6. Does the electrostatic field between the capacitor plates drive a steady current around the circuit? ■

## 6.1.2 Voltage drop and emf

Let's begin with something familiar. For a *conservative* electric field, $\mathbf{E}$, the **potential difference** between $\mathbf{r}_1$ and $\mathbf{r}_2$ is

$$V(\mathbf{r}_2) - V(\mathbf{r}_1) = -\int_{\mathbf{r}_1}^{\mathbf{r}_2} \mathbf{E} \cdot \mathrm{d}\mathbf{l}.$$

For our purposes, it is useful to express this in a different form. Changing signs on both sides of the equation, we obtain

$$V(\mathbf{r}_1) - V(\mathbf{r}_2) = \int_{\mathbf{r}_1}^{\mathbf{r}_2} \mathbf{E} \cdot \mathrm{d}\mathbf{l}.$$

The left-hand side of this equation is positive when the potential at $\mathbf{r}_1$ is greater than the potential at $\mathbf{r}_2$. For this reason, we shall call it the **potential drop** from $\mathbf{r}_1$ to $\mathbf{r}_2$. For a path that goes once around a closed loop, the start-point is identical to the end-point, so the potential drop around any closed loop is equal to zero.

Such terminology is unsuitable for electromagnetic induction. Non-conservative electric fields do not have potentials, so it is misleading (and wrong) to talk about potential differences in this context. However, we can make a more general definition:

The **voltage drop** along a fixed path $C$ is defined to be

$$V_{\text{drop}} = \int_C \mathbf{E} \cdot \text{d}\mathbf{l}, \tag{6.1}$$

where $\mathbf{E}$ is the electric field at an element $\delta\mathbf{l}$ along the path. Naturally enough, the SI unit of voltage drop is the volt.

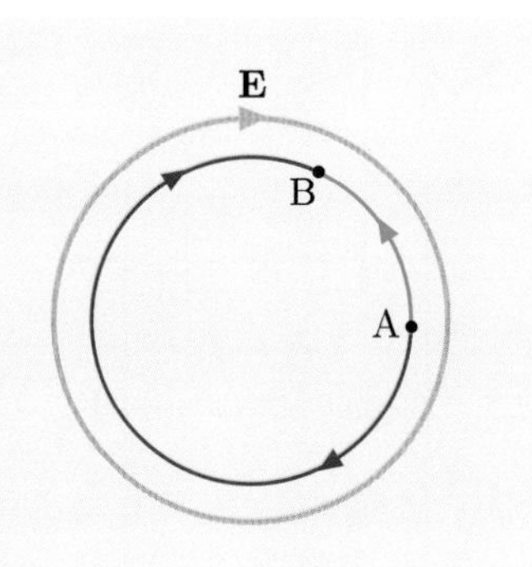


**Figure 6.7** The voltage drop from A to B depends on whether the red path or the blue path is followed.

The important feature of a voltage drop is that it refers to a specific path, $C$. The voltage drop may be different along different paths joining the same start- and end-points. For example, Figure 6.7 shows a non-conservative electric field which has constant magnitude around a circle. Clearly, the voltage drop from A to B along the blue curve is small and negative, while the voltage drop from A to B along the red curve is large and positive. It would therefore be meaningless to talk about the *voltage drop* from A to B without specifying the path followed. This is in sharp contrast to a *potential drop*, which depends only on the start- and end-points of the path. It is also worth noting that the path $C$ is fixed in space. This restriction is appropriate for the moment because we are considering currents in stationary circuits. At the end of the chapter, we shall consider circuits that are in motion, and revisit the concept of voltage drop under these more general conditions.

The second concept we need is that of an emf (pronounced ee-em-eff). We know that a continuous input of energy is needed to maintain a steady current in an ordinary circuit. This energy can be supplied by a variety of means, including dynamos, batteries, fuel cells, solar cells, thermocouples and piezoelectric devices. Suppose that the agencies responsible for maintaining the current in a given circuit convert energy $\delta W$ into electrical form in a time $\delta t$. This does not include any energy that is dissipated, but is the energy required to overcome the effects of dissipation throughout the circuit. During the time $\delta t$, a steady current $I$ flows in the circuit and the amount of charge transferred around the circuit is $\delta q = I\,\delta t$. The **emf** in the circuit is then defined to be

$$V_{\text{emf}} = \frac{\delta W}{\delta q}. \tag{6.2}$$

This is the *energy input per unit charge transferred around the circuit.* Since power is the rate of expenditure of energy, we also have

$$V_{\text{emf}} = \frac{1}{I}\frac{\delta W}{\delta t} = \frac{P}{I}, \tag{6.3}$$

where $P$ is the power that is converted into electrical form. We therefore see that the emf in a circuit is the *power supplied per unit current.* In steady-state conditions it is also equal to the *power dissipated per unit current.* Like current, emf has a sign. The emf is positive if it drives currents in the sense chosen for positive progression around a circuit, and it is negative if it drives currents in the opposite sense. The total emf in a circuit is the algebraic sum of all the emfs driving current around the circuit.

The term emf is an abbreviation for **electromotive force**. This is an unfortunate name because an emf is clearly not a force at all, in the scientific sense of the term. The unit of emf is the volt ($1\,\text{V} = 1\,\text{J}\,\text{C}^{-1}$), whereas the unit of force is the newton ($1\,\text{N} = 1\,\text{J}\,\text{m}^{-1}$). Also, an emf is defined around a closed loop, whereas a force is defined for a given particle at a given position and time. Some texts avoid this infelicity by using the term **electromotance** instead of emf. We will continue to talk about emf, but avoid the misleading phrase electromotive force.

### Induced emf

This chapter focuses on situations where an emf is produced by electromagnetic induction. Figure 6.8 shows a typical example — a magnet moves along the axis of a stationary wire ring, and the changing magnetic field induces a current to flow around the ring. You have already seen that the induced current is driven by a non-conservative electric field $\mathbf{E}$. The axial symmetry of the situation suggests that the electric field lines form circular loops, as shown in the diagram. This is unlike any electric field pattern you have seen previously in this book. The field lines do not start or end on charges, but form closed loops. There is no conflict with Gauss's law because the divergence of this electric field turns out to be equal to zero.

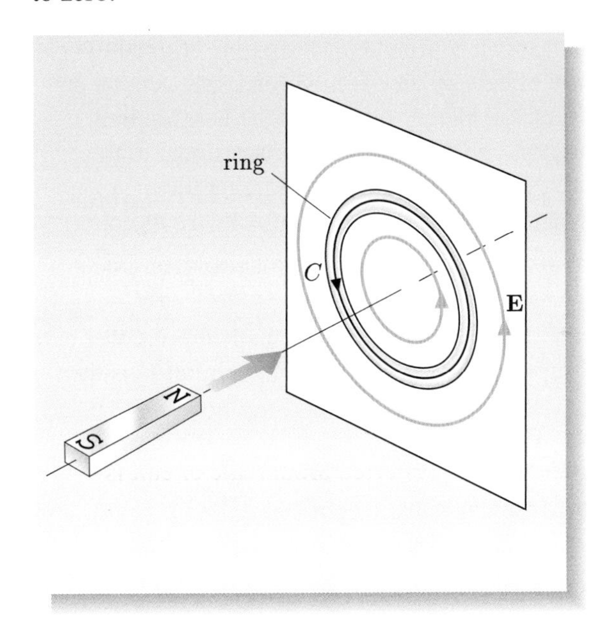


**Figure 6.8** The electric field produced by a changing magnetic field drives a current around a stationary wire ring.

Now, a charge $q$ experiences an electric force $q\mathbf{E}$, so the work done in transferring the charge around the closed path $C$ in the ring is

$$W = \oint_C q\mathbf{E} \cdot \mathrm{d}\mathbf{l}.$$

The emf around $C$ is the work done per unit charge:

$$V_{\text{emf}} = \oint_C \mathbf{E} \cdot \mathrm{d}\mathbf{l},$$

which is just the circulation of the electric field around $C$. Since this emf is associated with electromagnetic induction, it is called the **induced emf**. Comparing with Equation 6.1, we see that the induced emf is equal to the voltage drop around the complete closed path, $C$. This is equal to zero in static situations, which involve only conservative electric fields, but it is non-zero in the time-dependent situation of Figure 6.8.

### The emf of a battery

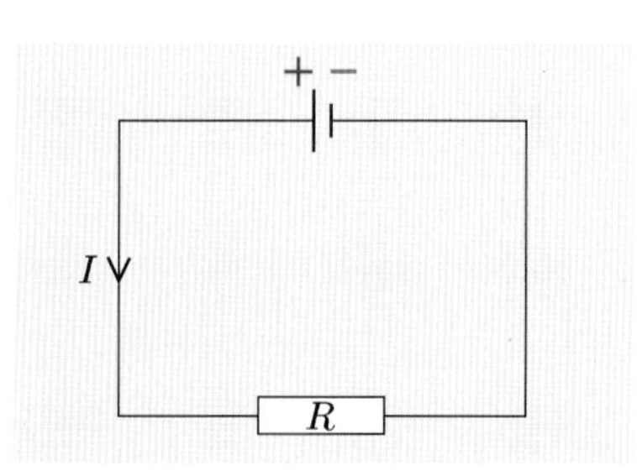


**Figure 6.9** A battery drives a current through a passive circuit.

A battery is a familiar source of emf. Although this book is not concerned with the physics of batteries, we give a very brief discussion here for the sake of comparison with electromagnetic induction.

Figure 6.9 shows a battery which drives a steady current through a resistor. In the circuit outside the battery, the charged plates drive a current from the positive terminal to the negative terminal, just as you would expect. But something more mysterious happens inside the battery, where the current flows from the negative plate to the positive plate. This internal current flow cannot be explained by an electrostatic field.

The inner workings of a battery are complicated. The crucial region is the interface between the battery plates and the surrounding conducting liquid, where atoms, electrons and ions combine and dissociate in various ways. These dynamical processes have chemical descriptions, but they are ultimately quantum mechanical in nature. This leads to a mismatch in language. Quantum mechanical descriptions generally involve energy levels and the way they are occupied, while classical electromagnetism deals with forces and fields. This gap is bridged by representing the quantum mechanical effects by an *effective* force that acts on charge carriers at the interface between the battery plates and the surrounding liquid. This force is short-range and non-conservative. It is proportional to the charge of the charge carriers and drives them forwards, overcoming the electrostatic force inside the battery and maintaining the anticlockwise direction of current flow in Figure 6.9.

Suppose that a charge $q$ experiences an electrostatic force $\mathbf{F}_{\text{estat}}$ due to the charged battery plates and an effective force $\mathbf{F}_{\text{eff}}$ due to quantum mechanical processes at the surfaces of the plates. The emf supplied by the battery in the circuit $C$ is then

$$V_{\text{emf}} = \frac{1}{q}\oint_C \mathbf{F}_{\text{estat}} \cdot \mathrm{d}\mathbf{l} + \frac{1}{q}\oint_C \mathbf{F}_{\text{eff}} \cdot \mathrm{d}\mathbf{l}.$$

The first integral on the right-hand side involves the electrostatic field $\mathbf{F}_{\text{estat}}/q$. Any electrostatic field has zero circulation around a closed loop, so this integral is equal to zero, and the emf reduces to

$$V_{\text{emf}} = \frac{1}{q}\oint_C \mathbf{F}_{\text{eff}} \cdot \mathrm{d}\mathbf{l}.$$

The emf in the circuit is due to quantum mechanical processes occurring on the battery plates. But, no matter what may be happening inside the battery, we can define an electrostatic potential *outside* the battery and discuss the potential differences across resistors, capacitors and other passive circuit components. This is legitimate because the electric field is conservative in the region *outside* the battery. From the perspective of the external circuit, the battery behaves like a black box which delivers a certain potential difference across its terminals. This is very different from the induced emf considered earlier. In Figure 6.8 a non-conservative electric field exists all around the circuit, making it impossible to define a potential difference. In the context of electromagnetic induction, we must always use the more general concept of a voltage drop along a given path.

### 6.1.3 Ohm's law

When a conducting loop is connected to a source of emf, an electric field exists inside its conducting wires. Mobile electrons in the wires are initially accelerated by the field, but their progress is impeded by collisions with impurities and with vibrating positive ions. Extremely rapidly, the current settles down, with the same value all around the circuit. You might wonder why this should happen — especially in the case of a battery, where the non-conservative forces driving the current are confined to the battery.

In fact, the current is non-uniform when it is first switched on, but a non-uniform current creates accumulations of charge around the circuit, which produce electrostatic fields. This is a self-regulating situation. The system soon settles down to a steady state, with a uniform flow of current and a static but non-uniform distribution of charge. This steady state is achieved so rapidly that we can usually ignore the initial transient stage. Even AC currents are normally taken to be uniform, though time-dependent, all around a conducting circuit.

In order to predict the electric current flowing in a circuit, we shall use **Ohm's law**. This law states that the voltage drop $V_{\text{drop}}$ across a conductor is proportional to the current $I$ flowing through the conductor, both quantities taken in the same direction. In terms of symbols,

$$V_{\text{drop}} = IR, \qquad (6.4)$$

where the proportionality factor $R$ is the **resistance** of the conductor. The SI unit of resistance is the **ohm** ($\Omega$). A conductor has a resistance of $1\,\Omega$ if it carries a current of $1\,\text{A}$ when the voltage drop across its ends is $1\,\text{V}$.

$1\,\Omega = 1\,\text{V}\,\text{A}^{-1}$

Ohm's law is well known, and is probably familiar to you from earlier studies. Nevertheless, it is worth noting that Ohm's law is not a fundamental law of electromagnetism, in the same league as Gauss's law. For one thing, it is not always true. Transistors, for example, show a highly non-linear relationship between voltage drop and current, and this non-linearity is an essential part of their function. However, it is an experimental fact that Ohm's law accurately describes the behaviour of most conductors, provided that they are maintained at fixed temperature, and it is normal practice to assume that Ohm's law is valid unless there is a definite reason for doing otherwise.

Unfortunately, the voltage drops across individual parts of a circuit may be unknown at the outset because they depend on the electrostatic fields that develop during the establishment of a uniform current. This difficulty can be overcome by using Ohm's law around a complete circuit. In this case, Ohm's law takes the form

$$V_{\text{emf}} = IR_{\text{circuit}}, \qquad (6.5)$$

where $V_{\text{emf}}$ is the emf around the circuit and $R_{\text{circuit}}$ is a proportionality constant that represents the total resistance of the circuit. If $V_{\text{emf}}$ and $R_{\text{circuit}}$ are known, we can use Equation 6.5 to find the current in the circuit, and then use Equation 6.4 to find the voltage drops across individual parts of the circuit.

Ohm's law can be used to assess the dangers of electric shock. Suppose that a current passes across the chest from one hand to another. Above 1 mA, an unpleasant tingling sensation is experienced. At 10–20 mA, fingers involuntarily clamp around a conductor, making it impossible to let go. A current of

These values are appropriate for mains frequency AC.

100–200 mA is sufficient to cause the heart to switch from its steady rhythm to useless random twitching. Normal heartbeat does not return spontaneously, but can be reactivated with suitable medical equipment. The resistance of the body depends on many factors, but is usually dominated by the resistance of the skin. Typical values range from $(3\,\Omega\,\mathrm{m}^2)/(\text{area of contact})$ for dry unbroken skin to $(0.05\,\Omega\,\mathrm{m}^2)/(\text{area of contact})$ for moist thin skin.

**Exercise 6.2** An unwary handyman grasps a live mains cable at $240\,\mathrm{V}$ and receives an electric shock. Assuming a contact area $0.50\,\mathrm{cm}^2$, will he survive?

**Exercise 6.3** A battery of internal resistance $r$ drives a current $I$ around a resistive circuit. Is the potential difference across the terminals of the battery equal to its emf?

**Exercise 6.4** A car battery with an emf of $12\,\mathrm{V}$ and an internal resistance of $r = 0.06\,\Omega$ is connected to a resistive circuit of resistance $R = 0.1\,\Omega$. How much power is expended by the battery? ■

## 6.2 Induction in a stationary circuit

### 6.2.1 Faraday's law

Electromagnetic induction is found in circuits that are stationary and in circuits that are in motion. Because the physics is rather different in these two cases, this section will continue to explore electromagnetic induction in *stationary* circuits in the presence of magnetic fields that vary in time.

Michael Faraday investigated the factors that influence the induced current, and reached some understanding of the basic physics involved. But Faraday described his findings pictorially, in terms of magnetic field lines, rather than equations. Maxwell set himself the task of translating Faraday's ideas into standard mathematical form. Eventually, in 1855, he succeeded. The basic law of electromagnetic induction is known today as Faraday's law. In modern notation, expressed in terms of electric and magnetic fields, this law can be stated as follows:

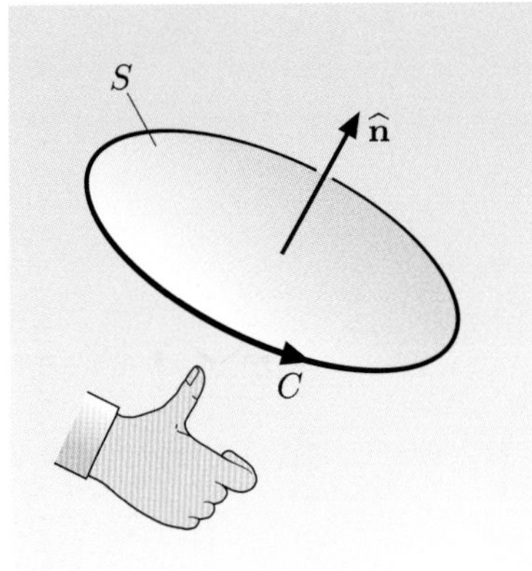


**Figure 6.10** The right-hand grip rule. With the fingers of the right hand curled in the sense of positive progression around $C$, the outstretched thumb points in the direction of the unit normal $\hat{\mathbf{n}}$ to the surface $S$.

**Faraday's law**

Suppose that $C$ is a closed loop that is fixed in space, and that $S$ is any open surface with $C$ as its perimeter. The sense of positive progression around $C$ and the unit normals to $S$ are linked by the usual right-hand grip rule (illustrated in Figure 6.10). Then **Faraday's law** states that

$$\oint_C \mathbf{E} \cdot \mathrm{d}\mathbf{l} = -\frac{\mathrm{d}}{\mathrm{d}t} \int_S \mathbf{B} \cdot \mathrm{d}\mathbf{S}. \qquad (6.6)$$

In other words, the induced emf around a closed loop $C$ is equal to the rate of decrease of magnetic flux over an open surface that has $C$ as its perimeter.

It is essential for $S$ to be an *open* surface. Closed surfaces do not have perimeters, and the magnetic flux over any closed surface is equal to zero (by the no-monopole law). Notice, however, that *any* open surface with perimeter $C$ can be used to calculate the rate of decrease of the magnetic flux. To see why this introduces no ambiguity, consider the two surfaces $S_1$ and $S_2$ shown in Figure 6.11. Both these surfaces are bounded by $C$ and oriented according to the right-hand grip rule. The purple volume between $S_1$ and $S_2$ is bounded by a closed surface $S$ whose unit normals all point outwards, into the exterior space. So, while one part of $S$ coincides with $S_1$, the remainder of $S$ coincides with the *reverse* of $S_2$ (that is, the surface obtained by reversing all the unit normals in $S_2$). Reversing the unit normals reverses the sign of the surface integral, so the magnetic flux over $S$ is

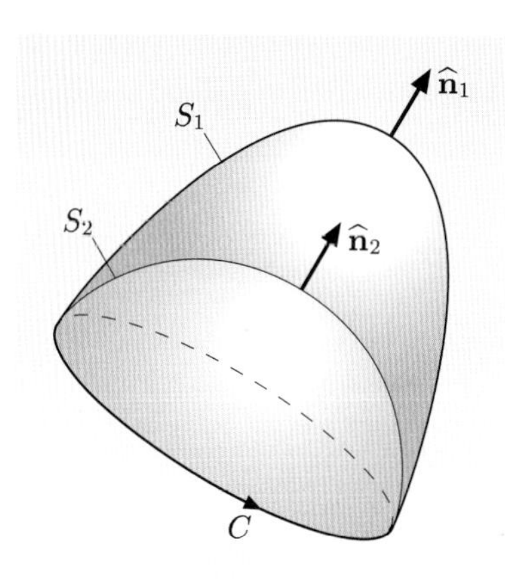


Figure 6.11 Two open surfaces $S_1$ and $S_2$ bounded by the same closed loop $C$ and oriented according to the right-hand grip rule.

$$\int_S \mathbf{B} \cdot \mathrm{d}\mathbf{S} = \int_{S_1} \mathbf{B} \cdot \mathrm{d}\mathbf{S} - \int_{S_2} \mathbf{B} \cdot \mathrm{d}\mathbf{S}.$$

The no-monopole law requires the left-hand side of this equation to be equal to zero, so the magnetic fluxes over $S_1$ and $S_2$ are identical. This shows that it does not matter which open surface with perimeter $C$ is chosen. If the closed path $C$ is a circle, it is natural to choose the disc bounded by this circle — any other choice would be perverse. But if $C$ has a more complicated non-planar shape, it is reassuring to know that the precise choice of $S$ is not critical, provided only that it is bounded by $C$ and oriented according to the right-hand grip rule.

**Exercise 6.5** A circular loop of radius 10 cm and resistance $4.0 \times 10^{-2}\,\Omega$ is placed in an increasing uniform magnetic field $\mathbf{B} = Kt^2\mathbf{e}_z$, where $K = 2.4\,\mathrm{T\,s^{-2}}$. The coil has its unit normal inclined at 30° to the $z$-axis. What is the magnitude of the current induced in this loop at time $t = 0.5\,\mathrm{s}$? ■

In many applications, the closed path $C$ contains a coil. The open surface $S$ then includes a region which looks something like a screw (Figure 6.12). This surface is a continuous sheet but has many folds, one for each turn of the coil. We are often interested in a situation where the turns are wound tightly together, and each fold of the surface can be approximated by a disc perpendicular to the axis of the coil. The rest of the open surface can usually be ignored. Then, if a uniform magnetic field is directed along the axis of the coil, the magnitude of the magnetic flux over the surface $S$ is $NBA$, where $N$ is the number of turns of the coil, $A$ is the cross-sectional area of each turn, and $B$ is the magnitude of the magnetic field. Notice that the rate of change of magnetic flux, and hence the induced emf, is enhanced by a factor of $N$ compared to a single loop. That is why coils, rather than single loops, are found in microphones, radio aerials and electric guitars.

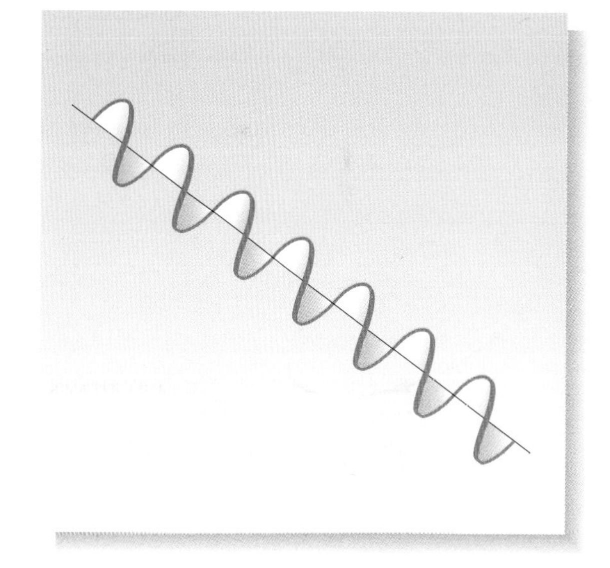

Figure 6.12 Part of an open surface bounded by a coil (shown in red).

Faraday's law is very general. It does not matter what causes the change in magnetic flux — it could be the motion of a magnet or a fluctuating current in a neighbouring circuit. And Faraday's law applies whether a conducting path is present or not. If the magnetic flux varies over an open surface $S$, the electric field has a circulation around the perimeter of $S$. If a conducting wire loop is placed around this perimeter, a current will flow through it. The current is a consequence of the non-conservative electric field, but this field exists whether the wire loop is present or not. It exists even in empty space.

**Essential skill**

Using Faraday's law to find an induced electric field.

### Worked Example 6.1

An infinitely long cylindrical solenoid of radius $R$ is aligned with the $z$-axis. The magnetic field inside the solenoid is uniform and varies as $\mathbf{B} = Kt\mathbf{e}_z$, where $K$ is a constant. There is no magnetic field outside the infinite solenoid. Find the induced electric field inside and outside the solenoid.

### Solution

The situation has axial symmetry around the axis of the solenoid and translational symmetry along this axis. It is therefore sensible to use cylindrical coordinates with the $z$-axis along the axis of the solenoid, and to assume that the electric field takes the form

$$\mathbf{E} = E_\phi(r)\,\mathbf{e}_\phi.$$

(The question does not require any justification of this assumption, but, for completeness, we note that: (1) any dependence on $\phi$ or $z$ is ruled out by axial and translational symmetry; (2) any $z$-component of the electric field is ruled out by reflection symmetry in a plane perpendicular to the axis of the solenoid; and (3) any radial component of the electric field is ruled out by Gauss's law, given the absence of a charge density.)

Inside the solenoid, we choose a circular path $C$ of radius $r < R$ as shown in Figure 6.13a. The corresponding open surface is a disc $S$, bounded by $C$, with its unit normal pointing in the positive $z$-direction. Faraday's law then gives

$$\begin{aligned}\oint_C \mathbf{E}\cdot\mathrm{d}\mathbf{l} &= E_\phi \times 2\pi r \\ &= -\frac{\mathrm{d}}{\mathrm{d}t}\int_S \mathbf{B}\cdot\mathrm{d}\mathbf{S} = -\frac{\mathrm{d}}{\mathrm{d}t}\left(Kt \times \pi r^2\right) = -K\pi r^2.\end{aligned}$$

So

$$E_\phi(r) = -\tfrac{1}{2}Kr \quad \text{and} \quad \mathbf{E} = -\tfrac{1}{2}Kr\,\mathbf{e}_\phi \quad \text{for } r < R.$$

Outside the solenoid, we choose a similar circular path $C$ and disc $S$, but with $r > R$ (Figure 6.13b). The field is restricted to the region inside the solenoid, so applying Faraday's law in this case gives

$$E_\phi \times 2\pi r = -\frac{\mathrm{d}}{\mathrm{d}t}\left(Kt \times \pi R^2\right) = -K\pi R^2.$$

Hence

$$E_\phi(r) = -\frac{KR^2}{2r} \quad \text{and} \quad \mathbf{E} = -\frac{KR^2}{2r}\,\mathbf{e}_\phi \quad \text{for } r > R.$$

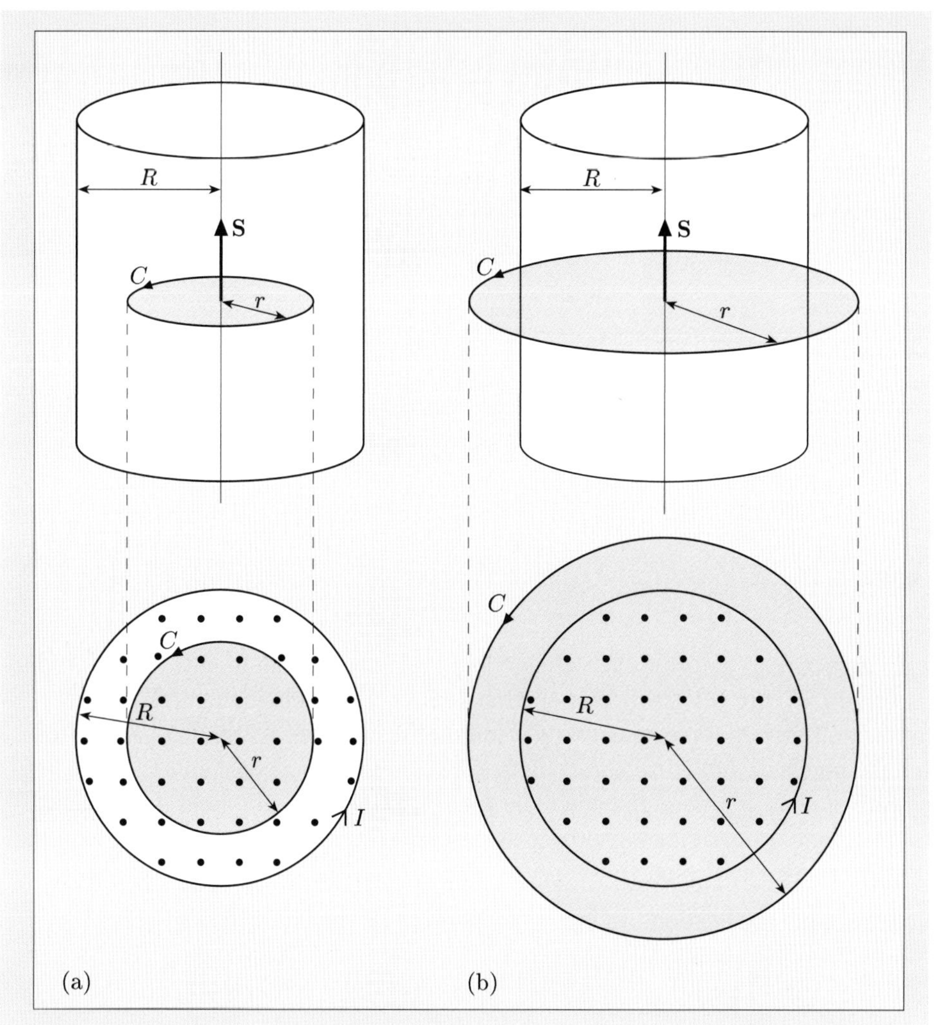


**Figure 6.13** The choice of closed loop $C$ and open surface $S$ used to apply Faraday's law (a) inside and (b) outside a solenoid. The upper half of the diagram shows perspective views, while the lower half shows plan views. The coils of the solenoid are omitted, for clarity.

In the above example, a non-conservative electric field exists in empty space, both inside and outside the infinite solenoid. It is interesting to note that an electric field is found outside the solenoid *even though there is no magnetic field there*. This follows directly from Faraday's law, because the magnetic flux over the disc $S$ in Figure 6.13b includes a time-dependent contribution from the region *inside* the solenoid. The presence of a non-conservative electric field outside the solenoid is readily confirmed by encircling a long solenoid by a conducting loop, as shown in Figure 6.14a. The electric field drives a current around the loop, and the current is observed to persist so long as the magnetic field inside the solenoid is changing. By contrast, a loop like that shown in Figure 6.14b carries practically no current. This is because the magnetic flux over the surface bounded by this loop is equal to zero outside an isolated infinite solenoid, and is practically constant outside a long solenoid in the static magnetic field of the Earth.

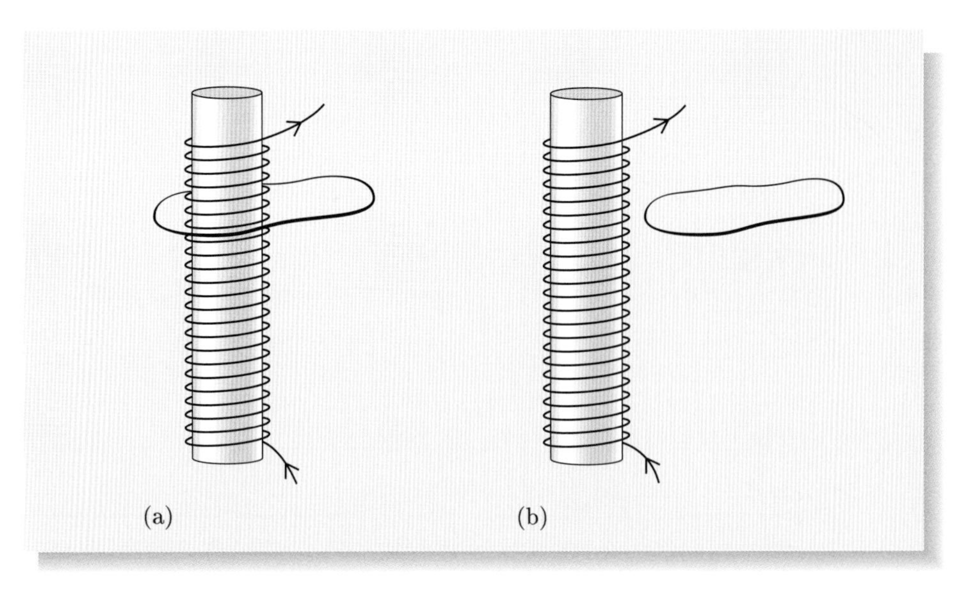


**Figure 6.14** Conducting loops placed (a) around and (b) outside a long solenoid carrying a varying current.

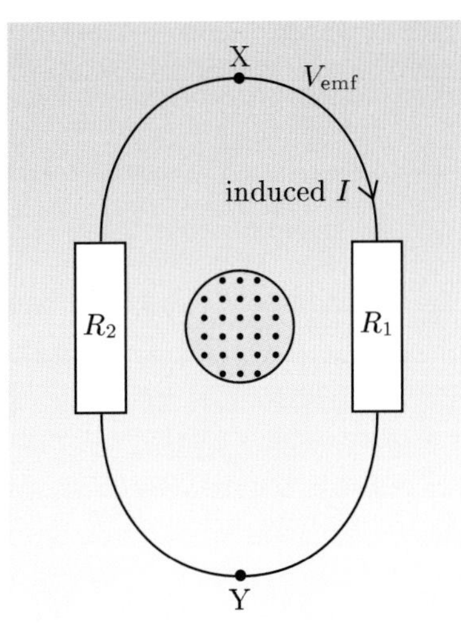


**Figure 6.15** Cross-sectional view of an infinite solenoid surrounded by a conducting loop.

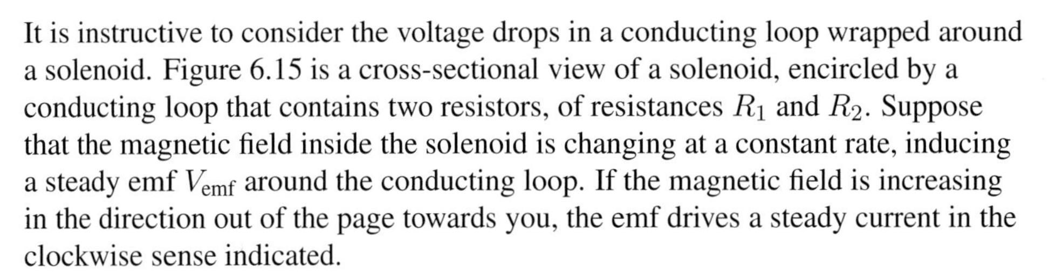

It is instructive to consider the voltage drops in a conducting loop wrapped around a solenoid. Figure 6.15 is a cross-sectional view of a solenoid, encircled by a conducting loop that contains two resistors, of resistances $R_1$ and $R_2$. Suppose that the magnetic field inside the solenoid is changing at a constant rate, inducing a steady emf $V_{emf}$ around the conducting loop. If the magnetic field is increasing in the direction out of the page towards you, the emf drives a steady current in the clockwise sense indicated.

Now a simple application of Ohm's law shows that the induced current is

$$I = \frac{V_{emf}}{R_1 + R_2}.$$

Further applications of Ohm's law then show that the voltage drop across resistor 1 is

$$V_1 = \frac{R_1}{R_1 + R_2} V_{emf} \quad \text{in the direction from X to Y,}$$

and the voltage drop across resistor 2 is

$$V_2 = \frac{R_2}{R_1 + R_2} V_{emf} \quad \text{in the direction from Y to X.}$$

Voltages are generally measured with a voltmeter — a device of high resistance which draws negligible current and gives a reading equal to the voltage drop across its terminals. It is therefore interesting to ask what a voltmeter reads when placed in the positions shown in Figures 6.16a and b.

- In Figure 6.16a, the red loop XYPQ has no magnetic flux through it. Faraday's law requires there to be no emf around this loop, so the voltmeter records a voltage drop of $V_1$, from Q to P.
- In Figure 6.16b, the red loop XYMN has no magnetic flux through it, and no emf around it. In this case, the voltmeter records a voltage drop of $V_2$, from M to N.

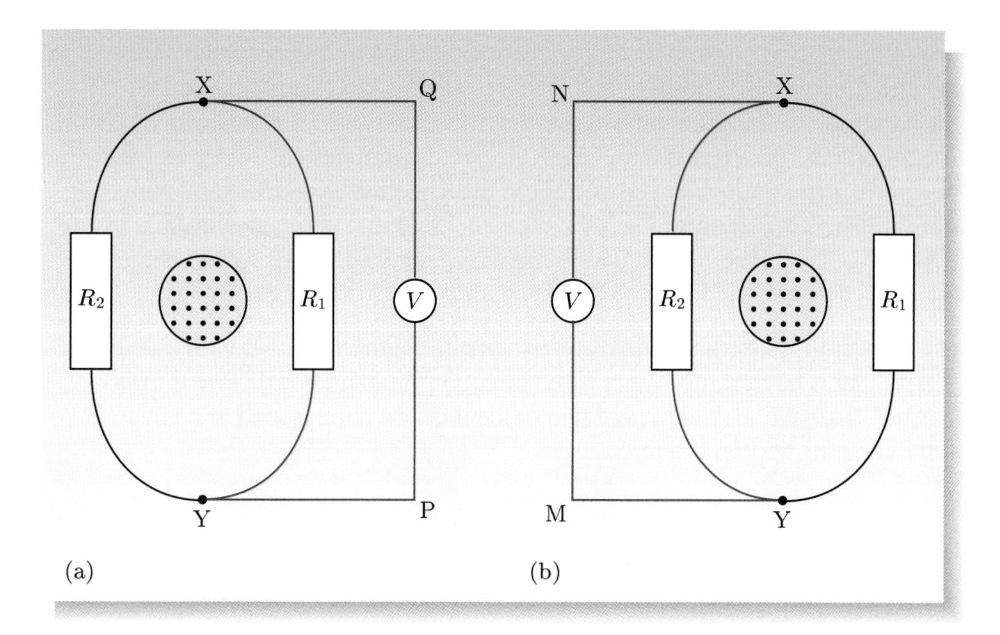


**Figure 6.16** Two positions for a voltmeter used to measure voltage drops around a solenoid.

It may seem strange that the reading on the voltmeter should depend on its location, but this is a consequence of the non-conservative nature of the electric field and the path-dependence of its line integrals. You will not be able to describe such phenomena if you cling to the notion of a potential difference between X and Y. The more general concept of a voltage drop *along a specified path* is essential.

### 6.2.2 The sign in Faraday's law

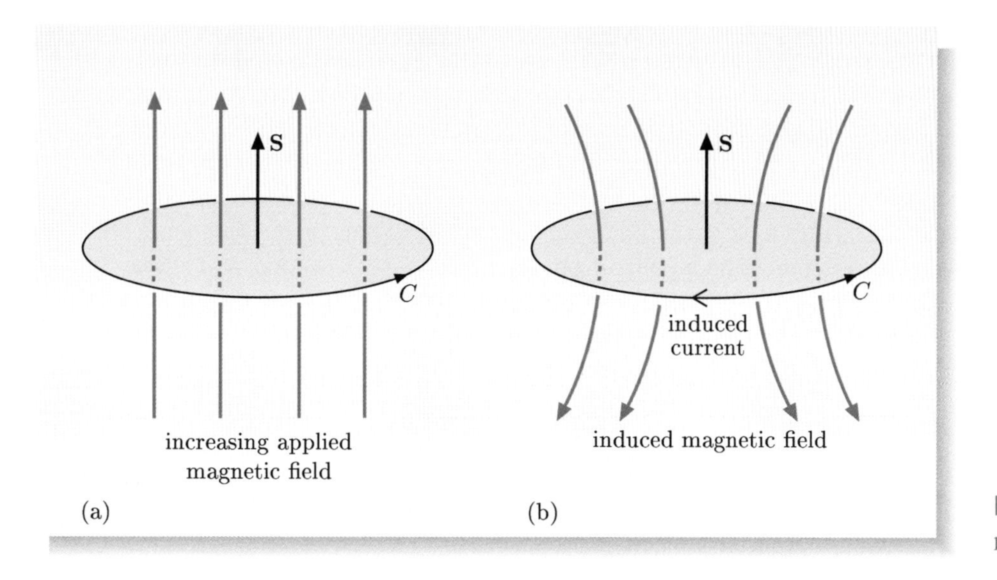


**Figure 6.17** The effect of the minus sign in Faraday's law.

The negative sign in Faraday's law tells us the direction of the electric field. Let's consider a definite case. Figure 6.17a shows a horizontal circular loop in an external magnetic field that points upwards and is increasing. We choose the open surface $S$ to be the disc bounded by the circular loop, and take the positive orientation of this disc to be upwards. Using the right-hand grip rule, the positive sense of circulation around the loop is then anticlockwise as seen from above. The magnetic flux over $S$ is positive and is increasing, so the minus sign on the right-hand side of Equation 6.6 tells us that the circulation of $\mathbf{E}$ is negative. With our conventions, this means that the electric field circulates clockwise as seen from above, driving the induced current in the same direction. As shown in Figure 6.17b, this current produces a magnetic field that points downwards inside the loop. So the magnetic field due to the induced current tends to counteract the increase in flux over $S$.

- Consider the same situation as that shown in Figure 6.17, but with a magnetic field that is decreasing. What is the direction of the induced current in this case? Does the magnetic field due to the induced current tend to counteract the decrease in flux over $S$?

- An argument similar to that given above shows that the right-hand side of Equation 6.6 is positive. This causes the electric field, and the current, to circulate anticlockwise as seen from above. This current produces a magnetic field that points upwards inside the loop, which tends to counteract the decrease in flux over $S$.

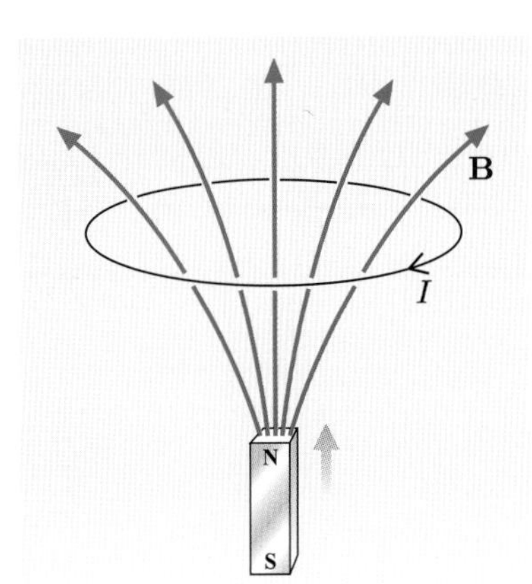


**Figure 6.18** An example of Lenz's law.

Notice how this works: the magnetic field produced by the induced current opposes the *change* in the magnetic field responsible for the current. This general feature of electromagnetic induction is called **Lenz's law**.

**Lenz's law**

The induced current flows in such a way that its magnetic flux opposes the *change* in the magnetic flux that produced it.

Lenz's law is part of Faraday's law, guaranteed by the minus sign on the right-hand side of Equation 6.6. One way of understanding its significance is to suppose that the increasing magnetic field in Figure 6.17 is produced by moving a bar magnet. Magnetic field lines emerge from the north pole end of the magnet, so we can achieve an increasing vertical field by moving the magnet towards the loop, led by its north pole (Figure 6.18). According to Lenz's law, the induced current produces a magnetic field which acts downwards on the magnet. This causes the magnet to be repelled from the loop, so work is done, and energy is used, in moving the magnet towards the loop. This makes good sense. It means that energy reserves must be expended to create electric power. The energy may come from a variety of sources, but nothing comes for free.

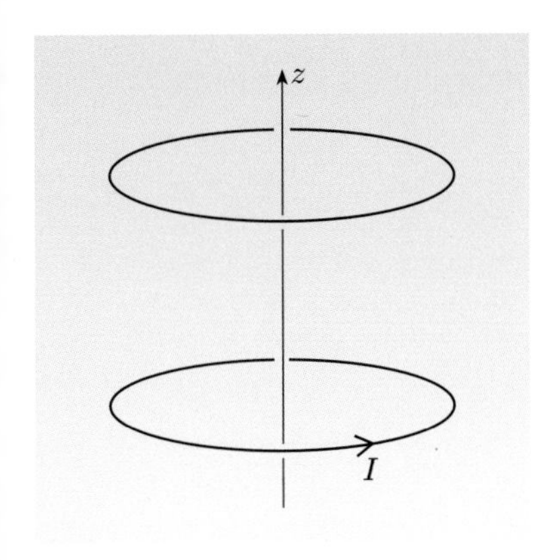


**Figure 6.19** Two conducting loops.

**Exercise 6.6** Figure 6.19 shows two conducting loops. The lower loop carries a current $I$ in the direction indicated. Use Lenz's law to find the direction of the induced current in the upper loop when (a) $I$ is increasing and (b) $I$ is decreasing.

### 6.2.3 Electromagnetic induction in action

Electromagnetic induction is applied in many different ways, and provides fertile ground for inventors. Mainly for interest, this section briefly mentions a few of the applications that have been developed.

### Power conversion

The motion of a magnet relative to a coil, driven by some external source of power, generates an emf. This basic fact underpins the working of the **alternator** of a car, which is an electric generator driven by the car engine. The alternating output is converted to a unidirectional current, and this is used to drive the electrical system of the car and to keep the battery charged.

On a much smaller scale, the vibrations of sound cause tiny relative displacements of magnets and coils, generating tiny currents that can be amplified and modified in various ways. This idea is used in moving-coil microphones, electric guitars and some of the seismometers that measure earthquakes.

### Transformers

A **transformer** is a device that converts low voltages into high voltages, or vice versa. For example, the 400 V output of a power station can be transformed to the 400 kV used in the UK national grid. The ignition system of a petrol engine contains a transformer that produces 1500 V across a small air gap in the spark plugs. This creates the spark that ignites the petrol–air mixture.

In a typical transformer, primary and secondary coils are wound on an iron core (Figure 6.20). For reasons that will be explained in Book 2, the magnetic field is guided by the iron core and confined to it. So, at any given instant, the magnetic flux has the same value over all cross-sections of the core. The output voltage is then determined by the input voltage and the ratio of the numbers of turns in the primary and secondary coils.

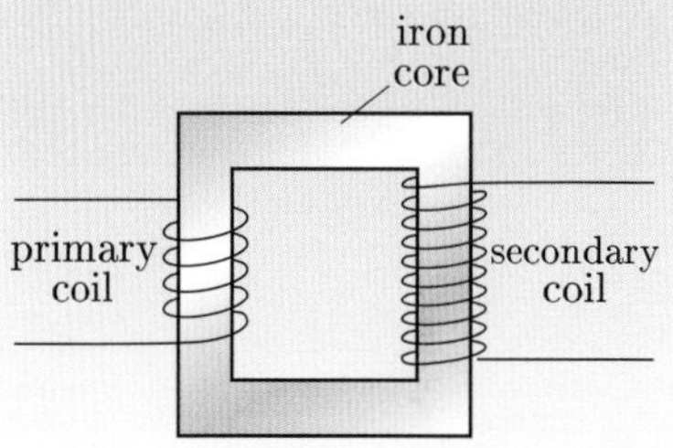

**Figure 6.20** A transformer, with primary and secondary coils wound on an iron core.

**Exercise 6.7** When an alternating voltage $V_1$ is applied across the primary coil of a transformer, the changing magnetic flux induces an alternating voltage $V_2$ across the secondary coil. Show that $V_2/V_1 = N_2/N_1$, where $N_1$ and $N_2$ are the numbers of turns in the primary and secondary coils. ■

### Magnetic storms

One or two days after a solar storm, the Earth experiences a sudden influx of charged particles. Most of these particles are deflected by the Earth's magnetic field, but small fluctuations are produced in the magnetic field at the Earth's surface. These fluctuations are called **magnetic storms**. They are widespread and sudden, and can induce damaging surges in the vast circuits that distribute electricity across countries and continents. The most severe incident in recent times occurred in March 1989, when 6 million people in Quebec lost electrical power for more than 9 hours.

**Exercise 6.8** Suppose that the vertical component of the Earth's magnetic field changes by 1.0% in 10 seconds. What emf is induced in a circular conducting loop of radius 600 km in a region where the vertical component of the magnetic field is normally $5.0 \times 10^{-5}$ T? ■

### Residual current devices

Many lives have been saved by **residual current devices**. In a typical example, the leads bringing current to and from an electrical appliance pass through an iron

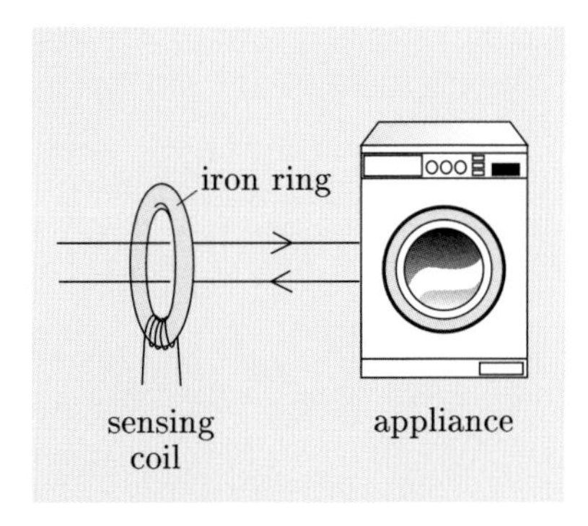


**Figure 6.21** A residual current device.

ring which has a sensing coil wound around it (Figure 6.21). In normal operation, the current through one lead is exactly opposite to the current through the other lead, so little magnetic flux passes through the sensing coil. But if something catastrophic occurs, a significant amount of current may flow to Earth (possibly via your body). In this case, the currents in the two leads no longer cancel, and a much larger magnetic flux passes through the sensing coil. At the moment of failure, the magnetic flux changes rapidly and a detectable current is induced in the sensing coil. This is used to trigger a mechanism that cuts off the current to the appliance.

### Probing structures

Electromagnetic induction is also used to detect metal objects below ground level. In a **metal detector**, an alternating current of frequency between 3 kHz and 30 kHz is sent through a transmitting coil. This produces an oscillating magnetic field which penetrates below ground level and induces currents in conducting objects. These currents themselves produce oscillating magnetic fields, which are detected by the currents they induce in a separate receiver coil. The receiver coil is designed in such a way that it picks up very little magnetic flux directly from the transmitting coil. Its current is amplified and converted into an audible tone.

A metal detector and a transcranial magnetic stimulator were illustrated in the Introduction to this chapter.

Although it sounds drastic, similar methods have been applied to the human body. In **transcranial magnetic stimulation** an alternating magnetic field is used to induce currents in the brain. Rather alarmingly, a magnetic field of 0.5 T is applied for less than a millisecond, producing a current pulse of a few kiloamps. The experience is not pleasant but is believed to cause no lasting harm. It is hoped that this technique will provide useful information about brain function.

## 6.3 The differential version of Faraday's law

The version of Faraday's law you have seen so far, namely

$$\oint_C \mathbf{E} \cdot \mathrm{d}\mathbf{l} = -\frac{\mathrm{d}}{\mathrm{d}t} \int_S \mathbf{B} \cdot \mathrm{d}\mathbf{S}, \qquad \text{(Eqn 6.6)}$$

is the **integral version of Faraday's law**. Like other laws in electromagnetism, it can be converted to an equivalent differential form. In order to achieve this, we recall that the open surface $S$ used in Faraday's law is fixed in space. So the only possible reason for a change in the magnetic flux over $S$ is a change in the magnetic field. This means that the rate of change of magnetic flux on the right-hand side of Equation 6.6 can be written as

$$\frac{\mathrm{d}}{\mathrm{d}t} \int_S \mathbf{B} \cdot \mathrm{d}\mathbf{S} = \int_S \frac{\partial \mathbf{B}}{\partial t} \cdot \mathrm{d}\mathbf{S}.$$

The use of ordinary differentiation outside the integral and partial differentiation inside the integral may seem odd, but is correct. Ordinary differentiation is appropriate outside the integral because the magnetic flux $\int_S \mathbf{B} \cdot \mathrm{d}\mathbf{S}$ is a function of time only. By contrast, the magnetic field inside the integral may depend on spatial coordinates as well as on time, so *partial* differentiation with respect to time is appropriate *inside* the integral.

We can also use the curl theorem to express the left-hand side of Equation 6.6 as

$$\oint_C \mathbf{E} \cdot d\mathbf{l} = \int_S \operatorname{curl} \mathbf{E} \cdot d\mathbf{S},$$

where $S$ is any open surface which has $C$ as perimeter. We choose this surface to be the same as that used to calculate the magnetic flux on the right-hand side of Equation 6.6. Combining these results, we can rewrite Faraday's law as

$$\int_S \left( \operatorname{curl} \mathbf{E} + \frac{\partial \mathbf{B}}{\partial t} \right) \cdot d\mathbf{S} = 0.$$

This equation is true for any open surface, irrespective of its position, orientation or size. Because it is true even for the tiniest scrap of surface, the integrand must vanish everywhere. We conclude that

$$\operatorname{curl} \mathbf{E} = -\frac{\partial \mathbf{B}}{\partial t}. \tag{6.7}$$

This is the **differential version of Faraday's law**. Although fixed loops and surfaces were used in its derivation, all traces of these have been left behind. Equation 6.7 is valid for all magnetic and electric fields at all places and times.

### Worked Example 6.2

**Essential skill**

Using the differential version of Faraday's law.

Consider again the situation described in Worked Example 6.1. An infinitely long cylindrical solenoid of radius $R$ is aligned with the $z$-axis. The uniform magnetic field inside the solenoid varies as $\mathbf{B} = Kt\mathbf{e}_z$, where $K$ is a constant, and there is no magnetic field outside the solenoid. Use the *differential* version of Faraday's law to find the form of the induced electric field inside and outside the solenoid. Do your answers agree with Worked Example 6.1?

#### Solution

As in Worked Example 6.1, we use axial and translational symmetry to assert that the induced electric field takes the form

$$\mathbf{E} = E_\phi(r)\mathbf{e}_\phi$$

in cylindrical coordinates. Using a formula listed inside the back cover of the book, we obtain

$$\operatorname{curl} \mathbf{E} = \frac{1}{r} \begin{vmatrix} \mathbf{e}_r & r\mathbf{e}_\phi & \mathbf{e}_z \\ \dfrac{\partial}{\partial r} & \dfrac{\partial}{\partial \phi} & \dfrac{\partial}{\partial z} \\ 0 & rE_\phi(r) & 0 \end{vmatrix} = \frac{1}{r}\frac{d}{dr}(rE_\phi)\mathbf{e}_z.$$

Inside the solenoid, $\partial \mathbf{B}/\partial t = K\mathbf{e}_z$, and the differential version of Faraday's law gives

$$\frac{d}{dr}(rE_\phi) = -Kr.$$

Integrating both sides, we obtain

$$E_\phi = -\tfrac{1}{2}Kr + \frac{A}{r},$$

where $A$ is an arbitrary constant of integration. This constant can be set equal to zero, because it would be unreasonable for the electric field to diverge as $r$ tends to zero.

Outside the solenoid, $\partial \mathbf{B}/\partial t = 0$, so the differential version of Faraday's law becomes $\text{curl}\,\mathbf{E} = \mathbf{0}$, which gives

$$\frac{\mathrm{d}}{\mathrm{d}r}(rE_\phi) = 0.$$

Integrating both sides, we obtain

$$E_\phi = \frac{C}{r},$$

where $C$ is another arbitrary constant of integration. The electric field must be continuous at the radius $R$ of the solenoid, so we can determine the value of $C$ by equating the two expressions for $E_\phi$ at $r = R$. This gives

$$-\tfrac{1}{2}KR = \frac{C}{R}, \quad \text{so} \quad C = -\tfrac{1}{2}KR^2.$$

Both inside and outside the solenoid, these answers agree with those obtained in Worked Example 6.1.

See also Worked Example 8.29.

It is worth noting that $\text{curl}\,\mathbf{E}$ vanishes outside the solenoid even though the electric field lines are circular there. This shows that you should not judge whether a field is irrotational solely on the basis of its field lines. Zero curl is consistent with circular field lines provided that the magnitude of the field decreases as $1/r$.

**Exercise 6.9** The electric field in a given region takes the form $\mathbf{E} = A\cos(ky - \omega t)\,\mathbf{e}_z$, where $A$, $k$ and $\omega$ are constants. What can be said about the magnetic field in this region? ■

## The significance of Faraday's law

Faraday's law, in either its integral version (Equation 6.6) or its differential version (Equation 6.7), is one of Maxwell's four laws of electromagnetism. It is a cornerstone of the whole subject of electromagnetism. It also introduces new aspects, unlike those discussed in previous chapters. Three points are worth emphasizing.

1. In Chapters 1–5 of this book, electric and magnetic fields were discussed independently. Now, Faraday's law links these two fields together. It is sometimes loosely said that a changing magnetic field causes a non-conservative electric field, but I will use more neutral language. Cause generally precedes effect, whereas Equation 6.7 shows that the time derivative of $\mathbf{B}$ and the curl of $\mathbf{E}$ coexist at the same time and place. It is therefore better to say that non-conservative electric fields and time-dependent magnetic fields go hand-in-hand. Where there is a non-conservative electric field there must be a time-dependent magnetic field, and where there is a time-dependent magnetic

field there must be a non-conservative electric field. They are two sides of the same coin.

2. Electromagnetic fields were originally introduced as ancillary concepts — useful tools that simplify the calculation of electric or magnetic forces. But Faraday's law suggests that the electromagnetic field has a *dynamics* of its own. The rate of change of the magnetic field at a given place and time is related to the curl of the electric field *at the same place and time*. By any standards, this is a major discovery, as Maxwell knew when he called his most important paper *A dynamical theory of the electromagnetic field*.

By 'dynamics', I mean an underlying theory that explains how the field changes with time.

3. Faraday's law tells us when an electric field can be treated as being electrostatic. If a magnetic field is constant throughout a given region, Faraday's law tells us that $\mathbf{E}$ is irrotational there ($\text{curl}\,\mathbf{E} = \mathbf{0}$). If the region is simply-connected, it follows that $\mathbf{E}$ is conservative, and this allows us to define an electrostatic potential, and to deduce the electric field by electrostatic methods.

   However, care is needed if the magnetic field is constant in a region that is not simply-connected (MT 8.9.5). In this case, Faraday's law still ensures that $\text{curl}\,\mathbf{E} = \mathbf{0}$, but we can no longer guarantee that $\mathbf{E}$ is conservative. For example, Worked Examples 6.1 and 6.2 described a situation where the magnetic field changes inside an infinitely long solenoid, but remains constant outside it. In this situation, the electric field is irrotational outside the solenoid, but the circular pattern of field lines shows that this field has a non-zero circulation, and so is not conservative.

## 6.4 Induction in a moving circuit

So far, you have seen that a current is induced in a stationary circuit when the magnetic flux through the circuit is changing. For example, a current is induced in a stationary coil when a magnet moves towards it. Now we shall consider what happens when a circuit moves in a static magnetic field. Instead of moving a magnet towards a stationary coil, we will move a coil towards a stationary magnet. Not surprisingly, a current is also induced in this case. While this may seem natural, it raises an interesting question.

- If the magnet is at rest, the magnetic field is time-independent. The differential version of Faraday's law then shows that the electric field is irrotational everywhere, and hence conservative. But we know that a conservative electric field cannot drive a current around a circuit, so why does a current flow in this case?

- The current must be driven by *magnetic* forces. When a conductor moves through a magnetic field, mobile charges in the conductor experience magnetic forces, and these forces drive the charges along the conductor.

To see how this works, consider the square conducting loop PQRS in Figure 6.22. This loop moves with velocity $\mathbf{v}$ to the right in a static magnetic field $\mathbf{B}$ that points into the page. For simplicity, let us suppose that any current in the loop is carried by *positive* charges, $q$, that are initially at rest relative to the loop, but are free to move within it. This simplifies the true situation, where *negatively*-charged electrons have zero *average* velocity relative to the loop, but does not affect any predictions of macroscopic current flow.

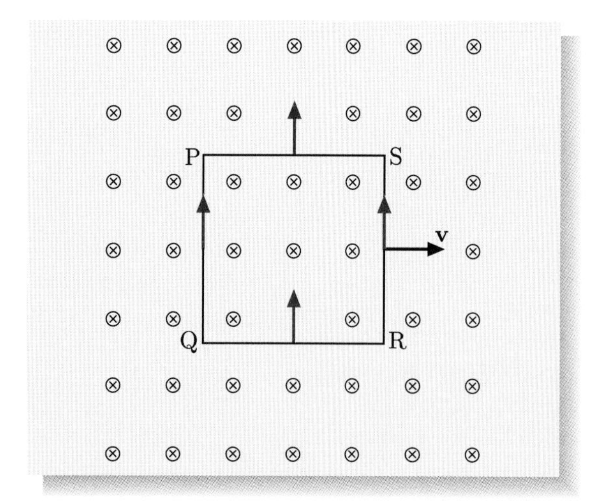


**Figure 6.22** A square conducting loop PQRS moving with velocity $\mathbf{v}$ in a static magnetic field $\mathbf{B}$ that points into the page. The red arrows indicate the magnetic forces acting on positive charge carriers in different parts of the loop.

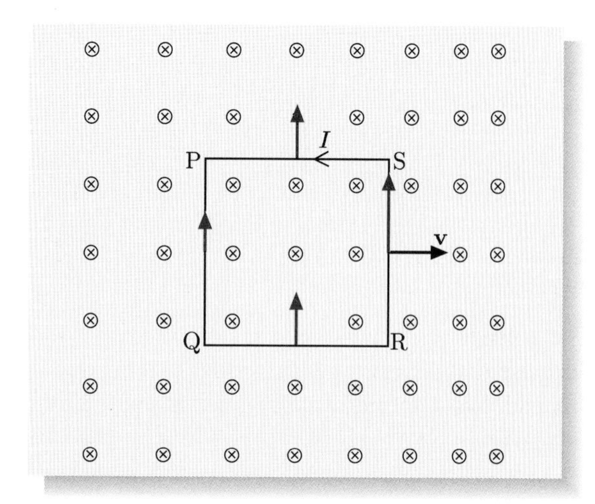


**Figure 6.23** A current is generated when a square conducting loop moves perpendicular to a *non-uniform* static magnetic field.

The mobile charge carriers move along with the loop, and so have velocity $\mathbf{v}$ in the magnetic field $\mathbf{B}$. They each experience a magnetic force $q\mathbf{v} \times \mathbf{B}$. Using the right-hand rule, the charge carriers experience magnetic forces in the directions shown by the red arrows in Figure 6.22. In sides QR and PS, they are pushed towards one side of the conductor but have no tendency to flow around the loop. In sides RS and QP, the magnetic forces push the charge carriers along the conductors. This can generate a current.

If the magnetic field is uniform, the tendency of the charge carriers in side RS to set up an anticlockwise current is exactly compensated by the tendency of the charge carriers in side QP to set up a clockwise current, so no current flows around the loop. But if the magnetic field is non-uniform, the cancellation is no longer exact and a current will flow around the loop. This is illustrated in Figure 6.23 for a case where the magnetic field is stronger at the leading edge of the loop (RS) than at the trailing edge (QP), leading to an anticlockwise current around the loop.

The current is driven by magnetic forces, although electrostatic forces may also arise in the process of establishing a uniform flow of charge all around the circuit. In the most general case, where the circuit moves and the magnetic field depends on time, the current is also driven by a non-conservative electric field. However, it is safe to say that in all cases, the induced current is driven by electromagnetic forces.

Now, suppose that a charge $q$ is transferred once around a conducting circuit $C$ that is moving in a magnetic field. You need not picture this in terms of a single particle making one lap of the circuit, but can think of a current $I$ flowing for a short time interval $\delta t$, with the charge $q = I\,\delta t$ flowing through each part in the circuit. The work done on the transferred charge is then

$$W = \oint_C q\,(\mathbf{E} + \mathbf{v} \times \mathbf{B}) \cdot \mathrm{d}\mathbf{l},$$

where $\mathbf{v}$ is the velocity of an element $\delta\mathbf{l}$ of the circuit. The corresponding emf is the work done per unit charge, so we define the **induced emf** to be

$$V_{\text{emf}} = \oint_C (\mathbf{E} + \mathbf{v} \times \mathbf{B}) \cdot \mathrm{d}\mathbf{l}. \tag{6.8}$$

A real circuit may contain additional sources of emf, such as batteries or thermocouples, but these are ignored in the present discussion.

The **voltage drop** across *part* of a moving circuit is defined in a similar way. Suppose that $C_1$ is a path that moves along with a circuit. At any given instant, this path has a definite shape but each point along the path has a velocity as well as a position. We then define the **voltage drop** along $C_1$ to be

$$V_{\text{drop}} = \int_{C_1} (\mathbf{E} + \mathbf{v} \times \mathbf{B}) \cdot \mathrm{d}\mathbf{l}. \tag{6.9}$$

This definition of voltage drop allows us to extend Ohm's law to moving circuits. If part of a moving circuit has resistance $R$, the voltage drop across this part of the circuit, taken along a path that moves along with it, obeys

$$V_{\text{drop}} = IR.$$

The voltage drop around the whole circuit is equal to the induced emf, so the current in the circuit is given by $I = V_{\text{emf}}/R_{\text{circuit}}$, where $R_{\text{circuit}}$ is the total resistance.

### Worked Example 6.3

**Essential skill**

Finding the current induced in a moving circuit.

Figure 6.24 shows two horizontal conducting rails. The rails are a distance $l$ apart, and are joined at their left-hand ends by a fixed conductor MN. A conducting bar PQ is perpendicular to the rails and completes the circuit MNPQ. The bar PQ slides over the rails, moving with velocity $\mathbf{v} = v\mathbf{e}_x$ to the right. A uniform magnetic field $\mathbf{B} = -B\mathbf{e}_z$ points vertically downwards throughout the whole region (*into* the page in Figure 6.24). Find the magnitude and direction of the current induced in the circuit MNPQ, assuming that this circuit has a constant resistance $R$.

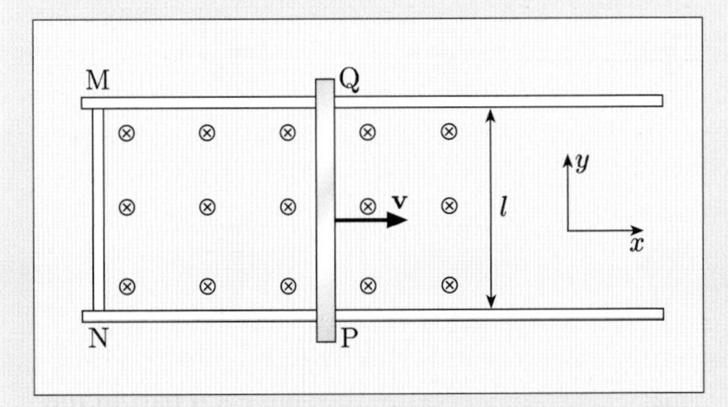


**Figure 6.24** For Worked Example 6.3.

**Solution**

The induced emf arises from magnetic forces in the moving bar PQ. To maintain a uniform current flow, there may also be an electrostatic field, but this does not contribute to the emf, because it is conservative and so has zero circulation around the circuit. At all points along the moving bar,

$$\mathbf{v} \times \mathbf{B} = v\mathbf{e}_x \times (-B\mathbf{e}_z) = Bv\mathbf{e}_y.$$

There is no contribution from the stationary parts of the circuit, so, integrating around the circuit in the sense MNPQ, we obtain

$$V_{\text{emf}} = Bvl.$$

Taking the positive sense of circulation to be MNPQ, the current is

$$I = \frac{Bvl}{R}.$$

Not surprisingly, this increases with $B$, $v$ and $l$, and decreases with $R$.

The current that we have just calculated persists in spite of the dissipative effects of resistance. Clearly, energy is needed to achieve this, so we should ask where this energy comes from. The answer is based on the fact that energy is needed to keep the bar moving.

We know that a current element $I\,\delta\mathbf{l}$ experiences a magnetic force

$$\delta\mathbf{F} = I\,\delta\mathbf{l} \times \mathbf{B}. \quad \text{(Eqn 3.12)}$$

The bar PQ contains many such current elements. Using the right-hand rule, we see that a magnetic force $\mathbf{F} = -BIl\mathbf{e}_x$ acts on the bar, pulling it to the left. To keep the bar moving at a steady velocity, a balancing external force $\mathbf{F}_{\text{ext}} = BIl\mathbf{e}_x$ must be applied to the bar, pushing it to the right. This force is supplied by some external agency — by you, if you are pushing the bar. In time $\delta t$, the bar moves a distance $v\,\delta t$ in the $x$-direction, and the work done by the external force is

$$\delta W = BIl \times v\,\delta t.$$

The power expended is therefore

$$P_{\text{ext}} = \frac{\mathrm{d}W}{\mathrm{d}t} = BIlv. \quad (6.10)$$

We already know that $V_{\text{emf}} = Bvl$, so we conclude that

$$P_{\text{ext}} = IV_{\text{emf}},$$

which is the power in the circuit. The energy books balance exactly. The mechanical energy spent by the agency that keeps the bar moving provides the energy needed to maintain a steady current in the circuit. Anticipating this result, and recalling that emf is the power supplied per unit current, Equation 6.10 provides us with an alternative way of calculating the emf. Dividing both sides of Equation 6.10 by the current $I$, we obtain $V_{\text{emf}} = P_{\text{ext}}/I = Bvl$, in agreement with Worked Example 6.3.

### A further check

The two different ways of calculating the emf are equivalent. To understand why, it may help to consider Figure 6.25. This shows a positive charge $q$ moving with drift velocity $\mathbf{v}_\mathrm{d}$ along the bar PQ, while the bar moves to the right with velocity $\mathbf{v}$. The resultant velocity of the charge is $\mathbf{v}_\mathrm{tot} = \mathbf{v}_\mathrm{d} + \mathbf{v}$.

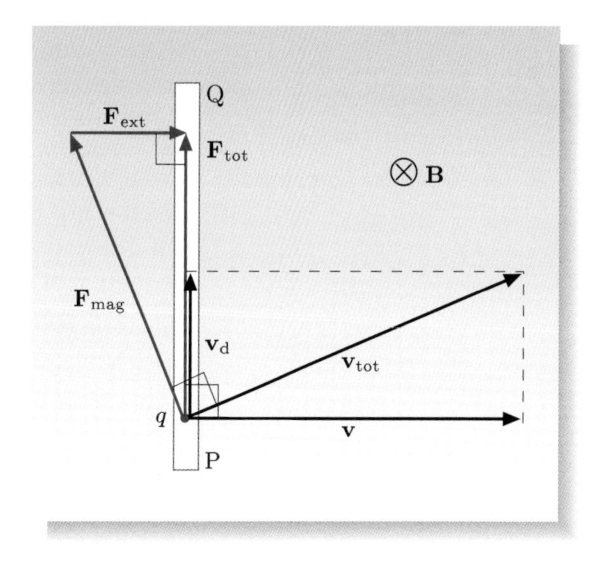


**Figure 6.25** A charge carrier $q$ has drift velocity $\mathbf{v}_\mathrm{d}$ along a bar PQ which is moving with velocity $\mathbf{v}$. A magnetic field $\mathbf{B}$ points into the page, away from you.

The charge $q$ experiences a magnetic force

$$\mathbf{F}_\mathrm{mag} = q(\mathbf{v}_\mathrm{tot} \times \mathbf{B}) = q(\mathbf{v}_\mathrm{d} \times \mathbf{B}) + q(\mathbf{v} \times \mathbf{B}).$$

The first term in the final expression represents a force pointing to the left. This is exactly cancelled by an external force $\mathbf{F}_\mathrm{ext} = -q(\mathbf{v}_\mathrm{d} \times \mathbf{B})$, which must be applied to keep the bar moving steadily.

The total force experienced by the charge is therefore

$$\mathbf{F}_\mathrm{tot} = \mathbf{F}_\mathrm{mag} + \mathbf{F}_\mathrm{ext} = q(\mathbf{v} \times \mathbf{B}),$$

which points along the bar PQ. The magnetic force $\mathbf{F}_\mathrm{mag}$ is perpendicular to $\mathbf{v}_\mathrm{tot}$, and cannot do any work. But the total force $\mathbf{F}_\mathrm{tot}$ acts in a different direction and, in time $\delta t$, does work $\delta W = \mathbf{F}_\mathrm{tot} \cdot \mathbf{v}_\mathrm{tot}\,\delta t$ on the charge. It is helpful to note that the three right-angles marked in Figure 6.25 imply that $\mathbf{F}_\mathrm{tot} \cdot \mathbf{v} = 0$, $\mathbf{F}_\mathrm{mag} \cdot \mathbf{v}_\mathrm{tot} = 0$ and $\mathbf{F}_\mathrm{ext} \cdot \mathbf{v}_\mathrm{d} = 0$. Using these scalar products, it is easy to see that

$$\begin{aligned}\mathbf{F}_\mathrm{tot} \cdot \mathbf{v}_\mathrm{tot} &= \mathbf{F}_\mathrm{tot} \cdot (\mathbf{v}_\mathrm{d} + \mathbf{v}) = \mathbf{F}_\mathrm{tot} \cdot \mathbf{v}_\mathrm{d} = q(\mathbf{v} \times \mathbf{B}) \cdot \mathbf{v}_\mathrm{d}\\ &= (\mathbf{F}_\mathrm{mag} + \mathbf{F}_\mathrm{ext}) \cdot \mathbf{v}_\mathrm{tot} = \mathbf{F}_\mathrm{ext} \cdot \mathbf{v}_\mathrm{tot} = \mathbf{F}_\mathrm{ext} \cdot (\mathbf{v}_\mathrm{d} + \mathbf{v}) = \mathbf{F}_\mathrm{ext} \cdot \mathbf{v}.\end{aligned}$$

Multiplying throughout by $\delta t$, the first line gives the work done by the force $q(\mathbf{v} \times \mathbf{B})$ when the charge makes a displacement $\delta \mathbf{l} = \mathbf{v}_\mathrm{d}\,\delta t$ along the bar, while the second line gives the work done by the external force $\mathbf{F}_\mathrm{ext}$ when the charge makes a sideways displacement $\mathbf{v}\,\delta t$ in the direction of the bar's motion. The equality of these two lines confirms that our two ways of calculating the emf are equivalent.

## 6.4.1 Faraday's law extended to moving circuits

The integral version of Faraday's law, as stated in Section 6.2, was confined to stationary circuits. This section will show that it can be extended to moving circuits as well.

Let's return to Worked Example 6.3. In this case, the magnetic flux through the rectangular loop MNPQ certainly changes with time. This is *not* because the magnetic field is time-dependent, but because the rectangular loop is expanding. It is easy to calculate the rate of change of magnetic flux through the loop. We choose the positive sense of circulation around the loop to be MNPQ, and take the open surface $S$ to be the rectangle bounded by MNPQ, with its unit normal pointing out of the page, towards you. The magnetic flux through $S$ is then $-Blx$, where $l$ and $x$ are the lengths of sides PQ and NP. The rate of change of magnetic flux is therefore

$$\frac{\mathrm{d}}{\mathrm{d}t}\int_S \mathbf{B} \cdot \mathrm{d}\mathbf{S} = \frac{\mathrm{d}}{\mathrm{d}t}(-Blx) = -Blv,$$

where $v$ is the speed of the conducting bar PQ. We recognize this as *minus* the emf calculated in Worked Example 6.3. So, in this example at least,

$$V_{\text{emf}} = -\frac{\mathrm{d}}{\mathrm{d}t}\int_S \mathbf{B} \cdot \mathrm{d}\mathbf{S},$$

which is just like an induced emf predicted from Faraday's law, except that the emf is now defined by Equation 6.8, and the changing magnetic flux arises from the motion of a circuit.

This is no coincidence, but turns out to be completely general. Suppose that we know how a vector field $\mathbf{F}$ varies in space and time *and* how the shape of a surface $S$ changes with time. Then we clearly have enough information to determine how the flux of $\mathbf{F}$ over $S$ varies with time, and therefore to find the rate of change of this flux. This is a purely mathematical problem, and it has a purely mathematical solution. The rate of change of the flux of any vector field $\mathbf{F}$ over a surface $S$ turns out to be

$$\frac{\mathrm{d}}{\mathrm{d}t}\int_S \mathbf{F} \cdot \mathrm{d}\mathbf{S} = \int_S \left(\frac{\partial \mathbf{F}}{\partial t} + \mathbf{v}\,\mathrm{div}\,\mathbf{F} - \mathrm{curl}(\mathbf{v} \times \mathbf{F})\right) \cdot \mathrm{d}\mathbf{S}, \tag{6.11}$$

where $\mathbf{v}$ is the velocity at a given point on $S$.

The proof of this formula would be a lengthy and unnecessary diversion. We shall simply treat it as a mathematical fact, valid for all smoothly-varying vector fields and surfaces. The scientific interest comes when we set $\mathbf{F} = \mathbf{B}$, a magnetic field. In this case the no-monopole law ensures that $\mathrm{div}\,\mathbf{B} = \mathbf{0}$, and the differential version of Faraday's law ensures that $\partial \mathbf{B}/\partial t = -\,\mathrm{curl}\,\mathbf{E}$, so Equation 6.11 becomes

$$\frac{\mathrm{d}}{\mathrm{d}t}\int_S \mathbf{B} \cdot \mathrm{d}\mathbf{S} = -\int_S \mathrm{curl}\,(\mathbf{E} + \mathbf{v} \times \mathbf{B}) \cdot \mathrm{d}\mathbf{S}.$$

Finally, using the curl theorem and interchanging left- and right-hand sides, we conclude that

$$\oint_C (\mathbf{E} + \mathbf{v} \times \mathbf{B}) \cdot \mathrm{d}\mathbf{l} = -\frac{\mathrm{d}}{\mathrm{d}t}\int_S \mathbf{B} \cdot \mathrm{d}\mathbf{S}, \tag{6.12}$$

where $C$ is the perimeter of $S$. Using the generalized definition of the induced emf in a moving circuit (Equation 6.8), we see that

$$V_{\text{emf}} = -\frac{\mathrm{d}}{\mathrm{d}t}\int_S \mathbf{B} \cdot \mathrm{d}\mathbf{S},$$

which is very similar to Faraday's law (Equation 6.6). There are two significant differences. For a moving circuit, the emf is defined to be the line integral of $\mathbf{E} + \mathbf{v} \times \mathbf{B}$ around the circuit, and the rate of decrease of magnetic flux includes contributions from the motion of the circuit. For these reasons, Equation 6.12 is called the **generalized Faraday law**. It is not counted as one of Maxwell's equations, but the above argument shows that it follows directly from the differential versions of two of Maxwell's equations — the no-monopole law and Faraday's law — which are valid for all electromagnetic fields. It is also worth noting that the generalized Faraday law contains the expression $(\mathbf{E} + \mathbf{v} \times \mathbf{B})$, even though its derivation made no use of the Lorentz force law. It is wonderful to see how these different aspects of electromagnetism fit together in a natural way.

The generalized Faraday law is useful in interpreting the behaviour of very highly conducting fluids, such as plasmas. A small closed loop in such a fluid will have a very low resistance. Various physical processes prevent the current from being too large, so Ohm's law, $V_{emf} = IR$, shows that the induced emf around the loop must be very small. Equation 6.12 then shows that the magnetic flux through the loop is almost constant. As the fluid churns and swirls, the imaginary closed loop changes shape, but the magnetic flux through the loop remains practically unchanged. This fact, known as **flux freezing**, is a key tool in understanding the dynamics of magnetic fields in stars such as the Sun.

### 6.4.2 Einstein's radical solution

This chapter has discussed two apparently different types of electromagnetic induction. Induction by a time-varying magnetic field in a stationary circuit is driven by non-conservative electric forces, while induction by a static magnetic field in a moving circuit is driven by magnetic forces.

When Einstein was a student, it was thought that all motion should be described relative to an 'ether'. For a circuit that is stationary relative to the ether, it was believed that the correct description of induction would involve non-conservative electric forces rather than magnetic forces. However, we have just seen that the two types of electromagnetic induction are united by the generalized Faraday law, making it impossible to tell the difference between them. This troubled Einstein. He thought it unreasonable for a theory to require detail in its descriptions, and at the same time deny experimenters any hope of gaining access to that detail. This was a major spur which led Einstein to his special theory of relativity.

Einstein's solution was radical. He abandoned the idea of a special reference frame defined by the ether, and assumed that the laws of physics, including Maxwell's laws of electromagnetism, are valid in *all* **inertial frames of reference**. This means that different inertial observers are free to use their own descriptions. One observer might describe induction in a circuit as being due to non-conservative electric forces, while another might describe it as being due to magnetic forces. Both descriptions are correct, but different observers have different representations of the electromagnetic field — a non-conservative electric field might exist in one reference frame and be absent in another. We have met this general feature of electromagnetism before (e.g. in Section 3.4). It is not hard to accept, because it is clear that a charge that is stationary in one reference frame (where it produces an electrostatic field) will be moving in another reference frame (where it produces both electric and magnetic fields).

An inertial frame of reference is one in which Newton's first law holds true; free particles do not accelerate.

A software package on the DVD allows you to explore the integral and differential versions of Faraday's law. This package is best studied some time after completing this chapter.

## Summary of Chapter 6

**Section 6.1** Steady currents in stationary circuits are driven by non-conservative electric fields. The voltage drop along a stationary path $C$ is the line integral of the electric field along $C$. The emf in a circuit is the work done per unit charge transferred around the circuit. Most current flows obey Ohm's law, $V = IR$, where $V$ is the voltage drop across a conductor of resistance $R$ carrying a current $I$.

**Section 6.2** The integral version of Faraday's law states that

$$\oint_C \mathbf{E} \cdot \mathrm{d}\mathbf{l} = -\frac{\mathrm{d}}{\mathrm{d}t} \int_S \mathbf{B} \cdot \mathrm{d}\mathbf{S},$$

that is, the induced emf around a stationary closed loop $C$ is the rate of decrease of the magnetic flux over an open surface $S$ bounded by $C$. The positive sense of progression around $C$ and the orientation of $S$ are linked by the right-hand grip rule. The minus sign in Faraday's law is consistent with Lenz's law, which states that an induced current flows in such a way that its magnetic flux opposes the *change* in the magnetic flux that produced it.

**Section 6.3** The differential version of Faraday's law states that

$$\operatorname{curl} \mathbf{E} = -\frac{\partial \mathbf{B}}{\partial t},$$

where $\mathbf{E}$ is the electric field at a given place and time, and $\mathbf{B}$ is the magnetic field at the same place and time. If a magnetic field is independent of time in a simply-connected region, the electric field is conservative there.

**Section 6.4** The voltage drop along a moving path $C$ is the line integral of $\mathbf{E} + \mathbf{v} \times \mathbf{B}$ along the path. This voltage drop appears in Ohm's law for the moving circuit: $V_{\text{drop}} = IR$. The induced emf around a moving circuit is the line integral of $\mathbf{E} + \mathbf{v} \times \mathbf{B}$ around the circuit. The generalized Faraday law states that the emf around a moving circuit is equal to the rate of decrease of magnetic flux through the circuit.

## Achievements from Chapter 6

*After studying this chapter you should be able to:*

**6.1** Explain the meanings of the newly defined (emboldened) terms and symbols, and use them appropriately.

**6.2** Define the terms voltage drop and emf for stationary paths and loops.

**6.3** State and apply Ohm's law.

**6.4** State and apply the integral form of Faraday's law for stationary circuits.

**6.5** State and apply the differential form of Faraday's law, and show how it follows from the integral form.

**6.6** Appreciate how the concepts of induced emf and voltage drop are extended to paths and circuits that are moving. State and apply the generalized Faraday law.

**6.7** Give examples of electromagnetic induction and its applications.

# Chapter 7 Maxwell's triumph

## Introduction

This chapter presents Maxwell's greatest triumph — the prediction that electromagnetic waves can propagate vast distances through empty space and the realization that light is itself an electromagnetic wave. Visible light has a very narrow range of wavelengths, but this tells us more about the sensitivity of our eyes than about the nature of electromagnetic radiation. A few years after Maxwell's death other types of electromagnetic radiation, including radio waves, X-rays and gamma rays, were discovered. Compared to light, radio waves have very long wavelengths, while X-rays and gamma rays have very short wavelengths. Different parts of the electromagnetic spectrum are used in different ways (Figure 7.1). Radio waves are used for broadcast radio and television, satellite communications and mobile phones. Gamma rays are used to treat cancer and X-rays are used in medical diagnosis. Yet all these waves have the same underlying description in terms of electric and magnetic fields.

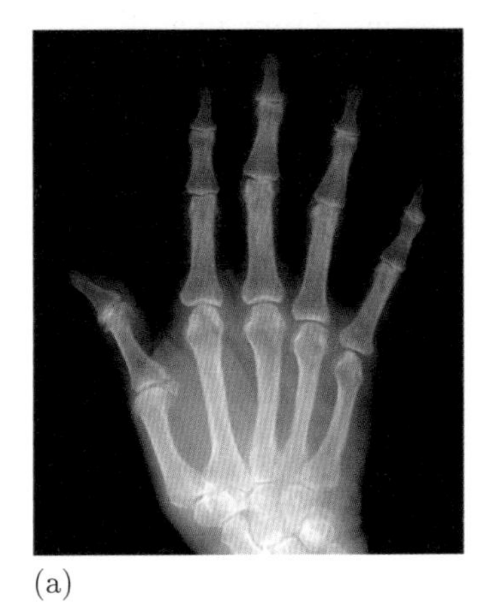

(a)

(b)

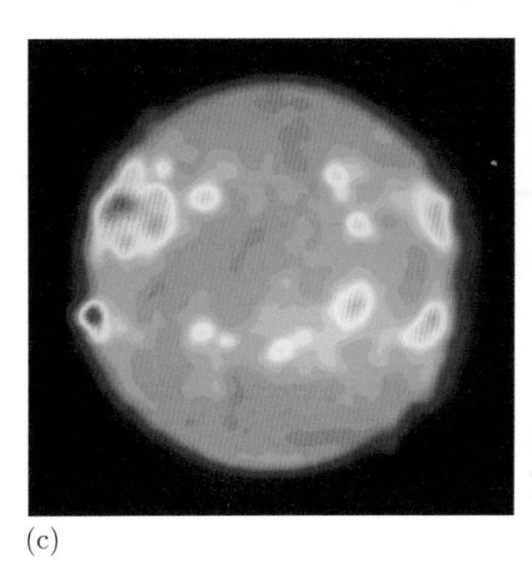

(c)

**Figure 7.1** (a) An X-ray image of a hand; (b) an infrared image of Hurricane Rita (2005) and (c) a radio image of the Sun taken at a wavelength of 2.8 cm. In (b) and (c) emission ranges from low (blue) to high (red).

Maxwell was in a position to predict the existence of electromagnetic waves because, by the mid-1860s, he had developed a comprehensive theory of electromagnetism. Much of this theory has been discussed in previous chapters. In particular, you have met three of Maxwell's four equations: *Gauss's law*, the *no-monopole law* and *Faraday's law*. These laws can be expressed in terms of volume, surface and line integrals or in terms of partial derivatives. Previous chapters emphasized the integral versions of Maxwell's equations, but we will now make more use of the differential versions.

- Write down the *differential* versions of Gauss's law, the no-monopole law and Faraday's law. Are these laws true under all circumstances?

- The three laws are:

$$\operatorname{div}\mathbf{E} = \frac{\rho}{\varepsilon_0} \qquad \text{(Gauss's law)},$$

$$\operatorname{div}\mathbf{B} = 0 \qquad \text{(the no-monopole law)},$$

$$\operatorname{curl}\mathbf{E} = -\frac{\partial \mathbf{B}}{\partial t} \qquad \text{(Faraday's law)},$$

where $\mathbf{E}$ and $\mathbf{B}$ are the electric and magnetic fields, $\rho$ is the charge density and $\varepsilon_0$ is the permittivity of free space. All three laws have general validity: they apply to time-varying situations as well as static or steady-state ones.

In Chapter 4, we also discussed *Ampère's law*, the differential version of which is

$$\operatorname{curl}\mathbf{B} = \mu_0\mathbf{J},$$

where $\mathbf{J}$ is the current density and $\mu_0$ is the permeability of free space. However, Ampère's law has a different status: it requires steady currents and is not valid for currents that vary in time. This means that Ampère's law is not general enough to count as one of Maxwell's four laws of electromagnetism.

Fortunately, Ampère's law can be rescued. Maxwell realized that an extra term, $\varepsilon_0\mu_0\partial\mathbf{E}/\partial t$, can be added to the right-hand side of Ampère's law. This term makes no difference in static situations, but it extends the validity of the law to general, time-varying situations. The extended equation is called the *Ampère–Maxwell law* and takes the form

$$\operatorname{curl}\mathbf{B} = \mu_0\mathbf{J} + \varepsilon_0\mu_0\frac{\partial \mathbf{E}}{\partial t}.$$

Our first task is to justify this law. To achieve this, we will make use of a basic principle of electromagnetism — the conservation of charge. You met this principle at the very beginning of this book, but we have not unlocked its full power yet. Section 7.1 will show that the law of conservation of charge leads to a relationship between current density and charge density known as the *equation of continuity*. This relationship will be used in Section 7.2 to help justify the Ampère–Maxwell law. Then, with all four of Maxwell's equations in place, we will be in a position to demonstrate that electromagnetic waves are a direct consequence of the laws of electromagnetism.

## 7.1 The equation of continuity

The conservation of charge is a basic tenet of electromagnetism. It can be simply expressed by the equation

$$\frac{\mathrm{d}Q_{\text{tot}}}{\mathrm{d}t} = 0,$$

where $Q_{\text{tot}}$ is the total charge in the Universe. However, such an equation does not really help us very much, because we are not usually concerned with anything as grand as the whole Universe. Moreover, it leaves out some important physics.

The most interesting aspect of the law of conservation of charge is that it applies locally as well as globally. If an electron were miraculously created here, and a proton were simultaneously, and equally miraculously, created on Mars, the total charge of the Universe would remain constant. But these two miracles would both violate the law of conservation of charge because they do not conserve charge *locally*, either here or on Mars. Electric charge is conserved in every region of space. We can therefore make a more powerful statement:

**The law of conservation of charge**

Any variation in the total charge within a closed surface must be due to charges that flow across the surface.

To express this law in mathematical terms, consider a volume $V$ bounded by the closed surface $S$ (Figure 7.2). Electric current is defined to be the rate of flow of charge across a surface so the law of conservation of charge tells us that

$$I = -\frac{\mathrm{d}Q}{\mathrm{d}t}, \qquad (7.1)$$

where $I$ is instantaneous current flowing outwards through $S$ into the exterior space and $Q$ is the instantaneous charge in the enclosed volume $V$. The minus sign arises because a current flowing outwards across the surface produces a *loss* of charge within the surface.

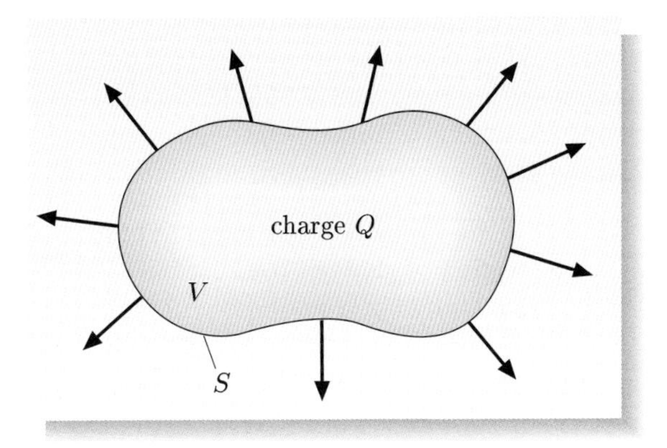


**Figure 7.2** The current flowing across the closed surface $S$ tells us the rate of loss of charge in the volume $V$ enclosed by $S$.

Now we can express the current $I$ as a surface integral of the current density $\mathbf{J}$:

$$I = \int_S \mathbf{J} \cdot \mathrm{d}\mathbf{S}.$$

Using the divergence theorem, we can also write this as

$$I = \int_V \operatorname{div} \mathbf{J}\, \mathrm{d}V. \qquad (7.2)$$

We can express the charge $Q$ as a volume integral of the charge density $\rho$:

$$Q = \int_V \rho\, \mathrm{d}V.$$

The rate of change of $Q$ within this volume is therefore

$$\frac{\mathrm{d}Q}{\mathrm{d}t} = \frac{\mathrm{d}}{\mathrm{d}t}\int_V \rho\,\mathrm{d}V = \int_V \frac{\partial\rho}{\partial t}\,\mathrm{d}V. \tag{7.3}$$

Note the use of ordinary differentiation outside the integral and partial differentiation inside the integral. Ordinary differentiation is appropriate outside the integral because $Q(t)$ is a function of time only. By contrast, the charge density depends on spatial coordinates as well as on time. These spatial coordinates remain fixed, so *partial differentiation* with respect to time is appropriate *inside* the integral.

Combining Equations 7.1, 7.2 and 7.3, we conclude that

$$\int_V \left(\frac{\partial\rho}{\partial t} + \operatorname{div}\mathbf{J}\right)\mathrm{d}V = 0.$$

The fact that this volume integral vanishes for all volumes (no matter how small) implies that the integrand must be equal to zero everywhere, so we have

$$\frac{\partial\rho}{\partial t} + \operatorname{div}\mathbf{J} = 0. \tag{7.4}$$

This is called the **equation of continuity**. It applies at each point in space and each instant in time and is a direct expression of the local law of conservation of charge. It is a fundamental fact about electromagnetism which applies in all situations and in all frames of reference.

The case of magnetostatics (discussed in Chapter 3), where all the currents are steady, is of special importance. In this case, we can argue that $\partial\rho/\partial t$ must be equal to zero. For, if $\partial\rho/\partial t$ were positive at any particular point, it would remain positive there *forever*, since all the currents are steady. This would lead to an unphysical boundless build-up of charge. A similar argument rules out a negative value of $\partial\rho/\partial t$. Therefore realistic steady currents are characterized by

$$\frac{\partial\rho}{\partial t} = \operatorname{div}\mathbf{J} = 0.$$

However, this is a very special situation. If the currents are not steady, we would expect concentrations of charge to build up in different regions, and then ebb away. In general, $\rho$ varies in time, and $\operatorname{div}\mathbf{J} \neq 0$.

**Exercise 7.1** A one-dimensional rod is aligned with the $z$-axis. At any point along the rod, the current density is given by

$$\mathbf{J}(z,t) = A\sin(kz - \omega t)\,\mathbf{e}_z,$$

where $k$, $\omega$ and $A$ are constants. What can be said about the charge density along the rod? You may assume that the time-average of charge density is zero at each point along the rod. ■

## 7.2 The Ampère–Maxwell law

### 7.2.1 Limitations of Ampère's law

In order to analyse the limitations of Ampère's law, and suggest ways of overcoming them, we need to use some properties of divergence. For ease of reference, these properties are given below:

### Some properties of divergence

1. The divergence of any curl is equal to zero:

$$\operatorname{div}(\operatorname{curl}\mathbf{F}) = 0. \tag{7.5}$$

2. A constant $k$ can be taken outside a divergence:

$$\operatorname{div}(k\mathbf{F}) = k\operatorname{div}\mathbf{F}. \tag{7.6}$$

3. A time derivative can be taken outside a divergence:

$$\operatorname{div}\left(\frac{\partial\mathbf{F}}{\partial t}\right) = \frac{\partial}{\partial t}(\operatorname{div}\mathbf{F}). \tag{7.7}$$

You can take these properties on trust if you wish, but it is easy enough to prove them by expanding both sides in Cartesian coordinates.

- Prove Equation 7.5.

- Expanding the left-hand side of Equation 7.5 gives

$$\begin{aligned}
&\frac{\partial}{\partial x}\left(\frac{\partial F_z}{\partial y} - \frac{\partial F_y}{\partial z}\right) + \frac{\partial}{\partial y}\left(\frac{\partial F_x}{\partial z} - \frac{\partial F_z}{\partial x}\right) + \frac{\partial}{\partial z}\left(\frac{\partial F_y}{\partial x} - \frac{\partial F_x}{\partial y}\right)\\
&= \left(\frac{\partial^2 F_z}{\partial x\partial y} - \frac{\partial^2 F_y}{\partial x\partial z}\right) + \left(\frac{\partial^2 F_x}{\partial y\partial z} - \frac{\partial^2 F_z}{\partial y\partial x}\right) + \left(\frac{\partial^2 F_y}{\partial z\partial x} - \frac{\partial^2 F_x}{\partial z\partial y}\right)\\
&= \left(\frac{\partial^2 F_z}{\partial x\partial y} - \frac{\partial^2 F_z}{\partial y\partial x}\right) + \left(\frac{\partial^2 F_x}{\partial y\partial z} - \frac{\partial^2 F_x}{\partial z\partial y}\right) + \left(\frac{\partial^2 F_y}{\partial z\partial x} - \frac{\partial^2 F_y}{\partial x\partial z}\right),
\end{aligned}$$

which vanishes because mixed partial derivatives do not depend on the order of partial differentiation.

Now let's examine the differential version of Ampère's law, which states that

$$\operatorname{curl}\mathbf{B} = \mu_0\mathbf{J}. \tag{Eqn 4.17}$$

The limitations of this law are revealed by taking the divergence of both sides. This gives

$$\operatorname{div}(\operatorname{curl}\mathbf{B}) = \operatorname{div}(\mu_0\mathbf{J}).$$

The divergence of any curl is equal to zero so, using Equation 7.6 and the equation of continuity, we have

$$0 = \mu_0\operatorname{div}\mathbf{J} = -\mu_0\frac{\partial\rho}{\partial t}.$$

We therefore see that Ampère's law requires the charge density to remain constant. Put another way:

Ampère's law fails when the charge density changes in time.

### 7.2.2 Generalizing Ampère's law

We need to generalize Ampère's law beyond the confines of static charge densities. Let's try adding an extra (and at this stage unknown) vector field, $\mathbf{K}$ to the right-hand side of the differential form of Ampère's law. The modified equation then reads

$$\operatorname{curl}\mathbf{B} = \mu_0\mathbf{J} + \mathbf{K}.$$

What can be said about the term $\mathbf{K}$? Taking the divergence of both sides of the modified equation, and using the fact that the divergence of any curl is equal to zero, we obtain

$$0 = \operatorname{div}(\mu_0\mathbf{J} + \mathbf{K}) = \mu_0 \operatorname{div}\mathbf{J} + \operatorname{div}\mathbf{K}.$$

So, using the equation of continuity (Equation 7.4), we have

$$\operatorname{div}\mathbf{K} = -\mu_0 \operatorname{div}\mathbf{J} = \mu_0 \frac{\partial \rho}{\partial t}.$$

Now Gauss's law tells us that

$$\rho = \varepsilon_0 \operatorname{div}\mathbf{E},$$

so, using Equation 7.7 to interchange the order of the time and space derivatives,

$$\frac{\partial \rho}{\partial t} = \varepsilon_0 \frac{\partial}{\partial t}(\operatorname{div}\mathbf{E}) = \varepsilon_0 \operatorname{div}\left(\frac{\partial \mathbf{E}}{\partial t}\right).$$

We conclude that

$$\operatorname{div}\mathbf{K} = \varepsilon_0\mu_0 \operatorname{div}\left(\frac{\partial \mathbf{E}}{\partial t}\right). \tag{7.8}$$

The *simplest* solution to this equation is

$$\mathbf{K} = \varepsilon_0\mu_0 \frac{\partial \mathbf{E}}{\partial t},$$

but there are other solutions as well. In fact, the most general solution is

$$\mathbf{K} = \varepsilon_0\mu_0 \frac{\partial \mathbf{E}}{\partial t} + \operatorname{curl}\mathbf{X}, \tag{7.9}$$

where $\mathbf{X}$ is any smooth vector field. You can easily verify that this satisfies Equation 7.8, because taking the divergence of both sides gives

$$\operatorname{div}\mathbf{K} = \varepsilon_0\mu_0 \operatorname{div}\left(\frac{\partial \mathbf{E}}{\partial t}\right) + \operatorname{div}(\operatorname{curl}\mathbf{X}),$$

and the last term vanishes, being the divergence of a curl.

This is as far as mathematical analysis can take us. It is not too surprising that we still have a choice to make. You should not expect to derive a *fundamental* law of physics from other laws. As a general rule, however, it is sensible to adopt the simplest law that is consistent with all the known facts. That is what Maxwell did, and we shall follow his lead. We assume that $\operatorname{curl}\mathbf{X} = \mathbf{0}$ in Equation 7.9, and replace Ampère's law by

$$\operatorname{curl}\mathbf{B} = \mu_0\mathbf{J} + \varepsilon_0\mu_0 \frac{\partial \mathbf{E}}{\partial t}. \tag{7.10}$$

This equation is called the **Ampère–Maxwell law** and the additional term, $\varepsilon_0\mu_0\partial\mathbf{E}/\partial t$, is called the **Maxwell term**. Some authors refer to the Maxwell term as $\mu_0$ times the *displacement current density*. We will not use this terminology in this book, but an optional appendix (best read *after* this section) describes the curious logic behind it. The Ampère–Maxwell law is the last of Maxwell's four equations of electromagnetism. It is believed to be true in all situations, both static and dynamic.

The above argument for the Ampère–Maxwell law is driven by theory. If we believe the law of conservation of charge (as we do), our mathematical analysis shows that Ampère's law must be modified for time-dependent situations. The simplest modification, consistent with Gauss's law and the equation of continuity, is then given by the Ampère–Maxwell law. Physics walks forward on the two legs of theory and experiment. Sometimes experiment strides ahead and reveals new facts which cry out for theoretical interpretation. The Ampère–Maxwell law is an early example of the opposite process — a law that emerged from a theoretical argument, and cried out for experimental confirmation.

In Maxwell's day, there was no *direct* experimental evidence requiring a modification to Ampère's law. The Maxwell term $\varepsilon_0\mu_0\partial\mathbf{E}/\partial t$ is usually very small in comparison with the term associated with the current density, $\mu_0\mathbf{J}$. For example, if a mains-frequency current is uniformly distributed throughout a copper wire, the Maxwell term in the wire is only about $5 \times 10^{-17}$ as large as $\mu_0 J$. On this basis, it is tempting to dismiss the Maxwell term as a practical irrelevance, but this would be a serious error of judgement. Although small, the Maxwell term can exist in empty space, where no real currents exist, and there it plays a vital role in sustaining the propagation of electromagnetic waves, as you will soon see. Ultimately, the existence of these waves provides the best evidence for the whole of Maxwell's theory, including the Maxwell term and the Ampère–Maxwell law.

**Exercise 7.2** Equation 7.10 is the differential version of the Ampère–Maxwell law. Show that the corresponding integral version is

$$\oint_C \mathbf{B} \cdot \mathrm{d}\mathbf{l} = \int_S \left(\mu_0\mathbf{J} + \varepsilon_0\mu_0\frac{\partial\mathbf{E}}{\partial t}\right) \cdot \mathrm{d}\mathbf{S} \tag{7.11}$$

where $C$ is a closed loop and $S$ is any open surface that has $C$ as its perimeter. The sense of positive progression around $C$ and the orientation of $S$ are related by the right-hand grip rule. ■

### 7.2.3 The Ampère–Maxwell law in action

To give some further insight into the Ampère–Maxwell law, we will now consider two situations where it plays a significant role.

#### An expanding sphere of charge

First consider an expanding spherically-symmetric ball of positive charge. This is not an implausible state of affairs. If the charges in the distribution are not held in place, their mutual repulsion leads to a spherically-symmetric expansion and a spherically-symmetric outward flow of current. You may recall from Chapter 4 that any spherically-symmetric distribution of current is magnetically silent — that is, it produces no magnetic field. This is true both outside and inside the

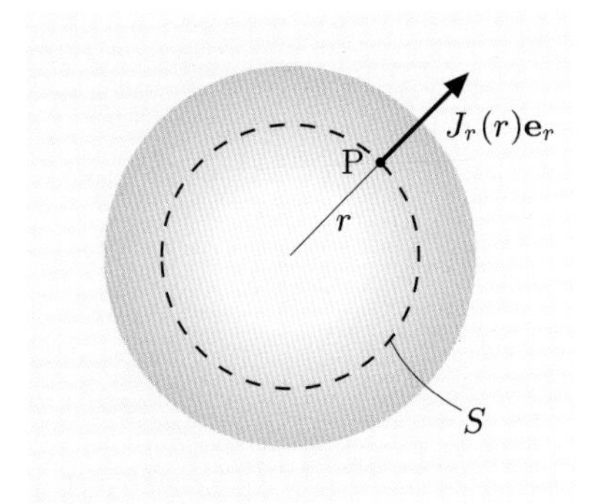


**Figure 7.3** An expanding sphere of charge.

current distribution. We will now show that this rather surprising result is fully consistent with the Ampère–Maxwell law.

Using a spherical coordinate system with its origin at the centre of the charge distribution, we consider a point P with radial coordinate $r$ (Figure 7.3). Because the charge distribution is spherically-symmetric, the electric field at P is

$$\mathbf{E} = \frac{Q_{\text{in}}}{4\pi\varepsilon_0 r^2}\,\mathbf{e}_r,$$

where $Q_{\text{in}}$ is the total charge inside a sphere of radius $r$ (the dashed sphere in Figure 7.3). The outward current through the surface of the dashed sphere is equal to the rate of decrease of charge inside it, so we have

$$\frac{\mathrm{d}Q_{\text{in}}}{\mathrm{d}t} = -\int_S \mathbf{J}\cdot\mathrm{d}\mathbf{S} = -J_r(r)\times 4\pi r^2,$$

where $S$ is the surface of the dashed sphere and $\mathbf{J} = J_r(r)\,\mathbf{e}_r$ is the current density on the surface of this sphere. It follows that the Maxwell term at point P on $S$ is

$$\varepsilon_0\mu_0\frac{\partial\mathbf{E}}{\partial t} = \varepsilon_0\mu_0\frac{1}{4\pi\varepsilon_0 r^2}\frac{\mathrm{d}Q_{\text{in}}}{\mathrm{d}t}\,\mathbf{e}_r = \mu_0\frac{-J_r(r)\times 4\pi r^2}{4\pi r^2}\,\mathbf{e}_r = -\mu_0\mathbf{J}.$$

Combining this equation with the Ampère–Maxwell law (Equation 7.10), we finally obtain

$$\operatorname{curl}\mathbf{B} = \mu_0\mathbf{J} + \varepsilon_0\mu_0\frac{\partial\mathbf{E}}{\partial t} = \mu_0\mathbf{J} - \mu_0\mathbf{J} = \mathbf{0},$$

which is consistent with $\mathbf{B} = \mathbf{0}$. Note that the Maxwell term is essential for this cancellation. Ampère's law would *wrongly* imply that $\operatorname{curl}\mathbf{B} \neq \mathbf{0}$ at points where $\mathbf{J} \neq \mathbf{0}$.

(Incidentally, $\operatorname{div}\mathbf{B}$ is also equal to zero, by virtue of the no-monopole law. Although we shall not prove it, the fact that *both* $\operatorname{curl}\mathbf{B}$ *and* $\operatorname{div}\mathbf{B}$ vanish everywhere, and the natural assumption that $\mathbf{B}$ tends to zero at infinity, turns out to be sufficient to guarantee that $\mathbf{B} = \mathbf{0}$ everywhere.)

### A capacitor with time-varying charges on its plates

Figure 7.4 shows a parallel plate capacitor with circular plates, which is being charged by steady currents flowing along straight wires. We know that there is a circular pattern of magnetic field lines around the wires, but what happens inside the capacitor, between the plates?

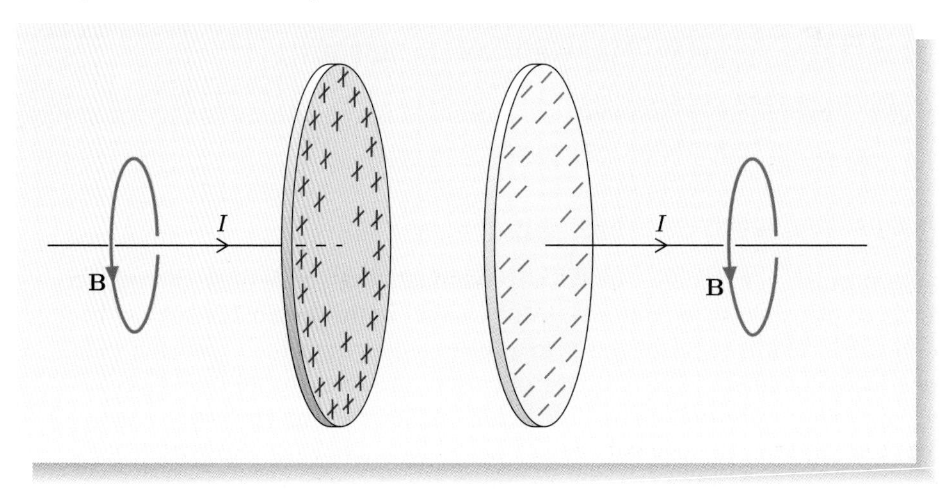


**Figure 7.4** Charging the plates of a capacitor.

The situation illustrated in Figure 7.4 is difficult to analyse quantitatively. Charge spreads out over the plates from the points of contact with the wires so, at any given moment, the plates are unevenly charged and radial currents flow over their surfaces. We will avoid such complications by imagining that the charge is conveyed by a uniform steady current density that is perpendicular to the full area of the plates. One way of approaching this ideal would be to replace the arrangement of Figure 7.4 by thick cylinders separated by a narrow gap, as in Figure 7.5. The gap between the cylinders is tiny compared to their diameters, so the system behaves like an infinite parallel plate capacitor, with the end-faces of the cylinders serving as the capacitor plates.

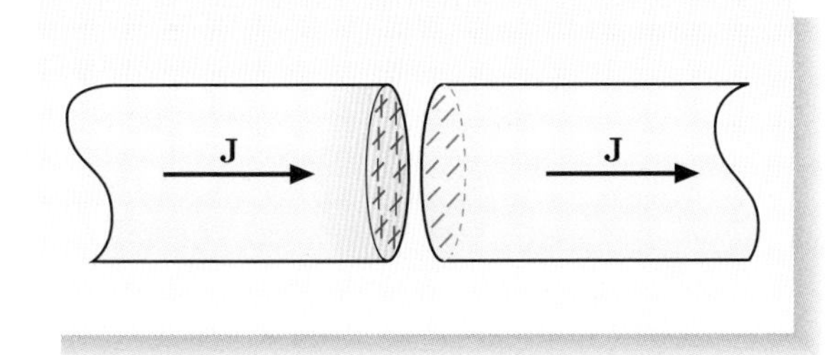


**Figure 7.5** A parallel plate capacitor formed from thick cylinders.

Between the plates, there is no charge flow so the current density **J** is equal to zero. However, the Maxwell term is non-zero there because the increasing charge on the plates produces a steadily increasing electric field between the plates. Taking the gap between the plates to be tiny (so that we can ignore edge effects), the electric field between the plates is uniform and has the instantaneous value

$$\mathbf{E} = \frac{Q(t)}{\varepsilon_0 A}\,\mathbf{e}_z, \tag{7.12}$$

See Chapter 5, Section 2.3.3.

where $Q(t)$ is the instantaneous charge on the positive plate, $A$ is the area of a plate and $\mathbf{e}_z$ is a unit vector pointing from the positive plate to the negative plate. The Maxwell term in the gap is

$$\varepsilon_0\mu_0\frac{\partial\mathbf{E}}{\partial t} = \frac{\mu_0}{A}\frac{\mathrm{d}Q}{\mathrm{d}t}\,\mathbf{e}_z,$$

so the differential version of the Ampère–Maxwell law in the gap is

$$\operatorname{curl}\mathbf{B} = \frac{\mu_0}{A}\frac{\mathrm{d}Q}{\mathrm{d}t}\,\mathbf{e}_z. \tag{7.13}$$

The corresponding integral equation is

$$\oint_C \mathbf{B}\cdot\mathrm{d}\mathbf{l} = \frac{\mu_0}{A}\frac{\mathrm{d}Q}{\mathrm{d}t}\int_S \mathbf{e}_z\cdot\mathrm{d}\mathbf{S}, \tag{7.14}$$

where $S$ is an open surface and $C$ is its perimeter.

Exploiting the axial symmetry of the situation, we use cylindrical coordinates with the $z$-axis along the line of symmetry. We also assume that the magnetic field has the form

$$\mathbf{B} = B_\phi(r,z)\,\mathbf{e}_\phi.$$

This form of the magnetic field can be justified by a reflection-symmetry argument similar to that given for an infinitely-long cylindrical conductor in

Chapter 4. For the moment, we have allowed for a *possible* dependence of $B_\phi$ on $z$. This is a wise precaution because the present situation does not have translational symmetry, but you will soon see that it is not necessary.

To apply the Ampère–Maxwell law, we choose the circular path $C$ shown in Figure 7.6, together with the disc $S$ that has $C$ as its boundary. Equation 7.14 then gives

$$B_\phi(r,z) \times 2\pi r = \frac{\mu_0}{A}\frac{\mathrm{d}Q}{\mathrm{d}t} \times \pi r^2.$$

So

$$B_\phi(r,z) = \frac{\mu_0 r}{2A}\frac{\mathrm{d}Q}{\mathrm{d}t}$$

and the magnetic field between capacitor plates is

$$\mathbf{B} = \frac{\mu_0 r}{2A}\frac{\mathrm{d}Q}{\mathrm{d}t}\mathbf{e}_\phi. \tag{7.15}$$

This is independent of $z$, and is also independent of time because we are assuming that the capacitor is being charged at a constant rate by a steady current.

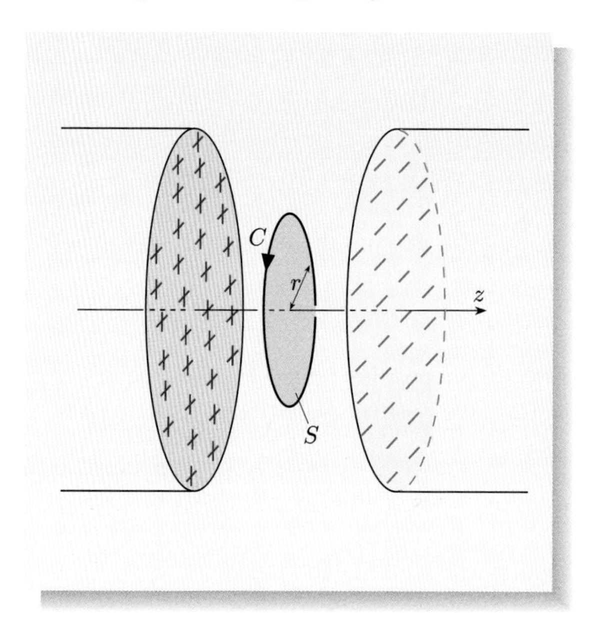


**Figure 7.6** A circular path $C$ and a disc $S$ used to find the magnetic field inside a capacitor that is being charged.

I should perhaps point out that I am *not* claiming that the Maxwell term *causes* the magnetic field inside the capacitor. It would be silly to neglect the currents that bring charge to the capacitor plates. These currents do not flow inside the capacitor, but there is nothing to prevent them from producing a magnetic field inside the capacitor. Indeed, if the gap between the plates is small, the magnetic field inside the capacitor due to external currents must overwhelm anything else. This may lead you to wonder why the above calculation, based on the Maxwell term, is valid. The logic is as follows. First, the time-varying charges on the capacitor plates produce a time-varying electric field between the plates. Then the Ampère–Maxwell law provides a relationship between the time-varying electric field and the circulation of the magnetic field. This relationship must be satisfied by all electric and magnetic fields, and it allows us to deduce the magnetic field from the known electric field *irrespective* of what the causes of these fields might be.

It is also instructive to calculate the magnetic field inside the capacitor by an alternative route. Instead of choosing $S$ to be a disc, we can take it to be the open cylinder shown in Figure 7.7, with its end-cap *outside* the capacitor. The unit normal to the end-cap is chosen to point along the positive $z$-axis, in accordance with the usual right-hand grip rule.

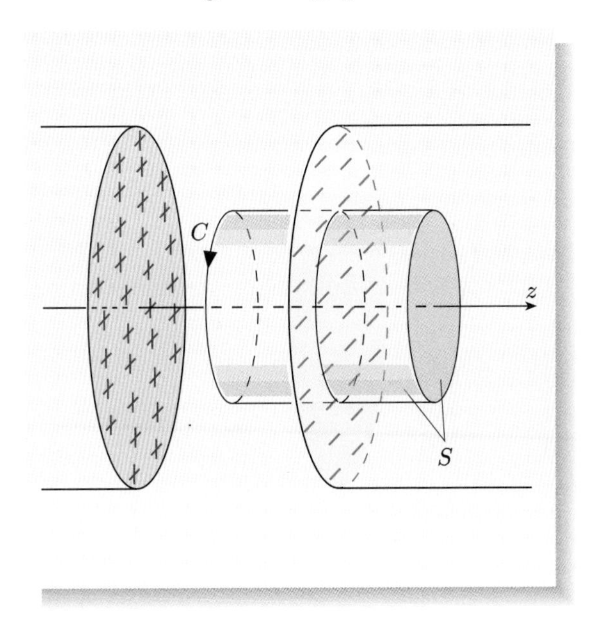


**Figure 7.7** A circular path $C$ and an open cylinder $S$ used to find the magnetic field inside the capacitor. The open cylinder has an end-cap on right, but no end-cap on the left.

Outside the infinite parallel plate capacitor, there is no time-dependent electric field, so there is no Maxwell term. However, there is the steady uniform current density that brings charge to the capacitor plates. This current density obviously obeys

$$J_z A = \frac{\mathrm{d}Q}{\mathrm{d}t}.$$

Now, both the Maxwell term inside the capacitor and the current density outside the capacitor are perpendicular to the capacitor plates (remember, we have carefully avoided any radial flow of current). So, if we apply the integral version of the Ampère–Maxwell law (Equation 7.11) to the surface in Figure 7.7, the curved sides of the cylinder contribute nothing, and we are left with an integral over the end-cap. The Ampère–Maxwell law then gives

$$B_\phi(r) \times 2\pi r = \mu_0 J_z \times \pi r^2 = \frac{\mu_0}{A}\frac{\mathrm{d}Q}{\mathrm{d}t} \times \pi r^2,$$

exactly as before. This shows why the Maxwell term is needed. Without it, these two methods of calculating the magnetic field inside the capacitor would give different answers, leading to a contradiction. Very similar calculations show that the magnetic field outside the capacitor is given by exactly the same expression, so there is no difference between the magnetic field inside and outside the capacitor.

Finally, it is interesting to note that the predictions of the Ampère–Maxwell law can be put to a direct experimental test. In 1973, Carver and Rajhel carried out a demonstration using the apparatus sketched in Figure 7.8. An *oscillating* voltage was applied across the circular plates of a large parallel plate capacitor, producing an oscillating electric field inside the capacitor. From the above argument, we would expect this to be accompanied by an oscillating $B_\phi$ field. The toroidal coil in Figure 7.8 was designed to detect this. The oscillating magnetic flux through the toroidal coil induced an oscillating voltage, which was easily detected on an oscilloscope.

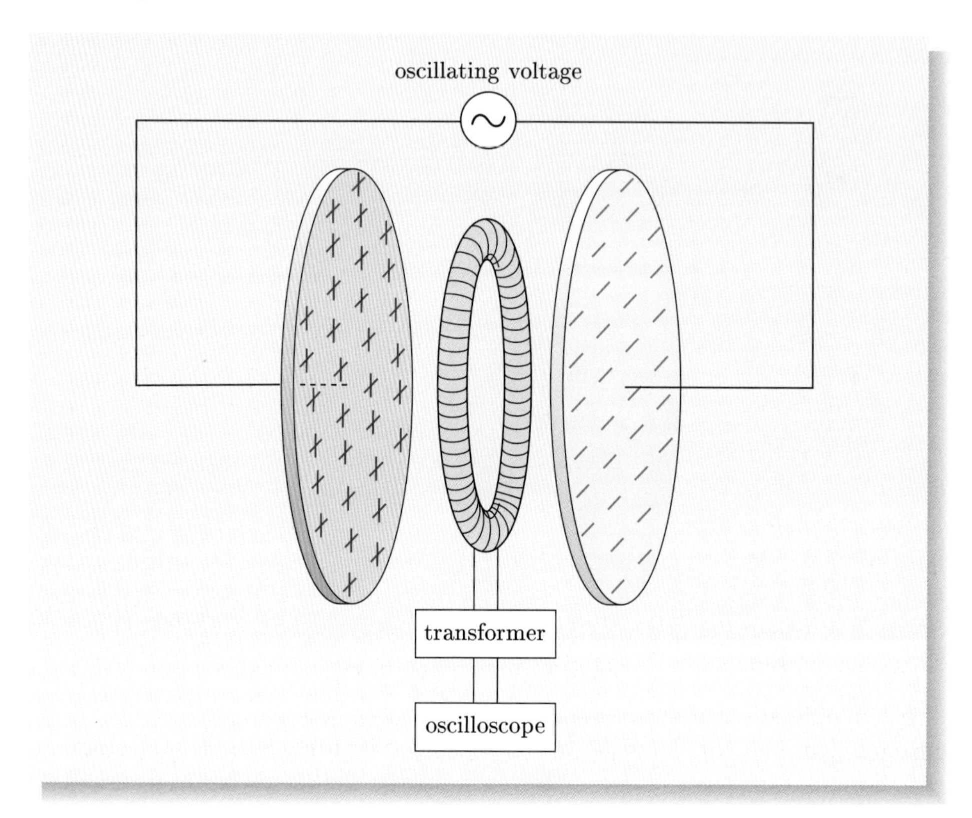


**Figure 7.8** A direct test of the Ampère–Maxwell law.

## 7.3 Maxwell's equations

We have reached a major milestone. All four of Maxwell's equations are now in place. This is an appropriate place to review their meaning and significance. We concentrate here on the differential versions, which are as follows:

$$\operatorname{div}\mathbf{E} = \frac{\rho}{\varepsilon_0}$$

$$\operatorname{div}\mathbf{B} = 0$$

$$\operatorname{curl}\mathbf{E} = -\frac{\partial \mathbf{B}}{\partial t}$$

$$\operatorname{curl}\mathbf{B} = \mu_0\mathbf{J} + \varepsilon_0\mu_0\frac{\partial \mathbf{E}}{\partial t}.$$

- Name the above equations.
- In the order presented, the equations are called: Gauss's law, the no-monopole law, Faraday's law and the Ampère–Maxwell law. These equations are listed inside the front cover of the book, but it would be a real advantage to remember them. This may come naturally, after sufficient use.

Maxwell's equations are of great generality. They apply to all charge and current densities, whether static or time-dependent. Together, they describe the dynamical behaviour of the electromagnetic field. Each of Maxwell's equations is a local equation, relating field quantities at each point in space and at each instant in time, so all trace of instantaneous action at a distance has been eliminated. The revolutionary nature of this description was recognized by Einstein, who wrote:

> 'The formulation of [Maxwell's] equations is the most important event in physics since Newton's time, not only because of their wealth of content, but also because they form a pattern for a new type of law ... Maxwell's equations are laws representing the structure of the field ... All space is the scene of these laws and not, as for mechanical laws, only points in which matter or charges are present.'

Maxwell's equations are partial differential equations. They link the spatial and temporal rates of change of electric and magnetic fields, and they show how these rates of change are related to the sources of the fields — charge and current densities. The spatial rates of change of the fields are neatly bundled up as $\operatorname{div}\mathbf{E}$, $\operatorname{div}\mathbf{B}$, $\operatorname{curl}\mathbf{E}$ and $\operatorname{curl}\mathbf{B}$ — divergences and curls. This, in itself, is an immense simplification. Each field has three components, which can be partially differentiated with respect to three coordinates, so there are 18 first-order spatial partial derivatives of the electric and magnetic fields. The divergences and curls collect these partial derivatives together, focusing attention on only eight quantities of interest (a scalar for each divergence and three components for each curl). Moreover, divergences and curls have clear physical interpretations, telling us how the fields spread out and circulate at each point.

Where do the electric and magnetic fields come from? The modern answer is that they come from *the terms in Maxwell's equations that describe matter* — the charge and current densities, $\rho$ and $\mathbf{J}$. To be explicit about this, we can re-order and rearrange Maxwell's equations so that the two source terms appear on the right-hand sides of the first two equations:

$$\operatorname{div}\mathbf{E} = \frac{\rho}{\varepsilon_0}$$

$$\operatorname{curl}\mathbf{B} - \varepsilon_0\mu_0\frac{\partial\mathbf{E}}{\partial t} = \mu_0\mathbf{J}$$

$$\operatorname{div}\mathbf{B} = 0$$

$$\operatorname{curl}\mathbf{E} + \frac{\partial\mathbf{B}}{\partial t} = 0.$$

In regions where there are no charges or currents, all four equations have zero on the right-hand sides. They then tell us the conditions that electric fields and magnetic fields must satisfy in empty space. These conditions describe the internal structure and dynamics of the electromagnetic field. We will discuss this dynamics in the next section, and you will see that it allows the propagation of wave-like disturbances — electromagnetic waves.

In regions where there are charges and currents, the first two equations have an additional role. They tell us how the electromagnetic field is coupled to matter, and the left-hand sides of these equations describe the response of the electromagnetic field to the local charge and current densities. The last two equations do not have this role, so Maxwell's equations are asymmetrical. The absence of source terms in the last two equations arises because magnetic monopoles, and monopole currents, are assumed to be non-existent.

When Maxwell introduced his equations, he expected them to apply in a special frame of reference — the frame of the stationary ether. This is not the modern view. We now believe equations apply in all **inertial frames of reference** — that is, all frames in which free particles move uniformly, with no acceleration. Maxwell's equations are also unaffected by time-reversal and by reflections in space.

Only one caveat need be mentioned. Maxwell's equations do not apply in non-inertial frames. In a rotating frame of reference, for example, the electric flux over a closed surface can be non-zero even though the surface encloses no net charge — a clear violation of Gauss's law. This should not alarm you. Most laws of physics, including the laws of conservation of energy and momentum, are restricted to inertial frames of reference, and Maxwell's equations are no exception. The use of inertial frames is implicitly assumed throughout this course.

**Exercise 7.3** Show that Maxwell's equations are unchanged by the operation of time-reversal, which changes $t \to -t$, $\mathbf{J} \to -\mathbf{J}$ and $\mathbf{B} \to -\mathbf{B}$, but leaves $\rho$ and $\mathbf{E}$ unchanged.

**Exercise 7.4** Show that the equation of continuity is contained within the Ampère–Maxwell law and Gauss's law. ■

# 7.4 Let there be light!

## 7.4.1 Electromagnetic waves

This section gives a brief introduction to light and electromagnetic waves. You will have the opportunity to revisit this material in the last book of the course.

The idea that light is an electromagnetic wave had occurred to Faraday while Maxwell was still a schoolboy, but Maxwell was the first person to possess a complete set of equations describing the dynamical behaviour of electric and magnetic fields. Believing that Faraday was correct, Maxwell set out to show that his equations have wave-like solutions that propagate through empty space at the speed of light.

Electric and magnetic fields are produced by charges and currents, but these fields also extend into surrounding regions of empty space. For example, charges and currents in the Sun produce electromagnetic fields which travel across almost empty space before reaching sunbathers on a beach on Earth. The detailed relationship between the fields and their sources will not be discussed here. Instead, we take the existence of time-varying electric and magnetic fields for granted, and concentrate on their propagation through space. In empty space, the charge and current densities are equal to zero, so Maxwell's equations become

$$\operatorname{div} \mathbf{E} = 0 \tag{7.16}$$

$$\operatorname{div} \mathbf{B} = 0 \tag{7.17}$$

$$\operatorname{curl} \mathbf{E} = -\frac{\partial \mathbf{B}}{\partial t} \tag{7.18}$$

$$\operatorname{curl} \mathbf{B} = \varepsilon_0 \mu_0 \frac{\partial \mathbf{E}}{\partial t}. \tag{7.19}$$

Our aim is to show that these equations have wave-like solutions which describe oscillating electric and magnetic fields that propagate through space. These wave-like solutions are called **electromagnetic waves**.

### Starting points

We begin by making some simplifying assumptions about the electric field. This is legitimate because we are not looking for the most general solution to Maxwell's equations, but only for special solutions that exhibit wave-like behaviour. We will ultimately check that our solutions for the fields satisfy all of Maxwell's equations, and hence obtain retrospective support for our initial assumptions.

If you drop a pebble in a pond, waves spread out in all directions on the surface. Many electromagnetic waves spread out radially like this, but we will consider a disturbance that propagates in a fixed direction, like the parallel beam from a searchlight. We will take the direction of propagation to be the $z$-axis. For simplicity, we assume that the electric field depends only on $z$ and $t$, and does not depend on $x$ or $y$ at all. At any given instant, the surfaces on which the electric field has a constant value are planes perpendicular to the $z$-axis. These planes are infinite in extent, corresponding to an infinitely wide beam. Disturbances of this type are called **plane waves**. We will also assume that the electric field oscillates along a fixed direction. Disturbances of this type are called **linearly polarized waves**.

With these assumptions, the electric field takes the form

$$\mathbf{E} = f(z,t)\,\mathbf{u}, \tag{7.20}$$

where $f(z,t)$ is some (as yet unspecified) function of $z$ and $t$ and $\mathbf{u} = u_x\,\mathbf{e}_x + u_y\,\mathbf{e}_y + u_z\,\mathbf{e}_z$ is a fixed unit vector. This electric field, and any associated magnetic field, must satisfy all four of Maxwell's equations in empty space. We will now show that this can be achieved *provided that* certain conditions are met. So our confirmation that electromagnetic waves can exist will also predict some of their properties.

### Getting agreement with Gauss's law

Substituting the assumed form of the electric field (Equation 7.20) into the empty-space version of Gauss's law (Equation 7.16) gives

$$\operatorname{div}\mathbf{E} = \frac{\partial f}{\partial x}\,u_x + \frac{\partial f}{\partial y}\,u_y + \frac{\partial f}{\partial z}\,u_z = 0.$$

The first two partial derivatives are equal to zero because $f$ does not depend on $x$ or $y$. So we obtain

$$\frac{\partial f}{\partial z}\,u_z = 0.$$

We are interested in disturbances that propagate in the $z$-direction, so can ignore the possibility that $\partial f/\partial z = 0$ everywhere. It follows that $u_z = 0$. This means that $\mathbf{u}$ is a unit vector perpendicular to the $z$-direction. With no loss in generality, we can choose $\mathbf{u}$ to be equal to $\mathbf{e}_x$. It is then appropriate to replace $f$ by $E_x$, and write Equation 7.20 in the form

$$\mathbf{E} = E_x(z,t)\,\mathbf{e}_x. \tag{7.21}$$

A wave of this type, in which the variable of interest oscillates perpendicular to the direction of propagation, is said to be **transverse**.

### Getting agreement with Faraday's law

Substituting Equation 7.21 into Faraday's law gives

$$\operatorname{curl}\mathbf{E} = \begin{vmatrix} \mathbf{e}_x & \mathbf{e}_y & \mathbf{e}_z \\ \dfrac{\partial}{\partial x} & \dfrac{\partial}{\partial y} & \dfrac{\partial}{\partial z} \\ E_x & 0 & 0 \end{vmatrix} = \frac{\partial E_x}{\partial z}\,\mathbf{e}_y = -\frac{\partial \mathbf{B}}{\partial t}. \tag{7.22}$$

This shows that a propagating electric wave is automatically accompanied by a transverse magnetic wave. The magnetic field oscillates in the $y$-direction, which is perpendicular to the direction of propagation and to the electric field. Expressing the magnetic field as

$$\mathbf{B} = B_y(z,t)\,\mathbf{e}_y, \tag{7.23}$$

Equation 7.22 requires that

$$\frac{\partial B_y}{\partial t} = -\frac{\partial E_x}{\partial z}. \tag{7.24}$$

This condition makes good sense. Faraday's law links the rate of change of the magnetic field to the spatial variation of the electric field. The consequences of this condition will be explored at the end of our analysis, after agreement with the remaining two Maxwell equations has been checked.

### Getting agreement with the no-monopole law

Substituting Equation 7.23 into the no-monopole law gives immediate agreement because

$$\operatorname{div} \mathbf{B} = \frac{\partial}{\partial y} B_y(z,t) = 0. \tag{7.25}$$

The no-monopole law is analogous to Gauss's law in empty space, and it leads to a similar conclusion: the magnetic wave must be transverse. This has already been established using Faraday's law, so no further conditions are added at this stage.

### Getting agreement with the Ampère–Maxwell law

Finally, our electric and magnetic fields must satisfy the Ampère–Maxwell law in empty space. Using Equations 7.21 and 7.23, we obtain

$$\operatorname{curl} \mathbf{B} = \begin{vmatrix} \mathbf{e}_x & \mathbf{e}_y & \mathbf{e}_z \\ \dfrac{\partial}{\partial x} & \dfrac{\partial}{\partial y} & \dfrac{\partial}{\partial z} \\ 0 & B_y & 0 \end{vmatrix} = -\frac{\partial B_y}{\partial z}\,\mathbf{e}_x = \varepsilon_0\mu_0 \frac{\partial E_x}{\partial t}\,\mathbf{e}_x,$$

which requires that

$$\varepsilon_0\mu_0 \frac{\partial E_x}{\partial t} = -\frac{\partial B_y}{\partial z}. \tag{7.26}$$

This condition is analogous to that obtained using Faraday's law. The Ampère–Maxwell law links the rate of change of the electric field to the spatial variation of the magnetic field.

### Pulling it all together

The electric and magnetic fields given by Equations 7.21 and 7.23 can satisfy all four of Maxwell's equations in empty space. Gauss's law and the no-monopole law are immediately satisfied because the fields are transverse. Faraday's law and the Ampère–Maxwell law will also be satisfied if we can find electric and magnetic fields that obey Equations 7.24 and 7.26.

We are looking for wave-like solutions, so it is sensible to try

$$E_x(z,t) = E_0 \sin\left(2\pi\left(\frac{z}{\lambda} - \frac{t}{T}\right)\right) \tag{7.27}$$

which is a typical expression for a monochromatic plane wave propagating in the $z$-direction. In this equation, $E_0$ is the maximum value of the electric field: this is

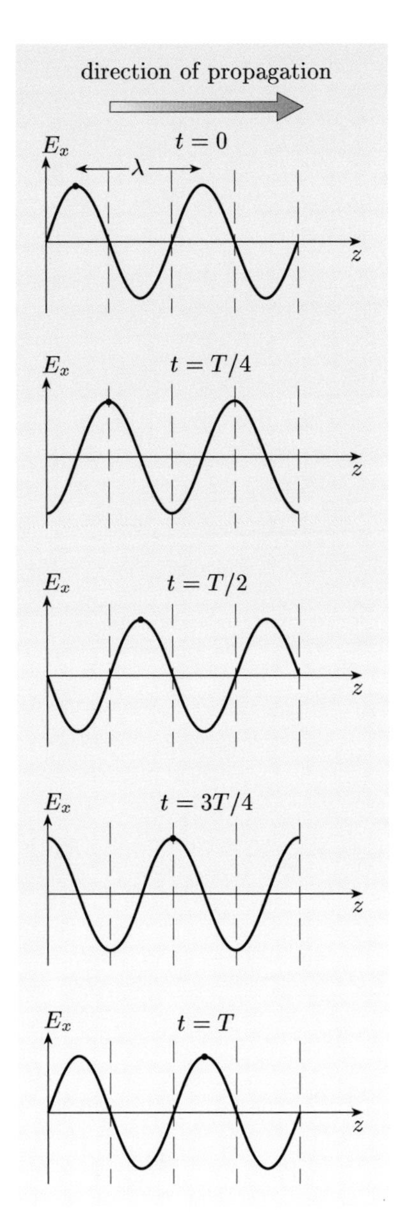


**Figure 7.9** A monochromatic plane wave propagating in the $z$-direction.

the **amplitude** of the wave. At any fixed time, $\lambda$ is the distance between successive wave crests: this is the **wavelength** of the wave. At any fixed position, $T$ is the time between successive wave crests: this is the **period** of the wave. Because there is only one wavelength associated with the wave, it is said to be **monochromatic**. Figure 7.9 shows the progression of the wave at times $t = 0$, $T/4$, $T/2$, $3T/4$ and $T$. The sinusoidal shape travels undistorted in the positive $z$-direction at the constant speed $c = \lambda/T$.

Equation 7.27 is more commonly written in the form

$$E_x(z,t) = E_0 \sin(kz - \omega t), \tag{7.28}$$

where $k = 2\pi/\lambda$ is the **wavenumber** of the wave and $\omega = 2\pi/T$ is the **angular frequency** (not to be confused with the **frequency** $f = 1/T$). The speed of the wave is then given by

$$c = \frac{\lambda}{T} = f\lambda = \frac{\omega}{k}.$$

Substituting this expression for the electric field into Equation 7.24 (a consequence of Faraday's law) we obtain

$$\frac{\partial B_y}{\partial t} = -\frac{\partial E_x}{\partial z} = -kE_0 \cos(kz - \omega t).$$

This equation can be integrated to give

$$B_y = \frac{k}{\omega} E_0 \sin(kz - \omega t) + K(x,y,z),$$

where $K(x,y,z)$ is any time-independent function. Time-independent fields such as $K$ can always exist, but they obviously play no part in the propagation of electromagnetic waves. It is therefore sensible to set $K = 0$. Remembering that the speed of the wave is given by $c = \omega/k$, we can write

$$B_y = B_0 \sin(kz - \omega t), \quad \text{where } B_0 = \frac{E_0}{c}. \tag{7.29}$$

Figure 7.10 shows how the electric and magnetic fields are related to one another. The electric and magnetic waves have similar shapes and are exactly in phase with one another. At all times $E = cB$, and both waves travel through empty space at the speed $c$.

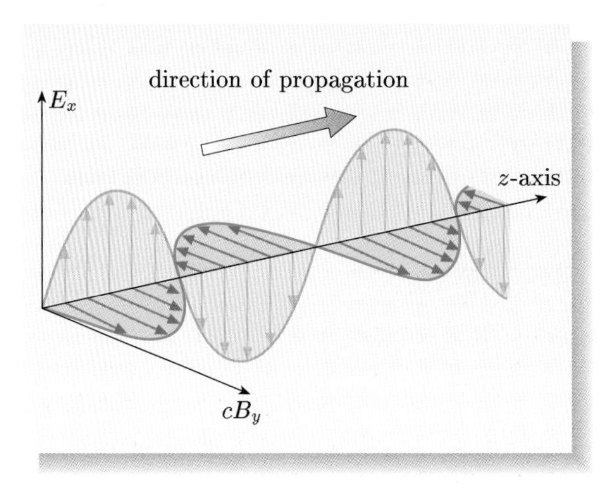


**Figure 7.10** An electromagnetic wave travelling in the $z$-direction.

Finally, we impose the condition given in Equation 7.26 (a consequence of the Ampère–Maxwell law). Rearranging this equation and inserting our expressions for the electric and magnetic fields (Equations 7.28 and 7.29), we obtain

$$\begin{aligned} 0 = \varepsilon_0\mu_0\frac{\partial E_x}{\partial t} + \frac{\partial B_y}{\partial z} &= -\omega\varepsilon_0\mu_0 E_0\cos(kz-\omega t) + kB_0\cos(kz-\omega t) \\ &= (kB_0 - \omega\varepsilon_0\mu_0 E_0)\cos(kz-\omega t) \\ &= kB_0(1-\varepsilon_0\mu_0 c^2)\cos(kz-\omega t), \end{aligned}$$

where we have used $\omega = ck$ and $E_0 = cB_0$ in the final line.

We therefore conclude that, in empty space, electromagnetic waves propagate at the fixed speed

$$c = \frac{1}{\sqrt{\varepsilon_0\mu_0}}. \qquad (7.30)$$

Now for the moment of truth. The constants $\varepsilon_0$ and $\mu_0$ can be found by measuring electrostatic and magnetostatic forces. In fact, the proportionality constant in Coulomb's law is

$$k_{\text{elec}} = \frac{1}{4\pi\varepsilon_0} = 8.988\times10^9\,\text{N}\,\text{m}^2\,\text{C}^{-2},$$

and the proportionality constant in the Biot–Savart law is

$$k_{\text{mag}} = \frac{\mu_0}{4\pi} = 10^{-7}\,\text{N}\,\text{A}^{-2}.$$

The speed of electromagnetic waves in empty space is the square root of the ratio of these proportionality constants:

$$c = \frac{1}{\sqrt{\varepsilon_0\mu_0}} = \sqrt{\frac{k_{\text{elec}}}{k_{\text{mag}}}} = 3.00\times10^8\,\text{m}\,\text{s}^{-1}.$$

To a fanfare of trumpets, we note that this is numerically the same as the measured speed of light in a vacuum. In 1865, Maxwell wrote:

> 'This velocity is so nearly that of light that it seems we have strong reason to conclude that light itself (including radiant heat, and other radiations if any) is an electromagnetic disturbance in the form of waves propagated through the electromagnetic field according to electromagnetic laws.'

Maxwell's 'strong reason' was irresistible — it is now fully accepted that light is an electromagnetic wave, with frequencies in the narrow band that our eyes can detect. Optics has become a branch of electromagnetism.

Maxwell also hinted that other electromagnetic waves, with frequencies beyond the visible range, might exist, but he suggested no mechanism for producing these waves. The problem was not just to generate the waves, but also to detect them and measure their properties. In 1887, Heinrich Hertz embarked on a magnificent series of experiments which succeeded in doing all of this (Figure 7.11). Feeding an oscillating current into a circuit containing two metal spheres, he created an oscillating electric dipole. This generated electromagnetic waves with wavelengths more than $10^7$ times greater than the wavelength of visible light. The

**Figure 7.11** Heinrich Hertz (1857–1894).

electric field of these waves was detected by the spark it produced across a narrow gap in a conducting metal loop. Using this primitive equipment, Hertz measured the speed of the waves and confirmed that it agreed with the known speed of light. He showed that the waves are transverse rather than longitudinal, and he observed refraction, reflection and focusing of the waves. Everything was similar to visible light, but on a much larger length-scale and a much more leisurely time-scale.

Hertz's work had a dual effect. It provided vital confirmation of Maxwell's theory, and it also led to rapid technological developments. In 1895 a radio signal was transmitted a distance of one mile; by 1900, the range had increased to 200 miles, and in 1901 a signal crossed the Atlantic. The first broadcasting radio station opened in Pittsburgh in 1920. The rest, as they say, is history. Society has been totally transformed by broadcast radio and television, satellite communication, mobile phones and wireless internet connection.

Today, the known electromagnetic spectrum extends over at least 20 orders of magnitude, from gamma rays to very low-frequency radio waves. There is no reason to believe that it does not stretch further, but there are practical difficulties in producing significant amounts of electromagnetic radiation at the extremes of frequency. Figure 7.12 shows the entire spectrum, with named regions characterized by their wavelength and frequency. The visible part of the spectrum occupies only a tiny fraction of the whole — from $4 \times 10^{14}$ Hz for red light to $8 \times 10^{14}$ Hz for violet light.

**Exercise 7.5** An electromagnetic wave is incident on a filter which absorbs all the electric field. Describe the magnetic field beyond the filter.

**Exercise 7.6** How many cycles of orange light pass a given point in $1.0 \times 10^{-14}$ s? (Orange light has a wavelength 600 nm.)

**Exercise 7.7** A moving charged particle travels at speed $v$ in the same direction as an electromagnetic wave. What is the ratio of the magnitudes of the electric and magnetic forces exerted on the particle by the electromagnetic wave? Under what conditions do these two force magnitudes become comparable? ■

**Figure 7.12** (See following page) The electromagnetic spectrum and its applications in various areas of medicine, technology and astronomy. The spectrum is displayed on logarithmic wavelength and frequency scales. Various parts of the spectrum are given the following abbreviations: extra long wave (ELW), long wave (LW), medium wave (MW), short wave (SW), very high frequency (VHF), ultra high frequency (UHF), terahertz (THz), infrared (IR) and ultraviolet (UV). The region indicated by the Sun symbol accounts for 99% of the Sun's output. The grey regions are significantly absorbed or reflected by the Earth's atmosphere, and so are of limited use to astronomers. The left-hand side of the diagram shows some typical lengths for comparisons with the wavelength scale. The right-hand side of the diagram shows how different wavelengths are used in applications. In some cases, a range of wavelengths is involved and a typical value is indicated.

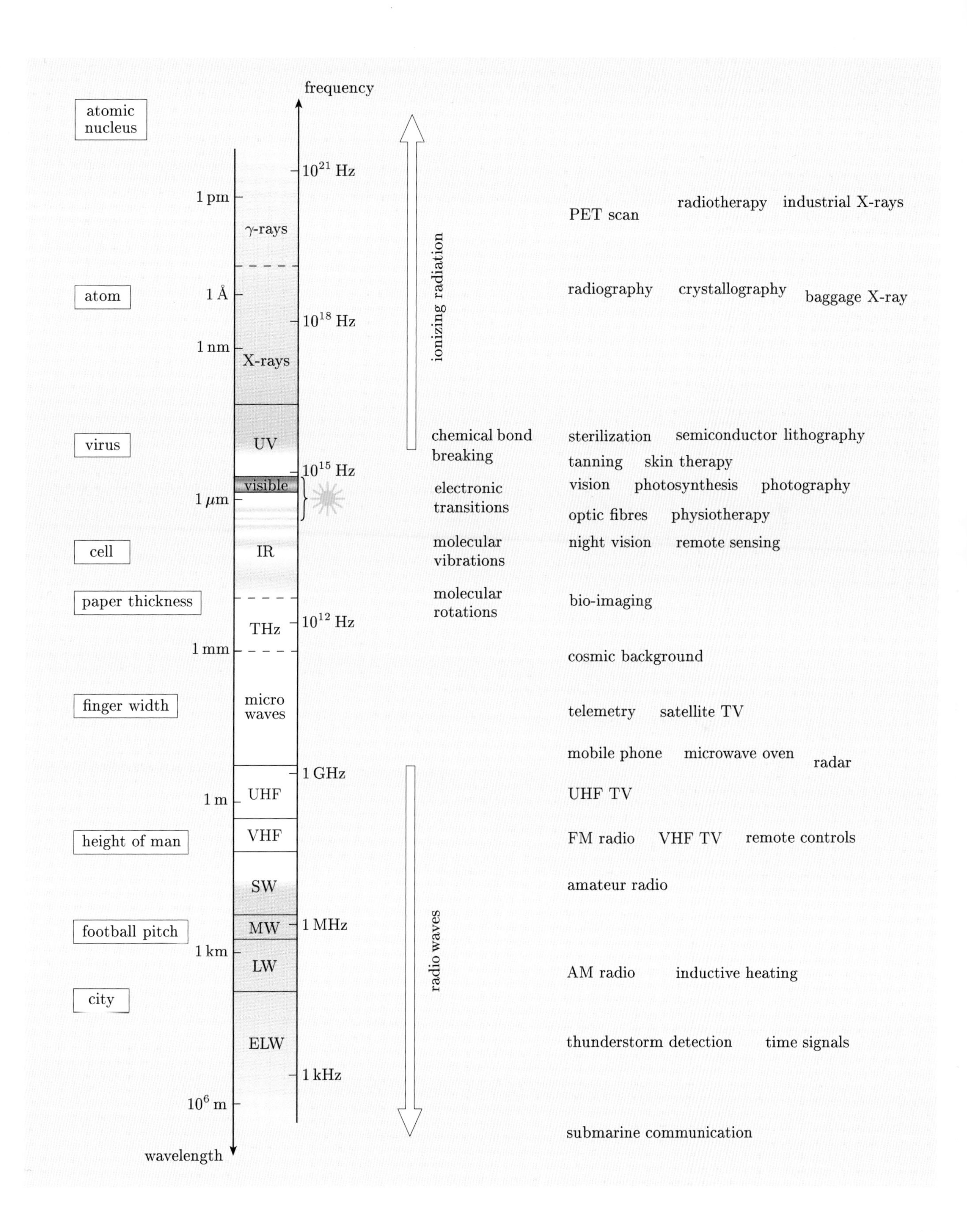
frequency
atomic nucleus
1 pm
$10^{21}$ Hz
γ-rays
PET scan
radiotherapy
industrial X-rays
atom
1 Å
$10^{18}$ Hz
1 nm
X-rays
ionizing radiation
radiography
crystallography
baggage X-ray
virus
UV
chemical bond breaking
sterilization
semiconductor lithography
tanning
skin therapy
$10^{15}$ Hz
visible
1 μm
electronic transitions
vision
photosynthesis
photography
optic fibres
physiotherapy
cell
IR
molecular vibrations
night vision
remote sensing
paper thickness
molecular rotations
bio-imaging
THz
$10^{12}$ Hz
1 mm
cosmic background
finger width
micro waves
telemetry
satellite TV
mobile phone
microwave oven
radar
1 GHz
1 m
UHF
UHF TV
height of man
VHF
FM radio
VHF TV
remote controls
SW
amateur radio
football pitch
MW
1 MHz
radio waves
1 km
LW
AM radio
inductive heating
city
ELW
thunderstorm detection
time signals
1 kHz
$10^6$ m
submarine communication
wavelength

### 7.4.2 The energy of electromagnetic waves

You saw in Chapter 5 that the energy density of an electric field $\mathbf{E}$ is

$$u_{\text{elec}} = \frac{1}{2}\varepsilon_0 E^2.$$

Although we will not prove it in this book, a very similar result applies to magnetic fields. The energy density of a magnetic field $\mathbf{B}$ is

$$u_{\text{mag}} = \frac{1}{2\mu_0}B^2.$$

It follows that an electromagnetic wave has a certain energy density, and as the wave travels through space, this energy is transported with it. Energy transport is clearly an important feature of electromagnetic waves, and explains how we can benefit from the energy generated in the Sun, $1.5 \times 10^8$ km away.

Let's compare the energy densities in the electric and magnetic waves in an electromagnetic wave. If $E$ and $B$ are the magnitudes of the electric and magnetic fields at a given point, we have

$$\frac{u_{\text{elec}}}{u_{\text{mag}}} = \frac{\varepsilon_0\mu_0 E^2}{B^2} = \frac{E^2}{c^2B^2}.$$

However, we know from Equations 7.28 and 7.29 that $E = cB$ at any point in an electromagnetic wave. So the electric and magnetic waves have equal energy densities.

In a small time interval $\Delta t$, the amount of energy transported across an area $\Delta S$, perpendicular to the direction of propagation of the wave, is given by the energy in the shaded volume in Figure 7.13. Allowing for the equal energy densities of the electric and magnetic waves, this is

$$\Delta U = (u_{\text{elec}} + u_{\text{mag}}) \times \Delta S \times c\,\Delta t = \varepsilon_0 c E^2\,\Delta S\,\Delta t.$$

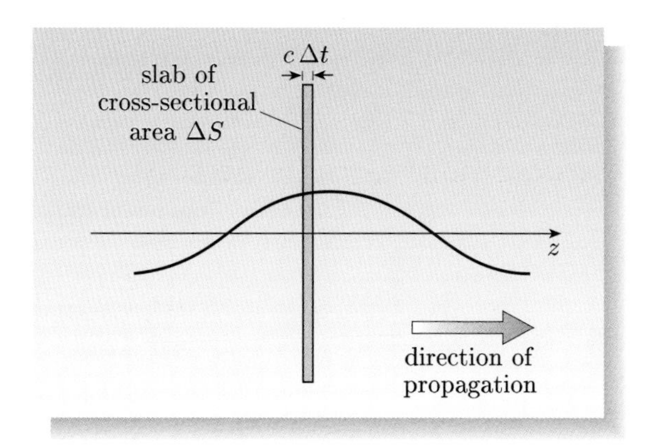


**Figure 7.13** The electromagnetic energy in the shaded volume has crossed the area $\Delta S$ in time $\Delta t$.

The energy flux is *per unit area*, and is a scalar field defined at each point in space. It has a different character from electric or magnetic fluxes which are not per unit area and are defined over specified surfaces.

The rate of transfer of energy per unit area perpendicular to the direction of propagation of the wave is called the **energy flux**, so we have

$$\text{energy flux} = \frac{\Delta U}{\Delta S\,\Delta t} = \varepsilon_0 c E^2.$$

The energy flux varies rapidly as peaks and troughs of the electromagnetic wave pass through the given area. Generally, we wish to know the average energy flux over one period of the wave. For a monochromatic, plane electromagnetic wave travelling in the $z$-direction, the electric field is proportional to $E_0 \cos(kz - \omega t)$, so we need to average $\cos^2(kz - \omega t)$ over one period. Using the identity $\cos^2\theta = (1 + \cos 2\theta)/2$, we have

$$\frac{1}{T}\int_0^T \cos^2(kz - \omega t)\,\mathrm{d}t = \frac{1}{2} + \left(\frac{1}{2T}\int_0^T \cos(2kz - 2\omega t)\,\mathrm{d}t\right).$$

Because $T = 2\pi/\omega$, the integral on the right-hand side is the integral of a cosine over a whole number of periods, and so is equal to zero. We therefore conclude that

$$\text{average energy flux} = \frac{1}{2}\varepsilon_0 c E_0^2 = \frac{1}{2}\sqrt{\frac{\varepsilon_0}{\mu_0}}\,E_0^2. \qquad (7.31)$$

**Exercise 7.8** At a receiver, a strong radio signal has an electric field of amplitude $0.01\ \mathrm{V\,m^{-1}}$. What is the average energy flux associated with this signal? ■

This is a suitable point at which to end this book. All of Maxwell's equations have been introduced, and you have seen that these equations permit electromagnetic waves to travel through empty space. Electric and magnetic fields are not just mathematical abstractions, but are real enough to transport energy from distant sources. You are bathed in various hues of light from the objects you see around you. Radio waves from radio and TV stations and a vast number of transmitting mobile phones are passing through you. In addition, there is a cosmic microwave background from the first minutes of the Universe and gamma rays from the most distant stars. No wonder Richard Feynman felt able to make the following judgement:

> 'From a long view of the history of mankind — seen from, say, ten thousand years from now — there can be little doubt that the most significant event of the 19th century will be judged as Maxwell's discovery of the laws of electrodynamics.'

**Figure 7.14** Maxwell, at the height of his powers in the mid-1860s.

## Appendix 7.1: A note on displacement current density

This appendix is optional reading. It is included for the sake of comparison with other texts.

The Ampère–Maxwell law,

$$\mathrm{curl}\,\mathbf{B} = \mu_0\mathbf{J} + \varepsilon_0\mu_0\frac{\partial\mathbf{E}}{\partial t}, \qquad \text{(Eqn 7.10)}$$

is sometimes expressed in the form

$$\mathrm{curl}\,\mathbf{B} = \mu_0(\mathbf{J} + \mathbf{J}_\mathrm{d}), \qquad (7.32)$$

where $\mathbf{J}_\mathrm{d} = \varepsilon_0\partial\mathbf{E}/\partial t$ is called the **displacement current density**. The Maxwell term is then equal to $\mu_0\mathbf{J}_\mathrm{d}$. Setting aside the adjective 'displacement' for the moment, this terminology appears to be reasonable because Equation 7.32 shows that $\mathbf{J}_\mathrm{d}$ has the same units as the current density $\mathbf{J}$. Regrouping and renaming terms in this way cannot affect our predictions, but it does affect the language we use to describe electromagnetism, and has provoked heated discussions between physicists.

The origins of the dispute go back to Maxwell himself, who did not know that charge is a property of particles, but thought of it as a distortion or displacement in the ether. With this background, Maxwell saw no reason to place the displacement current density on a different footing to the ordinary current density, and regarded both as contributing to a *total current density* $(\mathbf{J} + \mathbf{J}_\mathrm{d})$. Although this interpretation arose from a murky understanding of the nature of charge and current, it is still in fairly common use today.

This book gives a different description, which can be traced back to Lorentz. About twenty years after Maxwell's death, Lorentz promoted the modern view that charge is carried by particles, and that currents are just flows of charged particles. Lorentz insisted that charge and current densities are *only* sources of electric and magnetic fields. The term $\varepsilon_0\mu_0\partial\mathbf{E}/\partial t$ in the Ampère–Maxwell law is therefore regarded as part of the *response* of the electromagnetic field, not as one of its sources. This is why I have called it the 'Maxwell term' — a neutral expression which carries no implication that we are dealing with any kind of current density.

Although we cannot go into the details here, Lorentz solved Maxwell's equations to show that the values of the electric and magnetic fields at a given point and time (not just their divergences and curls) can be related to the charge and current densities throughout space. Because it takes time for information to travel from distant sources to the point at which the fields are measured, we need to know the charges and currents at times *before* the instant when the fields are measured. This delay emerges naturally from Lorentz's solutions to Maxwell's equations. An analogy can be drawn with throwing a stone into a pond. If you want to know about the ripples reaching the sides of the pond, you need to know about the motion of the stone at an earlier time, when it struck the water.

Things are very different in the description that treats the displacement current density as a source term. In this description, the spirit of Ampère's law is retained, while the definition of the total current density is modified. The Biot–Savart law is equivalent to Ampère's law, so this means that the Biot–Savart law can be extended to time-dependent situations *provided that* we use the total current density $(\mathbf{J} + \mathbf{J}_\mathrm{d})$ to define current elements. However, when we do this, it is essential to use the *present* values of $\mathbf{J}$ and $\mathbf{J}_\mathrm{d}$ — the values at the precise instant when the field is measured. No delays are involved. That is why I cannot take this description literally. Since the advent of relativity, it is much more natural to use Lorentz's description, which has all the expected delays built into it.

Having said all this, it is important to remember that we are only talking about semantics. If you hear that there is a debate about the existence of the displacement current, this will almost certainly be about the interpretation of the Ampère–Maxwell law, rather than about its validity. An analogy can be drawn with the concept of centrifugal force in mechanics. Modern textbooks describe this as the *fictitious* outward force you feel when you are swung in a circle, and tend to use the inward centripetal force instead. Taking a leaf from mechanics, the displacement current density might be called a *fictitious* current density, though I have never seen this done. No doubt, tradition and respect for Maxwell are inhibiting factors.

A software package on the DVD allows you to explore the differential version of the Ampère–Maxwell law. This package is best studied after completing this chapter.

## Summary of Chapter 7

**Section 7.1** The law of conservation of charge applies locally at each point and time, so any variation of the total charge within a closed surface must be due to charges that flow across the surface of the region. This principle leads to the equation of continuity:

$$\frac{\partial \rho}{\partial t} + \operatorname{div} \mathbf{J} = 0,$$

where $\rho$ is the charge density and $\mathbf{J}$ is the current density at any given point and time. In magnetostatic situations, $\partial\rho/\partial t = \operatorname{div}\mathbf{J} = 0$.

**Section 7.2** Ampère's law, $\operatorname{curl}\mathbf{B} = \mu_0\mathbf{J}$, is a law of magnetostatics. It applies when $\partial\rho/\partial t = \operatorname{div}\mathbf{J} = 0$. The appropriate generalization, valid for time-dependent charge and current densities, is the Ampère–Maxwell law:

$$\operatorname{curl}\mathbf{B} = \mu_0\mathbf{J} + \varepsilon_0\mu_0\frac{\partial \mathbf{E}}{\partial t}.$$

The extra term, $\varepsilon_0\mu_0\partial\mathbf{E}/\partial t$, on the right-hand side is called the Maxwell term.

**Section 7.3** Maxwell's four equations

$$\operatorname{div}\mathbf{E} = \frac{\rho}{\varepsilon_0}$$

$$\operatorname{div}\mathbf{B} = 0$$

$$\operatorname{curl}\mathbf{E} = -\frac{\partial \mathbf{B}}{\partial t}$$

$$\operatorname{curl}\mathbf{B} = \mu_0\mathbf{J} + \varepsilon_0\mu_0\frac{\partial \mathbf{E}}{\partial t}$$

describe the dynamical behaviour of electromagnetic fields. They are the same in all inertial frames of reference and are unaffected by time-reversal. They are not valid in rotating frames of reference.

**Section 7.4** An electromagnetic wave is an oscillating disturbance of electric and magnetic fields that propagates in accordance with Maxwell's equations. We concentrate on linearly polarized monochromatic plane waves. In empty space, the electric and magnetic waves are in phase with one another, with $B = E/c$. They are mutually perpendicular and transverse to the direction of propagation. In empty space, electromagnetic waves travel at speed $c = 1/\sqrt{\varepsilon_0\mu_0} = 3.00 \times 10^8\,\mathrm{m\,s^{-1}}$.

Electromagnetic waves with frequencies in the visible range, $4 \times 10^{14}$ Hz to $8 \times 10^{14}$ Hz, all called light, but the known electromagnetic spectrum also embraces radio waves, microwaves, infrared, ultraviolet, X-rays and gamma rays. Electromagnetic waves transport energy. The amount of energy carried by the magnetic wave is the same as that carried by the electric wave. The energy flux is the total energy transported per unit area per unit time across a plane area perpendicular to the direction of propagation of the electromagnetic wave. Averaging over a complete cycle,

$$\text{average energy flux} = \frac{1}{2}\sqrt{\frac{\varepsilon_0}{\mu_0}}E_0^2,$$

where $E_0$ is the amplitude of the electric wave.

## Achievements from Chapter 7

*After studying this chapter you should be able to:*

**7.1** Explain the meaning of the newly defined (emboldened) terms and symbols, and use them appropriately.

**7.2** State the equation of continuity and use it in simple problems.

**7.3** State the conditions under which Ampère's law is true and explain why it does not apply more generally.

**7.4** State the Ampère–Maxwell law and explain why it has a greater domain of validity than Ampère's law.

**7.5** State and name the differential versions of Maxwell's four laws of electromagnetism.

**7.6** Recall the properties of linearly polarized plane monochromatic electromagnetic waves in empty space, including their transverse nature, speed and energy flux.

# Part II: The mathematics of electromagnetism

# Chapter 8 Mathematical Toolkit

## Introduction

This toolkit describes the mathematics you need to know to study this book, and covers most of the mathematics needed in the whole course. The main topics covered are vector algebra and vector calculus. It is worth noting that vector notation did not become widespread until well into the twentieth century. Maxwell had his own vector notation (based on a Gothic alphabet) but, for his readers' benefit, wrote out all the components and partial derivatives in full. Modern notation mercifully protects us from such complexity.

## 8.1 Basic vector algebra

### 8.1.1 Scalars and vectors

Section 8.1 is best read before or during your study of Chapter 1.

Most physical quantities can be represented by scalars or vectors. The distinction between these two types of mathematical object is fundamental.

A **scalar quantity** is fully described by a single number, together with an appropriate unit of measurement. For example, mass, electric charge, temperature and energy are all scalar quantities. We talk of a mass of 4.7 kg or an electric charge of $-3.6$ C. Some scalars, such as mass, turn out to be non-negative but others, such as charge, can be positive, zero or negative. The **magnitude** of a scalar quantity is the size of the quantity ignoring any possible negative sign. By definition, a magnitude is always non-negative. If $Q$ is a scalar, we denote its magnitude by $|Q|$. For example, an electric charge of $Q = -3.6\,\mathrm{C}$ has a magnitude of $|Q| = 3.6\,\mathrm{C}$.

kg is the symbol for kilogram and C is the symbol for coulomb.

A **vector quantity** is characterized by both a magnitude *and* a direction in space. For example, force is a vector because, when you push something, you push it in a definite direction. Pushing upwards is not the same thing as pushing sideways. Velocity is also a vector, telling us the speed of a body and its direction of motion. Throughout this course, vectors will be indicated by being printed in bold font (e.g. **F**). In longhand, the same task is accomplished by underlining with straight or curly lines (e.g. $\underline{\mathrm{F}}$ or $\utilde{\mathrm{F}}$). The **magnitude** of the vector **a** can always be written as $|\mathbf{a}|$. More commonly, though, it is written simply as $a$. The absence of bold print (and of underlining) is sufficient to show that $a$ is not a vector. This raises the stakes somewhat. It becomes *absolutely essential* for you to underline vectors in your handwritten work and to use a bold font for vectors in any word-processed documents. Care is needed, but the discipline turns out to be useful. After a while, you will develop an instinct for the correct grammar. For example, it would be meaningless to equate a vector to a scalar, so an equation that begins $\mathbf{E} = \ldots$ must surely require some emboldening (or underlining) on the right-hand side.

## 8.1.2 The geometric picture of vectors

It is easy to picture a vector in geometric terms. Think of an arrow. The length of the arrow represents the magnitude of the vector and the direction of the arrow represents the direction of the vector. Under exceptional circumstances, a vector can have zero magnitude. In this case, the arrow shrinks to a point, and no special direction is singled out; the vector is then called the **zero vector**, $\mathbf{0}$. If two vectors, $\mathbf{a}$ and $\mathbf{b}$, have the same magnitude and the same direction we say that these vectors are *equal* to one another and write

$$\mathbf{a} = \mathbf{b}.$$

Strictly speaking, this equality does not imply that the arrows representing $\mathbf{a}$ and $\mathbf{b}$ are identical. The arrows must have the same length and they must point in the same direction, but they could be parallel to one another, with different starting points. The geometric picture of a vector and the notion of vector equality suggests various ways of combining vectors and scalars.

### Multiplying a vector by a scalar

We often need to multiply a vector by a scalar. In Newtonian mechanics, for example, momentum is defined as $\mathbf{p} = m\mathbf{v}$, where $m$ is mass (a scalar) and $\mathbf{v}$ is velocity (a vector). Figure 8.1 shows how the act of multiplying a vector by a scalar is interpreted. This is also called the **scaling** of a vector by a scalar.

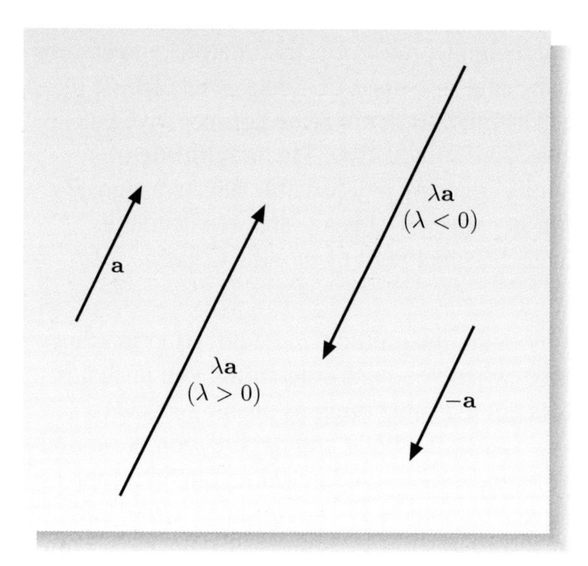


**Figure 8.1** Multiplying a vector by a scalar.

Given any vector $\mathbf{a}$ and any scalar $\lambda$, the product $\lambda\mathbf{a}$ is a new vector with magnitude $|\lambda|a$, pointing either parallel or antiparallel to $\mathbf{a}$. If $\lambda$ is positive, $\lambda\mathbf{a}$ points in the same direction as $\mathbf{a}$; if $\lambda$ is negative, $\lambda\mathbf{a}$ points in the opposite direction. Three special cases may be mentioned:

- $0\,\mathbf{a}$ has zero magnitude and is the zero vector, $\mathbf{0}$.
- The vector $-\mathbf{a}$ has the same magnitude as $\mathbf{a}$, but points in the opposite direction.

- $(1/a)\,\mathbf{a}$ is a vector of magnitude 1 (with no units) pointing in the same direction as $\mathbf{a}$. This vector is called the **unit vector** of $\mathbf{a}$ and is given the special symbol $\widehat{\mathbf{a}}$ (pronounced a-hat). Taking the equation $(1/a)\,\mathbf{a} = \widehat{\mathbf{a}}$, and multiplying both sides by $a$, we obtain

$$\mathbf{a} = a\,\widehat{\mathbf{a}}, \tag{8.1}$$

which neatly splits a vector into a product of two terms: $a$ gives the magnitude of the vector and $\widehat{\mathbf{a}}$ gives the direction of the vector. The units are contained in the magnitude, not the unit vector. Any unit vector is dimensionless and has magnitude 1; not 1 metre, 1 newton or 1 of anything else.

### Adding and subtracting vectors

We often need to add vectors, or subtract them from one another. For example, a single particle may simultaneously feel two different forces, $\mathbf{F}_1$ and $\mathbf{F}_2$. How does the particle respond? It responds just as if a single force, $\mathbf{F}_1 + \mathbf{F}_2$, had been applied to it. Here, $\mathbf{F}_1 + \mathbf{F}_2$ is the **vector sum** of the individual forces.

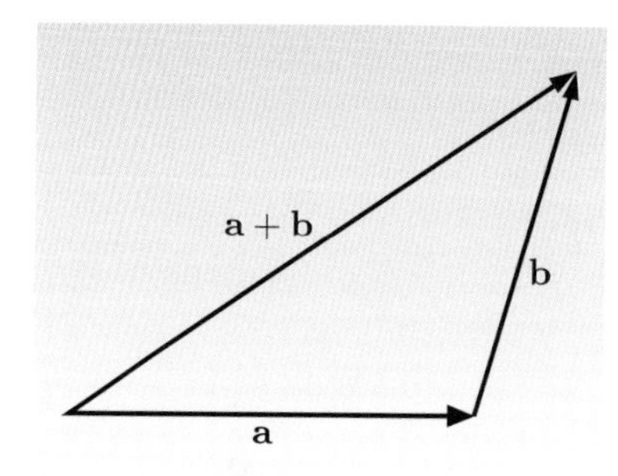


**Figure 8.2** The triangle rule for vector addition.

The geometric rule for adding two vectors is shown in Figure 8.2. Arrows representing the vectors are drawn with the head of the first arrow, $\mathbf{a}$, coincident with the tail of the second arrow, $\mathbf{b}$. The arrow joining the tail of $\mathbf{a}$ to the head of $\mathbf{b}$ then represents the vector sum $\mathbf{a} + \mathbf{b}$. This is called the **triangle rule**. Any number of vectors can be added together by repeated applications of this rule.

Vector subtraction is defined using scaling and vector addition. The vector $\mathbf{a} - \mathbf{b}$ is interpreted as the sum of $\mathbf{a}$ and $-\mathbf{b}$. We can then manipulate vector equations using the rules of ordinary algebra. For example, if $\mathbf{a} = \mathbf{b} + \lambda\mathbf{c}$, it follows that $\mathbf{c} = (\mathbf{a} - \mathbf{b})/\lambda$.

One use of vector subtraction is in describing the displacement of one point from another. Figure 8.3 shows two vectors $\mathbf{r}_1$ and $\mathbf{r}_2$ whose arrows start at the origin O and end at points 1 and 2. These vectors are called the **position vectors** of points 1 and 2. The figure also shows $\mathbf{r}_{12}$, which is the **displacement vector** of point 1 from point 2. Using the triangle rule, we see that

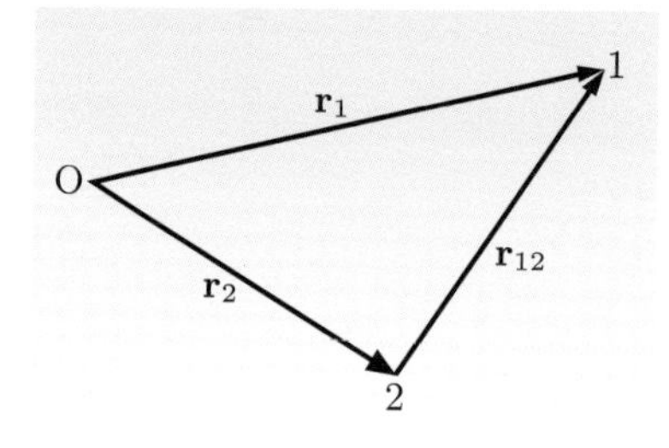


**Figure 8.3** The vector $\mathbf{r}_{12}$ is the displacement of point 1 from point 2.

$$\mathbf{r}_1 = \mathbf{r}_2 + \mathbf{r}_{12},$$

$$\text{so} \quad \mathbf{r}_{12} = \mathbf{r}_1 - \mathbf{r}_2. \tag{8.2}$$

Our notation is convenient because the indices 1 and 2 are in the same order on both sides of Equation 8.2. However, you will always have to remember that the displacement is *to* point 1 *from* point 2 — so the left-hand index labels the end-point and the right-hand index labels the start-point.

**Exercise 8.1** Rearrange the vector equation $6\mathbf{a} - 4\mathbf{b} + 2\mathbf{c} = \mathbf{0}$, to express $\mathbf{c}$ in terms of $\mathbf{a}$ and $\mathbf{b}$. ■

### 8.1.3 Vector components

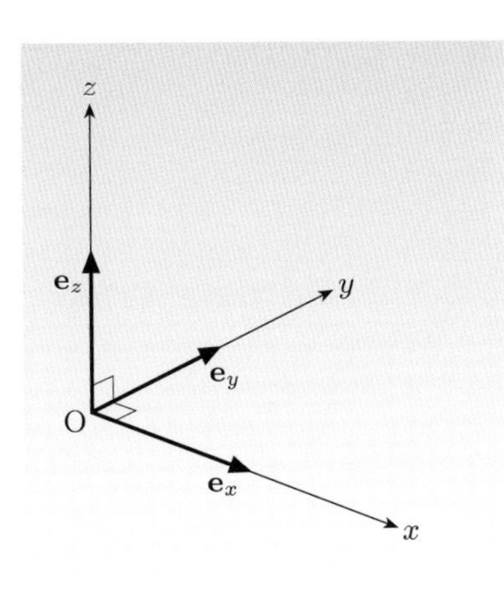


**Figure 8.4** A Cartesian coordinate system with its associated unit vectors. Cartesian unit vectors are sometimes denoted by $\mathbf{i}$, $\mathbf{j}$ and $\mathbf{k}$. However, these symbols have other meanings in electromagnetism. To avoid confusion we use $\mathbf{e}_x$, $\mathbf{e}_y$ and $\mathbf{e}_z$ from the outset.

An arrow gives a vivid image of a vector, but does not provide an efficient tool for calculations. It would be bad enough if we had to use the triangle rule on a sheet of paper, but vectors point in three-dimensional space, so we might be forced to build a three-dimensional sculpture with wires or rods. No thanks! Fortunately, there is a better way. Think of the instructions on a treasure map: from the large tree, walk 30 feet North, walk 20 feet East and dig 6 feet down. Any displacement can be specified by giving displacements along three standard directions, and something similar can be done for all vectors.

First, we create a **Cartesian coordinate system**, a set of three mutually perpendicular axes pointing outwards from an origin (Figure 8.4). The axes are called the $x$-axis, the $y$-axis and the $z$-axis. The unit vectors pointing in the directions of these axes are called **Cartesian unit vectors** and are given the symbols $\mathbf{e}_x$, $\mathbf{e}_y$ and $\mathbf{e}_z$. Since these are unit vectors, they have no units.

It is conventional to choose a **right-handed coordinate system** and Figure 8.5 shows how to do this, using the **right-hand rule**. Point the fingers of your right hand in the direction of the $x$-axis (Figure 8.5a), and bend them (rotating your wrist if necessary) in the direction of the $y$-axis (Figure 8.5b). If the outstretched thumb of your right hand points along the $z$-axis, your coordinate system is right-handed; otherwise it is left-handed. To begin with, the handedness of the coordinate system is of minor importance, but it will become significant later on. The signs in some equations involving magnetic fields depend on the handedness of the coordinate system so a definite choice must be made. We shall implicitly take all our coordinate systems to be right-handed.

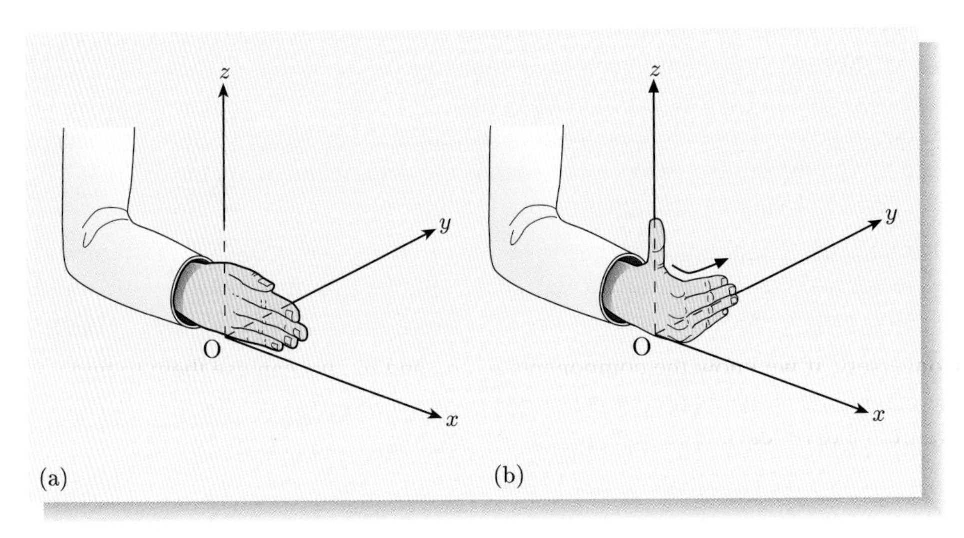


**Figure 8.5** Testing the handedness of a coordinate system.

Now, the crucial idea is that any vector can be split into a sum of other vectors, each aligned with a coordinate axis — that is, either parallel to the axis or antiparallel to the axis. Figure 8.6 shows an example of such a decomposition.

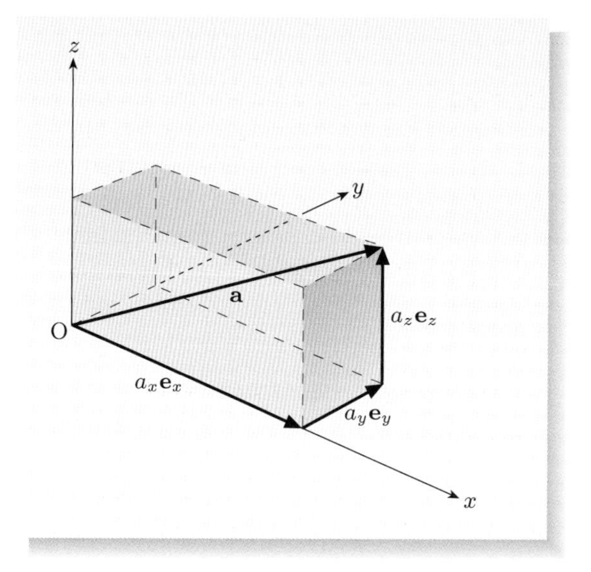


**Figure 8.6** Splitting the vector **a** into a sum of three vectors, each aligned with a coordinate axis.

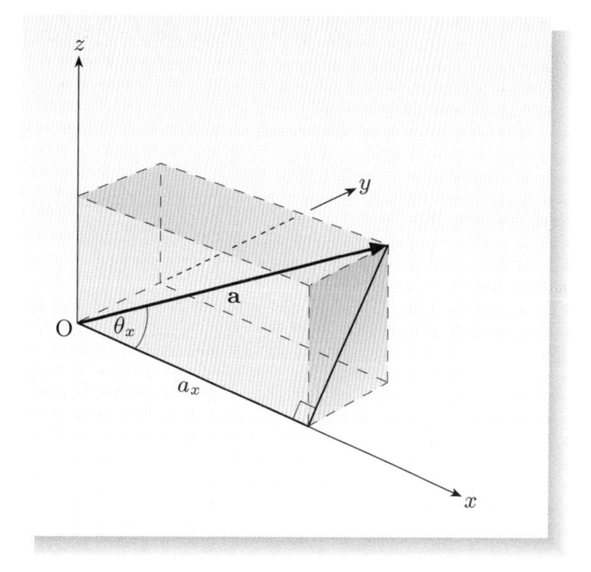


**Figure 8.7** Finding the $x$-component of a vector.

The vector along the $x$-axis can be written as $a_x\mathbf{e}_x$, where $a_x$ is a scalar. The vector along the $y$-axis can be written as $a_y\mathbf{e}_y$ and the vector along the $z$-axis can be written as $a_z\mathbf{e}_z$. It follows that any vector can be expressed in the form

$$\mathbf{a} = a_x\mathbf{e}_x + a_y\mathbf{e}_y + a_z\mathbf{e}_z. \tag{8.3}$$

The scalar quantities $a_x$, $a_y$ and $a_z$ are the **Cartesian components** of the vector (usually just called **components**). They have the same units as the vector, and may be positive, negative or zero.

If a vector has a known magnitude and a known direction, we can use trigonometry to find its components. From Figure 8.7 we see that

$$a_x = a\cos\theta_x,$$

where $a$ is the magnitude of the vector and $\theta_x$ is the angle between the direction of the vector and the $x$-axis. Similar formulae, with the appropriate angles, give the $y$- and $z$-components.

Conversely, if we know the components $a_x$, $a_y$ and $a_z$, we can use them to find the magnitude and direction of the vector **a**. Using Pythagoras's theorem twice in Figure 8.8 (overleaf), the magnitude of the vector is

$$a = \sqrt{a_x^2 + a_y^2 + a_z^2}. \tag{8.4}$$

The direction of the vector can be specified by giving the components of its unit vector, $\widehat{\mathbf{a}} = \mathbf{a}/a$. For example, the $x$-component of the unit vector $\widehat{\mathbf{a}}$ is

$$\frac{a_x}{a} = \cos\theta_x = \frac{a_x}{\sqrt{a_x^2 + a_y^2 + a_z^2}}, \tag{8.5}$$

with similar results for the $y$- and $z$-components.

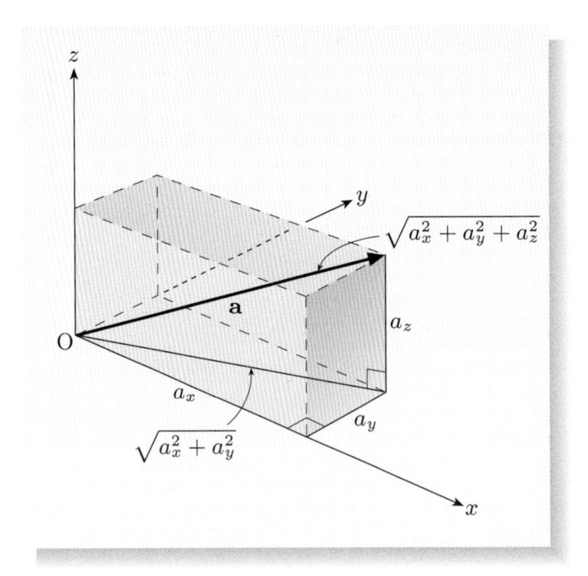


**Figure 8.8** Finding the magnitude of a vector using Pythagoras's theorem.

The vector operations introduced earlier all have simple interpretations in terms of components. To multiply a vector by a scalar, $\lambda$, we multiply each of its components by $\lambda$:

$$\lambda \mathbf{a} = (\lambda a_x)\mathbf{e}_x + (\lambda a_y)\mathbf{e}_y + (\lambda a_z)\mathbf{e}_z.$$

To add or subtract two vectors, we add or subtract their components:

$$\mathbf{a} + \mathbf{b} = (a_x + b_x)\mathbf{e}_x + (a_y + b_y)\mathbf{e}_y + (a_z + b_z)\mathbf{e}_z,$$

$$\mathbf{a} - \mathbf{b} = (a_x - b_x)\mathbf{e}_x + (a_y - b_y)\mathbf{e}_y + (a_z - b_z)\mathbf{e}_z.$$

In general, any vector equation can be expressed in terms of components. For example, the equation $\mathbf{a} = \mathbf{b}$ implies that

$$a_x\mathbf{e}_x + a_y\mathbf{e}_y + a_z\mathbf{e}_z = b_x\mathbf{e}_x + b_y\mathbf{e}_y + b_z\mathbf{e}_z.$$

We can equate corresponding components on both sides to obtain $a_x = b_x$, $a_y = b_y$ and $a_z = b_z$. So, one vector equation splits into three scalar equations for the components. Vector equations have the great advantage of brevity, but numerical calculations are usually carried out using the components.

Finally, let's see how some special vectors are represented in component notation:

- The **zero vector** has three zero components:

  $$\mathbf{0} = 0\mathbf{e}_x + 0\mathbf{e}_y + 0\mathbf{e}_z.$$

  It is different from the number 0, and is distinguished from 0 by using bold print or underlining. The zero vector could appear in an equation such as

  $$\mathbf{a} - \mathbf{a} = \mathbf{0}.$$

  It would not be correct to write this equation with the number 0 on the right-hand side. To do so would be to equate a vector to a scalar — something which makes no sense. The zero vector keeps everything in order, ensuring that both sides are vector quantities.

- The **position vector** of a point P in a coordinate system with origin O is

  $$\mathbf{r} = x\mathbf{e}_x + y\mathbf{e}_y + z\mathbf{e}_z,$$

  where $x$, $y$ and $z$ are the **Cartesian coordinates** of the point in the given coordinate system. The magnitude of the position vector,

  $$r = \sqrt{x^2 + y^2 + z^2},$$

  is the distance of the point from the origin.
- The **displacement vector** of point 1, with position vector

  $$\mathbf{r}_1 = x_1\mathbf{e}_x + y_1\mathbf{e}_y + z_1\mathbf{e}_z$$

  from point 2, with position vector

  $$\mathbf{r}_2 = x_2\mathbf{e}_x + y_2\mathbf{e}_y + z_2\mathbf{e}_z$$

  is

  $$\mathbf{r}_{12} = \mathbf{r}_1 - \mathbf{r}_2 = (x_1 - x_2)\mathbf{e}_x + (y_1 - y_2)\mathbf{e}_y + (z_1 - z_2)\mathbf{e}_z.$$

  The magnitude of the displacement vector,

  $$r_{12} = \sqrt{(x_1 - x_2)^2 + (y_1 - y_2)^2 + (z_1 - z_2)^2},$$

  is the distance between points 1 and 2.

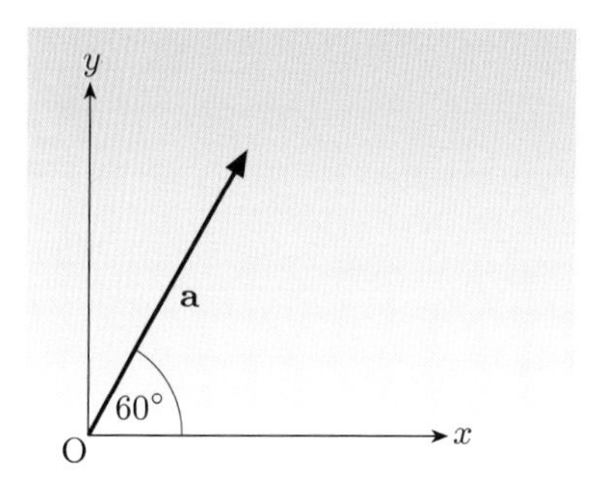


**Figure 8.9** For Exercise 8.2.

**Exercise 8.2** The vector $\mathbf{a}$ in Figure 8.9 lies in the $xy$-plane. Find the components of this vector.

**Exercise 8.3** The position vectors of two points A and B are $\mathbf{r}_\text{A} = (4\mathbf{e}_x - 3\mathbf{e}_y)$ m and $\mathbf{r}_\text{B} = (\mathbf{e}_x + \mathbf{e}_y)$ m, where the non-italic symbol m stands for metre. Find the displacement vector of A from B, the distance between A and B and the unit vector pointing from B towards A. ■

## 8.2 Products of vectors

Section 8.2 is best read before or during your study of Chapter 3. If you have not met scalar products before, you should read Section 8.2.1 before studying Chapter 2.

There are two ways of forming the product of two vectors, $\mathbf{a}$ and $\mathbf{b}$. The first method produces a scalar quantity, $\mathbf{a} \cdot \mathbf{b}$. This is called the *scalar product*, or the *dot product*, of the vectors. The second method produces a vector quantity, $\mathbf{a} \times \mathbf{b}$. This is called the *vector product*, or the *cross product*, of the vectors. In both cases the unit of the product is the product of the units of $\mathbf{a}$ and $\mathbf{b}$.

### 8.2.1 Scalar products

Scalar products occur throughout physics. For example, if a constant force $\mathbf{F}$ is applied to a particle while it moves through a displacement $\mathbf{s}$, the scalar product $\mathbf{F} \cdot \mathbf{s}$ is the work done by the force. This is the energy transferred to the particle.

The **scalar product** of two vectors $\mathbf{a}$ and $\mathbf{b}$ is a scalar quantity defined by

$$\mathbf{a} \cdot \mathbf{b} = ab\cos\theta, \tag{8.6}$$

where $a$ and $b$ are the magnitudes of the vectors and $\theta$ is the smaller of the two angles between their directions, which lies in the range $0 \leq \theta \leq \pi$ (Figure 8.10).

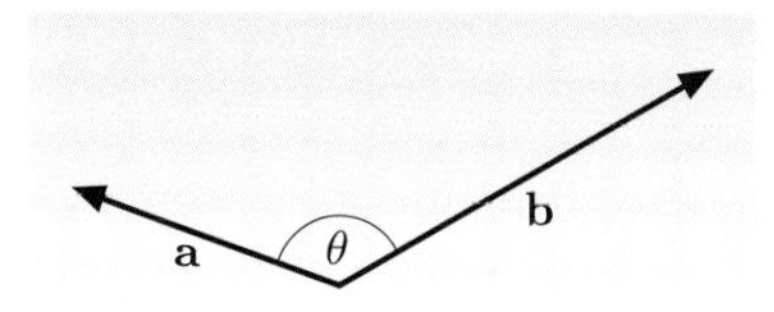


**Figure 8.10** Choosing the angle for the scalar product of two vectors. The angle $\theta$ used for the scalar product is always the smaller of the two angles between $\mathbf{a}$ and $\mathbf{b}$.

An equivalent definition can be given in terms of Cartesian components:

$$\mathbf{a} \cdot \mathbf{b} = a_x b_x + a_y b_y + a_z b_z. \tag{8.7}$$

You are free to use either definition, according to convenience. The value of the scalar product does not depend on the method of evaluation, or on the choice of coordinate system.

The magnitude of any vector $\mathbf{a}$ can be expressed in terms of a scalar product:

$$|\mathbf{a}| = a = \sqrt{a_x^2 + a_y^2 + a_z^2} = \sqrt{\mathbf{a} \cdot \mathbf{a}}.$$

The components of a vector can also be expressed as scalar products. For example

$$a_x = a \cos\theta_x = \mathbf{e}_x \cdot \mathbf{a},$$

where $\mathbf{e}_x$ is the unit vector in the $x$-direction.

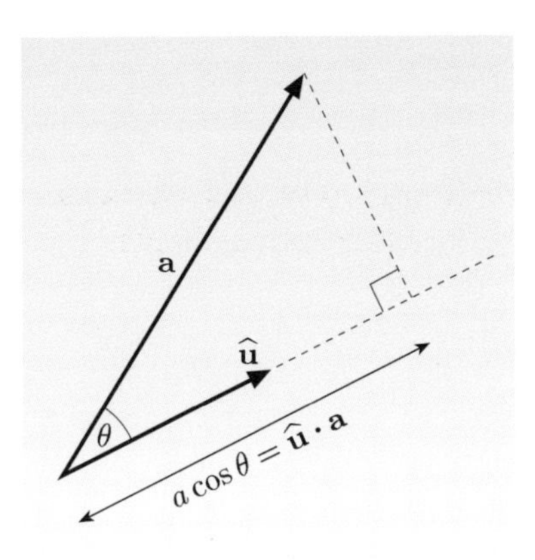


**Figure 8.11** The component of $\mathbf{a}$ in the direction of the unit vector $\widehat{\mathbf{u}}$.

More generally, if $\widehat{\mathbf{u}}$ is any unit vector, the quantity $\widehat{\mathbf{u}} \cdot \mathbf{a}$ is called the component of $\mathbf{a}$ in the direction of $\widehat{\mathbf{u}}$. The geometric significance of this quantity is illustrated in Figure 8.11. Scalar products can also be used to find the angle between two vectors. From Equation 8.6, we have

$$\cos\theta = \frac{\mathbf{a} \cdot \mathbf{b}}{ab}.$$

This provides a useful test. If $\mathbf{a}$ and $\mathbf{b}$ are non-zero vectors, and you want to know whether they are **orthogonal** (that is, perpendicular to one another), try taking their scalar product. The vectors are orthogonal if, and only if, $\mathbf{a} \cdot \mathbf{b} = 0$.

The simplest scalar products are those between Cartesian unit vectors. These vectors have unit magnitude so

$$\mathbf{e}_x \cdot \mathbf{e}_x = \mathbf{e}_y \cdot \mathbf{e}_y = \mathbf{e}_z \cdot \mathbf{e}_z = 1, \tag{8.8}$$

and they are mutually orthogonal so

$$\mathbf{e}_x \cdot \mathbf{e}_y = \mathbf{e}_y \cdot \mathbf{e}_z = \mathbf{e}_z \cdot \mathbf{e}_x = 0. \tag{8.9}$$

More generally, the scalar product has nearly all the properties you would expect of a product. For example, if $\mathbf{a} = \mathbf{b}$, and $\mathbf{c}$ is any vector, you can take the scalar product on both sides to form a valid scalar equation $\mathbf{c} \cdot \mathbf{a} = \mathbf{c} \cdot \mathbf{b}$. Moreover,

$$\mathbf{a} \cdot \mathbf{b} = \mathbf{b} \cdot \mathbf{a},$$

$$\mathbf{a} \cdot (\mathbf{b} + \mathbf{c}) = \mathbf{a} \cdot \mathbf{b} + \mathbf{a} \cdot \mathbf{c}$$

and

$$\mathbf{a} \cdot (\lambda \mathbf{b}) = \lambda(\mathbf{a} \cdot \mathbf{b}).$$

Scalar products can be evaluated using these properties to multiply out brackets, and using Equations 8.8 and 8.9 for the scalar products between unit vectors. The only restriction is that the scalar product cannot be extended to three vectors. It makes no sense to write $(\mathbf{a} \cdot \mathbf{b}) \cdot \mathbf{c}$. This is because $\mathbf{a} \cdot \mathbf{b}$ is a scalar quantity, and so cannot participate in a scalar product with a third vector, $\mathbf{c}$. However, it is perfectly reasonable to write $(\mathbf{a} \cdot \mathbf{b})\mathbf{c}$, which is the vector $\mathbf{c}$ scaled by the factor $\mathbf{a} \cdot \mathbf{b}$.

**Exercise 8.4** Evaluate the scalar product of $\mathbf{a} = \mathbf{e}_x - \mathbf{e}_y + \mathbf{e}_z$ and $\mathbf{b} = -\mathbf{e}_x - 3\mathbf{e}_y$.

**Exercise 8.5** Two vectors satisfy $\mathbf{a} \cdot \mathbf{b} = -ab$. What is the angle between them?

**Exercise 8.6** Show that, if $\mathbf{a}$ and $\mathbf{b}$ have the same magnitude and are neither parallel nor antiparallel, then $\mathbf{a} + \mathbf{b}$ is orthogonal to $\mathbf{a} - \mathbf{b}$. ■

### 8.2.2 Vector products

Section 8.2.2 is best read before or during your study of Chapter 3.

Vector products often arise in physics when rotational motion is involved. For example, torque and angular momentum are both defined as vector products.

The **vector product** of any two vectors $\mathbf{a}$ and $\mathbf{b}$ is a vector quantity defined by

$$\mathbf{a} \times \mathbf{b} = ab \sin\theta\, \widehat{\mathbf{n}}, \qquad (8.10)$$

where $a$ and $b$ are the magnitudes of the vectors and $\theta$ is the smaller angle between their directions, which means that $0 \leq \theta \leq \pi$ and $\sin\theta \geq 0$. The unit vector $\widehat{\mathbf{n}}$ is normal to the plane of $\mathbf{a}$ and $\mathbf{b}$ in a sense determined by the right-hand rule (Figure 8.12).

The word 'normal' is used as a synonym for 'perpendicular'.

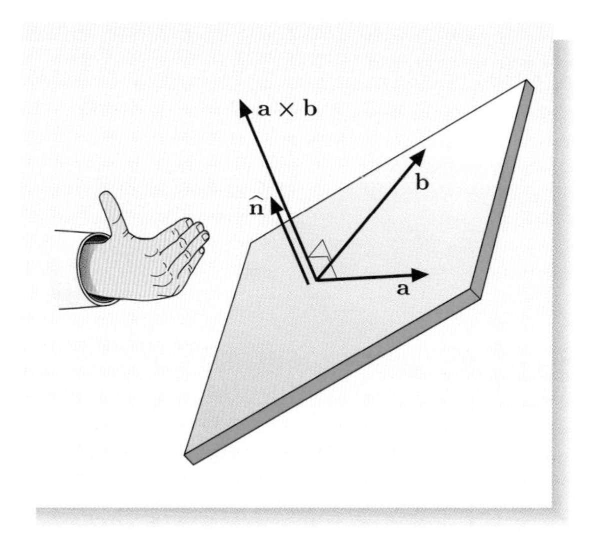


**Figure 8.12** Using the right-hand rule to find the direction of the vector product $\mathbf{a} \times \mathbf{b}$. First point the fingers of your right hand in the direction of $\mathbf{a}$, then bend them in the direction of $\mathbf{b}$. The outstretched thumb of your right hand points in the direction of $\mathbf{a} \times \mathbf{b}$, which has the same direction as the unit vector $\widehat{\mathbf{n}}$.

An equivalent definition can be given in terms of Cartesian components in a right-handed coordinate system:

$$\mathbf{a} \times \mathbf{b} = (a_y b_z - a_z b_y)\mathbf{e}_x + (a_z b_x - a_x b_z)\mathbf{e}_y + (a_x b_y - a_y b_x)\mathbf{e}_z. \qquad (8.11)$$

The fact that we need a right-handed coordinate system is related to the fact that a right-hand rule was used to find the direction of the unit vector $\widehat{\mathbf{n}}$ in Equation 8.10. Neither of these conventions need trouble us provided we stick to them. We will always use right-hand rules (rather than left-hand rules) and we have already made a firm decision to use only right-handed coordinate systems.

It is worth noting the strong pattern in Equation 8.11. The $x$-component of $\mathbf{a} \times \mathbf{b}$ is the difference of two terms. The first term is the $y$-component of $\mathbf{a}$ times the $z$-component of $\mathbf{b}$ (notice the natural order $x \to y \to z$); the second term takes these two components in the opposite order. The $y$- and $z$-components of the vector product follow similar patterns, based on cyclic permutations of the original order. This pattern can also be represented by a **determinant**:

$$\mathbf{a} \times \mathbf{b} = \begin{vmatrix} \mathbf{e}_x & \mathbf{e}_y & \mathbf{e}_z \\ a_x & a_y & a_z \\ b_x & b_y & b_z \end{vmatrix}, \tag{8.12}$$

which can be expanded out to give

$$\mathbf{a} \times \mathbf{b} = \begin{vmatrix} a_y & a_z \\ b_y & b_z \end{vmatrix} \mathbf{e}_x - \begin{vmatrix} a_x & a_z \\ b_x & b_z \end{vmatrix} \mathbf{e}_y + \begin{vmatrix} a_x & a_y \\ b_x & b_y \end{vmatrix} \mathbf{e}_z,$$

and Equation 8.11 is recovered when we expand the three $2 \times 2$ determinants.

Vector products can be used to define perpendicular directions in space. If two vectors $\mathbf{a}$ and $\mathbf{b}$ point in different directions, their vector product $\mathbf{a} \times \mathbf{b}$ is perpendicular to the plane that contains both $\mathbf{a}$ and $\mathbf{b}$. Vector products can also be used to test whether two vectors are aligned with one another (that is, either parallel or antiparallel). If $\mathbf{a}$ and $\mathbf{b}$ are non-zero vectors and $\mathbf{a} \times \mathbf{b} = \mathbf{0}$, then $\mathbf{a}$ and $\mathbf{b}$ are either parallel or antiparallel to each other. A trivial case arises when $\mathbf{a} = \mathbf{b}$, since $\mathbf{a} \times \mathbf{a} = \mathbf{0}$ for any vector $\mathbf{a}$, and $\mathbf{a}$ is always parallel to itself.

The simplest vector products are those between the Cartesian unit vectors of a right-handed coordinate system. We have

$$\mathbf{e}_x \times \mathbf{e}_x = \mathbf{e}_y \times \mathbf{e}_y = \mathbf{e}_z \times \mathbf{e}_z = \mathbf{0}, \tag{8.13}$$

and

$$\mathbf{e}_x \times \mathbf{e}_y = \mathbf{e}_z\,, \quad \mathbf{e}_y \times \mathbf{e}_z = \mathbf{e}_x\,, \quad \mathbf{e}_z \times \mathbf{e}_x = \mathbf{e}_y. \tag{8.14}$$

These results can be memorized by writing down:

$$\mathbf{e}_x \rightarrow \mathbf{e}_y \rightarrow \mathbf{e}_z,$$

(with an arrow returning from $\mathbf{e}_z$ to $\mathbf{e}_x$)

and noting that vector products of neighbouring unit vectors taken in the indicated sense of circulation give the remaining unit vector with a plus sign (e.g. $\mathbf{e}_y \times \mathbf{e}_z = \mathbf{e}_x$), while vector products taken in the opposite sense produce a minus sign (e.g. $\mathbf{e}_z \times \mathbf{e}_y = -\mathbf{e}_x$).

More generally, the vector product has *many* of the properties you would expect of a product. For example,

$$\mathbf{a} \times (\mathbf{b} + \mathbf{c}) = \mathbf{a} \times \mathbf{b} + \mathbf{a} \times \mathbf{c}$$

and

$$\mathbf{a} \times (\lambda \mathbf{b}) = (\lambda \mathbf{a}) \times \mathbf{b} = \lambda(\mathbf{a} \times \mathbf{b}).$$

However, there are some unusual properties which need special care. Firstly, the order of the vectors in a vector product is *crucial*. As Equation 8.11 shows,

This can also be seen by using the right-hand rule.

$$\mathbf{a} \times \mathbf{b} = -\mathbf{b} \times \mathbf{a}.$$

Secondly, if you take the vector product of a vector product, you must be careful to show how the terms are grouped. In general,

$$\mathbf{a} \times (\mathbf{b} \times \mathbf{c}) \neq (\mathbf{a} \times \mathbf{b}) \times \mathbf{c}.$$

For example,

$$\mathbf{e}_x \times (\mathbf{e}_y \times \mathbf{e}_y) = \mathbf{e}_x \times \mathbf{0} = \mathbf{0},$$

while

$$(\mathbf{e}_x \times \mathbf{e}_y) \times \mathbf{e}_y = \mathbf{e}_z \times \mathbf{e}_y = -\mathbf{e}_x.$$

Vector products can be evaluated by multiplying out brackets, and using Equations 8.13 and 8.14 for the vector products between Cartesian unit vectors.

**Exercise 8.7** Evaluate the vector product of $\mathbf{a} = 2\mathbf{e}_x + 3\mathbf{e}_y$ and $\mathbf{b} = 3\mathbf{e}_x + 2\mathbf{e}_y$.

**Exercise 8.8** If vector $\mathbf{a}$ is directed horizontally to the north and vector $\mathbf{b}$ is directed vertically upwards, what are the directions of $\mathbf{a} \times \mathbf{b}$ and $\mathbf{b} \times \mathbf{a}$?

**Exercise 8.9** When two vectors $\mathbf{a}$ and $\mathbf{b}$ are reflected in the $xy$-plane, their $z$-components are reversed and their $x$- and $y$- components are left unchanged. What happens to the components of the vector $\mathbf{c} = \mathbf{a} \times \mathbf{b}$ when it is reflected in the $xy$-plane? ■

### 8.2.3 Vector division?

Don't do it! To see why, recall how division works for numbers. The equation $4a = 12$ can be divided by 4 to give $a = 3$. There is no dispute about the result of this division because 3 is the *only* number that, when multiplied by 4, gives 12. By contrast, the equation $4\mathbf{e}_x \cdot \mathbf{a} = 12$ does not uniquely determine $\mathbf{a}$. One possibility is that $\mathbf{a} = 3\mathbf{e}_x$, but any combination of $\mathbf{e}_y$ or $\mathbf{e}_z$ could be added to $3\mathbf{e}_x$ without changing the value of the scalar product. Dividing by $4\mathbf{e}_x$ is therefore highly ambiguous. Mathematics, with its clear-cut = signs, cannot tolerate ambiguity, so division by a vector is illegal. Never write down anything like $1/\mathbf{a}$ because it is has no meaning.

### 8.2.4 Differentiating vectors and their products

If a vector $\mathbf{a}(t)$ depends on time, then one or more of its components depends on time, so we can write

$$\mathbf{a}(t) = a_x(t)\mathbf{e}_x + a_y(t)\mathbf{e}_y + a_z(t)\mathbf{e}_z.$$

The unit vectors $\mathbf{e}_x$, $\mathbf{e}_y$ and $\mathbf{e}_z$ are constant vectors, so the derivative of the vector is

$$\frac{\mathrm{d}\mathbf{a}}{\mathrm{d}t} = \frac{\mathrm{d}a_x}{\mathrm{d}t}\mathbf{e}_x + \frac{\mathrm{d}a_y}{\mathrm{d}t}\mathbf{e}_y + \frac{\mathrm{d}a_z}{\mathrm{d}t}\mathbf{e}_z.$$

To differentiate a vector with respect to a single variable, we just differentiate its components.

Sometimes we need to differentiate the product of two vectors. The usual rules for differentiating products apply:

$$\frac{\mathrm{d}}{\mathrm{d}t}(\mathbf{a}\cdot\mathbf{b}) = \mathbf{a}\cdot\frac{\mathrm{d}\mathbf{b}}{\mathrm{d}t} + \frac{\mathrm{d}\mathbf{a}}{\mathrm{d}t}\cdot\mathbf{b},$$

$$\frac{\mathrm{d}}{\mathrm{d}t}(\mathbf{a}\times\mathbf{b}) = \mathbf{a}\times\frac{\mathrm{d}\mathbf{b}}{\mathrm{d}t} + \frac{\mathrm{d}\mathbf{a}}{\mathrm{d}t}\times\mathbf{b},$$

though in the vector product case, we must be careful to preserve the ordering of the vectors throughout.

**Exercise 8.10** A particle of mass $m$ has velocity $\mathbf{v}$ and kinetic energy $\frac{1}{2}mv^2$. Use Newton's second law to show that the rate of change of the particle's kinetic energy is equal to $\mathbf{F}\cdot\mathbf{v}$, where $\mathbf{F}$ is the force on the particle. Hence show that, if $\mathbf{F}$ is always perpendicular to $\mathbf{v}$, the particle's kinetic energy remains constant. ■

### 8.2.5 Vector identities

A **vector identity** is a relationship between vectors that is *always* valid. For example, if $\mathbf{a}$, $\mathbf{b}$ and $\mathbf{c}$ are any vectors, it is always true that

$$\mathbf{a}\times(\mathbf{b}\times\mathbf{c}) = (\mathbf{a}\cdot\mathbf{c})\mathbf{b} - (\mathbf{a}\cdot\mathbf{b})\mathbf{c} \qquad (8.15)$$

and that

$$\mathbf{a}\cdot(\mathbf{b}\times\mathbf{c}) = (\mathbf{a}\times\mathbf{b})\cdot\mathbf{c}. \qquad (8.16)$$

To establish a vector identity it is usually a good idea to expand everything in terms of components and then compare both sides. For example, in the case of Equation 8.16, expanding the left-hand side gives

$$\mathbf{a}\cdot(\mathbf{b}\times\mathbf{c}) = a_x(b_yc_z - b_zc_y) + a_y(b_zc_x - b_xc_z) + a_z(b_xc_y - b_yc_x),$$

while expanding the right-hand side gives

$$(\mathbf{a}\times\mathbf{b})\cdot\mathbf{c} = (a_yb_z - a_zb_y)c_x + (a_zb_x - a_xb_z)c_y + (a_xb_y - a_yb_x)c_z.$$

Collecting together terms in $a_x$, $a_y$ and $a_z$, it is easy to see that these two expressions are equal, so Equation 8.16 has been explicitly confirmed. However, proving vector identities is not a central theme of this course. A short list of vector identities is given inside the back cover of the book. On the rare occasions that you will need to use one, I recommend that you simply look the identity up, and take it on trust.

## 8.3 Fields and coordinate systems

Section 8.3 is best read before or during your study of Chapter 2.

### 8.3.1 Scalar and vector fields

A **field** is a physical quantity which, at a given instant, has definite values throughout a region of space. The region may be the whole of space or a continuous set of points within it. It should not be a discrete set of isolated points.

As an example, consider the temperature in a room. The temperature may vary across the room — perhaps it is high near a stove and low near a window. Nevertheless, at a given instant, each point in the room has its own temperature, and we can talk of the *temperature field* in the room. Each point can be labelled by a position vector $\mathbf{r}$ or by a set of Cartesian coordinates, $x$, $y$ and $z$, so the temperature field can be represented by a function of the form $T(\mathbf{r})$ or $T(x, y, z)$. A time-varying temperature field is represented by $T(\mathbf{r}, t)$ or $T(x, y, z, t)$, where $t$ is the time. Sometimes it is appropriate to consider a two-dimensional region. For example, the temperature on the floor of the room might be represented by a function of the form $T(x, y)$.

It is important to distinguish between fields and their values. The temperature field over the whole of Britain is a function of position but, at any given place, a thermometer will read a single value. Maintaining this distinction is sometimes clouded by the fact that the symbol $T(x, y, z)$ can stand for the value of the temperature at a *particular* point $(x, y, z)$ or for the function that gives the temperature at a *general* point $(x, y, z)$ — that is, the temperature field.

Incidentally, you may have heard the words 'field' or 'force-field' used in science fiction films, where they generally mean something like 'a region of influence'. I hope you can see that the scientific meaning of a field is rather different. 'Region of influence' fails to convey the idea that a field is a function defined at all points in a region. And 'influence' is not always the relevant issue. We might be interested in a temperature field or a density field for reasons that have nothing to do with force.

All the fields you will meet in this course can be classified as being either scalar fields or vector fields.

- A **scalar field** is a field with scalar values throughout a region of space. Each point in the region has a particular scalar value of the field quantity.
- A **vector field** is a field with vector values throughout a region of space. Each point in the region has a particular magnitude and a direction of the field quantity.

The temperature field described above is a scalar field because temperature is a scalar quantity. An example of a vector field is provided by the wind velocity in the atmosphere. This is a field because wind velocity is defined at each point in the atmosphere. It is a vector field because wind velocity is a vector with a magnitude (the wind speed) and a direction (the wind direction). We represent the wind velocity field by a function of the form $\mathbf{v}(x, y, z, t)$, where the bold font explicitly shows the vector nature of the field. In electromagnetism, electric and magnetic fields are vector fields, but the electrostatic potential field is a scalar field.

Not every physical quantity can be described by a field. For example, we cannot sensibly define a mass field. A particle can have a mass but we cannot associate a mass with all the points in a material. The problem is that any region contains an infinite number of points so, if each point had a mass, the region would have an infinite mass, which is clearly unacceptable. We can, however, talk about the density at each point. Density is mass *per unit volume*, so the density at a given point is found by taking the ratio of mass to volume for a tiny volume centred on the point. Density is a scalar quantity defined at each point throughout a region, so there is no problem in defining a density field. Similar arguments apply to any quantity that is proportional to the size of the system. For example, we cannot define a charge field or an energy field, but we can define charge density and energy density fields. Both are scalar fields.

### Visualizing fields

Various representations are available to help us visualize how a field varies in space. All of these representations are described in Part I, in the context of electric fields (Chapter 1), magnetic fields (Chapter 3) and electrostatic potential fields (Chapter 5).

For vector fields, we can use arrow maps or field line patterns. An **arrow map** (Figure 8.13) displays arrows at a selection of points, with the length and direction of the arrow at a given point indicating the magnitude and direction of the vector field at the point. Alternatively, we can show a set of field lines (Figure 8.14). A **field line** is a continuous line that points in the direction of the field at each point along its path. A **field line pattern** tells us about the direction of the vector field, but does not automatically give quantitative information about the magnitude of the field.

For scalar fields, we simply draw lines (in two dimensions) or surfaces (in three dimensions) on which the field has a constant value (Figure 8.15). These are called **contour lines** (in 2D) or **contour surfaces** (in 3D), but more specific names are given in different circumstances (e.g. isobars for pressure, isotherms for temperature and equipotentials for electrostatic fields).

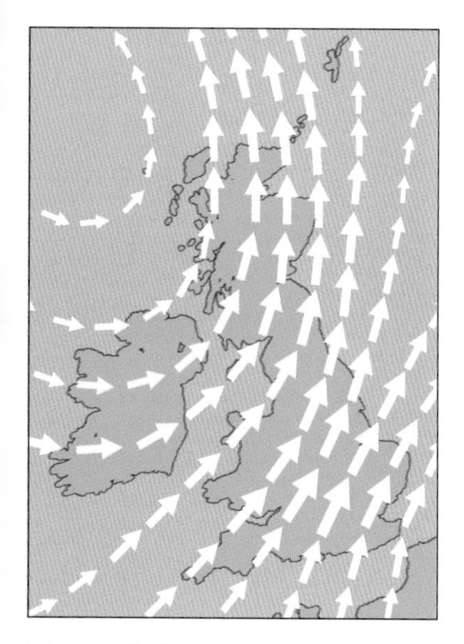

**Figure 8.13** An arrow map for a wind velocity field. May the largest arrows stay far from your roof!

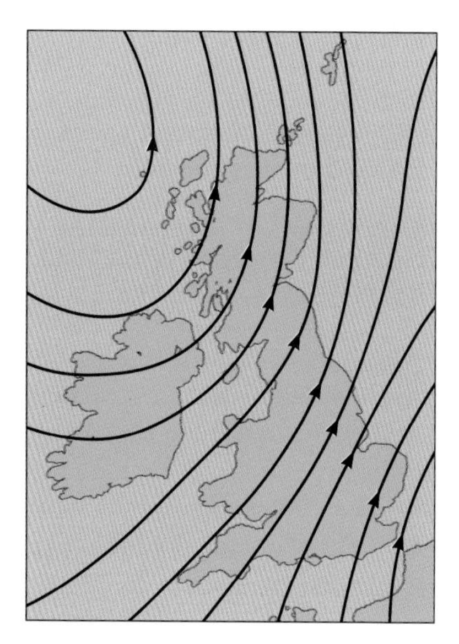

**Figure 8.14** A field line pattern for a wind velocity field.

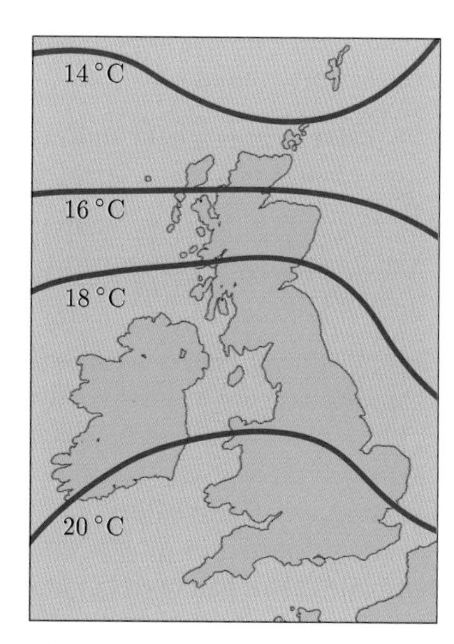


**Figure 8.15** Contour lines (isotherms) for a temperature field.

**Exercise 8.11** Classify the following as scalar or vector fields: the velocity of water in a river, the wind speed on Mars, the energy density around the Sun and the concentration of salt in the Atlantic Ocean. ■

## 8.3.2 Spherical and cylindrical coordinates

So far, we have concentrated on Cartesian coordinates, $x$, $y$ and $z$. However, fields are often described in other coordinate systems. If a field has spherical symmetry about a given point, it is sensible to use spherical coordinates centred on that point. If a system has cylindrical symmetry about a given axis, it is sensible to use cylindrical coordinates centred on the axis. You will need to use spherical and cylindrical coordinates throughout your studies of electromagnetism.

Animations of spherical and cylindrical coordinate systems are included on the DVD.

### Spherical coordinates

Figure 8.16 shows how the **spherical coordinates** $(r, \theta, \phi)$ of a point P are defined:

- The **radial coordinate** $r$ is the distance from the origin O to the point.
- The **polar coordinate** $\theta$ is the smaller of the angles between the positive $z$-axis and the line OP.
- The **azimuthal coordinate** $\phi$ is the angle between the positive $x$-axis and the projection of OP in the $xy$-plane. The sense of increasing $\phi$ is determined by a **right-hand grip rule**. With the thumb of the right hand pointing along the positive $z$-axis, the curled fingers of the right hand indicate the direction in which $\phi$ increases.

$\theta = 0$ when P lies on the positive $z$-axis.

$\phi = 0$ when the projection of P in the $xy$-plane coincides with the positive $x$-axis.

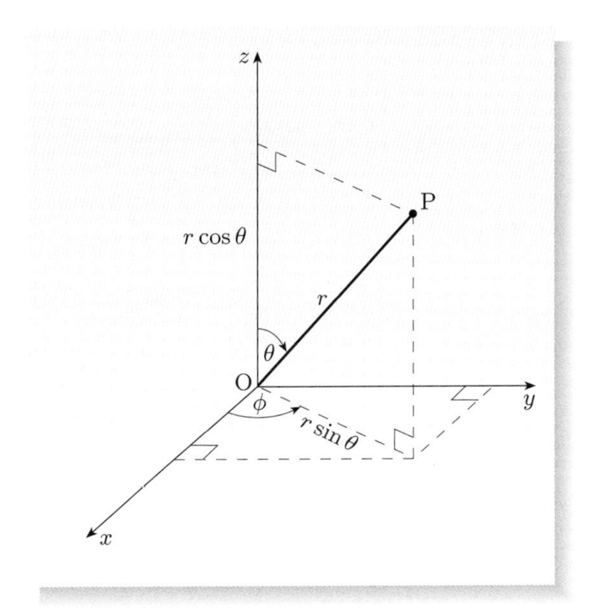


**Figure 8.16** The spherical coordinates $(r, \theta, \phi)$ of a point P.

Using trigonometry in Figure 8.16, we see that a point P with spherical coordinates $(r, \theta, \phi)$ has Cartesian coordinates

$$\begin{aligned} x &= r\sin\theta\cos\phi \\ y &= r\sin\theta\sin\phi \\ z &= r\cos\theta. \end{aligned} \tag{8.17}$$

The inverse transformations are

$$r = (x^2 + y^2 + z^2)^{1/2}$$

$$\cos\theta = \frac{z}{(x^2 + y^2 + z^2)^{1/2}}$$

$$\tan\phi = \frac{y}{x}.$$

We must restrict spherical coordinates to lie in the ranges:

$$0 \leq r < \infty, \quad 0 \leq \theta \leq \pi \quad \text{and} \quad 0 \leq \phi < 2\pi,$$

where we follow the usual convention of measuring angles in radians. These ranges allow spherical coordinates to cover the whole of space. Every point can be represented by a set of spherical coordinates. The given ranges also ensure that most points have only one set of spherical coordinates. The exceptions are points on the $z$-axis of Figure 8.16. Any value of $\phi$ can be chosen at these points and any values of $\theta$ and $\phi$ can be chosen at the origin.

As an example, Figure 8.17 shows how spherical coordinates can be used to locate places on Earth. The origin is at the centre of the Earth, the $z$-axis passes through the North Pole and the $x$-axis passes through a point in the Atlantic Ocean where the Equator meets the line of zero longitude (the Greenwich meridian). In this coordinate system, the spherical coordinates of Moscow are $r = 6400\,\text{km}$, $\theta = 0.60\,\text{rad} = 34°$ and $\phi = 0.66$ rad $= 38°$. The polar and azimuthal coordinates are closely related to latitude and longitude, but with some differences. Latitude is measured north and south of the Equator, while $\theta$ varies from 0 at the North Pole to $\pi$ at the South Pole. So, for example, the latitude of Moscow is $(90° - 34°)\,\text{N} = 56°\,\text{N}$. Longitude is measured east and west of the Greenwich meridian, with a jump at the international date line, while $\phi$ increases continuously from 0 to $2\pi$ as we lap the world once, travelling in an easterly direction.

To describe a scalar field $f$ in spherical coordinates we express it as a function of $r$, $\theta$ and $\phi$:

$$f = f(r, \theta, \phi).$$

To describe a vector field $\mathbf{F}$ in spherical coordinates we need suitable unit vectors. At any given point, we introduce the **spherical unit vectors** shown in Figure 8.18. Each unit vector points in a direction where one spherical coordinate changes and the other two remain fixed:

- $\mathbf{e}_r$ is in the direction of increasing $r$ and constant $\theta$ and $\phi$. This is the outward radial direction, pointing directly away from the origin.
- $\mathbf{e}_\theta$ is in the direction of increasing $\theta$ and constant $r$ and $\phi$.
- $\mathbf{e}_\phi$ is in the direction of increasing $\phi$ and constant $r$ and $\theta$.

In terms of our geographical example, if you stand at a given point on the Earth's surface, $\mathbf{e}_r$ points vertically upwards, $\mathbf{e}_\theta$ points southwards and $\mathbf{e}_\phi$ points eastwards. There are certain troublesome points. It is not possible to choose a unique outward radial direction at the origin, so the radial unit vector $\mathbf{e}_r$ is undefined there, as are $\mathbf{e}_\theta$ and $\mathbf{e}_\phi$. Standing at the South Pole, there is no direction southwards, so the polar unit vector $\mathbf{e}_\theta$ is undefined there. And the azimuthal unit vector $\mathbf{e}_\phi$ is not defined at either pole. These exceptions do not matter: our definitions work arbitrarily close to these points, and that is all we really need.

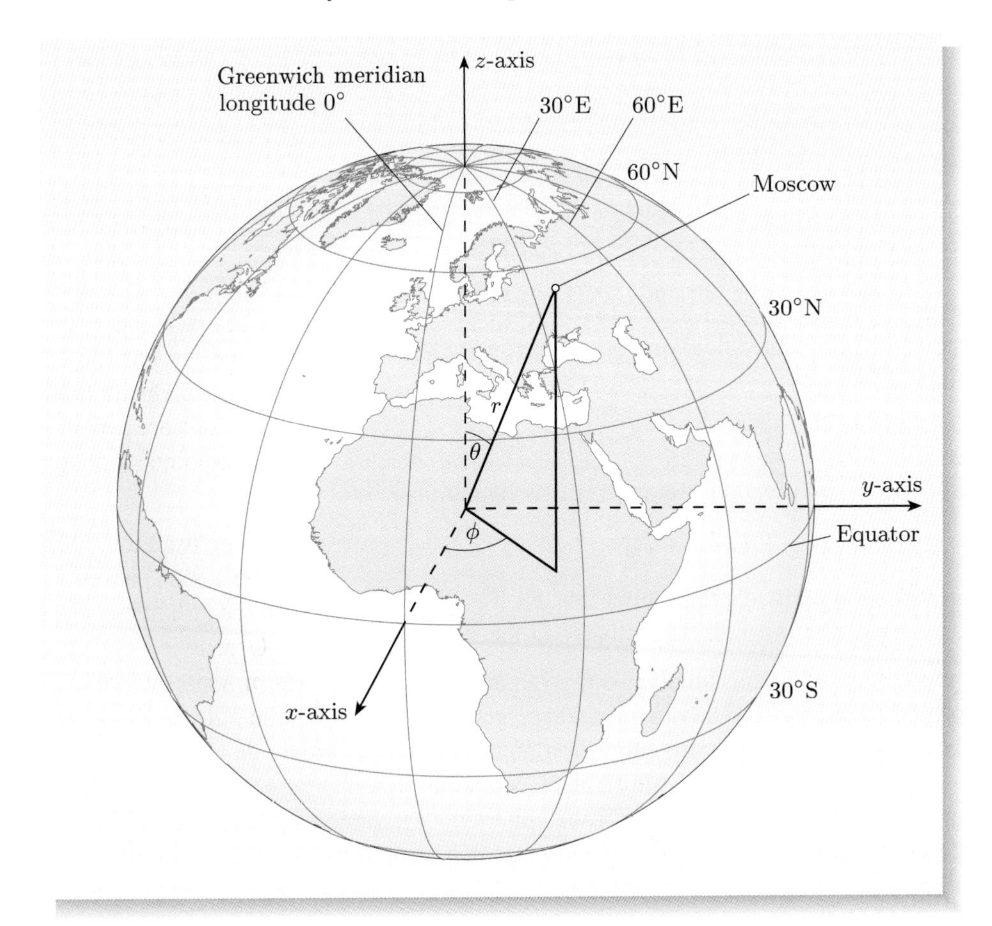


**Figure 8.17** Spherical coordinates of Moscow using a spherical coordinate system with its origin at the centre of the Earth, its $z$-axis passing through the North Pole, and its $x$-axis passing through the Greenwich meridian (longitude 0°).

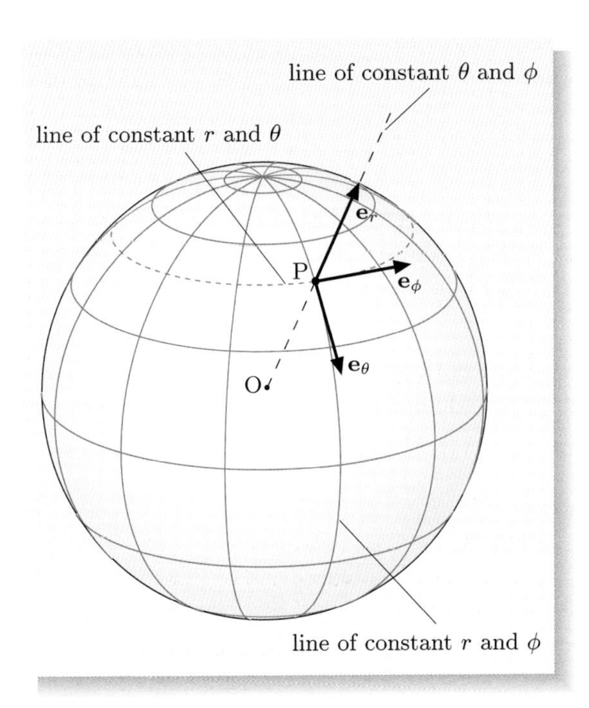


**Figure 8.18** Spherical unit vectors at a point P.

It is essential to realize that the directions of the spherical unit vectors vary from point to point. The notion of pointing radially outwards, for example, depends on where we are. The radial unit vector at the North Pole points in the opposite direction to the radial unit vector at the South Pole. More generally, every point $\mathbf{r}$ has its own set of unit vectors, $\mathbf{e}_r(\mathbf{r})$, $\mathbf{e}_\theta(\mathbf{r})$ and $\mathbf{e}_\phi(\mathbf{r})$. In this respect spherical unit vectors are unlike Cartesian unit vectors, which remain the same everywhere once we have chosen our axes.

At any given point $\mathbf{r}$, the triplet of vectors $(\mathbf{e}_r(\mathbf{r}), \mathbf{e}_\theta(\mathbf{r}), \mathbf{e}_\phi(\mathbf{r}))$ forms an orthogonal right-handed system. For example,

▶ Vector products are discussed in Section 8.2.2.

$$\mathbf{e}_r(\mathbf{r}) \cdot \mathbf{e}_\theta(\mathbf{r}) = 0 \quad \text{and} \quad \mathbf{e}_r(\mathbf{r}) \times \mathbf{e}_\theta(\mathbf{r}) = \mathbf{e}_\phi(\mathbf{r}).$$

The value of a vector field at $\mathbf{r}$ can therefore can be expanded in terms of these unit vectors:

$$\mathbf{F}(\mathbf{r}) = F_r(\mathbf{r})\,\mathbf{e}_r(\mathbf{r}) + F_\theta(\mathbf{r})\,\mathbf{e}_\theta(\mathbf{r}) + F_\phi(\mathbf{r})\,\mathbf{e}_\phi(\mathbf{r}). \tag{8.18}$$

In practice, such explicit notation is usually simplified to

$$\mathbf{F} = F_r\,\mathbf{e}_r + F_\theta\,\mathbf{e}_\theta + F_\phi\,\mathbf{e}_\phi,$$

but you should always remember that $F_r$, $F_\theta$, $F_\phi$, $\mathbf{e}_r$, $\mathbf{e}_\theta$ and $\mathbf{e}_\phi$ are all functions of position, and must all be evaluated at the same point.

Spherical coordinates can also be used to describe small displacements and small volume elements. Consider a small displacement $\delta\mathbf{l}$ from a point P with spherical coordinates $(r, \theta, \phi)$ to a neighbouring point with coordinates $(r + \delta r, \theta + \delta\theta, \phi + \delta\phi)$. This displacement is assumed to be so small that we can neglect any change in direction of the spherical unit vectors between the start-point and end-point and neglect terms that are second-order (or higher) in $\delta r$, $\delta\theta$ and $\delta\phi$. As shown in Figure 8.19a, the displacement can be split into separate displacements in the directions of $\mathbf{e}_r$, $\mathbf{e}_\theta$ and $\mathbf{e}_\phi$.

By second-order terms, we mean $(\delta r)^2$, $(\delta\theta)^2$, etc.

The radial displacement is simply $\delta r\,\mathbf{e}_r$. The displacement in the direction of $\mathbf{e}_\theta$ is along an arc of the blue circle in Figure 8.19b. This circle has radius $r$ and angular coordinate $\theta$, so the displacement is $r\,\delta\theta\,\mathbf{e}_\theta$. The displacement in the direction of $\mathbf{e}_\phi$ is along an arc of the red circle in Figure 8.19b. This circle has radius $r \sin\theta$ and angular coordinate $\phi$, so the displacement is $r \sin\theta\,\delta\phi\,\mathbf{e}_\phi$. Adding these three displacements together gives the displacement vector $\delta\mathbf{l}$ between the two neighbouring points $(r, \theta, \phi)$ and $(r + \delta r, \theta + \delta\theta, \phi + \delta\phi)$:

$$\delta\mathbf{l} = \delta r\,\mathbf{e}_r + r\,\delta\theta\,\mathbf{e}_\theta + r \sin\theta\,\delta\phi\,\mathbf{e}_\phi. \tag{8.19}$$

I have used the symbol $\delta\mathbf{l}$ for the displacement vector (rather than $\delta\mathbf{r}$) to avoid any confusion between the change in radial coordinate $\delta r$ and the length of the displacement,

$$\delta l = \sqrt{(\delta r)^2 + r^2(\delta\theta)^2 + r^2 \sin^2\theta(\delta\phi)^2},$$

Note that the displacement $\delta\mathbf{l}$ does not just depend on the *changes* in coordinates, $\delta r$, $\delta\theta$ and $\delta\phi$ — it also depends on the coordinates $r$ and $\theta$ themselves.

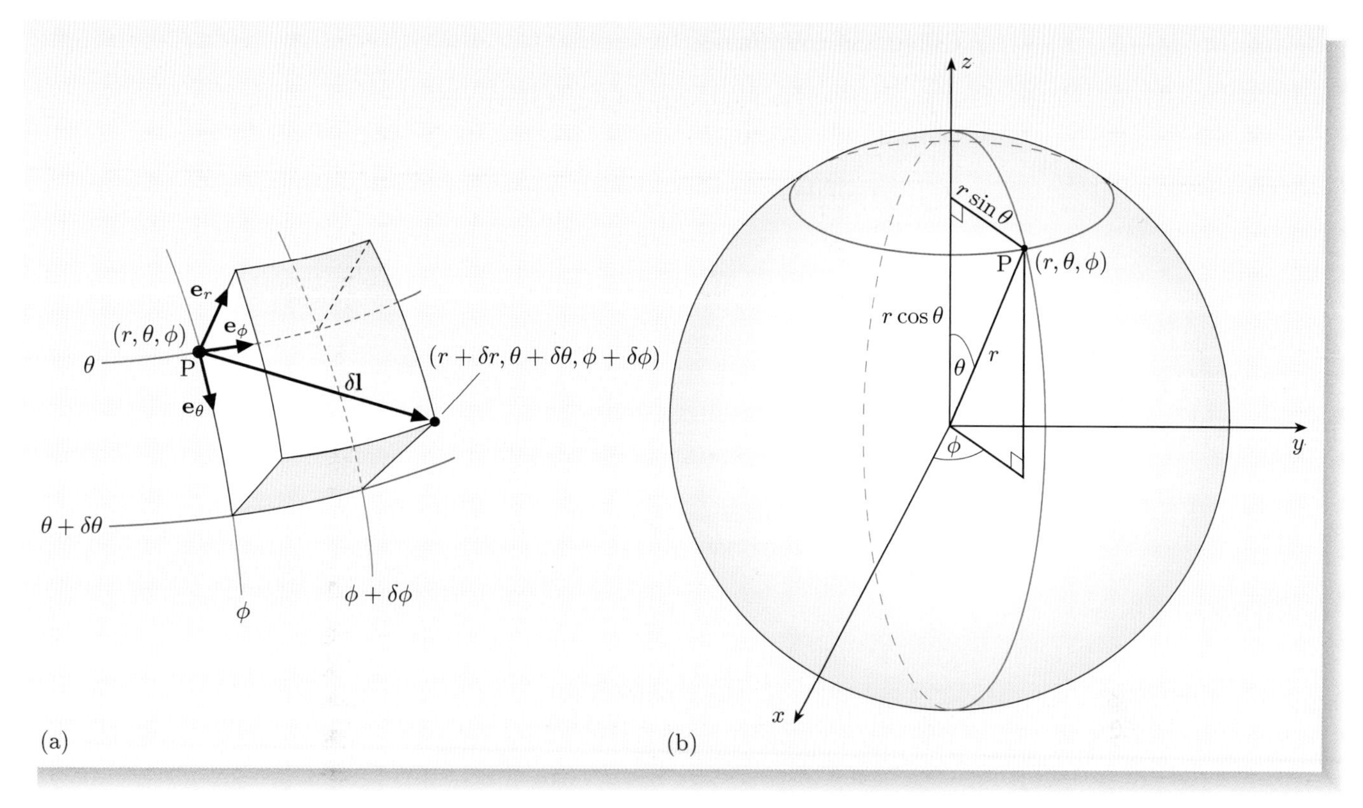


**Figure 8.19** (a) The displacement from $(r, \theta, \phi)$ to $(r + \delta r, \theta + \delta\theta, \phi + \delta\phi)$ can be split into separate displacements in the directions of $\mathbf{e}_r$, $\mathbf{e}_\theta$ and $\mathbf{e}_\phi$. (b) The displacement in the $\mathbf{e}_\theta$ direction is along an arc of the blue circle and the displacement in the $\mathbf{e}_\phi$ direction is along an arc of the red circle.

The coordinate $q$ could be $r$, $\theta$, or $\phi$ in the case of spherical coordinates, or $x$, $y$, or $z$ in Cartesian coordinates.

It is useful to introduce the notation of **scale factors**. For any coordinate $q$ and its associated unit vector $\mathbf{e}_q$, we consider a small change $\delta q$, while keeping the other coordinates fixed. Then the scale factor $h_q$ is defined as the factor by which $\delta q\, \mathbf{e}_q$ must be multiplied to give the resulting displacement.

Comparing with Equation 8.19, we see that the scale factors for spherical coordinates are

$$h_r = 1, \quad h_\theta = r \quad \text{and} \quad h_\phi = r \sin\theta,$$

in terms of which the displacement takes the symmetrical form

$$\delta\mathbf{l} = h_r\, \delta r\, \mathbf{e}_r + h_\theta\, \delta\theta\, \mathbf{e}_\theta + h_\phi\, \delta\phi\, \mathbf{e}_\phi. \tag{8.20}$$

Finally, because the spherical unit vectors are orthogonal, the small volume element shown in Figure 8.20 is very nearly a cube and so has volume

$$\delta V = (h_r\, \delta r) \times (h_\theta\, \delta\theta) \times (h_\phi\, \delta\phi).$$

Therefore the volume element in spherical coordinates is

$$\delta V = (\delta r) \times (r\, \delta\theta) \times (r \sin\theta\, \delta\phi) = r^2 \sin\theta\, \delta r\, \delta\theta\, \delta\phi. \tag{8.21}$$

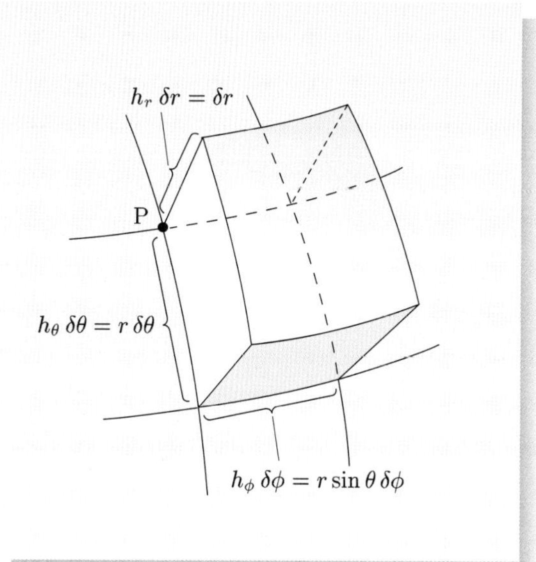


**Figure 8.20** A small volume element in spherical coordinates.

### Cylindrical coordinates

Figure 8.21 shows how the **cylindrical coordinates** $(r, \phi, z)$ of a point P are defined:

- The **radial coordinate** $r$ is the perpendicular distance from the $z$-axis to the point.
- The **azimuthal coordinate** $\phi$ is the azimuthal angle, that is, the angle between the positive $x$-axis and the projection of OP in the $xy$-plane. The sense of increasing $\phi$ is determined by a right-hand grip rule. With the thumb of the right hand pointing along the positive $z$-axis, the curled fingers of the right hand indicate the direction in which $\phi$ increases.
- The **axial coordinate** $z$ is identical to the Cartesian $z$-coordinate.

$\phi = 0$ when the projection of P in the $xy$-plane coincides with the positive $x$-axis.

Note that $r$ in cylindrical coordinates is *not* the same as $r$ in spherical coordinates. It is therefore important always to say which coordinate system is being used in a given situation.

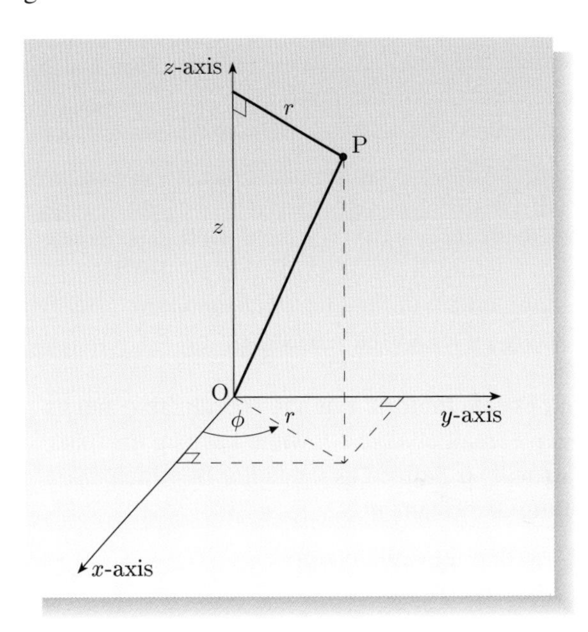


**Figure 8.21** The cylindrical coordinates $(r, \phi, z)$ of a point P.

Using trigonometry in Figure 8.21, we see that the cylindrical coordinates $(r, \phi, z)$ of a point P are related to the Cartesian coordinates $(x, y, z)$ of the same point by

$$\begin{aligned} x &= r\cos\phi \\ y &= r\sin\phi \\ z &= z. \end{aligned} \tag{8.22}$$

The inverse transformations are:

$$\begin{aligned} r &= (x^2 + y^2)^{1/2} \\ \tan\phi &= \frac{y}{x} \\ z &= z. \end{aligned}$$

The angle $\phi$ is measured in radians and the three coordinates are restricted to lie in the ranges:

$$0 \leq r < \infty, \quad 0 \leq \phi < 2\pi \quad \text{and} \quad -\infty < z < \infty.$$

These coordinates extend over the whole of space and most points have only one set of cylindrical coordinates. The only exceptions are points on the $z$-axis of Figure 8.21 (that is, points with $r = 0$). Any value of $\phi$ can be chosen at these points.

To describe a scalar field $f$ in cylindrical coordinates we express it as a function of $r$, $\phi$ and $z$:

$$f = f(r, \phi, z).$$

To describe a vector field $\mathbf{F}$ in cylindrical coordinates we use the **cylindrical unit vectors** shown in Figure 8.22. Each unit vector points in a direction in which one cylindrical coordinate changes while the other two remain fixed.

- $\mathbf{e}_r$ is in the direction of increasing $r$ and constant $\phi$ and $z$. This is in the outward radial direction, perpendicular to the $z$-axis.
- $\mathbf{e}_\phi$ is in the direction of increasing $\phi$ and constant $r$ and $z$.
- $\mathbf{e}_z$ is in the direction of increasing $z$ and constant $r$ and $\phi$.

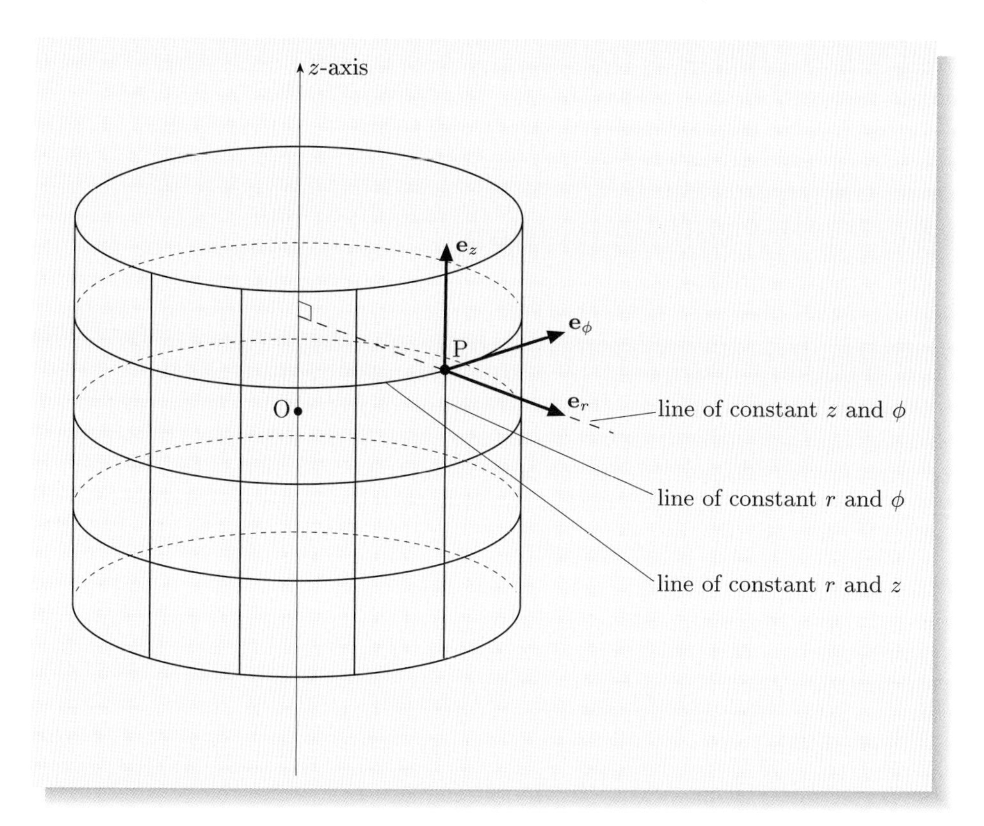


**Figure 8.22** Cylindrical unit vectors at a point P.

Although $\mathbf{e}_z$ maintains a constant direction, the other two unit vectors are functions of position. At any given point $\mathbf{r}$, the triplet of vectors $(\mathbf{e}_r(\mathbf{r}), \mathbf{e}_\phi(\mathbf{r}), \mathbf{e}_z)$ forms an orthogonal right-handed system with, for example,

$$\mathbf{e}_r(\mathbf{r}) \cdot \mathbf{e}_\phi(\mathbf{r}) = 0 \quad \text{and} \quad \mathbf{e}_r(\mathbf{r}) \times \mathbf{e}_\phi(\mathbf{r}) = \mathbf{e}_z.$$

The value of a vector field at $\mathbf{r}$ can therefore be expanded in terms of these unit vectors:

$$\mathbf{F}(\mathbf{r}) = F_r(\mathbf{r})\,\mathbf{e}_r(\mathbf{r}) + F_\phi(\mathbf{r})\,\mathbf{e}_\phi(\mathbf{r}) + F_z(\mathbf{r})\,\mathbf{e}_z, \tag{8.23}$$

but this is usually abbreviated to

$$\mathbf{F} = F_r\,\mathbf{e}_r + F_\phi\,\mathbf{e}_\phi + F_z\,\mathbf{e}_z,$$

with the position-dependence of $\mathbf{e}_r$ and $\mathbf{e}_\phi$ left implicit.

In cylindrical coordinates, a small displacement is given by

$$\delta\mathbf{l} = \delta r\,\mathbf{e}_r + r\,\delta\phi\,\mathbf{e}_\phi + \delta z\,\mathbf{e}_z. \tag{8.24}$$

The scale factors are therefore

$$h_r = 1, \quad h_\phi = r \quad \text{and} \quad h_z = 1,$$

and a small volume element about the point $(r, \phi, z)$ is

$$\delta V = h_r h_\phi h_z\,\delta r\,\delta\phi\,\delta z = r\,\delta r\,\delta\phi\,\delta z. \tag{8.25}$$

**Exercise 8.12** The scalar field $V(x, y, z) = A/(x^2 + y^2 + z^2)$, where $A$ is a constant, is expressed in Cartesian coordinates. Re-express this scalar field in (a) spherical and (b) cylindrical coordinates.

**Exercise 8.13** The vector field $\mathbf{F}(r) = (A/r^2)\,\mathbf{e}_r$, where $A$ is a constant, is expressed in spherical coordinates. Find expressions for $\mathbf{e}_r$ and $r^2$ in Cartesian coordinates and hence express the vector field $\mathbf{F}$ in Cartesian coordinates. ■

## 8.4 Partial differentiation

Section 8.4 is best read before or during your study of Chapter 2.

### 8.4.1 First partial derivatives

Any field is a function of position. In three-dimensional space, positions are specified by three coordinates, so fields are generally functions of three variables — four if time is included. We often need to know how rapidly a field is changing in a given direction. For example, we might want to know how rapidly a scalar field changes in the radial direction or how rapidly the $x$-component of a vector field varies in the $y$-direction. To deal with questions like this we must broaden the concept of differentiation to cope with functions of more than one variable.

You will be familiar with ordinary differentiation. Given a function $f(x)$ of the variable $x$, we can find its derivative $\mathrm{d}f/\mathrm{d}x$. The derivative is the *rate of change* of $f$ with respect to $x$. The value of the derivative at a given point is equal to the gradient of a graph of $f$ against $x$ at that point. The derivative is positive at a given point if $f$ increases with $x$ at that point. It is negative if $f$ decreases with $x$ at the point. Any calculus textbook will tell you how to calculate derivatives. There are rules for differentiating sums, products, quotients and functions of other functions, as well as specific rules dealing with standard functions.

We are interested in functions of more than one variable, and would like to extend the concept of differentiation to these functions. However, care is needed. For example, consider a function $f(x, y)$ of two independent variables, $x$ and $y$. If $x$

changes by $\Delta x$ and $y$ changes by $\Delta y$, the change in $f$ will depend on both $\Delta x$ and $\Delta y$. This is illustrated in the contour map shown in Figure 8.23. It follows that the rate of change of $f$ with respect to $x$ is ill-defined — *unless* we say what happens to $y$ while $x$ changes. The simplest possible choice is to insist that $y$ remains constant. This leads to the concept of partial differentiation.

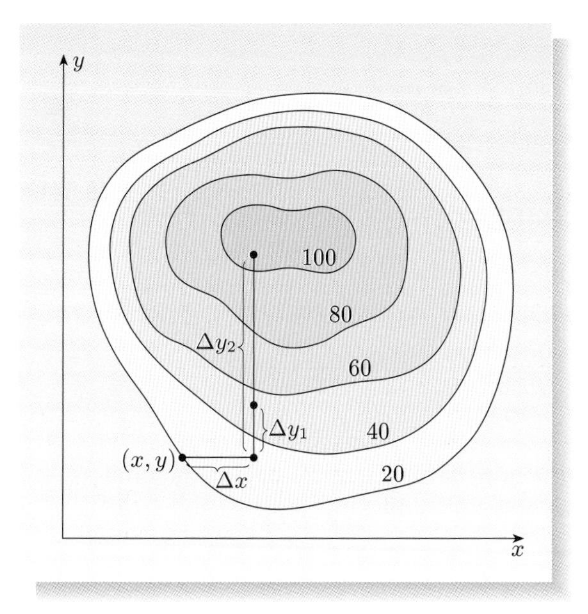


**Figure 8.23** Contour map of $f(x, y)$ with contours ranging from $f = 20$ to $f = 100$. Starting from a point $(x, y)$ and changing $x$ by a given amount $\Delta x$, the change in $f$ depends on the change in $y$. The contour lines show that the change in $f$ is greater when $\Delta x$ is accompanied by $\Delta y_2$ than by $\Delta y_1$.

The **partial derivative** of $f(x, y)$ with respect to $x$ is the rate of change of $f$ with respect to $x$ *when $y$ is held constant.* It is denoted by $(\partial f/\partial x)_y$, where the curly dees show that this is a *partial* derivative and the subscript $y$ reminds us that $y$ is held constant. The subscript is usually unnecessary. If we know that $f(x, y)$ is a function of $x$ and $y$, the fact that we are taking the partial derivative with respect to $x$ automatically implies that the other variable, $y$, is held constant. It is therefore sufficient to write

$$\frac{\partial f}{\partial x}$$

$\partial f/\partial x$ is pronounced as 'partial dee f by dee x'.

for the partial derivative of $f$ with respect to $x$, when $y$ is held constant. The partial derivative of $f$ with respect to $y$, when $x$ is held constant, is denoted by $\partial f/\partial y$. These ideas are easily extended to functions of many variables. Given a function $f(x_1, x_2, ..., x_n)$, the partial derivative of $f$ with respect to $x_i$ is written as $\partial f/\partial x_i$. This is the rate of change of $f$ with respect to $x_i$ *with all the other variables held constant.*

To calculate a partial derivative with respect to $x$ we just use the ordinary rules of differentiation, but remember to treat every variable, except $x$, as a constant. For example, if

$$f(x, y, z, t) = x^2y^2 \sin(\omega t) + z^4,$$

$$\frac{\partial f}{\partial x} = 2xy^2 \sin(\omega t).$$

In calculating this partial derivative, the factor $x^2$ is differentiated to give $2x$, whereas the factor $y^2 \sin(\omega t)$ is treated as a multiplicative constant which survives the differentiation unchanged and the term $z^4$ is treated as an additive constant whose derivative is zero. Using a similar argument we obtain

$$\frac{\partial f}{\partial t} = x^2 y^2 \omega \cos(\omega t).$$

**Exercise 8.14** If $f(x, y) = e^{2x} \cos(3y)$, find $\partial f/\partial x$ and $\partial f/\partial y$. ■

## 8.4.2 Estimating small changes

Given a function $f(x)$ of one variable, the derivative $\mathrm{d}f/\mathrm{d}x$ allows us to estimate the small change in $f$ that accompanies a small change in $x$. If $x$ changes by $\delta x$, the function $f$ changes by

$$\delta f = f(x + \delta x) - f(x) = \frac{\mathrm{d}f}{\mathrm{d}x}\,\delta x.$$

Strictly speaking, this is an approximation, but it becomes exact in the limit as $\delta x$ tends to zero and can be made as accurate as we like by taking $\delta x$ to be small enough.

We can extend this result to functions of many variables. Suppose we have a function $f(x, y, z)$ of variables $x$, $y$ and $z$. If we hold $y$ and $z$ constant and allow $x$ to change by a small amount $\delta x$, the change in $f$ is

$$\delta f = f(x + \delta x, y, z) - f(x, y, z) = \frac{\partial f}{\partial x}\,\delta x.$$

As with the case of one variable, this is an approximation which becomes exactly true in the limit as $\delta x$ tends to zero. More generally, $x$, $y$ and $z$ may all change. If we make arbitrary small changes $\delta x$, $\delta y$ and $\delta z$ to $x$, $y$ and $z$, the function $f$ changes by

$$\delta f = \frac{\partial f}{\partial x}\,\delta x + \frac{\partial f}{\partial y}\,\delta y + \frac{\partial f}{\partial z}\,\delta z. \tag{8.26}$$

This equation is known as the **chain rule of partial differentiation**. It is exact in the limit as $\delta x$, $\delta y$ and $\delta z$ tend to zero, and can be made as accurate as we like by taking $\delta x$, $\delta y$ and $\delta z$ to be small enough.

## 8.4.3 Higher partial derivatives

A function of a single variable can be differentiated once, twice or many times to produce higher-order derivatives. Something very similar can be done with partial derivatives. For example, if $f(x, y)$ is a function of $x$ and $y$, we can form the partial derivatives $\partial f/\partial x$ and $\partial f/\partial y$. These first-order partial derivatives are themselves functions of $x$ and $y$, so we can partially differentiate again with respect to $x$ or $y$ to obtain four second-order partial derivatives:

$$\frac{\partial^2 f}{\partial x^2} = \frac{\partial}{\partial x}\left(\frac{\partial f}{\partial x}\right),$$

$$\frac{\partial^2 f}{\partial y^2} = \frac{\partial}{\partial y}\left(\frac{\partial f}{\partial y}\right),$$

$$\frac{\partial^2 f}{\partial y \partial x} = \frac{\partial}{\partial y}\left(\frac{\partial f}{\partial x}\right),$$

$$\frac{\partial^2 f}{\partial x \partial y} = \frac{\partial}{\partial x}\left(\frac{\partial f}{\partial y}\right).$$

For example, if $f(x, y) = x^2 \sin y$, the first-order partial derivatives are

$$\frac{\partial f}{\partial x} = 2x \sin y,$$

$$\frac{\partial f}{\partial y} = x^2 \cos y.$$

Partially differentiating again, the second-order partial derivatives are

$$\frac{\partial^2 f}{\partial x^2} = \frac{\partial}{\partial x}(2x \sin y) = 2 \sin y,$$

$$\frac{\partial^2 f}{\partial y^2} = \frac{\partial}{\partial y}(x^2 \cos y) = -x^2 \sin y,$$

$$\frac{\partial^2 f}{\partial y \partial x} = \frac{\partial}{\partial y}(2x \sin y) = 2x \cos y,$$

$$\frac{\partial^2 f}{\partial x \partial y} = \frac{\partial}{\partial x}(x^2 \cos y) = 2x \cos y.$$

The last two partial derivatives are called **mixed partial derivatives** because they contain a mixture of partial differentiation with respect to $x$ and partial differentiation with respect to $y$. In one case we differentiate first with respect to $x$ (holding $y$ constant) and then with respect to $y$ (holding $x$ constant); in the other case this order of differentiation is reversed. The two partial differentiations occur one after the other, so there is no problem in holding a variable constant during the first differentiation and then allowing it to vary during the second. Notice that the two mixed partial derivatives are equal to one another. This turns out to be a general property, true for all 'well-behaved'smooth functions. It certainly applies to all the functions you will meet in this course. So you can safely assume that mixed partial derivatives do not depend on the order of partial differentiation.

**Exercise 8.15** If $f(x, t) = \sin(k(x - ct))$, where $k$ and $c$ are constants, show that

$$\frac{\partial^2 f}{\partial x^2} = \frac{1}{c^2}\frac{\partial^2 f}{\partial t^2}.$$

■

# 8.5 Volume and surface integrals

Section 8.5 is essential reading for Chapter 2.

This section shows how to integrate a scalar field over a volume and a vector field over a surface. These two ideas are connected. You will see later that the surface integral of a vector field is equal to the volume integral of a related scalar field.

## 8.5.1 Volume integrals

### Reminder of ordinary integration

You should be familiar with definite integrals of the form

$$I = \int_{x_{\min}}^{x_{\max}} f(x)\,\mathrm{d}x. \tag{8.27}$$

Such an integral is a kind of sum, suitable for functions of continuous variables, but it is *not* a sum of function values of the integrand. The integral is *not* related to a sum of the form

$$\sum_i f(x_i).$$

Instead, you should imagine dividing the range between $x_{\min}$ and $x_{\max}$ into many small steps, with the length of the $i^{\text{th}}$ step being equal to $\Delta x_i$. The integral is the limiting value of the sum

$$\sum_i f(x_i)\,\Delta x_i$$

when the steps have become infinite in number and infinitesimal in length ($i \to \infty$ and $\Delta x_i \to 0$).

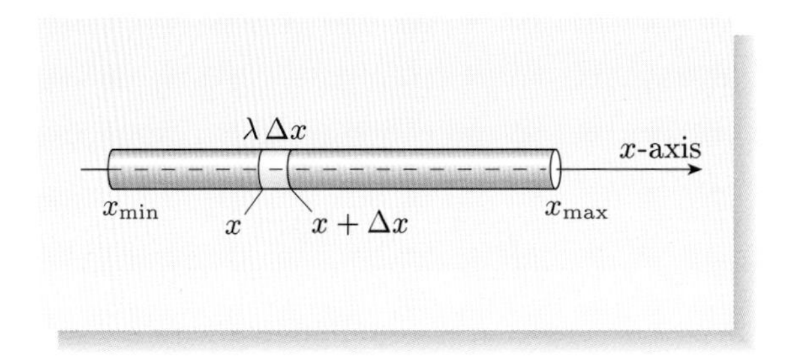


**Figure 8.24** A rod lying along the $x$-axis containing a mass element $\lambda\,\Delta x$.

To take a more physical case, imagine a long thin rod stretched out along the $x$-axis between $x_{\min}$ and $x_{\max}$ (Figure 8.24). The rod has a non-uniform mass per unit length. This non-uniformity is described by a function $\lambda(x)$, which is the mass per unit length of a segment at position $x$. In other words, the mass of the small element between $x$ and $x + \Delta x$ is $\lambda(x)\,\Delta x$. The total mass of the rod is approximated by

$$M \simeq \sum_i \lambda(x_i)\Delta x_i,$$

where the label $i$ runs over all the segments of the rod. Taking the limiting case of an infinite number of infinitesimal segments avoids any need to apologize for making approximations, and the total mass of the rod becomes

$$M = \int_{x_{\text{min}}}^{x_{\text{max}}} \lambda(x)\,\mathrm{d}x.$$

The integrand $\lambda(x)$ is a mass per unit length. This is integrated along the length of the rod to obtain the total mass.

### Extension to volume integrals

The integral discussed above involved a function that varies along the $x$-axis, and the integration was performed over a definite range of the $x$-axis. A **volume integral** generalizes this idea to three dimensions; we deal with functions that vary in three-dimensional space, and the integration is performed over a definite region of three-dimensional space, such as a cube or a sphere. Nevertheless, the basic idea of integration remains the same.

Suppose we have a function $f(\mathbf{r})$ which varies with position $\mathbf{r}$ in three-dimensional space. We want to integrate this function over a three-dimensional volume, $V$. This is achieved by dividing $V$ into many small volume elements. Suppose that the volume element containing the point $\mathbf{r}_i$ has volume $\Delta V_i$. Then we can form the sum

$$\sum_i f(\mathbf{r}_i)\,\Delta V_i,$$

where the label $i$ runs over all the volume elements $\Delta V_i$ in the volume $V$. Taking the limit of an infinite number of infinitesimal volume elements gives the required volume integral, which we write as

$$I = \int_V f(\mathbf{r})\,\mathrm{d}V. \tag{8.28}$$

The subscript $V$ on the integral sign indicates that the integral is taken over the volume $V$. This notation is less explicit than the use of limits in Equation 8.27 but it does serve to remind us that, when Equation 8.28 is approximated by a sum, all the volume elements must belong to $V$.

Let me be honest. If the volume $V$ is an irregular blob, the volume integral will be impossibly hard. Fortunately, we only need to consider simple cases, where both the volume $V$ and the function $f$ have high degrees of symmetry. The key to calculating volume integrals in these cases is to make full use of the symmetry. There are two main approaches, one informal and the other more formal. The informal method splits the volume of integration into carefully chosen volume elements. If possible, each volume element is labelled by a single variable and the integrand is taken to be constant throughout the element. The whole integral is then found by integrating over the variable that labels the volume elements. The following example illustrates how this works.

### Worked Example 8.1

A scalar field takes the form $f(r) = A/r$, where $A$ is a constant and $r$ is the distance from the origin. Calculate the volume integral $I = \int_V f(r)\,\mathrm{d}V$, where $V$ is a sphere of radius $R$, centred on the origin.

#### Solution

Because $f(r)$ depends only on the distance $r$ from the origin, it is sensible to divide the volume of the sphere into a set of nested spherical shells, each centred on the origin (Figure 8.25).

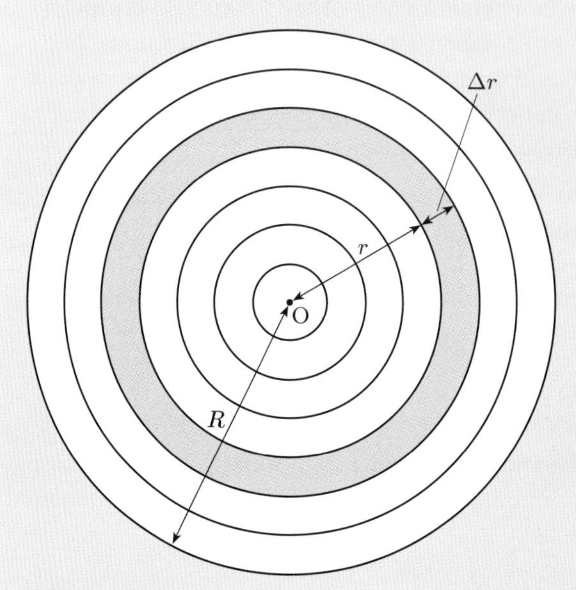


**Figure 8.25** Cross-sectional view of nested spherical shells, each of thickness $\Delta r$.

We concentrate on one of these shells of radius $r$ and thickness $\Delta r$. The volume of this shell is its surface area, $4\pi r^2$, times its thickness, $\Delta r$, so

$$\Delta V = 4\pi r^2\,\Delta r.$$

If the shell is thin enough, we can neglect any variation of $f$ in the shell. The contribution to the integral from this shell is therefore

$$\frac{A}{r} \times 4\pi r^2\,\Delta r = 4\pi A r\,\Delta r.$$

The integral over the whole sphere is found by adding contributions from all the spherical shells. Taking the limiting case of infinitely many shells of infinitesimal thickness, and integrating outwards from the centre of the sphere, $r = 0$, to its surface, $r = R$, we obtain

$$I = \int_0^R 4\pi A r\,\mathrm{d}r = 4\pi A\left[\frac{r^2}{2}\right]_0^R = 2\pi A R^2.$$

**Exercise 8.16** A scalar field takes the form $f(r) = Ar$, where $A$ is a constant and $r$ is the distance from the $z$-axis. Calculate the volume integral $I = \int_V f(r)\,\mathrm{d}V$, where $V$ is a cylinder of radius $R$ and length $L$, centred on the $z$-axis. ■

The remainder of Section 8.5.1 is optional reading.

Informal methods like these can cope with all the volume integrals you will meet in this book. However, to provide a flexible toolkit we will now show how volume integrals over spheres or cylinders can be approached more formally, using the spherical and cylindrical coordinate systems introduced in Section 8.3.2.

To integrate a scalar field over a sphere (or part of a sphere, such as a hemisphere), we use a spherical coordinate system with its origin at the centre of the sphere. In this coordinate system, the volume element is given by

$$\delta V = r^2 \sin\theta\,\delta r\,\delta\theta\,\delta\phi. \qquad \text{(Eqn 8.21)}$$

We need to select the limits that specify the volume of integration. A sphere of radius $R$ has coordinates in the range $0 \le r \le R$, $0 \le \theta \le \pi$ and $0 \le \phi < 2\pi$, so the volume integral can be written as

$$\int_{\text{sphere}} f(\mathbf{r})\,\mathrm{d}V = \int_{\phi=0}^{\phi=2\pi} \int_{\theta=0}^{\theta=\pi} \int_{r=0}^{r=R} f(r,\theta,\phi)\,r^2 \sin\theta\,\mathrm{d}r\,\mathrm{d}\theta\,\mathrm{d}\phi.$$

Note that, with $\mathrm{d}r$ placed innermost, the limits for $r$ are placed on the innermost integral sign — and so on, working outwards.

In particular, if $f$ depends only on $r$, the integral becomes

$$\begin{aligned}
\int_{\text{sphere}} f(r)\,\mathrm{d}V &= \int_{\phi=0}^{\phi=2\pi} \int_{\theta=0}^{\theta=\pi} \int_{r=0}^{r=R} f(r)\,r^2 \sin\theta\,\mathrm{d}r\,\mathrm{d}\theta\,\mathrm{d}\phi \\
&= \int_0^R f(r)\,r^2\,\mathrm{d}r \int_0^\pi \sin\theta\,\mathrm{d}\theta \int_0^{2\pi} \mathrm{d}\phi \\
&= \int_0^R f(r)\,r^2\,\mathrm{d}r \times 2 \times 2\pi \\
&= 4\pi \int_0^R f(r)\,r^2\,\mathrm{d}r.
\end{aligned}$$

For example, if $f = A/r$,

$$\int_{\text{sphere}} \frac{A}{r}\,\mathrm{d}V = 4\pi \int_0^R Ar\,\mathrm{d}r = 2\pi A R^2,$$

which agrees with Worked Example 8.1. However, the present method also works for functions that depend on the angular spherical coordinates. For example, if $f(r,\theta,\phi) = \cos^2\theta \sin^2\phi / r^2$, we have

$$\begin{aligned}
\int_{\text{sphere}} f(r,\theta,\phi)\,\mathrm{d}V &= \int_0^R \mathrm{d}r \int_0^\pi \cos^2\theta \sin\theta\,\mathrm{d}\theta \int_0^{2\pi} \sin^2\phi\,\mathrm{d}\phi \\
&= R \times \left[-\frac{\cos^3\theta}{3}\right]_0^\pi \times \pi = \frac{2\pi R}{3}.
\end{aligned}$$

Do not spend time working out lengthy integrals from first principles. The inside back cover of the book contains a list of standard integrals. Any integral needed in this book will either be elementary or will be in this list. At most, you may need to change the variable of integration or insert appropriate limits of integration.

A similar method can be used to evaluate volume integrals over cylinders (or parts of cylinders), but in this case we use cylindrical coordinates and the volume element is

$$\delta V = r\,\delta r\,\delta\phi\,\delta z. \qquad \text{(Eqn 8.25)}$$

A cylinder of radius $R$ and length $L$ has coordinates in the range $0 \leq r \leq R$, $0 \leq \phi < 2\pi$ and $-L/2 \leq z \leq L/2$, so the volume integral can be written as

$$\int_{\text{cylinder}} f(\mathbf{r})\,\mathrm{d}V = \int_{z=-L/2}^{z=+L/2} \int_{\phi=0}^{\phi=2\pi} \int_{r=0}^{r=R} f(r,\phi,z)\,r\,\mathrm{d}r\,\mathrm{d}\phi\,\mathrm{d}z.$$

If you need to integrate a function over all space, you can either use spherical coordinates (letting the upper limit of the $r$-coordinate tend to infinity) or use cylindrical coordinates (letting the upper limits of the $r$- and $z$-coordinates tend to infinity). However, you would be well-advised to choose the coordinate system in which the function takes the simplest possible form.

**Exercise 8.17** Calculate the volume integral over all space of the function $f(r) = \exp(-r^3)$, where $r$ is the distance from the origin. You may use the standard integral $\int r^2 \exp(-r^3)\,\mathrm{d}r = -\exp(-r^3)/3$. ■

## 8.5.2 Surface integrals

Surface integrals are used throughout science and technology. For example, in fluid mechanics they are used to calculate the amount of fluid flowing into a given region. They are also used to calculate the rate of heat loss through the walls, roof and floor of a house.

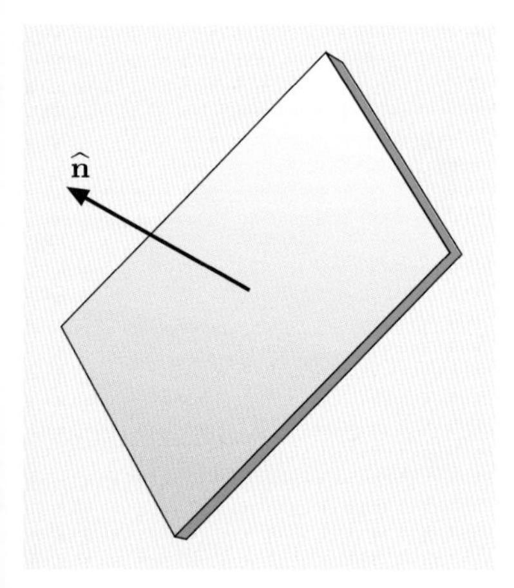


**Figure 8.26** The unit normal $\widehat{\mathbf{n}}$ of a plane.

### Area as a vector

You probably think of area as a scalar quantity — a certain number of square metres. This is good enough for areas drawn on a sheet of paper. More generally, though, we need to consider planes that are oriented in three-dimensional space. The simplest way to describe the orientation of a plane is to specify a unit vector $\widehat{\mathbf{n}}$ that is perpendicular to the plane (Figure 8.26). There are actually two such vectors, pointing in opposite directions, but this is not a problem — we just pick one of them and specify our selection clearly. The chosen unit vector is then called the **unit normal** of the plane.

For any given plane element, we can multiply the area $\Delta S$ of the element by its unit normal $\widehat{\mathbf{n}}$ to obtain the vector

$$\Delta\mathbf{S} = \Delta S\,\widehat{\mathbf{n}}.$$

This vector is called the **oriented area** of the plane element. It is perpendicular to the plane element and its magnitude is the area of the plane element.

### Flux over a plane element

Flux is a property of a vector field. Suppose a vector field $\mathbf{F}$ is defined throughout a region of space. We place a small plane element somewhere in this region (Figure 8.27). The plane element is small enough for the field to be taken as constant all over its surface. Then the **flux** of the vector field over the element is defined to be the normal component of the field (the component in the direction of the unit normal $\widehat{\mathbf{n}}$) times the area of the plane element:

$$\text{flux over element} = F_n\,\Delta S. \tag{8.29}$$

However, the normal component of the field is given by the scalar product

$$F_n = \mathbf{F} \cdot \widehat{\mathbf{n}} = F\cos\theta,$$

where $F$ is the magnitude of the vector field and $\theta$ is the angle between $\mathbf{F}$ and $\widehat{\mathbf{n}}$. So

$$\text{flux over element} = (\mathbf{F} \cdot \widehat{\mathbf{n}})\,\Delta S = \mathbf{F} \cdot (\widehat{\mathbf{n}}\,\Delta S) = \mathbf{F} \cdot \Delta\mathbf{S}. \tag{8.30}$$

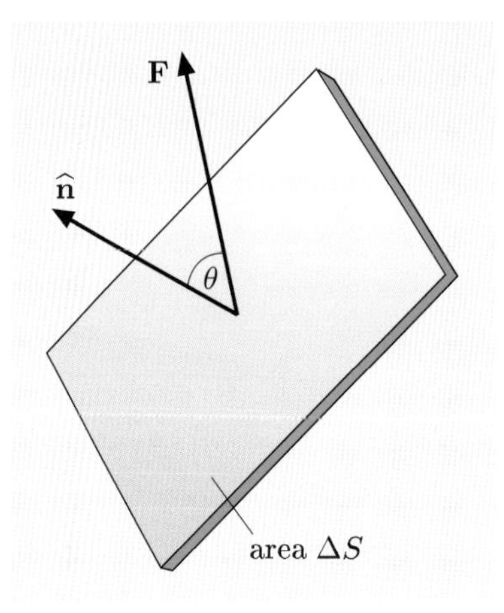


**Figure 8.27** The flux of a vector field over a small plane surface element $\Delta\mathbf{S} = \widehat{\mathbf{n}}\,\Delta S$.

▶ Scalar products are discussed in Section 8.2.1.

Hence, an alternative way of defining the flux is to say that it is the scalar product of the vector field (at the position of the element) and the oriented area of the element.

The name flux comes from the Latin for flow. This is not accidental because the flow of water provides useful insights into the meaning of flux. The velocity of water throughout a region of space can be described by a velocity vector field $\mathbf{v}(\mathbf{r})$. The flux of this vector field over a small plane element, $\Delta\mathbf{S}$, is

$$\text{flux of velocity} = \mathbf{v} \cdot \Delta\mathbf{S}.$$

This quantity has a simple interpretation. It is the rate of flow of water through the plane surface, measured in terms of volume per unit time. To see why, note from Figure 8.28 that the water that passes through the brown plane element $\Delta S$ in time $\Delta t$ is contained in the oblique parallelepiped.

This oblique parallelepiped has the same volume as the oblong brick, namely

$$\Delta V = \text{area of base} \times \text{height} = \Delta S \times (v\,\Delta t\cos\theta),$$

where $\theta$ is the angle between the direction of flow of the water and the unit normal $\widehat{\mathbf{n}}$ to the plane element of area $\Delta S$. So

$$\Delta V = (v\,\Delta S\cos\theta)\,\Delta t = (\mathbf{v} \cdot \Delta\mathbf{S})\,\Delta t,$$

and

$$\frac{\mathrm{d}V}{\mathrm{d}t} = \mathbf{v} \cdot \Delta\mathbf{S} = \text{flux of velocity}.$$

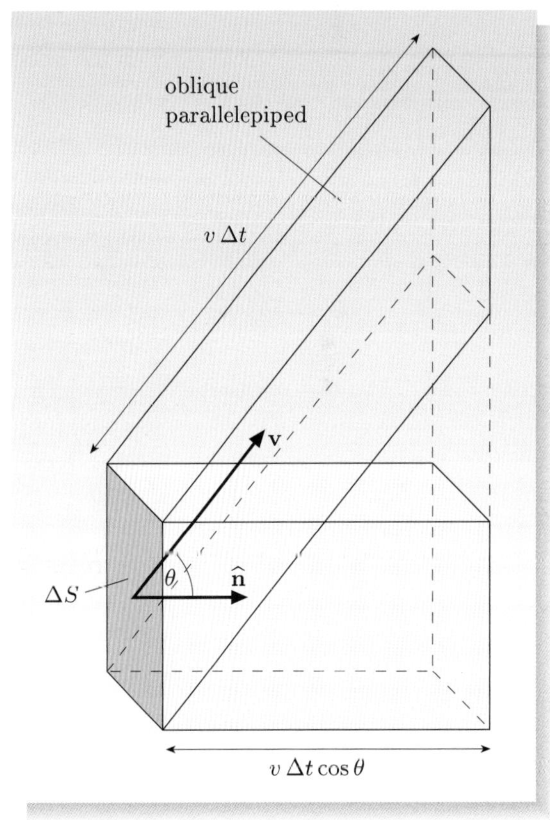


**Figure 8.28** The volume of water that passes the red plane element of area $\Delta S$ on the left in time $\Delta t$ is contained in the oblique parallelepiped, which has the same volume as the oblong brick with length $v\,\Delta t\cos\theta$.

This flux is positive if the direction of flow makes an acute angle with the unit normal, and is negative if the flow is in the opposite sense. For a given flow of water, the flux is greatest when the plane element is normal to the flow ($\widehat{\mathbf{n}}$ parallel to $\mathbf{v}$

and $\theta = 0°$). The flux is zero when the plane element is parallel to the flow ($\widehat{\mathbf{n}}$ perpendicular to $\mathbf{v}$ and $\theta = 90°$). Our general definition of flux is a mathematical abstraction of this concept which can be used for electric and magnetic fields, where nothing actually flows.

### Flux over an extended surface

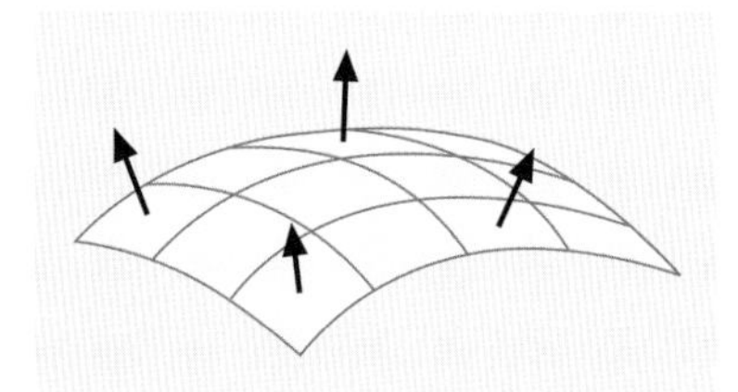

**Figure 8.29** Covering an extended surface with many small patches.

The definition of flux can be extended to larger surfaces, even if they are curved. To achieve this, we imagine covering the surface with many small patches (Figure 8.29). The patches are small enough for each to be treated as a plane element, and they are oriented consistently so that the unit normals of neighbouring patches are almost parallel, rather than almost antiparallel.

The flux over each patch can be found from Equation 8.30. To find the total flux over the whole surface we just add up the contributions of all the patches. We can avoid any inaccuracies by taking the limit of an infinite number of infinitesimal patches, so that the surface is fitted exactly. The resulting quantity is called the **surface integral** of the vector field over the surface. We write

$$\text{flux over surface } S = \int_S \mathbf{F} \cdot \mathrm{d}\mathbf{S}, \qquad (8.31)$$

where the right-hand side is our notation for the surface integral and the subscript $S$ on the integral sign shows that the integral is taken over a given surface $S$.

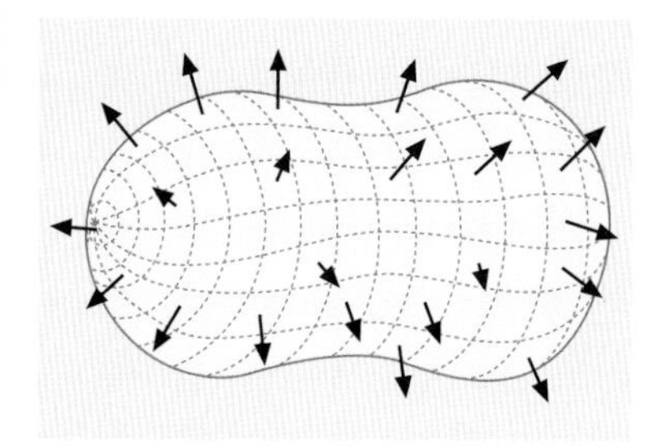

**Figure 8.30** The unit normals of a closed surface always point outwards.

Many of the surface integrals you will meet in electromagnetism will be over closed surfaces. A **closed surface** is one that separates space into two disconnected regions, one inside the surface and one outside. It is impossible to travel between these regions without crossing the surface. An **open surface** is one that fails to achieve this separation. The surface of an intact egg is an example of a closed surface; part of the eggshell after the egg has been cracked open is an open surface. For any closed surface it is conventional to choose the unit normals to point *outwards* (Figure 8.30). The flux of a vector field over a closed surface is therefore the flux *outwards* into the exterior space.

So much for definitions. What about practical calculations? First, the bad news; most surface integrals are very difficult, especially if the surface is irregularly-shaped or the vector field varies in a complicated way. Fortunately, we only need to consider simple cases. The surface will usually be that of a sphere or cylinder and the vector field will usually have a constant normal component on the surface, or on parts of the surface. With these advantages the surface integral can be found by multiplying the normal component of the field by an easily determined surface area.

**Worked Example 8.2**

The vector field $\mathbf{F}$ has the form $\mathbf{F} = (A/r^5)\,\mathbf{e}_r$, where $A$ is a constant and $\mathbf{e}_r$ is a unit vector pointing radially outwards from the origin. Calculate the flux of this vector field over a sphere of radius $R$, centred on the origin.

**Solution**

At all points on the surface of the sphere, the vector field points outwards, perpendicular to the surface. The normal component of the field has the constant value $A/R^5$ all over the spherical surface, so the flux is simply found by multiplying this normal component by the surface area $4\pi R^2$ of the sphere:

$$\text{flux} = \frac{A}{R^5} \times 4\pi R^2 = \frac{4\pi A}{R^3}.$$

**Exercise 8.18** The vector field $\mathbf{F}$ has the form $\mathbf{F} = (A/r)\,\mathbf{e}_r$, where $A$ is a constant and $\mathbf{e}_r$ is a unit vector pointing radially outwards from the $z$-axis in cylindrical coordinates. Calculate the flux of this vector field over the closed surface of a cylinder of radius $R$ and length $L$, centred on the $z$-axis. ■

## 8.6 The divergence of a vector field

Section 8.6 is essential reading for Chapter 2.

Given any vector field $\mathbf{F}$, we can define a scalar field called the divergence of $\mathbf{F}$. This section defines divergence and shows that a surface integral of $\mathbf{F}$ is related to a volume integral of the divergence of $\mathbf{F}$. The development hinges on a special property of flux — its additivity.

### 8.6.1 The additivity of flux

Suppose that a volume $V$ is split into many small volume elements. The principle of **additivity of flux** states that the flux of a vector field over the surface of the whole volume is the sum of the fluxes over the surfaces of all the volume elements. That is,

$$\int_S \mathbf{F} \cdot \mathrm{d}\mathbf{S} = \sum_i \int_{S_i} \mathbf{F} \cdot \mathrm{d}\mathbf{S}, \tag{8.32}$$

where $\mathbf{F}$ is the vector field, $S$ is the surface of the volume $V$ and $S_i$ is the surface of the $i^{\text{th}}$ volume element in $V$.

To establish this fact, consider two neighbouring volume elements $\Delta V_1$ and $\Delta V_2$ with surfaces $S_1$ and $S_2$ (Figure 8.31). The surfaces $S_1$ and $S_2$ contain a common boundary wall separating the two volume elements. At any point on this boundary wall, the unit normal $\widehat{\mathbf{n}}_1$ of $S_1$ points in the opposite direction to the unit normal $\widehat{\mathbf{n}}_2$ of $S_2$. This is because the unit normals of a closed surface point outwards. It follows that the flux contributed by the boundary wall section of $S_1$ is equal in magnitude and opposite in direction to the flux contributed by the boundary wall section of $S_2$. When we add up the fluxes over the surfaces of all the volume elements, the contributions from shared boundary walls all cancel out. The only surviving contributions come from the external surfaces, which together form the surface of the whole volume.

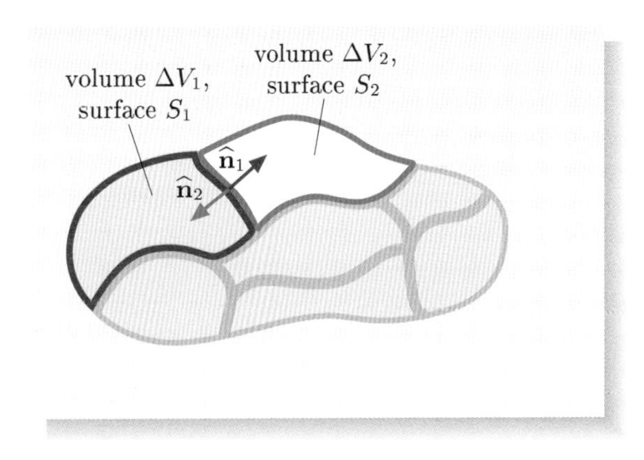


**Figure 8.31** Cross-sectional view of two neighbouring volume elements $\Delta V_1$ and $\Delta V_2$ with surfaces $S_1$ and $S_2$ shown in red and blue.

### 8.6.2 The divergence theorem

If the vector field $\mathbf{F}$ varies smoothly, and a small volume element is split into two similar pieces, the flux of $\mathbf{F}$ over the surface of each piece will be practically the same. The additivity of flux then requires the flux over the surface of each piece to be half the flux over the surface of the whole element. So, halving the volume halves the flux. More generally, the flux over the surface of any small volume element is proportional to the volume of the element. This suggests that the flux-to-volume ratio is a significant quantity.

The **divergence** of a vector field $\mathbf{F}$ at a given point $\mathbf{r}_i$ is defined by surrounding the point by a tiny volume element $\Delta V_i$, finding the flux of $\mathbf{F}$ over the surface of this volume element, and dividing by the volume $\Delta V_i$ of the element. It is denoted by $\operatorname{div}\mathbf{F}$ or if we wish to indicate the point of interest, by $\operatorname{div}\mathbf{F}(\mathbf{r}_i)$. So

div $\mathbf{F}$ is also written as $\boldsymbol{\nabla}\cdot\mathbf{F}$, as discussed in Section 8.10.

$$\operatorname{div}\mathbf{F}(\mathbf{r}_i) = \frac{1}{\Delta V_i}\int_{S_i} \mathbf{F}\cdot\mathrm{d}\mathbf{S}, \tag{8.33}$$

where $S_i$ is the surface enclosing the tiny volume element $\Delta V_i$ at $\mathbf{r}_i$.

Strictly speaking, divergence is defined in the limit where the volume element surrounding the point has become infinitesimally small. In this limit, the flux is exactly proportional to the volume of the element, and the flux-to-volume ratio tends to a definite value. The divergence of a vector field is the flux of the field *per unit volume*. Flux is a scalar quantity, so divergence is a scalar field.

Intuitively, divergence is a measure of the amount by which the field spreads outwards *per unit volume*. In the context of electrostatics, the electric field spreads outwards from positive charges and converges inwards towards negative charges. The divergence of the electric field is therefore positive at points where there is a positive charge density and negative at points where there is a negative charge density. It is zero where there is no charge. A second example relates to fluid flow. Suppose we treat the population of Manchester as a sort of fluid. This is like an ordinary fluid, but instead of molecules there are individual people. The velocity of this 'fluid' at any point is taken to be the average velocity of all the people in a small volume around the point. We assume that this varies smoothly over large length scales. Then the divergence of the velocity field is negative at places where people are gathering and positive at places where people are dispersing. At a football ground, the divergence is negative half an hour before the game begins and positive half an hour after it has ended.

Now let's return to Equation 8.32. This expresses the flux over a closed surface $S$ as a sum of terms. Each term in the sum is the flux over the surface $S_i$ of a volume element within the surface. Our aim is to replace this sum by a volume integral. This is achieved by combining Equations 8.32 and 8.33 to obtain

$$\int_S \mathbf{F}\cdot\mathrm{d}\mathbf{S} = \sum_i \operatorname{div}\mathbf{F}(\mathbf{r}_i)\,\Delta V_i.$$

Taking the limit of an infinite number of infinitesimal volume elements,

$$\int_S \mathbf{F}\cdot\mathrm{d}\mathbf{S} = \int_V \operatorname{div}\mathbf{F}\,\mathrm{d}V, \tag{8.34}$$

where $\mathbf{F}$ is a vector field and $\operatorname{div}\mathbf{F}$ is its divergence, $S$ is a closed surface and $V$ is the volume inside this surface. This result is called the **divergence theorem**. It tells us that the surface integral of a vector field over a closed surface is equal to the volume integral of the divergence of the field over the interior of the surface. The divergence theorem is a central pillar of vector calculus, of major importance in electromagnetism.

The divergence theorem was discovered independently by several people: Lagrange in 1764, Gauss in 1813, Green in 1828 and Ostrogradsky in 1831. The first two did not publish the theorem, but kept it in their personal papers. Green was an amateur mathematician with no connections to the academic world and only managed to publish it in an obscure pamphlet. It wasn't until 1831 that the theorem became well-known, just in time for the newly-developing science of electromagnetism. It is often called Gauss's theorem, but this risks confusion with Gauss's *law*; the two results are quite different — Equation 8.34 is a general theorem in mathematics while the Gauss's law is a law in physics specifically related to electromagnetism.

**Figure 8.32** Carl Friedrich Gauss (1777–1855).

### 8.6.3 Divergence as a derivative

▶ This section uses partial differentiation, which is discussed in Section 8.4.

You might wonder whether anything has been gained. Our definition of divergence involves a surface integral, so it is not clear that the right-hand side of Equation 8.34 is any simpler than the left-hand side. We can work on this though. Divergence involves surface integration over an *infinitesimal element*, and this leads to considerable simplification. In order to exploit this, we will take our volume element to be a cube aligned with the $x$-, $y$- and $z$-axes, with sides of length $\Delta L$ (Figure 8.33). We are interested in the flux of a vector field $\mathbf{F}$ over the surface of this cube.

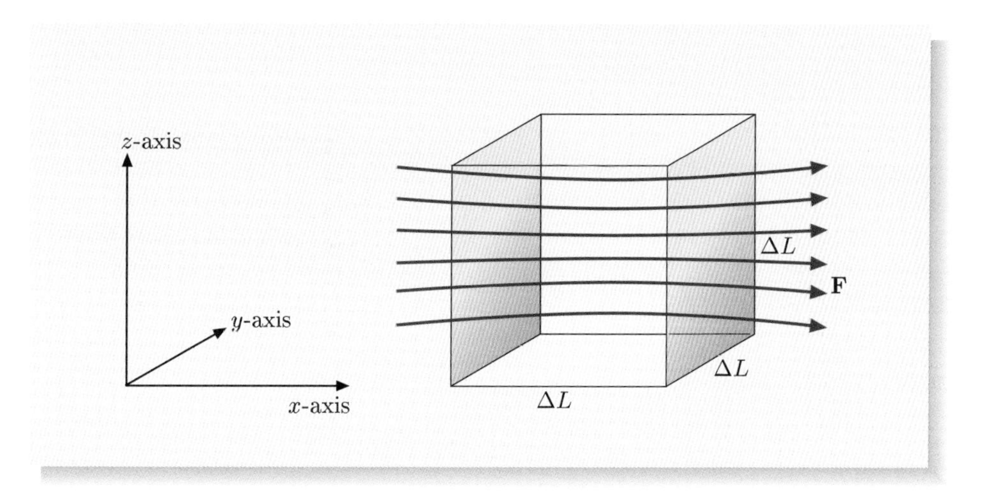


**Figure 8.33** A small cubic volume element threaded by the vector field $\mathbf{F}$.

The cube has six faces, and we must calculate the outward flux over each face, and then add them together. We start by considering the two shaded faces in Figure 8.33, which are perpendicular to the $x$-axis. The field on the left-hand face is $\mathbf{F}(x, y, z)$ and that on the right-hand face is $\mathbf{F}(x + \Delta L, y, z)$. To calculate the flux contribution of both faces, we need the component of the field perpendicular to the faces, that is the $x$-component. The flux contribution of both faces is then found by integrating $-F_x(x, y, z)$ over the left-hand face and integrating

$+F_x(x + \Delta L, y, z)$ over the right-hand face. The minus and plus signs occur because the outward normal of the left-hand face points in the negative $x$-direction, while the outward normal of the right-hand face points in the positive $x$-direction. In more physical terms they correspond to the fact that a field pointing along the positive $x$-axis has an inward flux on the left-hand face and an outward flux on the right-hand face. Because of this difference in sign, there would be no net flux if $F_x(x + \Delta L, y, z)$ were equal to $F_x(x, y, z)$. To get a non-zero flux, the field must vary as we move across the cube. To first order in $\Delta L$, we have

A partial derivative appears because $x$ varies while $y$ and $z$ remain constant.

$$F_x(x + \Delta L, y, z) - F_x(x, y, z) = \frac{\partial F_x}{\partial x}\,\Delta L,$$

so the net contribution of the pair of faces is obtained by integrating $(\partial F_x/\partial x)\,\Delta L$ over the right-hand face. In the limiting case of a tiny cube we can assume that $(\partial F_x/\partial x)\,\Delta L$ remains constant over the face, so the flux contribution from the pair of faces is

$$\frac{\partial F_x}{\partial x}\,\Delta L \times (\Delta L)^2 = \frac{\partial F_x}{\partial x}\,\Delta V,$$

where $\Delta V = (\Delta L)^3$ is the volume of the cube. A similar calculation can be performed for pairs of faces perpendicular to the $y$- and $z$-axes. Adding all these contributions together, we obtain the following expression for the total flux over the surface of the cube:

$$\text{flux} = \left(\frac{\partial F_x}{\partial x} + \frac{\partial F_y}{\partial y} + \frac{\partial F_z}{\partial z}\right)\Delta V.$$

Recalling that the divergence is the flux per unit volume, we conclude that

$$\operatorname{div}\mathbf{F} = \frac{\partial F_x}{\partial x} + \frac{\partial F_y}{\partial y} + \frac{\partial F_z}{\partial z}. \tag{8.35}$$

This formula gives us an explicit way of calculating a divergence in Cartesian coordinates. It also makes it easy to remember where the divergence goes in Equation 8.34. Because div **F** is a spatial derivative, its units are those of **F** divided by length. So, to get the same units on both sides of Equation 8.34, the divergence of **F** must belong in the volume integral, rather than in the surface integral.

### Worked Example 8.3

Find the divergence of the vector field $\mathbf{F} = x^2\mathbf{e}_x + y^2\mathbf{e}_y + z^2\mathbf{e}_z$. What is the value of div **F** at the point $(1, 2, 3)$ m?

#### Solution

Using Equation 8.35 for the divergence,

$$\operatorname{div}\mathbf{F} = \frac{\partial(x^2)}{\partial x} + \frac{\partial(y^2)}{\partial y} + \frac{\partial(z^2)}{\partial z} = 2x + 2y + 2z.$$

At the point $(1, 2, 3)$ m,

$$\operatorname{div}\mathbf{F} = 2 \times 1\,\text{m} + 2 \times 2\,\text{m} + 2 \times 3\,\text{m} = 12\,\text{m}.$$

**Exercise 8.19** Find the divergence of the vector field $\mathbf{F} = (\mathbf{a} \cdot \mathbf{r})\mathbf{e}_x + (\mathbf{b} \cdot \mathbf{r})\mathbf{e}_y + (\mathbf{c} \cdot \mathbf{r})\mathbf{e}_z$, where $\mathbf{a}$, $\mathbf{b}$ and $\mathbf{c}$ are constant vectors.

**Exercise 8.20** Use the divergence theorem to show that the surface integral of a constant vector field is zero over any closed surface. ■

### 8.6.4 Divergence in other coordinate systems

The definition of divergence as flux per unit volume is not restricted to any particular coordinate system, but the argument leading to Equation 8.35 used a cube with sides aligned in the $x$-, $y$- and $z$-direction, and this led to a formula involving derivatives with respect to Cartesian coordinates $x$, $y$ and $z$. This restriction can be removed by considering volume elements in other coordinate systems. I shall just quote the general result here, which applies to any **orthogonal coordinate system** — that is, one in which the three unit vectors, associated with the three coordinates, are mutually orthogonal. In an orthogonal coordinate system with coordinates $q_1$, $q_2$ and $q_3$ and scale factors $h_1$, $h_2$ and $h_3$, the divergence of $\mathbf{F}$ turns out to be

► Spherical and cylindrical coordinate systems are discussed in Section 8.3.2.

$$\operatorname{div} \mathbf{F} = \frac{1}{h_1 h_2 h_3} \left[ \frac{\partial}{\partial q_1}(h_2 h_3 F_1) + \frac{\partial}{\partial q_2}(h_1 h_3 F_2) + \frac{\partial}{\partial q_3}(h_1 h_2 F_3) \right], \quad (8.36)$$

where $F_1$, $F_2$ and $F_3$ are the components of $\mathbf{F}$ along the unit vectors $\mathbf{e}_1$, $\mathbf{e}_2$ and $\mathbf{e}_3$ that correspond to the coordinates $q_1$, $q_2$ and $q_3$.

Three special cases are important for us. In Cartesian coordinates, the scale factors are all equal to 1, so we recover Equation 8.35. In spherical coordinates

$$q_1 = r, \quad q_2 = \theta, \quad q_3 = \phi, \quad h_1 = 1, \quad h_2 = r \quad \text{and} \quad h_3 = r \sin\theta,$$

so the divergence becomes

$$\operatorname{div} \mathbf{F} = \frac{1}{r^2} \frac{\partial\,(r^2 F_r)}{\partial r} + \frac{1}{r \sin\theta} \frac{\partial\,(\sin\theta\, F_\theta)}{\partial \theta} + \frac{1}{r \sin\theta} \frac{\partial F_\phi}{\partial \phi}. \quad (8.37)$$

In cylindrical coordinates

$$q_1 = r, \quad q_2 = \phi, \quad q_3 = z, \quad h_1 = 1, \quad h_2 = r \quad \text{and} \quad h_3 = 1,$$

and the divergence becomes

$$\operatorname{div} \mathbf{F} = \frac{1}{r} \frac{\partial}{\partial r}(r\, F_r) + \frac{1}{r} \frac{\partial F_\phi}{\partial \phi} + \frac{\partial F_z}{\partial z}. \quad (8.38)$$

Equations of this type are collected together inside the back cover of this book. You are not expected to prove or remember them, but you should know of their existence. You will need to recognize when to use them, and be prepared to look them up and apply them when it is necessary to do so.

**Worked Example 8.4**

Consider the vector field $\mathbf{F} = A\mathbf{r}$, where $A$ is a constant. Find the divergence of this vector field using (a) spherical coordinates and (b) Cartesian coordinates.

**Solution**

(a) In spherical coordinates,

$$\mathbf{F} = A\mathbf{r} = (Ar)\mathbf{e}_r,$$

so $F_r = Ar$ and $F_\theta = F_\phi = 0$.

Therefore the divergence of the vector field $\mathbf{F}$ is

$$\operatorname{div}\mathbf{F} = \frac{1}{r^2}\frac{\partial(r^2 \times Ar)}{\partial r} = \frac{1}{r^2}\frac{\partial(Ar^3)}{\partial r} = \frac{3Ar^2}{r^2} = 3A.$$

(b) In Cartesian coordinates, the vector field takes the form

$$\mathbf{F} = A(x\mathbf{e}_x + y\mathbf{e}_y + z\mathbf{e}_z),$$

so the divergence is

$$\operatorname{div}\mathbf{F} = \frac{\partial(Ax)}{\partial x} + \frac{\partial(Ay)}{\partial y} + \frac{\partial(Az)}{\partial z} = 3A,$$

as before.

**Exercise 8.21** Use the divergence theorem to calculate the flux of the vector field $\mathbf{F} = A\mathbf{r}$ over the surface of an arbitrary region of volume $V$. Check your answer by direct calculation of the flux over the surface of a sphere of radius $R$, centred on the origin.

**Exercise 8.22** A vector field $\mathbf{E}$ is spherically symmetric and takes the form $\mathbf{E} = f(r)\,\mathbf{e}_r$ in spherical coordinates. If $\operatorname{div}\mathbf{E} = 0$ at all points except the origin, show that $f(r)$ is inversely proportional to $r^2$.

**Exercise 8.23** A vector field $\mathbf{E}$ is cylindrically symmetric and takes the form $\mathbf{E} = f(r)\,\mathbf{e}_r$ in cylindrical coordinates. If $\operatorname{div}\mathbf{E} = 0$ at all points not on the $z$-axis, show that $f(r)$ is inversely proportional to $r$, the distance from the $z$-axis. ■

## 8.7 Line integrals

Section 8.7 is essential reading for Chapter 4.

Line integrals arise in many areas of physics. Perhaps the most familiar example is that of work in mechanics. Think of a particle that experiences a constant force $\mathbf{F}$ while undergoing a displacement $\delta\mathbf{l}$. The work done by this force is given by the scalar product

$$\delta W = \mathbf{F} \cdot \delta\mathbf{l}. \tag{8.39}$$

More generally, the particle may experience a force that varies with position, and the particle may move along a curve. In this case, the total work done can be approximated by dividing the curve into many short segments. The force remains almost constant over a short segment, so the work done within a segment is still given by Equation 8.39. The total work done along the curve is then approximated by adding contributions from all the segments. This approximation becomes exact in the limit of taking an infinite number of infinitesimal segments. When this limit is taken, the total work is said to be the *line integral of the force along the curve.*

The concept of a line integral can be extended to any vector field, $\mathbf{F}(\mathbf{r})$, and any directed curve, C. A **directed curve** is a path with an associated sense of progression, leading from a start-point to an end-point. The path could be a straight line, an intricate curve or a **closed loop** with identical start- and end-points. The directed curve is approximated by many directed line elements, each described by a displacement vector $\delta\mathbf{l}_i$, pointing in the sense of progression along the curve (Figure 8.34). For each line element, we take the scalar product $\mathbf{F}_i \cdot \delta\mathbf{l}_i$, where $\mathbf{F}_i$ is the value of the field at the position of the line element. We then add together contributions from all the line elements. The **line integral** is the limiting value of this sum when the line elements become infinitesimal and the curve is fitted exactly. This gives a scalar quantity whose units are those of the vector field times length.

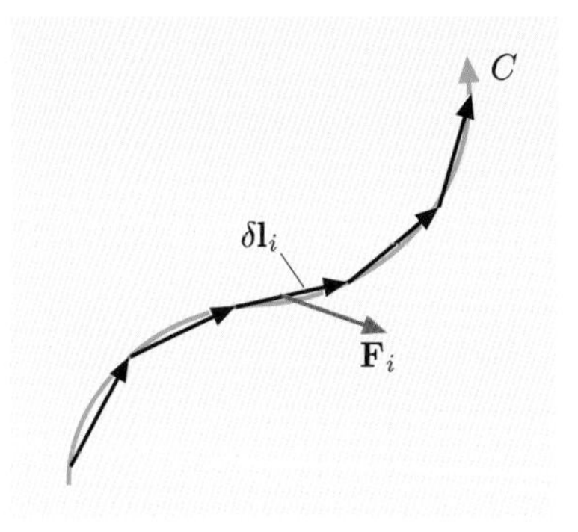


**Figure 8.34** Approximating a directed curve $C$ by a set of directed line elements such as $\delta\mathbf{l}_i$.

The line integral of $\mathbf{F}$ along a given directed curve $C$ is denoted by

$$\int_C \mathbf{F} \cdot \mathrm{d}\mathbf{l}.$$

The line integral of $\mathbf{F}$ around a *closed loop* $C$ is written as

$$\oint_C \mathbf{F} \cdot \mathrm{d}\mathbf{l},$$

with a circle in the middle of the integral sign. This line integral is called the **circulation** of $\mathbf{F}$ around $C$.

All the line integrals you need to evaluate in this book are quite straightforward. The following worked example is a typical case.

### Worked Example 8.5

A vector field is expressed in cylindrical coordinates as $\mathbf{F}(\mathbf{r}) = kr\mathbf{e}_\phi$. The field lines of this vector field are concentric circles around the $z$-axis, as shown in Figure 8.35. Calculate the line integral of $\mathbf{F}$ along $C_1$, a circle of radius $R$ centred on the origin and perpendicular to the $z$-axis, circulating in the same sense as $\mathbf{e}_\phi$.

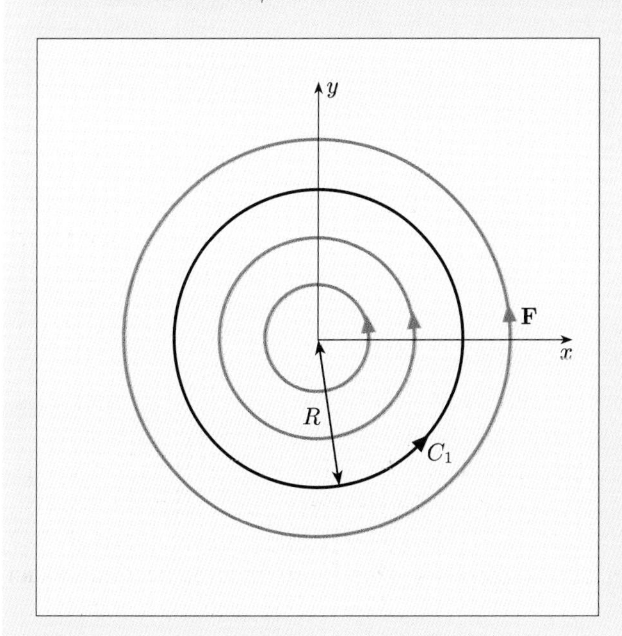


**Figure 8.35** A vector field $\mathbf{F}$ whose field lines are concentric circles around the $z$-axis is to be integrated round a circular path $C_1$. The $z$-axis points out of the page, towards you.

**Solution**

The circle $C_1$ has radius $R$. At each point on this circle, the vector field has magnitude $kR$ and points in the same direction as the path taken round the circle. If the circle is divided into many segments, each segment contributes $kR$ times the length of the segment. So the line integral is given by $kR$ times the circumference $2\pi R$ of the circle. That is,

$$\int_{C_1} \mathbf{F} \cdot \mathrm{d}\mathbf{l} = 2\pi k R^2.$$

This argument can be presented in a more formal way. Suppose that $C_1$ is split into many small directed line elements. A directed line element with cylindrical coordinates $(R, \phi, z)$ can be expressed as $\delta\mathbf{l} = R\,\delta\phi\,\mathbf{e}_\phi$. At the position of this line element, the vector field has the value $\mathbf{F} = kR\mathbf{e}_\phi$, so the contribution of the line element to the line integral is

$$\mathbf{F} \cdot \delta\mathbf{l} = (kR\mathbf{e}_\phi) \cdot (R\,\delta\phi\,\mathbf{e}_\phi) = kR^2\,\delta\phi.$$

Integrating over all the directed line elements then gives

$$\int_{C_1} \mathbf{F} \cdot \mathrm{d}\mathbf{l} = \int_0^{2\pi} kR^2\,\mathrm{d}\phi = 2\pi k R^2,$$

as before.

When defining a line integral we must specify a vector field and a directed curve. The direction along the curve matters. If $C_1$ is a directed curve from A to B and $C_2$ is the same curve but taken from B to A, we have

$$\int_{C_1} \mathbf{F} \cdot \mathrm{d}\mathbf{l} = -\int_{C_2} \mathbf{F} \cdot \mathrm{d}\mathbf{l}.$$

The precise curve also matters. It is not sufficient to say that a line integral starts at point A and ends at point B. In general, we need to know the path chosen to join these points because different paths starting at A and ending at B have different line integrals. The following example illustrates this fact.

**Worked Example 8.6**

Figure 8.36 shows a red path, $C_1$, and a blue path, $C_2$. Calculate the line integral of the vector field $\mathbf{F} = x\mathbf{e}_y$ along each of these paths.

**Solution**

A small directed line element along either of the paths can be written as $\delta\mathbf{l} = \delta x\,\mathbf{e}_x + \delta y\,\mathbf{e}_y$. Taking the scalar product with the vector field $\mathbf{F} = x\mathbf{e}_y$ gives

$$\mathbf{F} \cdot \delta\mathbf{l} = x\delta y.$$

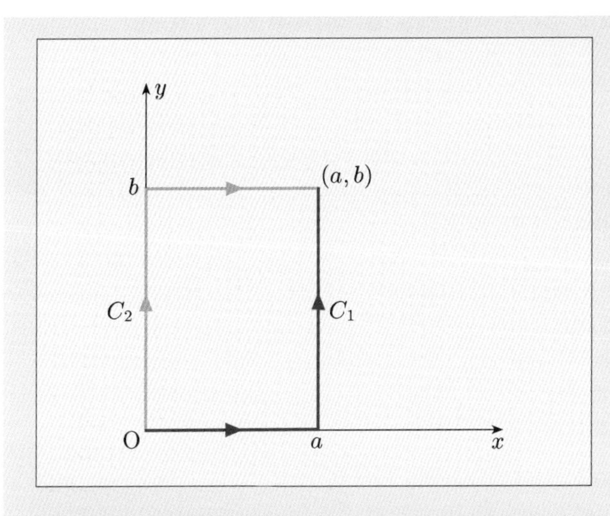


**Figure 8.36** Two different paths, $C_1$ and $C_2$, each starting at the origin and ending at $(a, b)$.

The elements of each path that run parallel to the $x$-axis have $\delta y = 0$, and therefore make no contribution. The elements of each path that run parallel to the $y$-axis have $x =$ constant, but different constant values of $x$ are experienced along $C_1$ and $C_2$. Along $C_1$ we have $x = a$, so

$$\int_{C_1} \mathbf{F} \cdot \mathrm{d}\mathbf{l} = \int_0^b a\,\mathrm{d}y = ab.$$

Along $C_2$ we have $x = 0$, so

$$\int_{C_2} \mathbf{F} \cdot \mathrm{d}\mathbf{l} = \int_0^b 0\,\mathrm{d}y = 0.$$

Although line integrals generally depend on the choice of path, there are exceptions. Some special vector fields have the wonderful property that all their line integrals depend only on the start-point and end-point of the path used. Such line integrals will be discussed later, in Section 8.9.

**Exercise 8.24** For the vector field described in Worked Example 8.5, calculate the line integral around $C_2$, a circle of radius $R$ centred on the origin and lying in the $xz$-plane.

**Exercise 8.25** For the vector field described in Worked Example 8.6, calculate the line integral along $C_3$, a straight-line path starting at $(0, 0)$ and ending at $(a, b)$. ■

## 8.8 The curl of a vector field

Given any vector field $\mathbf{F}$, we can define a new vector field called the curl of $\mathbf{F}$. This section defines curl and shows that a line integral of $\mathbf{F}$ around a closed loop is related to a surface integral of the curl of $\mathbf{F}$. We begin by introducing a convention for the sense of progression around the perimeter of an open surface.

Section 8.8 is essential reading for Chapter 4.

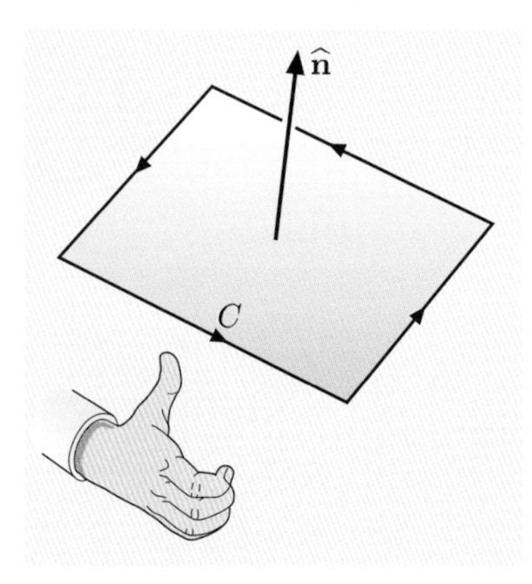


**Figure 8.37** The right-hand grip rule determines the sense of progression around the perimeter of a plane element.

### 8.8.1 A convention for perimeters of open surfaces

You know that each plane element has a unit normal $\widehat{\mathbf{n}}$, that is, a unit vector pointing perpendicular to the element. Of course, there are two directions perpendicular to the plane element, opposite to one another. In order to specify the plane element we must choose one of these directions as the unit normal. Now consider the perimeter of the plane element. This is a closed loop which can be traversed in two senses (clockwise or anticlockwise). We adopt a convention which links the choice of unit normal to the positive sense of progression around the perimeter. The convention uses the **right-hand grip rule** shown in Figure 8.37 — with the thumb of your right hand pointing in the direction of the unit normal of a plane element, the curled fingers of your right hand indicate the positive sense of progression around the perimeter of the element.

An extended open surface also has a perimeter. The open surface can be covered by a patchwork of tiny plane elements. In this case, the unit normals of the plane elements are chosen to point in consistent directions, so that neighbouring patches have unit normals that are nearly parallel, rather than nearly antiparallel. This defines a consistent sense of progression around the perimeter of each patch, and hence around the perimeter of the whole surface. The sense of progression becomes important when we consider a line integral around the perimeter of an open surface. The line integral is always taken in the sense of positive progression, determined by the right-hand grip rule. Some of Maxwell's equations implicitly assume that this has been done.

**Exercise 8.26** An open surface lies in the plane of the paper, with its unit normal pointing out of the plane of the paper towards you. Is the positive sense of progression around the perimeter of this element clockwise or anticlockwise, from your viewpoint? ■

### 8.8.2 The additivity of circulation

Now, suppose that an open surface is divided into many surface elements which are oriented consistently, so that their perimeters are all traversed in the same sense. The principle of **additivity of circulation** states that the circulation of a vector field around the perimeter of the whole surface is the sum of its circulations around the perimeters of all the surface elements. That is,

$$\oint_C \mathbf{F} \cdot \mathrm{d}\mathbf{l} = \sum_i \oint_{C_i} \mathbf{F} \cdot \mathrm{d}\mathbf{l}, \qquad (8.40)$$

where $\mathbf{F}$ is the vector field, $C$ is the perimeter of the whole surface and $C_i$ is the perimeter of the $i^{\text{th}}$ surface element.

To establish this fact, consider two neighbouring surface elements $\Delta S_1$ and $\Delta S_2$ with perimeters $C_1$ and $C_2$ (Figure 8.38). These perimeters have a common section, AB, which forms a boundary between the two surface elements. Our convention requires both perimeters to be traversed in the same sense, taken to be anticlockwise in the diagram. This means that AB is traversed in one sense (from A to B) for $C_1$ and in the opposite sense (from B to A) for $C_2$. When we calculate the sum of the line integrals of a vector field around the perimeters of all the surface elements, the contribution from AB in $C_1$ cancels the contribution from BA in $C_2$. More generally, the contributions from all common boundaries between surface elements cancel out, leaving only contributions from curves that form the perimeter of the whole surface.

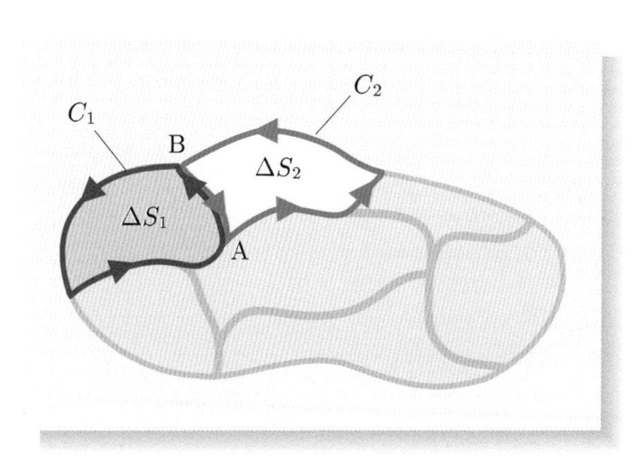


**Figure 8.38** Two neighbouring surface elements $\Delta S_1$ and $\Delta S_2$ with perimeters $C_1$ and $C_2$ shown in red and blue.

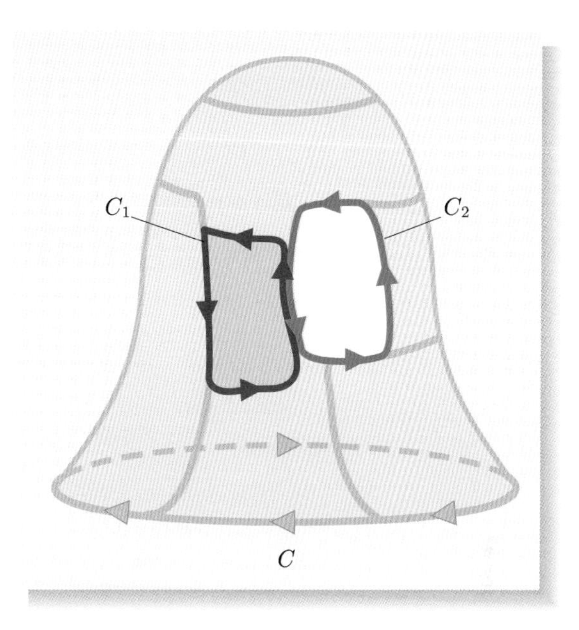


**Figure 8.39** The additivity of circulation applies to open surfaces of any shape, not just planar ones.

We need not even assume that all the surface elements lie in the same plane. For example, Figure 8.39 shows a bell-shaped surface divided into many surface elements. The above argument continues to work in this case, so the circulation around the opening of the bell is the sum of the circulations around the perimeters of all the patches on the surface of the bell.

## 8.8.3 The curl theorem

If the vector field $\mathbf{F}$ varies smoothly, and a small surface element is split into two similar pieces, the circulation of $\mathbf{F}$ around the perimeter of each piece will be practically the same. The additivity of circulation then requires that the circulation around the perimeter of each piece is half the circulation around the perimeter of the whole element. So, halving the area halves the circulation. More generally, the circulation around the perimeter of any small surface element is proportional to the area of the element. This suggests that the circulation-to-area ratio is a significant quantity.

The situation is similar to that encountered for divergence, but with one significant difference. The surface element can be oriented in many different ways, each giving a different circulation. So we get different values of the circulation per unit area for plane elements oriented in different directions. We are therefore led to consider a *vector* quantity, called the **curl** of $\mathbf{F}$ and denoted by $\operatorname{curl}\mathbf{F}$. At any given point, the *component* of $\operatorname{curl}\mathbf{F}$ in the direction of the unit vector $\widehat{\mathbf{n}}_i$ is the circulation per unit area for a small plane element centred on the

$\operatorname{curl}\mathbf{F}$ is also written as $\boldsymbol{\nabla} \times \mathbf{F}$, as discussed in Section 8.10.

point, with unit normal $\widehat{\mathbf{n}}_i$. In terms of symbols, the component of $\operatorname{curl}\mathbf{F}$ in the direction of the unit vector $\widehat{\mathbf{n}}_i$ is

$$(\operatorname{curl}\mathbf{F}) \cdot \widehat{\mathbf{n}}_i = \frac{1}{\Delta S_i} \oint_{C_i} \mathbf{F} \cdot \mathrm{d}\mathbf{l}, \tag{8.41}$$

where the line integral is taken round the perimeter $C_i$ of a small plane element which has area $\Delta S_i$ and unit normal $\widehat{\mathbf{n}}_i$ and is situated at the point where the curl is evaluated. The direction of $\widehat{\mathbf{n}}_i$ and the positive sense of circulation around $C_i$ are linked by the right-hand grip rule, as always.

Strictly speaking, curl is defined in the limit where the plane element has become infinitesimally small. In this limit, the circulation is exactly proportional to the area of the element, and the circulation per unit area tends to a definite value. The component of the curl of a vector field in the direction of a unit vector is the circulation of the field *per unit area perpendicular to the unit vector*. Three independent components of $\operatorname{curl}\mathbf{F}$ can be defined at each point in space, so curl is a vector field.

Intuitively, curl is a measure of the local swirling tendency of a vector field per unit area. The $z$-component of the curl, for example, is a measure of the local swirling tendency per unit area in the $xy$-plane. For example, imagine a leaf floating on the surface of a river. In addition to moving downstream, the leaf will, in general, rotate about a vertical axis. If the water velocity is described by the vector field $\mathbf{v}$, the vertical component of $\operatorname{curl}\mathbf{v}$ at the position of the leaf is proportional to the rate of rotation of the leaf. In a domestic setting, water going down the plughole of a bath tends to form vortices, within which the water velocity has a non-zero curl.

Now let's return to the additivity of circulation. Suppose we have an open surface $S$ with perimeter $C$, then Equation 8.40 gives the circulation around $C$ as a sum of terms. Each term is the circulation around the perimeter of a small surface element. Our aim is to replace this sum by a surface integral over $S$. This is achieved by combining Equations 8.40 and 8.41 to obtain

$$\oint_C \mathbf{F} \cdot \mathrm{d}\mathbf{l} = \sum_i (\operatorname{curl}\mathbf{F}) \cdot \widehat{\mathbf{n}}_i \, \Delta S_i$$

Recalling that $\widehat{\mathbf{n}}_i \, \Delta S_i = \Delta\mathbf{S}_i$ is the oriented area of the surface element and taking the limiting case of an infinite number of infinitesimal surface elements, we conclude that

$$\oint_C \mathbf{F} \cdot \mathrm{d}\mathbf{l} = \int_S \operatorname{curl}\mathbf{F} \cdot \mathrm{d}\mathbf{S}, \tag{8.42}$$

where $C$ is a closed loop and $S$ is any open surface that has $C$ as its perimeter. This result is called the **curl theorem**. It tells us that the line integral of a vector field around a closed loop is equal to the surface integral of the curl of the field over any surface bounded by the loop.

**Figure 8.40** Sir George Gabriel Stokes (1819–1903).

The curl theorem is just as important as the divergence theorem, and plays a central role in electromagnetism. It is often called **Stokes's theorem**, though the connection with Stokes is a bit shaky. The theorem was actually discovered in 1850 by William Thompson (Lord Kelvin) who told his friend, George Stokes (Figure 8.40), about it in a postscript to a letter. Stokes set it as a demanding problem in an examination, which was taken by a young student, J. Clerk Maxwell. Perhaps exams have their uses, after all!

### 8.8.4 Curl as a derivative

You have seen that the divergence of a vector field can be expressed as a combination of partial derivatives; in Cartesian coordinates,

$$\operatorname{div} \mathbf{F} = \frac{\partial F}{\partial x} + \frac{\partial F}{\partial y} + \frac{\partial F}{\partial z}. \qquad \text{(Eqn 8.35)}$$

This formula is useful because it allows us to find the divergence of any given vector field. We will now show that $\operatorname{curl} \mathbf{F}$ can also be expressed in terms of partial derivatives.

Let's concentrate on the $z$-component of $\operatorname{curl} \mathbf{F}$. To find this, we take the line integral of $\mathbf{F}$ around a tiny square element with unit normal $\mathbf{e}_z$ (Figure 8.41). This square element has sides of length $\Delta L$ which are aligned with the $x$- and $y$-axes. To conform with the right-hand grip rule, the perimeter of the square is traversed in an anticlockwise sense, as indicated in the diagram.

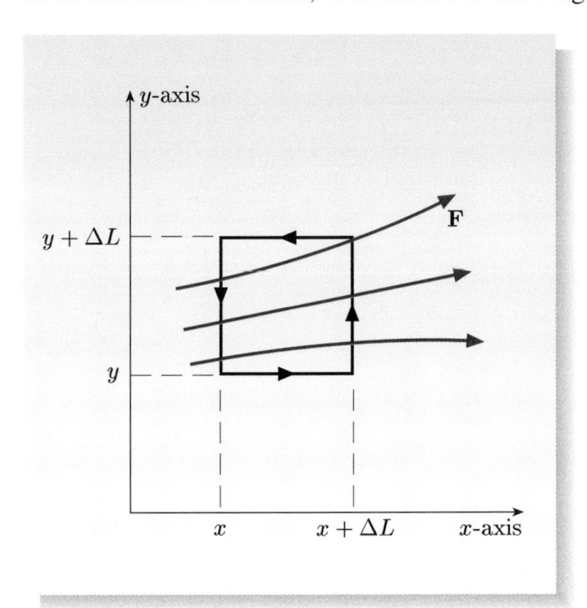


**Figure 8.41** A square plane element used to obtain an expression for the $z$-component of $\operatorname{curl} \mathbf{F}$.

Consider first the contribution to the line integral from the pair of sides parallel to the $y$-axis. Along these sides we must integrate $F_y$ over $y$. On the left-hand path, $F_y(x, y, z)$ is integrated from $y + \Delta L$ to $y$. This is equivalent to integrating $-F_y(x, y, z)$ from $y$ to $y + \Delta L$. On the right-hand path $F_y(x + \Delta L, y, z)$ is integrated from $y$ to $y + \Delta L$. So the total contribution from the two paths is obtained by integrating

$$F_y(x + \Delta L, y, z) - F_y(x, y, z)$$

from $y$ to $y + \Delta y$. This would vanish if $F_y(x + \Delta L, y, z)$ were equal to $F_y(x, y, z)$. To get a non-zero contribution to the circulation, the field must vary as we move across the square. To first order in $\Delta L$, we have

$$F_y(x + \Delta L, y, z) - F_y(x, y, z) = \frac{\partial F_y}{\partial x}\, \Delta L.$$

In the limiting case of an infinitesimal square we can assume that $(\partial F_y/\partial x)\,\Delta L$ remains constant along a side of the square, so the net contribution from the pair of sides parallel to the $y$-axis is

$$\int_y^{y+\Delta L} \frac{\partial F_y}{\partial x}\,\Delta L\,\mathrm{d}y = \frac{\partial F_y}{\partial x}\,(\Delta L)^2 = \frac{\partial F_y}{\partial x}\,\Delta S,$$

where $\Delta S$ is the area of the square. A similar calculation can be performed for the pair of sides parallel to the $x$-axis, and produces a contribution $(-\partial F_x/\partial y)\,\Delta S$. Adding both sets of contribution gives the circulation round the square:

$$\text{circulation} = \left(\frac{\partial F_y}{\partial x} - \frac{\partial F_x}{\partial y}\right)\Delta S.$$

Recalling that the $z$-component of the curl is the circulation per unit area, we conclude that

$$(\operatorname{curl}\mathbf{F})_z = \frac{\partial F_y}{\partial x} - \frac{\partial F_x}{\partial y}. \qquad (8.43)$$

The $x$- and $y$-components of the curl can be worked out in a similar way, leading to the final result:

$$\operatorname{curl}\mathbf{F} = \left(\frac{\partial F_z}{\partial y} - \frac{\partial F_y}{\partial z}\right)\mathbf{e}_x + \left(\frac{\partial F_x}{\partial z} - \frac{\partial F_z}{\partial x}\right)\mathbf{e}_y + \left(\frac{\partial F_y}{\partial x} - \frac{\partial F_x}{\partial y}\right)\mathbf{e}_z. \qquad (8.44)$$

There is a strong pattern in this formula, reminiscent of a vector product. The terms in the second and third parentheses can be obtained from the first term by cyclically permuting the $x$, $y$, $z$ labels (i.e. by making the substitutions $x \to y$, $y \to z$, $z \to x$). This pattern can be represented succinctly as a determinant:

$$\operatorname{curl}\mathbf{F} = \begin{vmatrix} \mathbf{e}_x & \mathbf{e}_y & \mathbf{e}_z \\ \dfrac{\partial}{\partial x} & \dfrac{\partial}{\partial y} & \dfrac{\partial}{\partial z} \\ F_x & F_y & F_z \end{vmatrix}. \qquad (8.45)$$

### Worked Example 8.7

Find the curl of the vector field $\mathbf{V} = -\omega y\mathbf{e}_x + \omega x\mathbf{e}_y$, which describes the velocity at points on a solid disk rotating at constant angular speed $\omega$ around the $z$-axis.

**Solution**

Using Equation 8.45 for the curl,

$$\operatorname{curl}\mathbf{V} = \begin{vmatrix} \mathbf{e}_x & \mathbf{e}_y & \mathbf{e}_z \\ \dfrac{\partial}{\partial x} & \dfrac{\partial}{\partial y} & \dfrac{\partial}{\partial z} \\ -\omega y & \omega x & 0 \end{vmatrix} = \left(\frac{\partial}{\partial x}(\omega x) - \frac{\partial}{\partial y}(-\omega y)\right)\mathbf{e}_z = 2\omega\mathbf{e}_z.$$

So the curl is constant over the disk and points along the axis of rotation.

**Exercise 8.27** Find the curl of the vector field $\mathbf{V} = kx\mathbf{e}_y$, where $k$ is a constant.

**Exercise 8.28** Verify explicitly that the curl theorem is true for the vector field $\mathbf{V} = kx\mathbf{e}_y$, integrated around a square ABCD in the $xy$-plane, where $\mathrm{A} = (0, 0)$, $\mathrm{B} = (L, 0)$, $\mathrm{C} = (L, L)$ and $\mathrm{D} = (0, L)$. ■

### 8.8.5 Curl in other coordinate systems

It is also possible to express curl in other coordinate systems. In any coordinate system with coordinates $q_1$, $q_2$ and $q_3$, mutually orthogonal unit vectors $\mathbf{e}_1$, $\mathbf{e}_2$ and $\mathbf{e}_3$ and scale factors $h_1$, $h_2$ and $h_3$, the curl turns out to be

$$\operatorname{curl}\mathbf{F} = \frac{1}{h_1 h_2 h_3}\begin{vmatrix} h_1\mathbf{e}_1 & h_2\mathbf{e}_2 & h_3\mathbf{e}_3 \\ \dfrac{\partial}{\partial q_1} & \dfrac{\partial}{\partial q_2} & \dfrac{\partial}{\partial q_3} \\ h_1F_1 & h_2F_2 & h_3F_3 \end{vmatrix}.$$

The scale factors given earlier mean that, in spherical coordinates,

$$\operatorname{curl}\mathbf{F} = \frac{1}{r^2\sin\theta}\begin{vmatrix} \mathbf{e}_r & r\,\mathbf{e}_\theta & r\sin\theta\,\mathbf{e}_\phi \\ \dfrac{\partial}{\partial r} & \dfrac{\partial}{\partial \theta} & \dfrac{\partial}{\partial \phi} \\ F_r & rF_\theta & r\sin\theta F_\phi \end{vmatrix}, \tag{8.46}$$

and in cylindrical coordinates,

$$\operatorname{curl}\mathbf{F} = \frac{1}{r}\begin{vmatrix} \mathbf{e}_r & r\,\mathbf{e}_\phi & \mathbf{e}_z \\ \dfrac{\partial}{\partial r} & \dfrac{\partial}{\partial \phi} & \dfrac{\partial}{\partial z} \\ F_r & rF_\phi & F_z \end{vmatrix}. \tag{8.47}$$

I encourage you to treat these equations as tools of the trade. You will not need them very often, and you should not try to memorize them, since you can look them up when you need to use them.

**Worked Example 8.8**

A vector field $\mathbf{F}$ is spherically symmetric and takes the form $\mathbf{F} = f(r)\,\mathbf{e}_r$ in spherical coordinates. Show that the curl of this field vanishes at all points that are not on the $z$-axis.

**Solution**

Using Equation 8.46 gives

$$\operatorname{curl}\mathbf{F} = \frac{1}{r^2\sin\theta}\begin{vmatrix} \mathbf{e}_r & r\,\mathbf{e}_\theta & r\sin\theta\,\mathbf{e}_\phi \\ \dfrac{\partial}{\partial r} & \dfrac{\partial}{\partial \theta} & \dfrac{\partial}{\partial \phi} \\ f(r) & 0 & 0 \end{vmatrix}.$$

This is equal to zero because $f(r)$ does not depend on $\theta$ or $\phi$ and $r^2\sin\theta \neq 0$ away from the $z$-axis.

**Exercise 8.29** A vector field $\mathbf{B}$ is cylindrically symmetric and takes the form $\mathbf{B} = f(r)\,\mathbf{e}_\phi$ in cylindrical coordinates. If $\operatorname{curl}\mathbf{B} = \mathbf{0}$ at all points not on the $z$-axis, show that $f(r)$ is inversely proportional to $r$, the distance from the $z$-axis. ■

## 8.9 Conservative vector fields

Section 8.9 is essential reading for Chapter 5.

### 8.9.1 Zero circulation and path-independence

The circulation of a vector field around a closed loop is not equal to zero in general. For example, the work done moving a particle around a closed loop $C$ is given by the line integral $\oint_C \mathbf{F} \cdot \mathrm{d}\mathbf{l}$, where $\mathbf{F}$ is the force acting on the particle. If the force has to overcome friction or air resistance the total work done is non-zero, even though the particle returns to its initial position. A second example is provided by a magnetic field. Magnetic field lines form closed loops and the line integral of the magnetic field around such a loop is clearly non-zero. However, this section considers a special type of vector field which does have zero circulation.

This definition of a conservative field is distinct from the idea of energy conservation. For example, a magnetic field is non-conservative, but a charged particle moving in a magnetic field does not dissipate energy.

**Definition of a conservative field**

A vector field is said to be **conservative** in a given region if its circulation around any closed loop in the region is equal to zero. If the region is left unspecified, the field is taken to be conservative in the whole of space.

**Worked Example 8.9**

A vector field takes the form $\mathbf{E} = f(r)\,\mathbf{e}_r$ in spherical coordinates, where $f(r) > 0$. Is this field conservative?

**Solution**

Consider an arbitrary path $C$. In spherical coordinates, an element of this path is

$$\delta\mathbf{l} = \delta r\,\mathbf{e}_r + r\,\delta\theta\,\mathbf{e}_\theta + r\sin\theta\,\delta\phi\,\mathbf{e}_\phi, \qquad \text{(Eqn 8.19)}$$

so

$$\mathbf{E} \cdot \delta\mathbf{l} = (f(r)\,\mathbf{e}_r) \cdot (\delta r\,\mathbf{e}_r + r\,\delta\theta\,\mathbf{e}_\theta + r\sin\theta\,\delta\phi\,\mathbf{e}_\phi) = f(r)\,\delta r.$$

The line integral of $\mathbf{F}$ along $C$ is

$$\int_C \mathbf{E} \cdot \mathrm{d}\mathbf{l} = \int_{r_1}^{r_2} f(r)\,\mathrm{d}r,$$

where $r_1$ and $r_2$ are the radial coordinates of the start- and end-points of the path. We are interested in the case where $C$ is a closed loop. In this case, the start-point and end-point are identical so $r_1 = r_2$, and the integral vanishes. This is true for any closed path, so $\mathbf{E}$ is conservative throughout its region of definition.

This calculation is relevant to the electric field of a spherically symmetric charge distribution centred on the origin.

**Exercise 8.30** A vector field takes the form $\mathbf{B} = f(r)\,\mathbf{e}_\phi$ in cylindrical coordinates, where $f(r) > 0$. Is this field conservative? ■

Conservative fields have several important properties that follow from their definition. First, we can show that the line integral of a conservative vector field does not depend on the precise path that joins the start-point to the end-point.

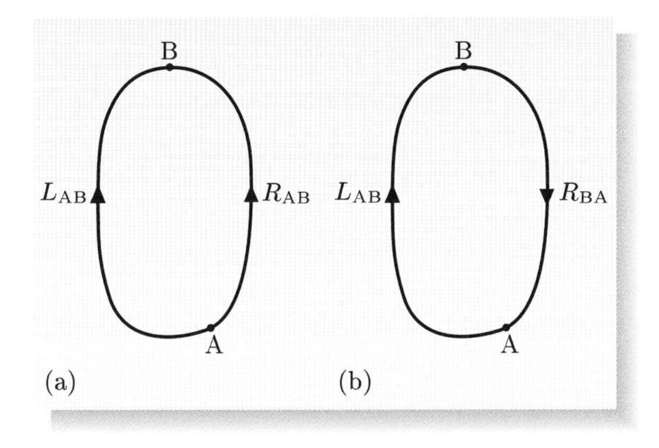


**Figure 8.42** (a) Two paths from A to B. (b) Similar paths to (a), but with the right-hand path reversed.

For example, consider the line integral of a vector field **F** along the two paths from A to B shown in Figure 8.42a. Let $L_{AB}$ and $R_{AB}$ be the line integrals of **F** along the left-hand and right-hand paths respectively. Also, let $R_{BA}$ be the line integral of **F** along the reverse right-hand path, from B to A, as shown in Figure 8.42b. Reversing the direction of the path reverses the sign of all the displacements in the line integral, so $R_{AB} = -R_{BA}$. Consequently,

$$L_{AB} - R_{AB} = L_{AB} + R_{BA}.$$

The expression on the right-hand side is the line integral of **F** around a closed loop, from A to B and back to A again. By definition, this is equal to zero for a conservative vector field so we conclude that $L_{AB} = R_{AB}$. This argument applies to any path from A to B that lies entirely within the region where **F** is conservative, so we can make the following statement:

If a vector field **F** is conservative within a given region, any line integral of **F** within this region depends only on the start-point and end-point of the path, and not on its detailed shape.

The fact that the line integral of a conservative field depends only on the start- and end-points of the path is reflected in our notation. A typical line integral is written as $\int_C \mathbf{F} \cdot \mathrm{d}\mathbf{l}$, supplemented by a detailed description of the path $C$. This is necessary because different paths usually produce different answers. But the line integral of a *conservative* field can be written simply as $\int_A^B \mathbf{F} \cdot \mathrm{d}\mathbf{l}$, where A and B are the start- and end-points of the path. No additional information about the path is needed in this case.

If you are asked to calculate the line integral of a vector field **F** along a complicated path, it is worth considering whether the field is conservative. If so, you are entitled to replace the complicated path by a simpler path joining the same start- and end-points. This trick is illustrated by the following worked example.

**Worked Example 8.10**

The vector field $\mathbf{F} = (x^2 + y^2)\mathbf{e}_x + 2xy\mathbf{e}_y$ is conservative. Calculate the line integral of $\mathbf{F}$ along a semicircular path in the $xy$-plane, with start-point $(-R, 0, 0)$, end-point $(R, 0, 0)$ and mid-point $(0, R, 0)$.

**Solution**

We are told that $\mathbf{F}$ is a conservative field, so we can replace the semicircular path by a straight-line path along the $x$-axis. Along this path the line integral becomes

$$\int_{-R}^{R} (x^2 + 0)\,\mathrm{d}x = \left[\frac{x^3}{3}\right]_{-R}^{R} = \frac{2}{3}R^3.$$

*Note*: To use this trick you must be sure that the field is conservative. The wording of this question supplies the necessary assurance. More generally, Section 8.9.5 will show how to test whether a given vector field is conservative.

### 8.9.2 The scalar potential field

The fact that a conservative field has path-independent line integrals allows us to introduce a new scalar field as follows. Suppose that the vector field $\mathbf{F}$ is conservative in a region $R$ (Figure 8.43). Within this region we choose a fixed reference point $\mathbf{r}_0$ and a path leading from $\mathbf{r}_0$ to a point $\mathbf{r}$. Then we define

$$f(\mathbf{r}) = -\int_{\mathbf{r}_0}^{\mathbf{r}} \mathbf{F} \cdot \mathrm{d}\mathbf{l} + f_0, \tag{8.48}$$

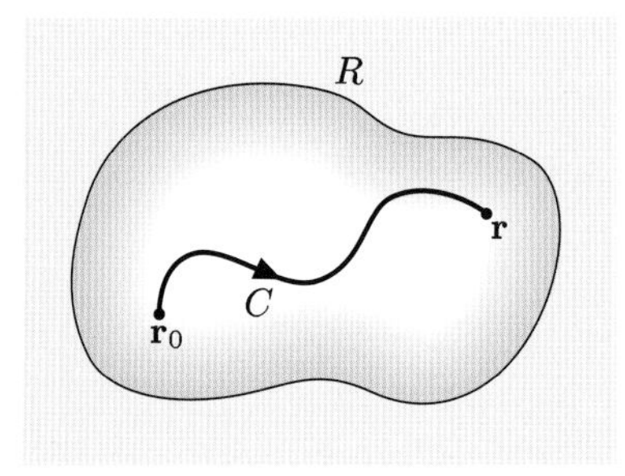


**Figure 8.43** A path $C$ used to define the scalar potential field at a point $r$ in a region $R$.

where $f_0$ is a constant. Because $\mathbf{F}$ is conservative, the line integral does not depend on the path and Equation 8.48 specifies a unique scalar at each point $\mathbf{r}$ in $R$: it defines a scalar field known as the **scalar potential**. The minus sign in Equation 8.48 is a matter of convention. It is omitted in some branches of physics, such as fluid mechanics, but is always included in electromagnetism and mechanics. At the reference point itself,

$$f(\mathbf{r}_0) = -\int_{\mathbf{r}_0}^{\mathbf{r}_0} \mathbf{F} \cdot \mathrm{d}\mathbf{l} + f_0 = f_0,$$

so $f_0$ is the value of the scalar potential at the reference point. Usually, this is set equal to zero, giving

$$f(\mathbf{r}) = -\int_{\mathbf{r}_0}^{\mathbf{r}} \mathbf{F} \cdot \mathrm{d}\mathbf{l}.$$

In many cases, the scalar potential is set equal to zero at points infinitely far away from the origin. We then say that the zero of the scalar potential is at infinity.

Equation 8.48 shows that a line integral from the reference point to another point in $R$ can be expressed in terms of the scalar potential. This property can be extended slightly. Using the fact that

$$\int_{\mathbf{r}_1}^{\mathbf{r}_2} \mathbf{F} \cdot \mathrm{d}\mathbf{l} = \int_{\mathbf{r}_0}^{\mathbf{r}_2} \mathbf{F} \cdot \mathrm{d}\mathbf{l} - \int_{\mathbf{r}_0}^{\mathbf{r}_1} \mathbf{F} \cdot \mathrm{d}\mathbf{l},$$

we can express any line integral in $R$ as a difference of scalar potential values:

$$\int_{\mathbf{r}_1}^{\mathbf{r}_2} \mathbf{F} \cdot \mathrm{d}\mathbf{l} = -\left(f(\mathbf{r}_2) - f(\mathbf{r}_1)\right) \tag{8.49}$$

In electromagnetism, $\mathbf{F}$ might be the electrostatic force acting on a particle. The left-hand side is then interpreted as the work done by the electrostatic force, which is *minus* the work done by the balancing external force, which must be applied to move the particle from $\mathbf{r}_1$ to $\mathbf{r}_2$. The right-hand side is minus the corresponding change in electrostatic potential energy.

**Exercise 8.31** A vector field is represented in spherical coordinates as $\mathbf{F} = (A/r^2)\,\mathbf{e}_r$, where $A$ is a positive constant. Taking the zero of potential to be at infinity, find the scalar potential field corresponding to $\mathbf{F}$. ■

### 8.9.3 The gradient of a scalar field

The scalar potential $f$ is defined in terms of a line integral of a conservative vector field $\mathbf{F}$. This process can be reversed. We can also represent $\mathbf{F}$ as a combination of partial derivatives of $f$.

To see how this works, consider two neighbouring points, $(x, y, z)$ and $(x + \delta x, y, z)$ separated by a tiny displacement $\delta x$ in the $x$-direction. In this case, Equation 8.49 gives

$$f(x + \delta x, y, z) - f(x, y, z) \simeq -F_x\,\delta x.$$

Dividing by $\delta x$ and taking the limit as $\delta x$ tends to 0, gives

$$\frac{\partial f}{\partial x} = -F_x,$$

where I have used partial derivative notation because the displacement is one in which $x$ varies while $y$ and $z$ are held constant. Similar results apply to displacements in the $y$- and $z$-directions, so we conclude that

$$\mathbf{F} = F_x\mathbf{e}_x + F_y\mathbf{e}_y + F_z\mathbf{e}_z = -\left(\frac{\partial f}{\partial x}\mathbf{e}_x + \frac{\partial f}{\partial y}\mathbf{e}_y + \frac{\partial f}{\partial z}\mathbf{e}_z\right).$$

The right-hand side of this equation is usually written in more compact form. For any scalar field $f(x, y, z)$, we define the **gradient** of the field to be

$$\operatorname{grad} f = \frac{\partial f}{\partial x}\,\mathbf{e}_x + \frac{\partial f}{\partial y}\,\mathbf{e}_y + \frac{\partial f}{\partial z}\,\mathbf{e}_z. \tag{8.50}$$

$\operatorname{grad}\phi$ is also written as $\boldsymbol{\nabla}\phi$, as discussed in Section 8.10.

Using this notation, we can make the following statement:

If a vector field $\mathbf{F}$ is conservative in a region $R$, we can always find a scalar field $f$ such that

$$\mathbf{F} = -\operatorname{grad} f \tag{8.51}$$

throughout $R$.

This is a good point to summarize what has been established so far.

**Properties of a conservative vector field**

If a vector field $\mathbf{F}$ is conservative in a region $R$, we now know that:

C1 The circulation of $\mathbf{F}$ around any closed loop in $R$ is equal to zero.

C2 The line integral of $\mathbf{F}$ along any path in $R$ depends only on the start-point and end-point of the path.

C3 The line integral of $\mathbf{F}$ along any path in $R$ can be expressed as minus the difference between the values of a scalar field at the end-point and start-point of the path.

C4 The vector field $\mathbf{F}$ can be represented as minus the gradient of a scalar field.

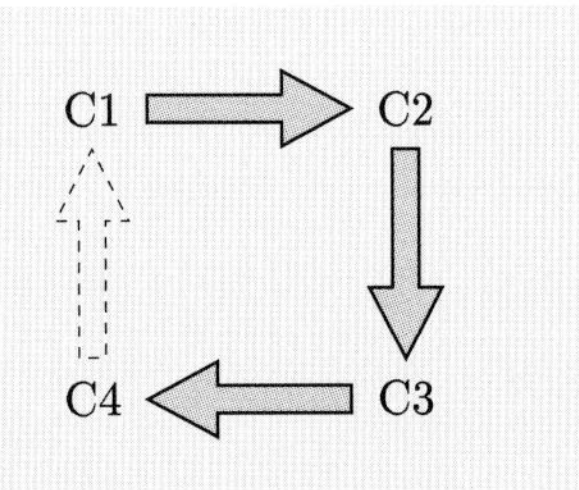


**Figure 8.44** Properties of conservative vector fields.

Property C1 provided us with a definition of a conservative vector field. We then followed a linear argument, showing that C1 implies C2, C2 implies C3 and C3 implies C4. This chain of implications is indicated by the solid arrows in Figure 8.44. The arrows only flow in one direction, so we cannot yet claim that C1, C2, C3 and C4 are equivalent statements. For example, we have shown that C4 is true for conservative fields, but we have not yet ruled out the possibility that C4 might be true for other fields, which are not conservative. This gap will now be remedied. We will show that:

If a vector field $\mathbf{F}$ can be represented as

$$\mathbf{F} = -\operatorname{grad} f$$

throughout a region $R$, then $\mathbf{F}$ is conservative in $R$.

In other words, we will close the logical circle by establishing the dashed arrow in Figure 8.44. To do this, we use the gradient representation to write

$$\oint_C \mathbf{F} \cdot \mathrm{d}\mathbf{l} = -\oint_C (\operatorname{grad} f) \cdot \mathrm{d}\mathbf{l},$$

where $C$ is any closed loop in $R$. Taking the scalar product of $\operatorname{grad} f$ and a tiny displacement $\delta\mathbf{l} = \delta x\, \mathbf{e}_x + \delta y\, \mathbf{e}_y + \delta z\, \mathbf{e}_z$ gives

$$\begin{aligned}(\operatorname{grad} f) \cdot \delta\mathbf{l} &= \left(\frac{\partial f}{\partial x}\,\mathbf{e}_x + \frac{\partial f}{\partial y}\,\mathbf{e}_y + \frac{\partial f}{\partial z}\,\mathbf{e}_z\right) \cdot (\delta x\, \mathbf{e}_x + \delta y\, \mathbf{e}_y + \delta z\, \mathbf{e}_z) \\ &= \frac{\partial f}{\partial x}\,\delta x + \frac{\partial f}{\partial y}\,\delta y + \frac{\partial f}{\partial z}\,\delta z \\ &= \delta f, \end{aligned} \qquad (8.52)$$

where the last step follows from the chain rule of partial differentiation (Equation 8.26). The circulation around $C$ can then be expressed as

$$\oint_C \mathbf{F} \cdot \mathrm{d}\mathbf{l} = -\oint_C \mathrm{d}f,$$

which is equal to 0 because $f$ returns to its initial value when we travel once around the loop. Hence the circulation vanishes and $\mathbf{F}$ is conservative.

Now, the chain of implications in Figure 8.44 is closed. It is possible to start with any one of the properties and work our way around the chain to prove all the others. This means that all four properties stand or fall together. If one is true, they are all true and the vector field is conservative; if one is false, they are all false and the vector field is non-conservative.

**Exercise 8.32** Use the formula $\mathbf{F} = -\operatorname{grad} f$ to find a scalar potential for the vector field $\mathbf{F} = (x^2 + y^2)\,\mathbf{e}_x + 2xy\,\mathbf{e}_y$. ■

## 8.9.4 More about the gradient

We will now explore the meaning of the gradient in more detail. The gradient of a scalar field $f$ is a vector field whose Cartesian components are given by Equation 8.50. These components give the rates of change of $f$ in the $x$-, $y$- and $z$-directions. In general, the component of $\operatorname{grad} f$ in any direction is the rate of change of $f$ in that direction.

The vector nature of $\operatorname{grad} f$ is not apparent in our notation (nothing is underlined or printed in bold type), but you should remember that the values of $\operatorname{grad} f$ have both magnitude and direction. To interpret the magnitude and direction of $\operatorname{grad} f$, it is helpful to revisit Equation 8.52, which we write in the form

$$\delta f = (\operatorname{grad} f) \cdot \delta\mathbf{r}, \tag{8.53}$$

where $\delta f = f(\mathbf{r} + \delta\mathbf{r}) - f(\mathbf{r})$ is the change in $f$ between two neighbouring points and $\operatorname{grad} f$ is the gradient of $f$ at the point $\mathbf{r}$.

The scalar field $f$ has surfaces on which the value of the field remains constant. If the displacement $\delta\mathbf{r}$ is tangential to such a surface, $\delta f = 0$ so

$$(\operatorname{grad} f) \cdot \delta\mathbf{r} = 0.$$

The vanishing scalar product implies that $\operatorname{grad} f$ is perpendicular to $\delta\mathbf{r}$. This is true for every displacement parallel to the surface of constant $f$, so the direction of $\operatorname{grad} f$ at any point is perpendicular to the surface of constant $f$ at that point. This is illustrated in Figure 8.45.

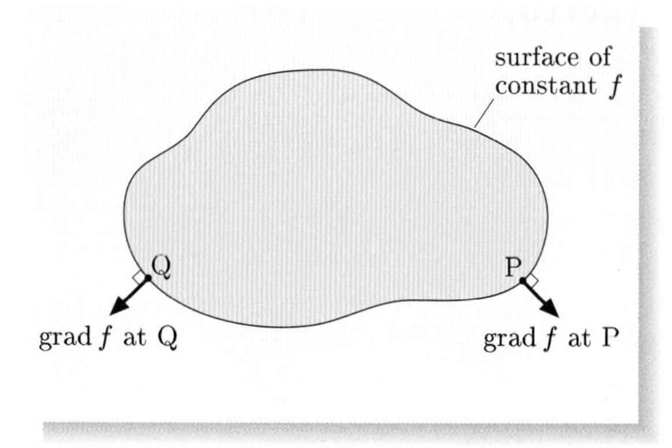


**Figure 8.45** The gradient of $f$ at any point is perpendicular to the surface of constant $f$ at that point. (Two-dimensional representation.)

By contrast, if $\delta\mathbf{r}$ is parallel to $\operatorname{grad} f$, the right-hand side of Equation 8.53 reaches its maximum possible value, $|\operatorname{grad} f| \times |\delta\mathbf{r}|$. This shows that $\operatorname{grad} f$ is in the direction of steepest increase of $f$ and the magnitude of grad $f$ is the rate of increase of $f$ in this direction.

We are interested in gradients in the context of the formula $\mathbf{F} = -\operatorname{grad} f$, which relates a conservative vector field to a scalar potential field. The minus sign in this formula means that, at any given point, the direction of $\mathbf{F}$ is the direction of steepest *decrease* of $f$ and the magnitude of $\mathbf{F}$ is the rate of *decrease* of $f$ in this direction. In the case of gravity near to the Earth's surface, the surfaces of constant gravitational potential are horizontal sheets. The gravitational potential decreases most rapidly in the direction that points vertically downwards; this is the direction of the corresponding vector field, the gravitational acceleration.

Finally, we consider the line integrals of a gradient field. We know that grad $f$ is a conservative vector field, so any line integral of grad $f$ depends only on its start- and end-points. Using Equation 8.52 we have

$$\int_{\mathbf{r}_1}^{\mathbf{r}_2} (\operatorname{grad} f) \cdot \mathrm{d}\mathbf{l} = \int_{\mathbf{r}_1}^{\mathbf{r}_2} \mathrm{d}f = f(\mathbf{r}_2) - f(\mathbf{r}_1), \qquad (8.54)$$

so the line integral of grad $f$ along a particular path is simply the difference between the values of $f$ at the start-point and end-point of the path. This result is called the **gradient theorem**.

**Exercise 8.33** Find the gradient of the scalar field $f = xyz$ at the point $\mathrm{P} = (1, 1, 0)$. In what direction away from P does the field $f$ increase most rapidly?

### Gradient in other coordinate systems

The gradient of a scalar field can also be expressed in other coordinate systems. In any coordinate system with coordinates $q_1$, $q_2$ and $q_3$, mutually orthogonal unit vectors $\mathbf{e}_1$, $\mathbf{e}_2$ and $\mathbf{e}_3$ and scale factors $h_1$, $h_2$ and $h_3$, the gradient turns out to be

$$\operatorname{grad} f = \frac{1}{h_1}\frac{\partial f}{\partial q_1}\mathbf{e}_1 + \frac{1}{h_2}\frac{\partial f}{\partial q_2}\mathbf{e}_2 + \frac{1}{h_3}\frac{\partial f}{\partial q_3}\mathbf{e}_3.$$

The scale factors given in Section 8.3.2 mean that, in spherical coordinates,

$$\operatorname{grad} f = \frac{\partial f}{\partial r}\mathbf{e}_r + \frac{1}{r}\frac{\partial f}{\partial \theta}\mathbf{e}_\theta + \frac{1}{r\sin\theta}\frac{\partial f}{\partial \phi}\mathbf{e}_\phi, \qquad (8.55)$$

and in cylindrical coordinates

$$\operatorname{grad} f = \frac{\partial f}{\partial r}\mathbf{e}_r + \frac{1}{r}\frac{\partial f}{\partial \phi}\mathbf{e}_\phi + \frac{\partial f}{\partial z}\mathbf{e}_z. \qquad (8.56)$$

As usual, my advice is that you should regard these equations as a resource. You are not expected to prove or remember them, but you should know of their existence. You will need to know when to use them, and be prepared to look them up and apply them when necessary.

**Exercise 8.34** A scalar potential field takes the form $f(\mathbf{r}) = K/r^6$ where $r$ is the distance from the origin. Find the corresponding vector field $\mathbf{F}$ and evaluate the line integral of $\mathbf{F}$ along a path from point A (with $r = a$) to point B (with $r = b$).

### 8.9.5 Irrotational vector fields

Conservative vector fields have a final important property, which has a different status from the properties C1 to C4 mentioned earlier. You have seen that any conservative vector field can be written in the form

$$\mathbf{F} = -\operatorname{grad} f,$$

where $f$ is the scalar potential. Taking the curl of both sides of this equation in Cartesian coordinates gives

$$\operatorname{curl} \mathbf{F} = -\operatorname{curl}(\operatorname{grad} f) = -\begin{vmatrix} \mathbf{e}_x & \mathbf{e}_y & \mathbf{e}_x \\ \dfrac{\partial}{\partial x} & \dfrac{\partial}{\partial y} & \dfrac{\partial}{\partial z} \\ \dfrac{\partial f}{\partial x} & \dfrac{\partial f}{\partial y} & \dfrac{\partial f}{\partial z} \end{vmatrix} = \mathbf{0},$$

where the last step is established by expanding the determinant and using the fact that mixed partial derivatives do not depend on the order of partial differentiation. For example,

$$(\operatorname{curl} \mathbf{F})_x = -\left[\frac{\partial}{\partial y}\left(\frac{\partial f}{\partial z}\right) - \frac{\partial}{\partial z}\left(\frac{\partial f}{\partial y}\right)\right] = 0.$$

A vector field whose curl vanishes is said to be **irrotational**, so we have the following result:

If a vector field $\mathbf{F}$ is conservative in a given region, it is also irrotational in that region.

The converse is true under special circumstances. For example, if $\mathbf{F}$ is irrotational throughout the whole of space, it is also conservative. To see why, let $C$ be any closed loop. Then the curl theorem tells us that

$$\oint_C \mathbf{F} \cdot \mathrm{d}\mathbf{l} = \int_S \operatorname{curl} \mathbf{F} \cdot \mathrm{d}\mathbf{S},$$

where $S$ is an open surface whose boundary is $C$ (Figure 8.46). The irrotational nature of $\mathbf{F}$ means that $\operatorname{curl} \mathbf{F} = \mathbf{0}$, so the surface integral on the right-hand side is equal to zero. It follows that the circulation of $\mathbf{F}$ around $C$ is equal to zero. This applies to any closed loop, so $\mathbf{F}$ is conservative.

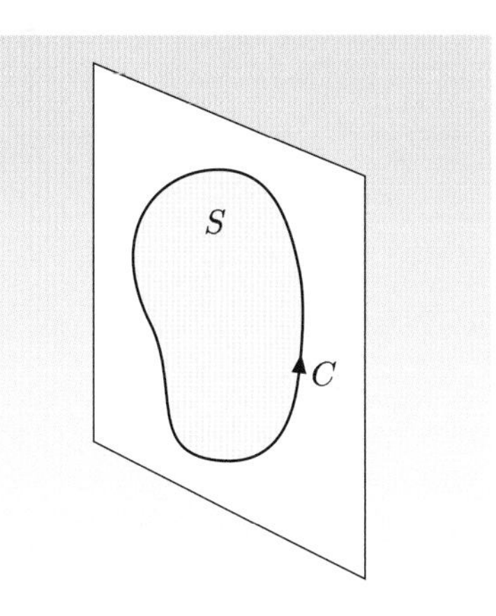


**Figure 8.46** Using the curl theorem around a closed loop $C$, which is the only boundary of an open surface $S$.

This argument can be extended to other regions. For example, suppose that $\mathbf{F}$ is irrotational throughout a region $R$ that consists of the whole of space *except for some isolated holes*. Then, given any closed loop $C$ in $R$, we can still find an open surface that has $C$ as its perimeter and avoids all the holes. The surface will have undulations where it avoids the holes, but this does not prevent us from using the curl theorem, so the argument goes through just as before.

However, there are some regions where it is impossible to find a surface that avoids all the holes. For example, suppose that $\mathbf{F}$ is irrotational throughout a region $R$ which consists of the whole of space *except for the entire $z$-axis*. Figure 8.47 shows a closed loop $C_1$ that encircles the $z$-axis. In this case it is

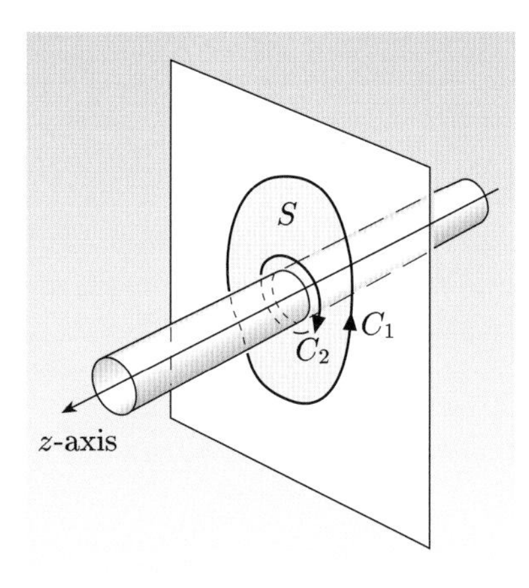


**Figure 8.47** Using the curl theorem in a region that excludes the $z$-axis. The open surface $S$ is bounded by both $C_1$ and $C_2$

impossible to find an open surface in $R$ with $C_1$ as its only boundary — another boundary such as $C_2$ is inevitably present. The curl theorem continues to apply in this situation, provided both $C_1$ and $C_2$ are taken into account:

$$\oint_{C_1} \mathbf{F} \cdot \mathrm{d}\mathbf{l} + \oint_{C_2} \mathbf{F} \cdot \mathrm{d}\mathbf{l} = \int_S \operatorname{curl} \mathbf{F} \cdot \mathrm{d}\mathbf{S}.$$

If $\mathbf{F}$ is irrotational throughout the region, the right-hand side is again equal to zero. It follows that the two circulations on the left-hand side cancel. However, we cannot deduce that either of these circulations is equal to zero, so we cannot establish that $\mathbf{F}$ is conservative. The essential difference between a space with isolated holes and a space with the $z$-axis removed can be characterized more precisely.

A **simply-connected region** is one in which any closed loop can be continuously distorted and shrunk to a point without leaving the region.

For example the whole of space is simply-connected and so is a solid sphere. A thick spherical shell is also simply-connected because we can shrink any closed loop within the shell down to a point. For the same reason, a typical Swiss cheese (with isolated bubbles in it) is simply-connected. However, three-dimensional space with the $z$-axis removed, or with a torus-shaped tunnel removed, is not simply-connected.

If you picture a closed loop $C$, leaving a visible trail behind as it collapses down to a point, this trail defines an open surface whose only boundary is $C$. Such open surfaces provide the conditions needed to establish that an irrotational field is conservative. We therefore reach the following conclusion:

If a vector field is irrotational in a *simply-connected* region, it is also conservative in that region.

The requirement for simple-connectedness has real consequences. For example, consider a vector field $\mathbf{B}$ given in cylindrical coordinates by

$$\mathbf{B} = \frac{A}{r}\,\mathbf{e}_\phi \quad \text{for } r \neq 0.$$

This is the form of the magnetic field outside an infinitely-long straight wire of negligible thickness. Using Equation 8.47 for the curl of a vector field in cylindrical coordinates, we obtain

$$\operatorname{curl} \mathbf{B} = \frac{1}{r}\begin{vmatrix} \mathbf{e}_r & r\,\mathbf{e}_\phi & \mathbf{e}_z \\ \dfrac{\partial}{\partial r} & \dfrac{\partial}{\partial \phi} & \dfrac{\partial}{\partial z} \\ 0 & r(A/r) & 0 \end{vmatrix},$$

which is equal to zero for $r \neq 0$. The vector field $\mathbf{B}$ is therefore irrotational in the whole of space excluding the $z$-axis. Nevertheless, $\mathbf{B}$ is not conservative. Its field lines are circles and the circulation $\mathbf{B}$ around any of these circles is non-zero (as you saw in Exercise 8.30).

In order to confirm that a given vector field is conservative we can take the curl of the field and verify that this vanishes throughout a region. This is called the **curl test**. However this test only works in a simply-connected region. In electromagnetism, the space outside a set of isolated point charges is simply-connected, but the space outside an electrical circuit is not simply-connected. The curl test is therefore appropriate for the electrostatic fields produced by point charges, but is inappropriate for magnetostatic fields. Magnetostatic fields are irrotational outside current flows, but they are not conservative.

**Exercise 8.35** The following vector fields are defined throughout the whole of space. Which are conservative?

$$\mathbf{F} = (x^2 + y^2)\,\mathbf{e}_x + 2xy\,\mathbf{e}_y,$$
$$\mathbf{G} = (x^2 - y^2)\,\mathbf{e}_x + 2xy\,\mathbf{e}_y,$$
$$\mathbf{H} = \text{grad}(x^2 + xy + z^2).$$

## 8.9.6 Integrating fields — a summary

In a spirit of review, it is worth noting that a common thread binds together the divergence theorem (Equation 8.34), the curl theorem (Equation 8.42) and the gradient theorem (Equation 8.54). Each equation relates the derivative of a field, integrated over a finite region, to a contribution of the field coming from the *boundary* of the region. This is illustrated in Figure 8.48.

- In the *divergence theorem*, the region is a three-dimensional volume, the derivative of the field is a divergence, and the boundary of the volume is a two-dimensional closed surface.
- In the *curl theorem*, the region is a two-dimensional surface, the derivative of the field is a curl, and the boundary of the surface is a one-dimensional closed loop.
- In the *gradient theorem*, the region is a one-dimensional directed curve, the derivative of the field is a gradient, and the boundary of the curve is just two points — its start-point and its end-point.

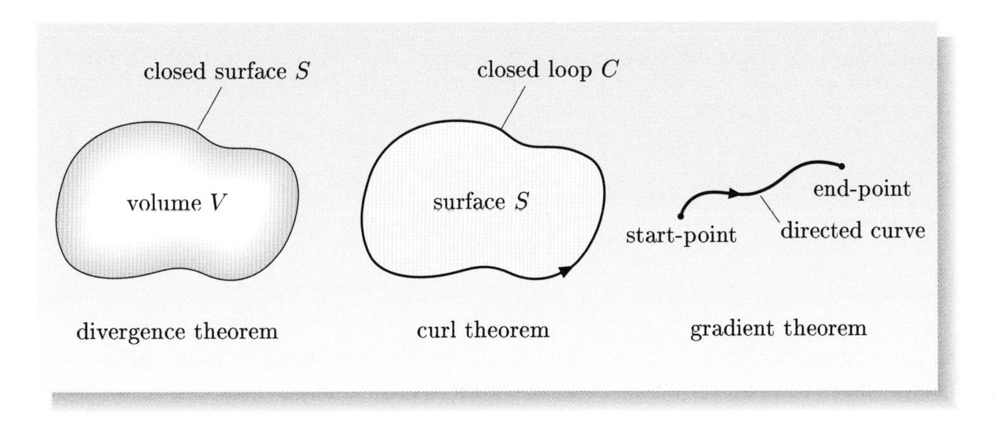


**Figure 8.48** The divergence, curl and gradient theorems.

These three great theorems can be thought of as 3-dimensional, 2-dimensional and 1-dimensional generalizations of the fundamental theorem of calculus, which states that

$$\int_a^b \frac{\mathrm{d}f}{\mathrm{d}x}\,\mathrm{d}x = f(b) - f(a),$$

and so relates the integral of the derivative of a function to the behaviour of the function at the limits of the interval of integration.

## 8.10 Further topics in vector calculus

Section 8.10 is not needed for the physics chapters of this book, but is included for completeness.

### 8.10.1 Del notation

An alternative notation based on the symbol $\boldsymbol{\nabla}$ (pronounced del) is often used in vector calculus. Before describing this notation, it is worth remarking that the operation of partial differentiation can be described in terms of the object $\partial/\partial x$. The idea is that $\partial/\partial x$ *operates* on a function $f(x,y,z)$ and converts it to another function, the partial derivative $\partial f/\partial x$. We say that $\partial/\partial x$ is an **operator**.

In this spirit, we introduce the **del operator**

$$\boldsymbol{\nabla} = \frac{\partial}{\partial x}\,\mathbf{e}_x + \frac{\partial}{\partial y}\,\mathbf{e}_y + \frac{\partial}{\partial z}\,\mathbf{e}_z, \qquad (8.57)$$

The del operator has three Cartesian components, $\partial/\partial x$, $\partial/\partial y$ and $\partial/\partial z$, associated with the $x$, $y$ and $z$-directions, and is therefore a *vector* operator. That is why $\boldsymbol{\nabla}$ is printed in bold type, and why you must underline it in your written work. The partial differentiations do not act on the Cartesian unit vectors $\mathbf{e}_x$, $\mathbf{e}_y$ and $\mathbf{e}_z$ (which are constant vectors) but they do act on any function placed to the right of the del operator.

When the del operator acts on a scalar field $f(x,y,z)$ it gives

$$\boldsymbol{\nabla} f = \frac{\partial f}{\partial x}\,\mathbf{e}_x + \frac{\partial f}{\partial y}\,\mathbf{e}_y + \frac{\partial f}{\partial z}\,\mathbf{e}_z = \operatorname{grad} f.$$

For any vector field

$$\mathbf{F} = F_x\,\mathbf{e}_x + F_y\,\mathbf{e}_y + F_z\,\mathbf{e}_z,$$

we can form two types of product with $\boldsymbol{\nabla}$.

Taking the *scalar* product gives

$$\begin{aligned}\boldsymbol{\nabla}\cdot\mathbf{F} &= \left(\frac{\partial}{\partial x}\,\mathbf{e}_x + \frac{\partial}{\partial y}\,\mathbf{e}_y + \frac{\partial}{\partial z}\,\mathbf{e}_z\right)\cdot\left(F_x\,\mathbf{e}_x + F_y\,\mathbf{e}_y + F_z\,\mathbf{e}_z\right)\\ &= \frac{\partial F_x}{\partial x} + \frac{\partial F_y}{\partial y} + \frac{\partial F_z}{\partial z}\\ &= \operatorname{div}\mathbf{F}.\end{aligned}$$

Taking the *vector* product gives

$$\nabla \times \mathbf{F} = \left(\frac{\partial}{\partial x}\mathbf{e}_x + \frac{\partial}{\partial y}\mathbf{e}_y + \frac{\partial}{\partial z}\mathbf{e}_z\right) \times (F_x\,\mathbf{e}_x + F_y\,\mathbf{e}_y + F_z\,\mathbf{e}_z)$$

$$= \begin{vmatrix} \mathbf{e}_x & \mathbf{e}_y & \mathbf{e}_z \\ \dfrac{\partial}{\partial x} & \dfrac{\partial}{\partial y} & \dfrac{\partial}{\partial z} \\ F_x & F_y & F_z \end{vmatrix}$$

$$= \operatorname{curl}\mathbf{F}.$$

So the gradient, divergence and curl operations, which are central to vector calculus, are all represented simply and compactly in terms of the del operator $\nabla$.

The del notation has other advantages. It makes the formulae for grad, div and curl in Cartesian coordinates easy to remember. It also reminds us that $\nabla f$ and $\nabla \times \mathbf{F}$ are vector fields and that $\nabla \cdot \mathbf{F}$ is a scalar field. It can even can help us avoid errors. For example, the equation $\rho = \nabla V$ looks wrong because the non-bold print on the left indicates a scalar field while the bold print on the right indicates a vector field. A scalar can never be equal to a vector, so this equation makes no sense, either grammatically or physically. By contrast, the equation $\mathbf{E} = -\nabla V$ makes perfect sense, and is one you will meet in electromagnetism.

The identification of $\nabla f$, $\nabla \cdot \mathbf{F}$ and $\nabla \times \mathbf{F}$ as gradient, divergence and curl was carried out in Cartesian coordinates. It is also possible to define the del operators in other coordinate systems, but it is not very useful to do so. The difficulty is that the unit vectors in a non-Cartesian coordinate system generally vary from point to point. So, for example, when using the expression for del in a spherical coordinate system to calculate the divergence of a vector field, it is necessary to differentiate the unit vectors $\mathbf{e}_r$, $\mathbf{e}_\theta$ and $\mathbf{e}_\phi$ with respect to $r$, $\theta$ and $\phi$. This is an unwelcome chore, and it is generally much easier to use Equation 8.37 directly. In spite of this practical difficulty, $\nabla f$, $\nabla \cdot \mathbf{F}$ and $\nabla \times \mathbf{F}$ are taken as synonyms for $\operatorname{grad} f$, $\operatorname{div}\mathbf{F}$ and $\operatorname{curl}\mathbf{F}$, no matter what coordinate system is being used.

## 8.10.2 Vector calculus identities

A **vector calculus identity** is a formula that involves grads, divs or curls and is valid for all fields. For example,

$$\operatorname{div}(\operatorname{curl}\mathbf{F}) = 0 \quad \text{i.e.} \quad \nabla \cdot (\nabla \times \mathbf{F}) = 0 \quad \text{for } any \text{ vector field } \mathbf{F}, \tag{8.58}$$

and

$$\operatorname{curl}(\operatorname{grad} f) = \mathbf{0} \quad \text{i.e.} \quad \nabla \times (\nabla f) = \mathbf{0} \quad \text{for } any \text{ scalar field } f. \tag{8.59}$$

There are many other vector calculus identities, some of which are listed inside the back cover of this book. For example, the third book of this course will use the identity

I pronounce this as: curl of curl F equals grad of div F minus del squared F.

$$\operatorname{curl}(\operatorname{curl}\mathbf{F}) = \operatorname{grad}(\operatorname{div}\mathbf{F}) - \nabla^2\mathbf{F}, \tag{8.60}$$

that is

$$\nabla \times (\nabla \times \mathbf{F}) = \nabla(\nabla \cdot \mathbf{F}) - \nabla^2\mathbf{F}.$$

where the operator $\nabla^2$ is defined to be

$$\nabla^2 = (\boldsymbol{\nabla} \cdot \boldsymbol{\nabla}) = \frac{\partial^2}{\partial x^2} + \frac{\partial^2}{\partial y^2} + \frac{\partial^2}{\partial z^2} \tag{8.61}$$

in Cartesian coordinates and is called the **Laplacian operator**.

Of course, you are under no obligation to prove or memorize identities. You can always look them up on the inside back cover of the book and treat them as standard tools ready for use.

To establish these identities we can work in Cartesian coordinates. This may seem restrictive, but it is not. Div, curl and grad have definitions that are independent of coordinate system, so if we succeed in proving a vector identity in one coordinate system, it must be true in all others. To prove Equation 8.58, for example, we write

$$\boldsymbol{\nabla}\cdot(\boldsymbol{\nabla}\times\mathbf{F}) = \frac{\partial}{\partial x}\left(\frac{\partial F_z}{\partial y} - \frac{\partial F_y}{\partial z}\right) + \frac{\partial}{\partial y}\left(\frac{\partial F_x}{\partial z} - \frac{\partial F_z}{\partial x}\right) + \frac{\partial}{\partial z}\left(\frac{\partial F_y}{\partial x} - \frac{\partial F_x}{\partial y}\right).$$

If you multiply out the brackets and use the fact that the order of differentiation in mixed partial derivatives does not matter, you will see that the terms on the right-hand side cancel out in pairs, leaving zero as required.

### 8.10.3 The Laplacian operator

The previous section introduced the Laplacian operator, $\nabla^2$, expressed in Cartesian coordinates. For any scalar field $f(x, y, z)$,

$$\nabla^2 f = \frac{\partial^2 f}{\partial x^2} + \frac{\partial^2 f}{\partial y^2} + \frac{\partial^2 f}{\partial z^2},$$

For any vector field $\mathbf{F}(x, y, z)$,

$$\nabla^2 \mathbf{F} = \frac{\partial^2 \mathbf{F}}{\partial x^2} + \frac{\partial^2 \mathbf{F}}{\partial y^2} + \frac{\partial^2 \mathbf{F}}{\partial z^2},$$

which has $x$-component

$$(\nabla^2 \mathbf{F})_x = \nabla^2 F_x = \frac{\partial^2 F_x}{\partial x^2} + \frac{\partial^2 F_x}{\partial y^2} + \frac{\partial^2 F_x}{\partial z^2}.$$

The Laplacian can also be represented in other coordinate systems, but care is needed as different formulae apply to scalar and vector fields. For a scalar field $f$,

$$\nabla^2 f = \boldsymbol{\nabla} \cdot (\boldsymbol{\nabla} f) = \operatorname{div} \operatorname{grad} f.$$

In spherical coordinates, Equations 8.37 and 8.55 give

$$\nabla^2 f = \frac{1}{r^2}\frac{\partial}{\partial r}\left(r^2 \frac{\partial f}{\partial r}\right) + \frac{1}{r^2 \sin\theta}\frac{\partial}{\partial \theta}\left(\sin\theta \frac{\partial f}{\partial \theta}\right) + \frac{1}{r^2 \sin^2\theta}\frac{\partial^2 f}{\partial \phi^2}. \tag{8.62}$$

In cylindrical coordinates, Equations 8.38 and 8.56 give

$$\nabla^2 f = \frac{1}{r}\frac{\partial}{\partial r}\left(r \frac{\partial f}{\partial r}\right) + \frac{1}{r^2}\frac{\partial^2 f}{\partial \phi^2} + \frac{\partial^2 f}{\partial z^2}. \tag{8.63}$$

These formulae do not apply to a vector field $\mathbf{F}$. Instead, we rearrange Equation 8.60 to obtain

$$\nabla^2 \mathbf{F} = \operatorname{grad}(\operatorname{div} \mathbf{F}) - \operatorname{curl}(\operatorname{curl} \mathbf{F}),$$

and then use the appropriate expressions for grad, div and curl in the required coordinate system. This leads to very lengthy formulae for $\nabla^2 \mathbf{F}$, which will not be required in this course.

# Solutions to exercises

**Ex 1.1** When you run a comb through your hair you may succeed in removing some of the comb's electrons, leaving it with a net positive charge. Because electromagnetic forces are so strong, you need only remove a few electrons, too few to make a significant difference to the comb's mass. The lost electrons are transferred to your hair, so there is no conflict with the conservation of charge. When brought close to a scrap of paper, the comb attracts negatively-charged electrons in the paper and repels positively-charged ions. The electrons move slightly towards the comb and the ions move slightly further away. This slight charge displacement explains the attraction. Electric forces decrease with increasing distance, so the attraction of the electrons overcomes the repulsion of the ions, and the overall force on the scrap of paper is attractive, towards the comb.

**Ex 1.2** No. This follows immediately from the definition that distinguishes electric and magnetic forces.

**Ex 1.3** Yes. Particle A experiences different electromagnetic forces in the two cases shown in Figures 1.3a and 1.3b. This particle is stationary, so it experiences no magnetic force. It therefore experiences different electric forces in the two cases and this must be due to the motion of particle B.

**Ex 1.4** No, because an electron is not a point charge. Because of its spin, a stationary electron behaves like a miniature magnet, and can experience a magnetic force even when it is stationary. In most practical situations this force is negligible, but our classification of electric and magnetic forces avoids this possible complication by referring only to point charges.

**Ex 1.5** According to the back cover, the charge-to-mass ratio of an electron is

$$\frac{-e}{m} = -\frac{1.60 \times 10^{-19}\,\mathrm{C}}{9.11 \times 10^{-31}\,\mathrm{kg}} = -1.76 \times 10^{11}\,\mathrm{C\,kg^{-1}}.$$

So one gram of electrons has charge $q = -1.76 \times 10^{11}\,\mathrm{C\,kg^{-1}} \times 10^{-3}\,\mathrm{kg} = -1.76 \times 10^{8}\,\mathrm{C}$ and Coulomb's law gives an electrostatic force of magnitude

$$\begin{aligned} F &= \frac{1}{4\pi\varepsilon_0}\frac{q^2}{r^2} \\ &= 8.99 \times 10^{9}\,\mathrm{N\,m^2\,C^{-2}} \times \frac{(-1.76 \times 10^{8}\,\mathrm{C})^2}{(1.5 \times 10^{11}\,\mathrm{m})^2} \\ &= 1.2 \times 10^{4}\,\mathrm{N}. \end{aligned}$$

This is greater than the weight of one tonne of matter at the Earth's surface, in spite of the enormous separation of the charges! Of course, it would not be easy to gather one gram of electrons together in a small region — the repulsive forces would be enormous.

**Ex 1.6** Yes. To see this, exchange the indices 1 and 2 throughout Equation 1.2, to obtain

$$\mathbf{F}_{21} = \frac{1}{4\pi\varepsilon_0}\frac{q_2 q_1}{r_{21}^2}\,\widehat{\mathbf{r}}_{21}.$$

Since $r_{21} = r_{12}$ and $\widehat{\mathbf{r}}_{21} = -\widehat{\mathbf{r}}_{12}$, we conclude that $\mathbf{F}_{21} = -\mathbf{F}_{12}$. These forces are equal in magnitude and opposite in direction, in agreement with Newton's third law.

**Ex 1.7** Figure S1.1 shows the arrangement of charges and a suitable choice of coordinate system.

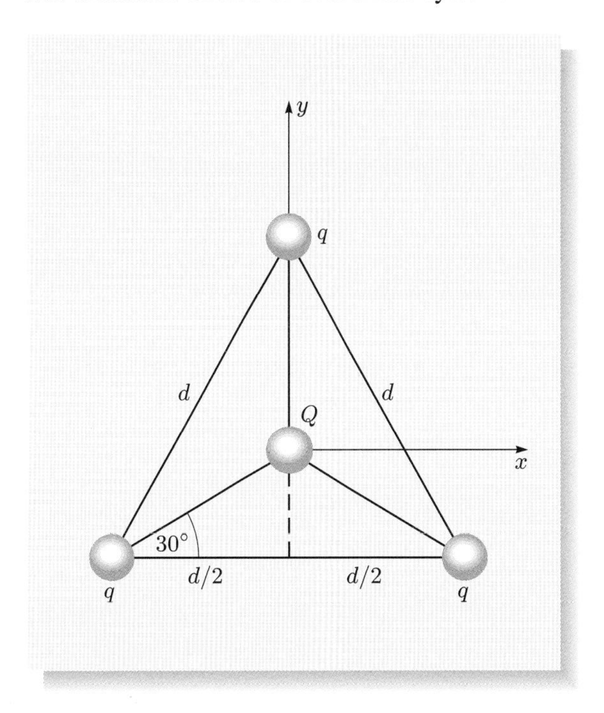


**Figure S1.1** Arrangement of charges for Exercise 1.7.

The $x$-component of the force on the central charge $Q$ vanishes by symmetry. The distance separating a corner of the triangle from its centre is $(d/2)/\cos 30° = d/\sqrt{3}$ so the $y$-component of the force on $Q$ is

$$\frac{1}{4\pi\varepsilon_0}\frac{(\sqrt{3})^2 qQ}{d^2}\big((2\cos 60°)\,\mathbf{e}_y - \mathbf{e}_y\big) = 0.$$

where $\mathbf{e}_y$ is the Cartesian unit vector in the $y$-direction. So the force on the central charge $Q$ vanishes no matter what value is chosen for $Q$.

Now consider the force on a charge $q$ at the corner of the triangle. Worked Example 1.1 showed that each corner charge experiences a force of magnitude $\sqrt{3}\,q^2/4\pi\varepsilon_0 d^2$ due to the charges in the other two corners. This force points away from the centre of the triangle. The electrostatic force due to $Q$ must balance this. Adding forces in the direction away from the centre of the triangle, we require that

$$\frac{\sqrt{3}}{4\pi\varepsilon_0}\frac{q^2}{d^2} + \frac{3}{4\pi\varepsilon_0}\frac{qQ}{d^2} = 0.$$

So $Q = -q/\sqrt{3} = -0.58\,q$. This argument works for all the charges at the corners of the triangle, ensuring that they all experience zero electrostatic force.

**Ex 1.8** First, we find the displacement vector and distance between the particles. From the given Cartesian coordinates,

$$\begin{aligned}\mathbf{r}_1 - \mathbf{r}_2 &= [(3-2)\mathbf{e}_x + (2-4)\mathbf{e}_y + (-1-1)\mathbf{e}_z]\ \mathrm{m}\\ &= (\mathbf{e}_x - 2\mathbf{e}_y - 2\mathbf{e}_z)\,\mathrm{m},\end{aligned}$$

therefore

$$|\mathbf{r}_1 - \mathbf{r}_2| = \sqrt{1^2 + (-2)^2 + (-2)^2}\ \mathrm{m} = 3\,\mathrm{m}.$$

Then Coulomb's law (Equation 1.3) gives

$$\begin{aligned}\mathbf{F}_{12} &= \bigg(8.99\times 10^9 \times 9\times 10^{-5}\\ &\qquad \times (-3)\times 10^{-5} \times \frac{\mathbf{e}_x - 2\mathbf{e}_y - 2\mathbf{e}_z}{3^3}\bigg)\ \mathrm{N}\\ &= (-0.90\mathbf{e}_x + 1.8\mathbf{e}_y + 1.8\mathbf{e}_z)\ \mathrm{N},\end{aligned}$$

to two significant figures.

**Ex 1.9** All the charges lie in the $xy$-plane as shown in Figure S1.2, so we can ignore the $z$-coordinates.

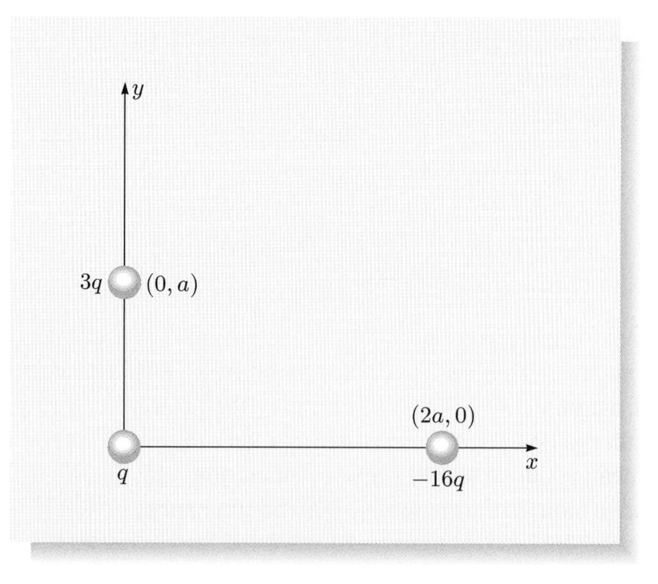


**Figure S1.2** The arrangement of charges in Exercise 1.9.

The electrostatic force on the charge $q$ at the origin is

$$\begin{aligned}\mathbf{F} &= \frac{1}{4\pi\varepsilon_0}\frac{-16q\times q}{(2a)^2}(-\mathbf{e}_x) + \frac{1}{4\pi\varepsilon_0}\frac{3q\times q}{a^2}(-\mathbf{e}_y)\\ &= \frac{1}{4\pi\varepsilon_0}\frac{q^2}{a^2}(4\mathbf{e}_x - 3\mathbf{e}_y).\end{aligned}$$

This force has magnitude

$$|\mathbf{F}| = \frac{1}{4\pi\varepsilon_0}\frac{q^2}{a^2}\sqrt{4^2 + (-3)^2} = \frac{5}{4\pi\varepsilon_0}\frac{q^2}{a^2}$$

and is in the direction of the unit vector

$$\widehat{\mathbf{F}} = \frac{\mathbf{F}}{|\mathbf{F}|} = \frac{1}{5}(4\mathbf{e}_x - 3\mathbf{e}_y) = (0.8\mathbf{e}_x - 0.6\mathbf{e}_y).$$

**Ex 1.10** The SI unit of force is the newton (N) and the SI unit of charge is the coulomb (C). It follows that the SI unit of electric field is newtons per coulomb ($\mathrm{N\,C^{-1}}$).

*Comment*: Electric fields are also expressed in volts per metre ($\mathrm{V\,m^{-1}}$). This is just an alternative way of representing newtons per coulomb, as you will see when the volt is defined in Chapter 5.

**Ex 1.11** Place a test charge $q$ at any point $\mathbf{r} \neq \mathbf{r}_0$. This test charge experiences an electric force

$$\mathbf{F} = \frac{1}{4\pi\varepsilon_0}\frac{q\,q_0}{|\mathbf{r} - \mathbf{r}_0|^3}(\mathbf{r} - \mathbf{r}_0)$$

due to the charge $q_0$. The electric field at $\mathbf{r}$ is found by dividing this force by the value of the test charge, so

$$\mathbf{E}(\mathbf{r}) = \frac{\mathbf{F}}{q} = \frac{1}{4\pi\varepsilon_0}\frac{q_0}{|\mathbf{r} - \mathbf{r}_0|^3}(\mathbf{r} - \mathbf{r}_0).$$

This equation provides a formula for the electric field at all points except at the position occupied by the source charge $q_0$ (where the electric field is undefined). The field has a magnitude that is proportional to the charge $q_0$ and inversely proportional to the square of the distance from the charge. It points radially outwards from the source charge if $q_0$ is positive and points radially inwards towards the source charge if $q_0$ is negative.

**Ex 1.12** The proton is accelerated by a constant force of magnitude $F = qE$. This causes the proton to undergo an acceleration of magnitude $a = qE/m$. Because this acceleration is constant, the final speed of the proton is $v = at$, where $t$ is the time spent in the field. Thus,

$$t = \frac{v}{a} = \frac{mv}{qE}$$
$$= \frac{1.67 \times 10^{-27}\,\text{kg} \times 1.0 \times 10^{7}\,\text{m}\,\text{s}^{-1}}{1.6 \times 10^{-19}\,\text{C} \times 100\,\text{N}\,\text{C}^{-1}}$$
$$= 1.0 \times 10^{-3}\,\text{s},$$

where the final units of seconds are obtained using the conversion

$$1\,\text{N} = 1\,\text{kg}\,\text{m}\,\text{s}^{-2}.$$

A useful table of unit conversions appears inside the front cover of the book.

*Comment*: It is reasonable to use Newtonian mechanics in this question because any relativistic corrections are of order $\frac{1}{2}v^2/c^2 < 10^{-3}$.

**Ex 1.13** The field lines were sketched in Figure 1.13c. Our task here is to use symmetry principles to justify this pattern. Consider the electric field at any point near the sheet. If the sheet is rotated about its normal, any component of the electric field in the plane of the sheet must also rotate. However, the charge distribution is unaffected by such a rotation, so the electric field cannot change. We conclude that the electric field cannot have a component in the plane of the sheet, and is therefore perpendicular to the sheet. (Figure 1.13c shows that the field points *away* from a positively-charged sheet but this fact cannot be deduced from symmetry.)

An alternative argument uses some aspects of Coulomb's law. Consider a ring of charge in the plane centred on a point directly below the point P at which the field is measured (Figure S1.3). The ring is divided into similar segments which are grouped in pairs at opposite ends of a diameter, for example A and B.

Using Coulomb's law, it is easy to see that the electric field due to a pair has no component in the plane of the sheet; contributions from the two segments cancel out. Each ring is made up of pairs of segments and the whole plane can be thought of as a collection of rings, so the electric field of the whole sheet must be perpendicular to the sheet.

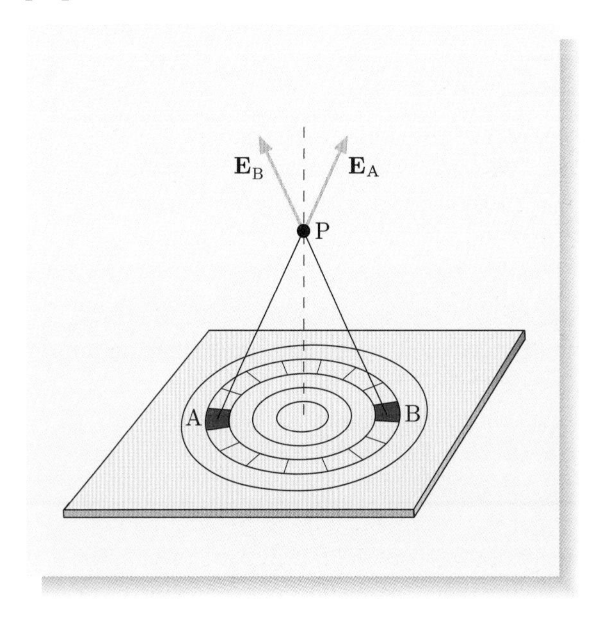


**Figure S1.3** Splitting a plane into rings and a ring into segments.

**Ex 1.14** The charge distribution is unchanged by rotations around the central axis of the cylinder. At points on the central axis, these rotations would change the radial component of the electric field. The electric field on the central axis is therefore directed along the axis. The charge distribution is also unchanged by a rotation of 180° perpendicular to the axis of symmetry, passing through the mid-point of the cylinder. This implies that the electric field pattern has a similar symmetry, and has a magnitude that depends only on the distance from the mid-point. These features are shown in Figure S1.4 (overleaf).

The electric field vanishes at the mid-point because contributions from each half of the cylinder exactly cancel those from the opposite half. At points on the axis near the mid-point, there is still some cancellation but this is no longer exact. The electric field therefore grows in magnitude as we move along the axis away from the mid-point. The maximum field is expected to occur just beyond the ends of the cylinder because cancellation from different parts of the cylinder only ceases once we step outside the cylinder. Eventually, far enough from the ends of the cylinder, the inverse-square

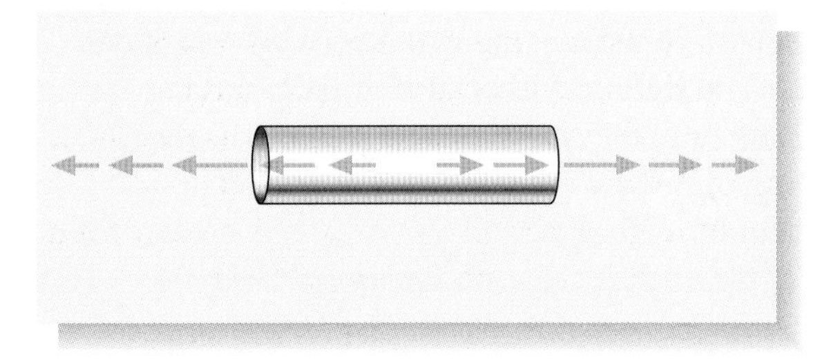

**Figure S1.4** Arrow map along the axis of a uniformly-charged cylinder.

nature of Coulomb's law becomes the most important factor and the electric field decreases.

**Ex 2.1** The surface of the cube consists of three pairs of opposite faces. Consider one pair, A and B. The electric field is constant, so has the same value on these faces. However, a cube is a closed surface so the outward unit normal of A points in the opposite direction to the outward unit normal of B. Therefore, the normal component of the electric field on A is minus the normal component of the electric field on B. Flux contributions cancel out for all pairs of opposite faces, so the flux over the whole cube vanishes.

**Ex 2.2** In cases (a), (c), (d), (f), (g) and (h), the total electric flux is unchanged because the total charge within the closed surface is unchanged. In cases (b) and (e), the total electric flux changes because the total charge within the closed surface changes.

**Ex 2.3** No, if the photon had a non-zero mass, the electric field of a point charge would be expected to decay exponentially at large distances (Chapter 1, p. 23). Such a deviation from an inverse square law would undermine our proof of Gauss's law.

To show explicitly that Gauss's law would fail in this case, consider a charge outside an enormous closed surface that contains no charges. With the electric field decaying exponentially, the electric flux on the distant side of the surface (far away from the charge) is negligible, while the electric flux on the near side of the surface (close to the charge) is still sizeable. Hence the total flux over the closed surface is non-zero even though it contains no charge. I hasten to add that this failure of Gauss's law is purely hypothetical — no photon mass has ever been detected.

**Ex 2.4** The charge distribution is spherically symmetrical, so we proceed exactly as in Worked Example 2.2. We again argue that the electric field is spherically symmetrical and hence choose spherical Gaussian surfaces centred on the origin.

(a) Outside the spherical distribution of charge we choose a spherical Gaussian surface with radius $r > R$. This closed surface contains the whole charge $Q$ of the sphere, which can be calculated as in Worked Example 2.1:

$$\begin{aligned} Q &= \int_0^R \rho(r) \times 4\pi r^2 \, \mathrm{d}r \\ &= \int_0^R Ar \times 4\pi r^2 \, \mathrm{d}r \\ &= 4\pi A \int_0^R r^3 \, \mathrm{d}r \\ &= \pi A R^4. \end{aligned}$$

Calculation of the field exactly repeats part (a) of Worked Example 2.2, leading to

$$\mathbf{E}(\mathbf{r}) = \frac{Q}{4\pi\varepsilon_0 \, r^2} \, \mathbf{e}_r = \frac{AR^4}{4\varepsilon_0 \, r^2} \, \mathbf{e}_r,$$

where $\mathbf{e}_r$ is the radial unit vector at the point $\mathbf{r}$.

(b) Inside the spherical distribution of charge we choose a spherical Gaussian surface with $r < R$. This closed surface contains only part of the total charge. The enclosed charge is

$$\begin{aligned} Q_{\text{enc}} &= \int_0^r \rho(s) \times 4\pi s^2 \, \mathrm{d}s \\ &= \int_0^r A\, s \times 4\pi s^2 \, \mathrm{d}s \\ &= 4\pi A \int_0^r s^3 \, \mathrm{d}s \\ &= \pi A \, r^4. \end{aligned}$$

The electric field is perpendicular to the Gaussian surface and has a constant normal component, $E_r(r)$, on this surface so Gauss's law gives

$$E_r(r) \times 4\pi r^2 = \frac{Q_{\text{enc}}}{\varepsilon_0} = \frac{\pi A \, r^4}{\varepsilon_0},$$

so

$$E_r(r) = \frac{A\, r^2}{4\varepsilon_0} \quad \text{and} \quad \mathbf{E}(\mathbf{r}) = \frac{A\, r^2}{4\varepsilon_0} \, \mathbf{e}_r.$$

These answers can (and should!) be checked as in Worked Example 2.2.

**Ex 2.5** The electric field strength increases as we approach the hailstone. In the air around the hailstone, the field reaches its greatest magnitude on the surface of the hailstone; this is where breakdown will start. Suppose that the hailstone has radius $R$ and total charge $Q$ and that the radial component of its electric field is $E_r$. Then, choosing a spherical Gaussian surface at the surface of the hailstone and applying Gauss's law we obtain

$$E_r(R) \times 4\pi R^2 = \frac{Q}{\varepsilon_0}.$$

The magnitude of the electric field at the surface of the hailstone is $|E_r(R)|$. Equating this to the breakdown field, $E_\text{b}$, we obtain

$$\frac{|Q|}{4\pi\varepsilon_0 R^2} = E_\text{b},$$

so

$$\begin{aligned}|Q| &= 4\pi\varepsilon_0 R^2 \times E_\text{b}\\ &= 4\pi \times 8.85 \times 10^{-12}\,\text{C}^2\,\text{N}^{-1}\,\text{m}^{-2}\\ &\qquad \times (3.0 \times 10^{-3}\,\text{m})^2 \times 1.0 \times 10^6\,\text{N}\,\text{C}^{-1}\\ &= 1.0 \times 10^{-9}\,\text{C}.\end{aligned}$$

Any charge greater than this would produce an electric field at the surface of the hailstone above $E_\text{b}$, resulting in charge leakage, which will continue until the field at the surface of the hailstone dips below $E_\text{b}$. In this context, a nanocoulomb is a very large charge!

**Ex 2.6** Choose a spherical Gaussian surface at the Earth's surface. Applying Gauss's law over this surface we obtain

$$E_r(R) \times 4\pi R^2 = \frac{Q}{\varepsilon_0},$$

where $E_r(R)$ is the radial component of the field at the Earth's surface, $R$ is the radius and $Q$ is the total charge of planet Earth. Thus,

$$\begin{aligned}Q &= 4\pi\varepsilon_0 R^2 \times E_r(R)\\ &= 4\pi \times 8.85 \times 10^{-12}\,\text{C}^2\,\text{N}^{-1}\,\text{m}^{-2}\\ &\qquad \times (6.6 \times 10^6\,\text{m})^2 \times (-100\,\text{N}\,\text{C}^{-1})\\ &= -4.8 \times 10^5\,\text{C}.\end{aligned}$$

Because the electric field points down towards the Earth, the radial component of the electric field is negative and Gauss's law gives a negative charge on planet Earth.

**Ex 2.7** Yes. Gauss's law applies whether the charges are stationary or not. The argument leading to Equation 2.7 can therefore be repeated without modification, provided that $\lambda$ is interpreted as the charge per unit length of the *moving* cylinder. This remark turns out to be significant because of special relativistic effects. Although the charge on the cylinder is invariant, the moving cylinder undergoes length contraction. It follows that the charge per unit length, $\lambda$, is greater for a moving cylinder than for a stationary cylinder!

In applying Gauss's law, we assume that the electric field around the moving infinite cylinder has cylindrical symmetry. To completely answer the question, we should justify this assumption. Clearly, the symmetry of the situation demands that the field is unchanged by rotations around the axis of the cylinder and by translations along the axis of the cylinder. However, it is not obvious that the field must be perpendicular to the axis of the cylinder; at first sight, the field lines might slope at some angle that depends on the speed of the cylinder. In fact, this does not happen. Section 1.5.2 explained that the electric field of a uniformly-moving charge is unchanged by a reflection in the plane that contains the charge and is perpendicular to its line of motion. The field of a uniformly-moving cylinder is the sum of such fields, so it must have this reflection symmetry at all points along the axis. This forces the field to be perpendicular to the axis of the cylinder. The derivation of Equation 2.7 from Gauss's law then proceeds as before.

**Ex 2.8** (a) Yes. The expression in Equation 2.7 does not depend on the radius of the cylinder, so it would remain valid if the cylinder were compressed radially to a uniform line of charge along the central axis.

(b) No. Inside the cylinder we use a cylindrical Gaussian surface of radius $r < R$ and length $\Delta l$. The enclosed charge is smaller than $\lambda\,\Delta l$ so the electric field is smaller than that given by Equation 2.7.

**Ex 2.9** The simplest way of tackling this problem is to use Equation 2.8 and the principle of superposition. In the gap between the plates, the total field is

$$\mathbf{E} = \frac{\sigma_1}{2\varepsilon_0}\,\mathbf{e}_n + \frac{\sigma_2}{2\varepsilon_0}\,(-\mathbf{e}_n),$$

where $\mathbf{e}_n$ points into the gap away from plate 1 and $(-\mathbf{e}_n)$ points into the gap away from plate 2. Consequently,

$$\mathbf{E} = \frac{\sigma_1 - \sigma_2}{2\varepsilon_0}\,\mathbf{e}_n.$$

As expected, there is no field in the gap if $\sigma_1 = \sigma_2$, and we recover the usual expression for the field in an infinite parallel plate capacitor if $\sigma_1 = -\sigma_2$.

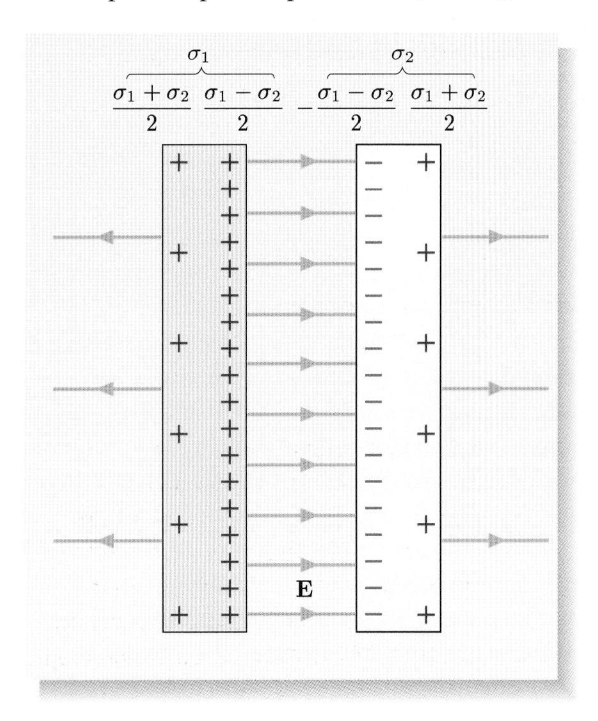


**Figure S2.1** Capacitor plates with general charge densities (drawn for the case $\sigma_2 < 0 < \sigma_1$).

It is more challenging to derive this result directly from Gauss's law, but it can be done. To ensure that there is no electric field inside either plate, the inner and outer surfaces of the plates must have the surface charge densities shown in Figure S2.1. (Check that this distribution of charge produces the required vanishing fields inside the plates, if you wish.) Then, using Gauss's law over the surface of a pillbox that straddles the inner surface of one of the plates, we recover our previous answer.

**Ex 2.10** The spherical distribution of charge produces a spherically-symmetric electric field of the form $\mathbf{E}(\mathbf{r}) = E_r(r)\,\mathbf{e}_r$ so we use spherical coordinates. Applying Gauss's law and using Equation 2.12 gives

$$\frac{1}{r^2}\frac{\mathrm{d}}{\mathrm{d}r}(r^2E_r) = \frac{Ar}{\varepsilon_0},$$

so

$$\frac{\mathrm{d}}{\mathrm{d}r}(r^2E_r) = \frac{Ar^3}{\varepsilon_0}.$$

Integrating both sides with respect to $r$,

$$r^2E_r = \frac{Ar^4}{4\varepsilon_0} + C,$$

where $C$ is an arbitrary constant of integration. Thus,

$$E_r = \frac{Ar^2}{4\varepsilon_0} + \frac{C}{r^2}.$$

The field must remain finite at the origin (indeed it vanishes there by symmetry) so $C = 0$ and

$$E_r = \frac{Ar^2}{4\varepsilon_0},$$

which reassuringly agrees with the answer to Exercise 2.4.

**Ex 2.11** Taking the divergence of the electric field,

$$\begin{aligned}\operatorname{div}\mathbf{E} &= \frac{\partial}{\partial x}(Ax^3) + \frac{\partial}{\partial y}(Ay^3) + \frac{\partial}{\partial z}(-Az^3)\\ &= 3Ax^2 + 3Ay^2 - 3Az^2\\ &= 3A(x^2+y^2-z^2).\end{aligned}$$

So Gauss's law gives

$$\rho = \varepsilon_0\operatorname{div}\mathbf{E} = 3A\varepsilon_0(x^2+y^2-z^2).$$

This charge density is positive at points in the $z = 0$ plane and negative at points on the $z$-axis (where $x^2 + y^2 = 0$). The region must therefore contain both positive and negative charges.

*Comment*: The charge density we have calculated is that required to provide consistency with Gauss's law within the region. Other charges could exist outside the region, and may be partially responsible for the field.

**Ex 3.1** The divergence of the current density is

$$\begin{aligned}\operatorname{div}\mathbf{J} &= \frac{\partial}{\partial x}Ax(y-z)\\ &\quad + \frac{\partial}{\partial y}Ay(z-x) + \frac{\partial}{\partial z}Az(x-y)\\ &= A(y-z) + A(z-x) + A(x-y)\\ &= 0,\end{aligned}$$

so this current can persist without any accumulation of charge, and it might continue until someone wakes me up!

**Ex 3.2** The magnitude of the current density is $1.0\,\mathrm{A}/(\pi\times(5.0\times10^{-4}\,\mathrm{m})^2) = 1.3\times10^6\,\mathrm{A\,m^{-2}}$. This current is carried by electrons of charge $-e$ so

Equation 3.3 gives

$$v = \frac{J}{ne} = \frac{1.3 \times 10^{6}\,\mathrm{A\,m^{-2}}}{8.5 \times 10^{28}\,\mathrm{m^{-3}} \times 1.60 \times 10^{-19}\,\mathrm{C}} = 9.6 \times 10^{-5}\,\mathrm{m\,s^{-1}}.$$

*Comment*: This is well below snail's pace. An individual electron takes about an hour to travel one foot along the wire. Fortunately, we don't have to wait this long to get a light bulb to shine; electrical energy travels much more rapidly than the drift speed of individual electrons.

**Ex 3.3** No. The unit vector $\widehat{\mathbf{r}}_{12}$ is parallel to the current element $I_2\,\delta\mathbf{l}_2$ so the vector product $I_2\,\delta\mathbf{l}_2 \times \widehat{\mathbf{r}}_{12}$ vanishes.

**Ex 3.4** Using Equations 3.5 and 3.9 we obtain

$$\frac{F_{\mathrm{mag}}}{F_{\mathrm{elec}}} = \frac{\mu_0 I^2/2\pi d}{\lambda^2/2\pi\varepsilon_0 d} = \varepsilon_0\mu_0\frac{I^2}{\lambda^2},$$

where $I$ is the current and $\lambda$ is the charge of the conduction electrons per unit length of wire. Suppose that the wire has cross-sectional area $A$ and that its conduction electrons, each of charge $-e$, have number density $n$ and drift speed $v$. Then $|I| = nevA$ and $|\lambda| = neA$ so $I^2/\lambda^2 = v^2$ and

$$\frac{F_{\mathrm{mag}}}{F_{\mathrm{elec}}} = \varepsilon_0\mu_0 v^2.$$

Using the results of Exercise 3.2 we conclude that

$$\frac{F_{\mathrm{mag}}}{F_{\mathrm{elec}}} = 8.85 \times 10^{-12} \times 4\pi \times 10^{-7} \times (9.6 \times 10^{-5})^2 = 1.0 \times 10^{-25}.$$

*Note*: $F_{\mathrm{elec}}$ is enormous compared to $F_{\mathrm{mag}}$, but is exactly balanced by attractive forces between the conduction electrons and the positive ions, so the much smaller magnetic force $F_{\mathrm{mag}}$ is detectable.

**Ex 3.5** Substituting $z = 0$ in Equation 3.13, and taking the magnitude of both sides gives

$$B = \frac{\mu_0\,|I|}{2a}.$$

Alternatively, working from first principles, a current element $I\,\delta\mathbf{l}$ produces a magnetic field at O of magnitude

$$\delta B = \frac{\mu_0}{4\pi}\frac{|I|\,\delta l \times a \times \sin 90^\circ}{a^3} = \frac{\mu_0}{4\pi}\frac{|I|\,\delta l}{a^2},$$

in a direction perpendicular to the loop. All current elements in the loop produce identical magnetic field contributions, pointing in the same direction. The magnitude of the total magnetic field is obtained by integrating $\delta l$ round the circumference of the loop. Since

$$\int_{\mathrm{loop}} \mathrm{d}l = 2\pi a,$$

this gives

$$B = \frac{\mu_0}{4\pi}\frac{|I| \times 2\pi a}{a^2} = \frac{\mu_0\,|I|}{2a},$$

as before.

**Ex 3.6** Using Equation 3.12 and applying the right-hand rule, the magnetic force on side PQ acts vertically downwards and the magnetic force on side RS acts vertically upwards. The magnetic forces on QR and SP act horizontally and outwards, away from the centre of the loop. The forces on QR and SP cancel out, but the forces on PQ and RS create a torque on the loop, causing it to rotate about a horizontal axis perpendicular to $\mathbf{B}$. Equilibrium is achieved when the loop lies in a vertical plane; then all the magnetic forces act in the plane of the loop and cancel out.

**Ex 3.7** The magnetic field lines are helices, wrapped around the wire.

It is interesting to note that, as the uniform magnetic field parallel to the wire increases, the pitch of the helix *increases*, moving successive turns of the helix further apart. This example shows that it is impossible, in general, to gauge the strength of a magnetic field by counting the number of times its magnetic field lines cross a given plane. The general rule of thumb — that magnetic field lines are closer together where the magnetic field is stronger — is not infallible.

**Ex 3.8** They attract one another. For example, Figure S3.1 shows the two magnetic dipoles (loop 1 and loop 2) aligned with the $z$-axis, together with the magnetic field of loop 2. This magnetic field points upwards along the $z$-axis and has an outward radial component just off the $z$-axis as the field lines bend round to form closed loops. Using the right-hand rule, this magnetic field causes the loop 1 to feel a magnetic force with a negative $z$-component. The red arrows in the diagram show contributions to the force from two current elements in loop 1. Adding the magnetic forces on all current elements in loop 1, the force components perpendicular to the $z$-axis cancel out while the negative $z$-components reinforce one another. The upper dipole (loop 1) is therefore attracted to the lower dipole (loop 2).

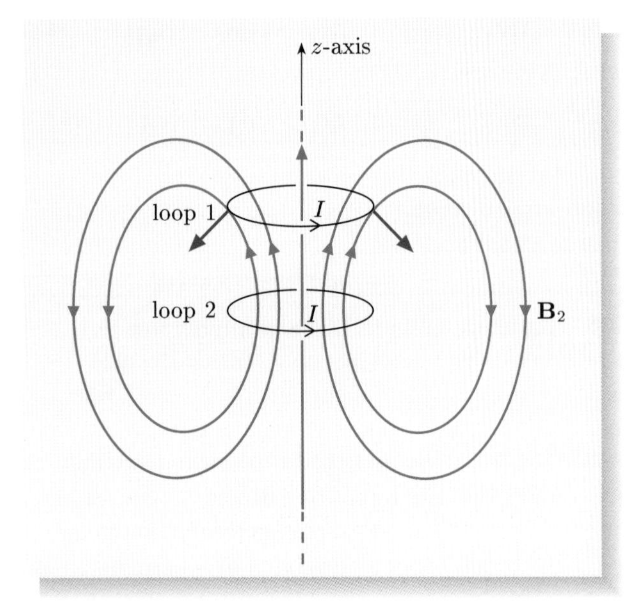


**Figure S3.1** The magnetic field due to current loop 2 produces a downward magnetic force on current loop 1.

**Ex 3.9** Let $r_E$ and $r_J$ be the radii of orbit of the Earth and Jupiter, and let $B_E$ and $B_J$ be the magnitudes of the Sun's dipolar magnetic field at these radii. A dipolar field decreases as $1/r^3$ so $B_J/B_E = (r_E/r_J)^3$. Rearranging this equation,

$$\begin{aligned} B_J &= \left(\frac{r_E}{r_J}\right)^3 \times B_E \\ &= \left(\frac{1.5}{8.2}\right)^3 \times 3.0 \times 10^{-10}\,\text{T} \\ &= 1.8 \times 10^{-12}\,\text{T}. \end{aligned}$$

**Ex 3.10** Substituting the given velocity into the magnetic force law gives

$$\begin{aligned} \mathbf{F}_{\text{mag}} &= q\mathbf{v} \times \mathbf{B} \\ &= q\begin{vmatrix} \mathbf{e}_x & \mathbf{e}_y & \mathbf{e}_z \\ 0 & 0 & v_z \\ B_x & B_y & B_z \end{vmatrix} \\ &= q\left(-v_z B_y \mathbf{e}_x + v_z B_x \mathbf{e}_y\right). \end{aligned}$$

Equating this to $F_x\mathbf{e}_x + F_y\mathbf{e}_y$, we conclude that

$$B_y = -F_x/qv_z \quad \text{and} \quad B_x = F_y/qv_z.$$

No information is available about $B_z$. As expected, the magnetic force determines the components of the magnetic field perpendicular to the particle's motion, but it tells us nothing about the component of the magnetic field parallel to the particle's motion.

**Ex 3.11** The Lorentz force on the electron must vanish so $\mathbf{E} + \mathbf{v} \times \mathbf{B} = \mathbf{0}$. Taking the $x$-component of this equation gives

$$E_x + (v_y B_z - v_z B_y) = E - vB = 0, \quad \text{so } E/B = v.$$

**Ex 3.12** (a) If the current carriers were positively charged, the magnetic field would deflect them onto the face $z = d$ in Figure 3.21 which is not what is observed. So the charge-carriers are negatively-charged and flow in the opposite direction to the current. The magnetic force still deflects them towards the face $z = d$, but the electric field now points from right to left, as required.

(b) Under steady-state conditions the charge carriers experience no net force and the electric and magnetic forces cancel out. So $qE = qvB$ and $v = E/B$. The current is related to the drift speed $v$ of the carriers by $|I| = nevA$, so the number density of the carriers is

$$\begin{aligned} n &= \frac{|I|}{evA} \\ &= \frac{|I|B}{eAE} \\ &= \frac{1.5\,\text{A} \times 3.0 \times 10^{-2}\,\text{T}}{1.60 \times 10^{-19}\,\text{C} \times 2.0 \times 10^{-6}\,\text{m}^2 \times 3.0\,\text{N}\,\text{C}^{-1}} \\ &= 4.7 \times 10^{22}\,\text{m}^{-3}. \end{aligned}$$

**Ex 4.1** Taking the divergence of each vector field gives

(a) $\operatorname{div} \mathbf{V}_1 = 0$,

(b) $\operatorname{div} \mathbf{V}_2 = C(2x + 2y - 2z)$,

(c) $\operatorname{div} \mathbf{V}_3 = C(z + z - 2z) = 0$.

The divergence of $\mathbf{V}_1$ and the divergence of $\mathbf{V}_3$ vanish everywhere, so $\mathbf{V}_1$ and $\mathbf{V}_3$ could be magnetic fields. The divergence of $\mathbf{V}_2$ does not vanish everywhere, so $\mathbf{V}_2$ could not be a magnetic field.

**Ex 4.2** The magnetic field takes the form $\mathbf{B} = B_z\mathbf{e}_z$ so the differential version of the no-monopole law gives

$$\operatorname{div} \mathbf{B} = \frac{\partial B_z}{\partial z} = 0.$$

Hence $B_z$ is independent of $z$ and $\mathbf{B}$ does not depend on $z$, in either direction or magnitude. (It could depend on $x$ or $y$.)

**Ex 4.3** The integral version of *Ampère's law* states that the *circulation* of the *magnetic field*, taken *around any closed path*, is proportional to the *total current through any open surface* bounded by the *closed path*.

**Ex 4.4** The symmetry of the situation suggests use of cylindrical coordinates, with the $z$-axis along the central axis of the tube. Using axial and translational symmetry, the magnetic field takes the form

$$\mathbf{B}(\mathbf{r}) = B_\phi(r)\,\mathbf{e}_\phi.$$

Consider the circular path $C$ shown in Figure S4.1, which is centred on and perpendicular to the axis of the tube and has radius $r < a$. The line integral of the magnetic field around this circle is $B_\phi(r) \times 2\pi r$. The circle is the perimeter of a disk lying entirely in the central hole of the tube. No current flows through this disk, so Ampère's law gives

$$B_\phi(r) \times 2\pi r = 0.$$

For $r \neq 0$ we obtain $B_\phi(r) = 0$. This shows that the magnetic field is zero everywhere inside the hole, with the possible exception of the central axis itself. In fact, the magnetic field vanishes here as well because we can safely assume that it is a smoothly varying function with no sudden discontinuities.

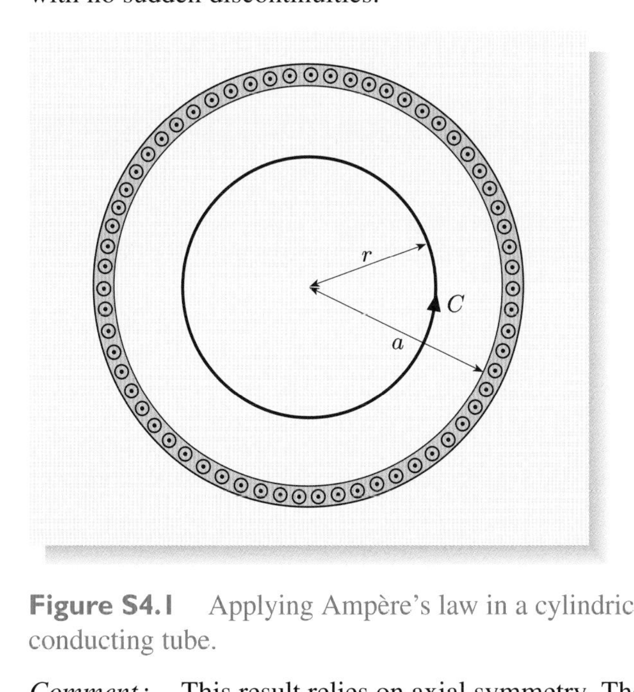


**Figure S4.1** Applying Ampère's law in a cylindrical conducting tube.

*Comment*: This result relies on axial symmetry. The magnetic field need not be zero inside a hole of square cross-section or inside a cylindrical hole that is off-centre, although its circulation around a closed path within the hole would be zero.

**Ex 4.5** The planar symmetry prompts use of Cartesian coordinates (Figure S4.2). Translational symmetry in the $x$- and $y$-directions ensures that the components of the magnetic field do not depend on $x$ or $y$, so

$$\mathbf{B}(\mathbf{r}) = B_x(z)\,\mathbf{e}_x + B_y(z)\,\mathbf{e}_y + B_z(z)\,\mathbf{e}_z.$$

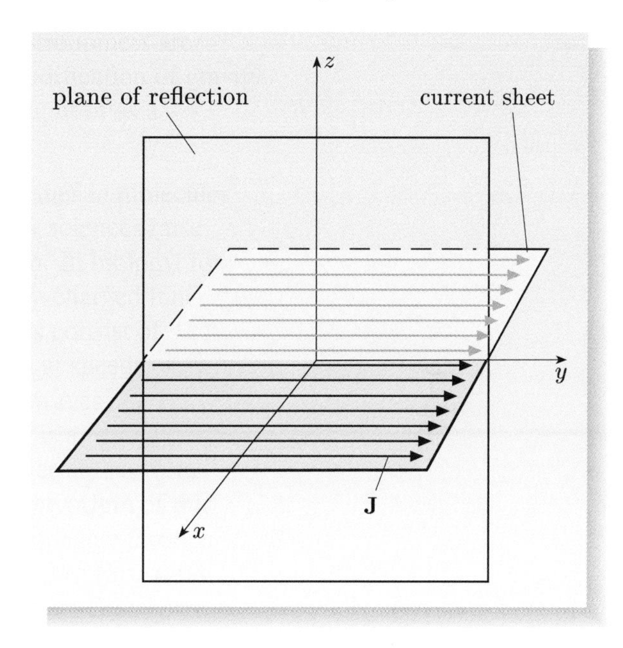


**Figure S4.2** A sheet in the $xy$-plane carrying current in the $y$-direction.

Consider a reflection of the current sheet in a plane perpendicular to the $x$-axis. This reflection does not change the current distribution. Using the reflection rule for magnetic fields, the reflection reverses the $y$- and $z$-components of the magnetic field, which are parallel to the plane of reflection, so the symmetry principle tells us that the $y$- and $z$-components are both equal to zero. We conclude that

$$\mathbf{B}(\mathbf{r}) = B_x(z)\,\mathbf{e}_x.$$

*Comment*: This is a complete answer to the question, and is as far as symmetry arguments can take us. However, you will see in Exercise 4.10 that $B_x(z)$ does not depend on the distance from the infinite sheet of current.

**Ex 4.6** Choose the circular loop $C$ of radius $r$ shown in Figure S4.3, lying inside the toroidal solenoid. The circulation of the magnetic field around the loop is

$$\int_C \mathbf{B} \cdot \mathrm{d}\mathbf{l} = B \times 2\pi r.$$

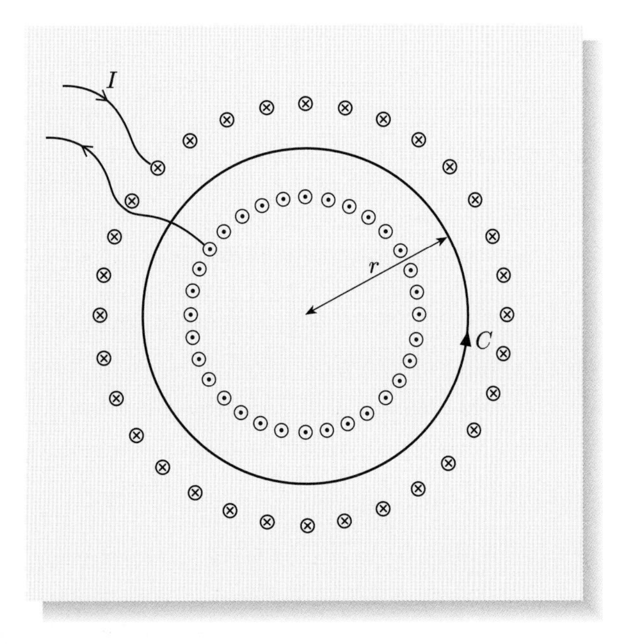


**Figure S4.3** Applying Ampère's law to a toroidal solenoid.

The interior of the loop $C$ is a circular disc. The total current flowing through this disc is

$$I_{\text{tot}} = N \times I.$$

Finally, Ampère's law gives

$$B \times 2\pi r = \mu_0 N \times I,$$

so

$$B = \frac{\mu_0 NI}{2\pi r} \quad \text{within the toroidal solenoid.}$$

This is similar to the magnetic field strength inside a long straight solenoid, but with the number of turns per unit length, $n$, being replaced by $N/2\pi r$. The field is greatest at the inner radius and smallest at the outer radius of the toroidal solenoid.

**Ex 4.7** The differential version of *Ampère's law* states that, at each point in space, the *curl* of the *magnetic field* is proportional to the *current density*.

**Ex 4.8** Working in Cartesian coordinates, the divergence of curl $\mathbf{B}$ is

$$\begin{aligned}\operatorname{div}(\operatorname{curl}\mathbf{B}) = {} & \frac{\partial}{\partial x}\left(\frac{\partial B_z}{\partial y} - \frac{\partial B_y}{\partial z}\right) \\ & + \frac{\partial}{\partial y}\left(\frac{\partial B_x}{\partial z} - \frac{\partial B_z}{\partial x}\right) \\ & + \frac{\partial}{\partial z}\left(\frac{\partial B_y}{\partial x} - \frac{\partial B_x}{\partial y}\right).\end{aligned}$$

Regrouping terms on the right-hand side gives

$$\begin{aligned}&\left(\frac{\partial^2 B_z}{\partial x \partial y} - \frac{\partial^2 B_z}{\partial y \partial x}\right) + \left(\frac{\partial^2 B_x}{\partial y \partial z} - \frac{\partial^2 B_x}{\partial z \partial y}\right) \\ &\qquad + \left(\frac{\partial^2 B_y}{\partial z \partial x} - \frac{\partial^2 B_y}{\partial x \partial z}\right),\end{aligned}$$

which vanishes because mixed partial derivatives do not depend on the order of partial differentiation. Taking the divergence of both sides of Equation 4.17 then gives

$$\operatorname{div}\mathbf{J} = \frac{1}{\mu_0}\operatorname{div}(\operatorname{curl}\mathbf{B}) = 0.$$

So the current density is divergence-free. This is characteristic of a steady current density, as explained in Section 3.1.

**Ex 4.9** The spatial derivatives of the components of a uniform magnetic field vanish so $\operatorname{curl}\mathbf{B} = \mathbf{0}$, and hence $\mathbf{J} = \operatorname{curl}\mathbf{B}/\mu_0 = \mathbf{0}$, throughout the region.

**Ex 4.10** Because there are no currents, the differential version of Ampère's law gives $\operatorname{curl}\mathbf{B} = \mathbf{0}$. Taking the $y$-component of this equation,

$$\frac{\partial B_x}{\partial z} - \frac{\partial B_z}{\partial x} = 0.$$

Using the fact that $B_z = 0$, we see that $B_x(z)$ is a constant.

*Comment*: This result is relevant to the situation described in Exercise 4.5.

**Ex 5.1** Working in Cartesian coordinates, we have

$$\begin{aligned}\frac{\partial}{\partial x}\left(\frac{1}{r^3}\right) &= \frac{\partial}{\partial x}(x^2 + y^2 + z^2)^{-3/2} \\ &= -\frac{3}{2}(x^2 + y^2 + z^2)^{-5/2} \times 2x \\ &= -\frac{3x}{r^5},\end{aligned}$$

with similar results for $\partial/\partial y$ and $\partial/\partial z$. So,

$$\operatorname{curl}\mathbf{F} = \begin{vmatrix} \mathbf{e}_x & \mathbf{e}_y & \mathbf{e}_z \\ \dfrac{\partial}{\partial x} & \dfrac{\partial}{\partial y} & \dfrac{\partial}{\partial z} \\ Ax/r^3 & Ay/r^3 & Az/r^3 \end{vmatrix}$$

$$= -\frac{3A}{r^5}\big((yz - zy)\mathbf{e}_x + (zx - xz)\mathbf{e}_y + (xy - yx)\mathbf{e}_z\big).$$

This is equal to zero everywhere (except possibly at $r = 0$ where the curl is undefined). The vector field $\mathbf{F}$ therefore passes the curl test for electrostatic fields.

*Comment*: Alternatively, you could spot that

$$\mathbf{F} = \frac{A}{r^3} \times \mathbf{r} = \frac{A}{r^2} \times \mathbf{e}_r,$$

where $\mathbf{e}_r$ is the radial unit vector in spherical coordinates. This field has the same form as that of a point charge. We can therefore use our previous analysis in spherical coordinates (p.118) to show that $\operatorname{curl}\mathbf{F} = \mathbf{0}$ for $r \neq 0$.

**Ex 5.2** The electrostatic potential at a point $\mathbf{r}$ is given by

$$V(\mathbf{r}) = -\int_{\mathbf{r}_0}^{\mathbf{r}} \mathbf{E} \cdot \mathrm{d}\mathbf{l},$$

where $\mathbf{r}$ and $\mathbf{r}_0$ have radial cylindrical coordinates $r$ and $r_0$. The electric field is given by $\mathbf{E} = \lambda/(2\pi\varepsilon_0 r)\,\mathbf{e}_r$, where $\mathbf{e}_r$ is the unit radial vector in cylindrical coordinates. For an arbitrary small displacement $\delta\mathbf{l}$, we have

$$\mathbf{E} \cdot \delta\mathbf{l} = \frac{\lambda}{2\pi\varepsilon_0 r}\,\mathbf{e}_r \cdot \delta\mathbf{l} = \frac{\lambda}{2\pi\varepsilon_0 r}\,\delta r,$$

where $\delta r$ is the change in radial cylindrical coordinate. It follows that the potential is independent of $\phi$ and $z$, and we will write it as $V(r)$. Hence,

$$V(r) = -\int_{r_0}^{r} \frac{\lambda}{2\pi\varepsilon_0 s}\,\mathrm{d}s,$$

where I have changed the variable of integration to $s$ in order to avoid confusion with the upper limit of integration, $r$. Evaluating the integral gives

$$V(r) = -\frac{\lambda}{2\pi\varepsilon_0}\Big[\ln s\Big]_{r_0}^{r} = \frac{\lambda}{2\pi\varepsilon_0}\ln\left(\frac{r_0}{r}\right).$$

If a charge $q$ is initially at distance $d$ from the line of charge, and moves to a distance $d/2$ from the line of charge, the change in its electrostatic potential energy is

$$\Delta U = qV(d/2) - qV(d)$$

$$= \frac{q\lambda}{2\pi\varepsilon_0}\left[\ln\left(\frac{2r_0}{d}\right) - \ln\left(\frac{r_0}{d}\right)\right]$$

$$= \frac{q\lambda}{2\pi\varepsilon_0}\ln 2.$$

*Comment*: It is not possible to place the zero of potential at infinity in this exercise because the potential increases without limit as $r$ increases. This unusual situation arises because the charge distribution is infinite in extent. However, it is not a problem, as it is perfectly acceptable to choose the potential to be zero at $r = r_0$, a finite distance from the line of charge.

**Ex 5.3** Far from the nucleus, the electrostatic potential energy of the alpha particle is negligible. The total energy of the alpha particle is therefore equal to its initial kinetic energy $U_{\text{kin}} = 1.23 \times 10^{-13}\,\text{J}$.

At the point of closest approach in a head-on collision, the alpha particle comes instantaneously to rest. At this point, the total energy of the alpha particle is equal to its electrostatic potential energy. Let the alpha particle have charge $q$ and the gold nucleus have charge $Q$. The electrostatic potential of the nucleus is

$$V(r) = \frac{Q}{4\pi\varepsilon_0 r},$$

so, at the distance of closest approach, $r_{\text{min}}$, the electrostatic potential energy of the alpha particle is

$$qV(r_{\text{min}}) = \frac{qQ}{4\pi\varepsilon_0 r_{\text{min}}}.$$

Setting this equal to the initial kinetic energy $U_{\text{kin}}$ and solving for $r_{\text{min}}$ gives

$$r_{\text{min}} = \frac{qQ}{4\pi\varepsilon_0 U_{\text{kin}}}$$

$$= \frac{3.20 \times 10^{-19}\,\text{C} \times 1.26 \times 10^{-17}\,\text{C}}{4\pi \times 8.85 \times 10^{-12}\,\text{C}^2\,\text{N}^{-1}\,\text{m}^{-2} \times 1.23 \times 10^{-13}\,\text{J}}$$

$$= 2.95 \times 10^{-13}\,\text{m}.$$

**Ex 5.4** The electric field is given by

$$\mathbf{E} = -\operatorname{grad} V$$

$$= \frac{\partial(Axy)}{\partial x}\mathbf{e}_x + \frac{\partial(Axy)}{\partial y}\mathbf{e}_y + \frac{\partial(Axy)}{\partial z}\mathbf{e}_z$$

$$= Ay\mathbf{e}_x + Ax\mathbf{e}_y.$$

Any vector field that can be expressed as the gradient of a scalar function is conservative.

**Ex 5.5** The charge on an electron is $-e$, where $e$ is positive, so the electrostatic force on an electron is $\mathbf{F} = -(-e)\,\mathrm{grad}\,V = e\,\mathrm{grad}\,V$. Thus $\mathbf{F}$ is positive in the direction of grad $V$, which is the direction of steepest increase of $V$. Therefore electrons are attracted towards regions of higher potential. Since $U = (-e)V$, this corresponds to regions in which their electrostatic potential energy is lower.

**Ex 5.6** No. If an electrostatic field line were to cross an equipotential surface at A and again at B, the work done transporting a test charge $q$ from A to B along the field line would be non-zero. This is impossible since A and B are on the same equipotential and therefore have the same electrostatic potential.

**Ex 5.7** The situation is illustrated in Figure S5.1.

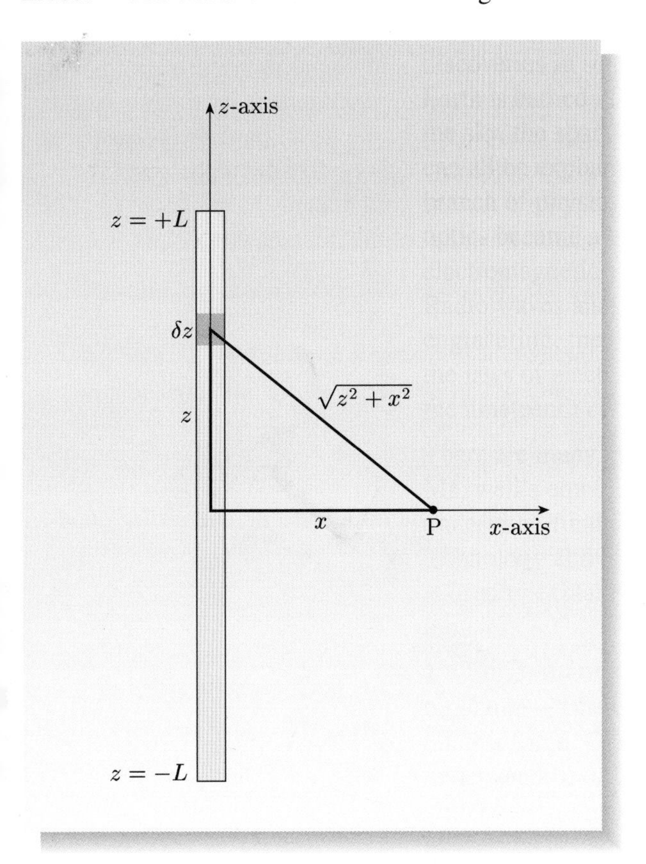


**Figure S5.1** Calculating the potential of a finite line of charge ($-L \le z \le L$).

The line element at position $z$ and of length $\delta z$ has charge $\lambda\,\delta z$ and is a distance $\sqrt{z^2 + x^2}$ from the point P on the $x$-axis. This element contributes a potential

$$\delta V = \frac{1}{4\pi\varepsilon_0}\frac{\lambda\,\delta z}{\sqrt{z^2 + x^2}}.$$

Integrating over the linear charge distribution gives

$$\begin{aligned} V &= \frac{\lambda}{4\pi\varepsilon_0}\int_{-L}^{L}\frac{1}{\sqrt{z^2 + x^2}}\,\mathrm{d}z \\ &= \frac{\lambda}{4\pi\varepsilon_0}\left[\ln(\sqrt{z^2 + x^2} + z)\right]_{z=-L}^{z=L} \\ &= \frac{\lambda}{4\pi\varepsilon_0}\ln\left(\frac{\sqrt{L^2 + x^2} + L}{\sqrt{L^2 + x^2} - L}\right), \end{aligned}$$

where the integration was carried out using a standard integral listed inside the back cover.

This answer diverges as $L \to \infty$, and so makes no sense in this limit. (To obtain an expression for the electrostatic potential of an infinite line of charge, we must carry out the direct evaluation of a line integral. This has already been done in Exercise 5.2.)

**Ex 5.8** In equilibrium, the two spheres are at the same potential so using Equation 5.18, the final charges on the spheres obey

$$\frac{Q_1}{R_1} = \frac{Q_2}{R_2}.$$

Also, the conservation of charge gives

$$Q_1 + Q_2 = 2Q.$$

Solving for $Q_1$ and $Q_2$ we obtain

$$Q_1 = \frac{2R_1}{R_1 + R_2}Q \quad\text{and}\quad Q_2 = \frac{2R_2}{R_1 + R_2}Q.$$

The larger sphere has a greater charge. Nevertheless, the smaller sphere has a greater surface electric field. (The spheres are widely separated, so the surface electric field on each sphere is proportional to charge/radius$^2$.)

**Ex 5.9** The potential difference between the ground and the base of the cloud is

$$V = Ed = 5000\,\mathrm{V\,m^{-1}} \times 1.0 \times 10^3\,\mathrm{m} = 5.0 \times 10^6\,\mathrm{V}.$$

The capacitance of the ground–cloud system is

$$\begin{aligned} C &= \frac{\varepsilon_0 A}{d} \\ &= \frac{8.85 \times 10^{-12}\,\mathrm{C^2\,N^{-1}\,m^{-2}} \times 20.0 \times 10^6\,\mathrm{m^2}}{1.0 \times 10^3\,\mathrm{m}} \\ &= 1.77 \times 10^{-7}\,\mathrm{F}. \end{aligned}$$

The total energy stored in the system is therefore

$$U = \frac{1}{2}CV^2$$
$$= \frac{1}{2} \times 1.77 \times 10^{-7}\,\text{F} \times (5.0 \times 10^6\,\text{V})^2$$
$$= 2.2 \times 10^6\,\text{J},$$

where the units have been combined using $1\,\text{F} = 1\,\text{C}\,\text{V}^{-1}$ and $1\,\text{J} = 1\,\text{C}\,\text{V}$.

**Ex 5.10** (a) If the plates are left connected to the battery their potential difference is fixed by the potentials of the battery terminals and so remains equal to $V$. The electric field strength in the gap is given by $E = V/d$ which increases as the gap is reduced. (This means that the charge $Q$ on the plates increases.)

(b) If the plates are disconnected from the battery, their charges remain fixed. The electric field strength in the gap is given by $E = Q/A\varepsilon_0$, where $A$ is the area of each plate, and this remains fixed. The potential difference between the plates is given by $V = Ed$, so this decreases as the gap narrows.

*Comment*: The second case reminds us that the potential of an electrically isolated conductor is not fixed, but depends on position. In principle, it is safe for a spaceship from Earth to visit a distant planet that has a much higher potential than on Earth because the potential of the spacecraft will have adjusted to be the same as the potential of the planet just in time for landing!

**Ex 6.1** No. Any electrostatic field is conservative and cannot drive a steady current around a circuit. Note that we cannot assume that the electric field is zero outside the capacitor plates, even in principle. The electrostatic field outside the capacitor must be such that the line integral of **E** around ABCD is equal to zero.

**Ex 6.2** Unusually in this book, the answer is 'maybe'. With good luck, the handyman's resistance to current flow will be of order

$$(3\,\Omega\,\text{m}^2)/(0.5 \times 10^{-4}\,\text{m}^2) = 6.0 \times 10^4\,\Omega,$$

and the current flowing through his heart will be

$$240/6.0 \times 10^4\,\text{A} = 4.0\,\text{mA}$$

— painful, but not fatal. With bad luck, his resistance will be

$$(0.05\,\Omega\,\text{m}^2)/(0.5 \times 10^{-4}\,\text{m}^2) = 1000\,\Omega,$$

leading to a probably fatal current of

$$240/1000\,\text{A} = 0.24\,\text{A}.$$

*Comment*: Needless to say, you should never take risks with mains electricity. Many factors can influence the outcome, including your general state of health.

**Ex 6.3** Let the resistance of the external part of the circuit be $R$, and let the internal resistance of the battery be $r$. Then the potential difference across the battery terminals is $V = IR$, and the emf of the battery is $V_{\text{emf}} = I(R + r)$. Real batteries always have some internal resistance, so $V = V_{\text{emf}} - Ir$ is always less than $V_{\text{emf}}$. The potential difference across the terminals of a battery approaches its emf as the current $I$ drawn from the battery tends to zero.

**Ex 6.4** The current drawn from the battery is

$$I/(R + r) = 12\,\text{V}/(0.16\,\Omega) = 75\,\text{A}.$$

So the power expended by the battery is

$$P = IV_{\text{emf}} = 75\,\text{A} \times 12\,\text{V} = 900\,\text{W}.$$

**Ex 6.5** We choose the surface $S$ to be the disc whose perimeter is the circular loop with its unit normal inclined at 30° to the $z$-axis. The magnetic flux over this disc is

$$\int_S \mathbf{B} \cdot \text{d}\mathbf{S} = Kt^2 \int_S \mathbf{e}_z \cdot \text{d}\mathbf{S}$$
$$= Kt^2 \times A\cos 30^\circ = \frac{\sqrt{3}}{2}AKt^2,$$

where $A$ is the area of the disc. Faraday's law then gives

$$V_{\text{emf}} = -\frac{\text{d}}{\text{d}t}\left(\frac{\sqrt{3}}{2}AKt^2\right) = -\sqrt{3}AKt.$$

The magnitude of the induced current is then found from Ohm's law:

$$|I| = \left|\frac{V_{\text{emf}}}{R}\right|$$
$$= \frac{\sqrt{3}AKt}{R}$$
$$= \frac{\sqrt{3} \times \pi(0.10\,\text{m})^2 \times 2.4\,\text{T}\,\text{s}^{-2} \times 0.5\,\text{s}}{4.0 \times 10^{-2}\,\Omega}$$
$$= 1.6\,\text{A}$$

(using $1\,\text{T} = 1\,\text{V}\,\text{s}\,\text{m}^{-2} = 1\,\text{A}\,\Omega\,\text{s}\,\text{m}^{-2}$).

*Comment*: The induced current is time-dependent, so it produces a time-dependent magnetic flux through the loop. *In principle*, this changing magnetic flux should be taken into account when calculating the induced emf and current. In the present case, however, the rate of change of magnetic flux due to the induced current turns out to be much smaller than the rate of change of magnetic flux due to the externally applied magnetic field (by a factor of order $10^{-5}$). We are therefore justified in ignoring this effect in this exercise.

**Ex 6.6** For definiteness, we take the open surface $S$ associated with the upper loop to be a disc bounded by the upper loop, with its unit normal pointing in the positive $z$-direction. Then, using the right-hand grip rule, the lower loop produces a positive magnetic flux over $S$.

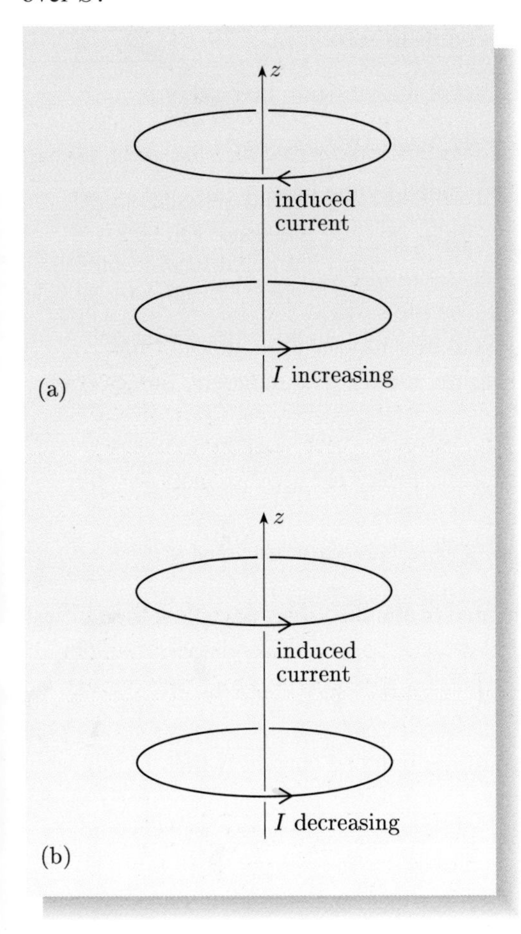


**Figure S6.1** The direction of the induced current in the upper loop depends on whether the current in the lower loop is increasing or decreasing.

(a) If $I$ is increasing, the magnetic flux over $S$ is increasing. Lenz's law requires the induced current to produce a compensating negative flux over $S$. Using the right-hand grip rule again, the induced current must flow in the direction shown in Figure S6.1a.

(b) If $I$ is decreasing, the magnetic flux over $S$ is decreasing. Lenz's law requires the induced current to produce a compensating positive flux over $S$. Using the right-hand grip rule again, the induced current must flow in the direction shown in Figure S6.1b.

**Ex 6.7** Let $\Phi(t)$ be the magnetic flux over a cross-section of the core. This is the magnetic flux through any single turn in the primary or secondary coils. The total magnetic flux through the primary coil is $N_1\Phi(t)$, while the total magnetic flux through the secondary coil is $N_2\Phi(t)$. Using Faraday's law, the voltage drops across the primary and secondary coils are

$$V_1 = -N_1\frac{\mathrm{d}\Phi}{\mathrm{d}t} \quad \text{and} \quad V_2 = -N_2\frac{\mathrm{d}\Phi}{\mathrm{d}t},$$

which immediately gives the required result: $V_2/V_1 = N_2/N_1$.

**Ex 6.8** Let's assume that the magnetic field changes at a constant rate. Then Faraday's law gives an induced emf of magnitude

$$\begin{aligned} V_{\text{emf}} &= \frac{0.01 \times 5.0 \times 10^{-5}\,\text{T} \times \pi(6 \times 10^5\,\text{m})^2}{10\,\text{s}} \\ &= 57\,\text{kV} \end{aligned}$$

(using $1\,\text{T} = 1\,\text{V}\,\text{s}\,\text{m}^{-2}$).

**Ex 6.9** Taking the curl of the electric field, we obtain

$$\begin{aligned} \text{curl}\,\mathbf{E} &= \begin{vmatrix} \mathbf{e}_x & \mathbf{e}_y & \mathbf{e}_z \\ \dfrac{\partial}{\partial x} & \dfrac{\partial}{\partial y} & \dfrac{\partial}{\partial z} \\ 0 & 0 & E_z \end{vmatrix} \\ &= \frac{\partial E_z}{\partial y}\mathbf{e}_x = -Ak\sin(ky - \omega t)\,\mathbf{e}_x. \end{aligned}$$

So Faraday's law gives

$$\frac{\partial B_x}{\partial t} = +Ak\sin(ky - \omega t),$$

$$\frac{\partial B_y}{\partial t} = 0 \quad \text{and} \quad \frac{\partial B_z}{\partial t} = 0.$$

Integrating these equations with respect to time, we conclude that

$$\mathbf{B} = \frac{Ak}{\omega}\cos(ky - \omega t) + \mathbf{B}_0,$$

where $\mathbf{B}_0$ is any time-independent magnetic field.

**Ex 7.1** The current density only has a $z$-component, so the equation of continuity becomes

$$\frac{\partial \rho}{\partial t} = -\,\text{div}\,\mathbf{J} = -\frac{\partial J_z}{\partial z} = -kA\cos(kz - \omega t).$$

Integrating with respect to time, the charge density is

$$\rho(z,t) = \frac{k}{\omega} A \sin(kz - \omega t) + C(z),$$

where $C(z)$ is an arbitrary function. In general, it is necessary to allow for such a function, which describes a fixed charge density distributed along the rod. However, $C(z)$ is the time-average of the charge density at position $z$, which is equal to zero according to information given in the question. Hence,

$$\rho(z,t) = \frac{k}{\omega} A \sin(kz - \omega t) = \frac{k}{\omega} J_z(z,t).$$

**Ex 7.2** Taking the surface integral of both sides of Equation 7.10 over an open surface $S$ gives

$$\int_S \operatorname{curl} \mathbf{B} \cdot \mathrm{d}\mathbf{S} = \int_S \left( \mu_0 \mathbf{J} + \varepsilon_0 \mu_0 \frac{\partial \mathbf{E}}{\partial t} \right) \cdot \mathrm{d}\mathbf{S}.$$

Using the curl theorem on the left-hand side we obtain

$$\oint_C \mathbf{B} \cdot \mathrm{d}\mathbf{l} = \int_S \left( \mu_0 \mathbf{J} + \varepsilon_0 \mu_0 \frac{\partial \mathbf{E}}{\partial t} \right) \cdot \mathrm{d}\mathbf{S},$$

where the sense of positive progression around $C$ and the orientation of $S$ are related by the right-hand grip rule. This is the required integral version of the Ampère–Maxwell law.

**Ex 7.3** Applying the transformation rules for time-reversal given in the question does not affect Gauss's law. The remaining Maxwell equations transform as follows:

$$\operatorname{div}(-\mathbf{B}) = 0,$$

$$\operatorname{curl} \mathbf{E} = -\frac{\partial(-\mathbf{B})}{\partial(-t)} \quad \text{and}$$

$$\operatorname{curl}(-\mathbf{B}) = \mu_0(-\mathbf{J}) + \varepsilon_0 \mu_0 \frac{\partial(\mathbf{E})}{\partial(-t)}.$$

In each case, the transformed equation can be rearranged to recover the original Maxwell equation, so Maxwell's equations are unchanged by time-reversal.

**Ex 7.4** Taking the divergence of the Ampère–Maxwell law (Equation 7.10) gives

$$\operatorname{div}(\operatorname{curl} \mathbf{B}) = \mu_0 \operatorname{div} \mathbf{J} + \varepsilon_0 \mu_0 \operatorname{div} \left( \frac{\partial \mathbf{E}}{\partial t} \right).$$

The left-hand side is equal to zero (from Equation 7.5). Interchanging the divergence and time derivative on the right-hand side and cancelling the factor $\mu_0$, then gives

$$\operatorname{div} \mathbf{J} + \frac{\partial}{\partial t} (\varepsilon_0 \operatorname{div} \mathbf{E}) = 0.$$

Using Gauss's law, $\operatorname{div} \mathbf{E} = \rho/\varepsilon_0$, we finally obtain

$$\operatorname{div} \mathbf{J} + \frac{\partial \rho}{\partial t} = 0,$$

which is the equation of continuity. Maxwell wrote down the equation of continuity alongside his other equations, but it is not counted as one of his four laws of electromagnetism because it is a consequence of two of the other laws.

**Ex 7.5** The electric wave does not exist beyond the filter, so its curl is equal to zero there. There can be no curl due to electrostatic fields either because electrostatic fields have zero curl. Faraday's law, $\operatorname{curl} \mathbf{E} = -\partial \mathbf{B}/\partial t$, therefore shows that the magnetic field must be independent of time beyond the filter. There is no magnetic wave beyond the filter.

**Ex 7.6** In time $\Delta t$, a wave crest moves a distance $\Delta z = c\,\Delta t$. If $n$ cycles of the wave pass the given point in this time, $n\lambda = c\,\Delta t$ so

$$n = \frac{c\,\Delta t}{\lambda} = \frac{(3 \times 10^8\,\mathrm{m\,s^{-1}}) \times (1.0 \times 10^{-14}\,\mathrm{s})}{600 \times 10^{-9}\,\mathrm{m}} = 5.$$

**Ex 7.7** The magnitude of the electric force is $qE$. Because the magnetic wave is transverse, perpendicular to the velocity of the particle, the magnitude of the magnetic force is $qvB$. In an electromagnetic wave, $E = cB$, so the ratio of the force magnitudes is

$$\frac{F_{\text{mag}}}{F_{\text{elec}}} = \frac{qvB}{qE} = \frac{v}{c}.$$

The magnetic force is much smaller than the electric force for non-relativistic particles, but the two forces become comparable for a charged particle that travels close to the speed of light.

**Ex 7.8** The average energy flux is

$$\frac{1}{2}\sqrt{\frac{\varepsilon_0}{\mu_0}}E_0^2 = \frac{1}{2}\sqrt{\frac{8.85 \times 10^{-12}\,\mathrm{C^2\,m^{-2}\,N^{-1}}}{4\pi \times 10^{-7}\,\mathrm{N\,A^{-2}}}} \times (0.01\,\mathrm{V\,m^{-1}})^2$$
$$= 1.3 \times 10^{-7}\,\mathrm{W\,m^{-2}},$$

using the unit conversions $1\,\mathrm{C} = 1\,\mathrm{A\,s}$, $1\,\mathrm{A\,V} = 1\,\mathrm{W}$ and $1\,\mathrm{N\,m\,s^{-1}} = 1\,\mathrm{W}$.

*Comment*: The small value of this energy flux shows that amplification is an essential function of any radio receiver.

**Ex 8.1** Subtracting $6\mathbf{a} - 4\mathbf{b}$ from each side gives

$$2\mathbf{c} = -(6\mathbf{a} - 4\mathbf{b}) \quad \text{so} \quad \mathbf{c} = 2\mathbf{b} - 3\mathbf{a}.$$

**Ex 8.2** Taking components in the $x$- and $y$-directions:

$$a_x = a\cos 60^\circ = \tfrac{1}{2}a,$$
$$a_y = a\cos 30^\circ = \tfrac{\sqrt{3}}{2}a.$$

The $z$-component is zero because the vector lies in the $xy$-plane.

**Ex 8.3** The displacement vector of A from B is

$$\begin{aligned}\mathbf{r}_{\text{AB}} &= (4\mathbf{e}_x - 3\mathbf{e}_y)\,\text{m} - (\mathbf{e}_x + \mathbf{e}_y)\,\text{m}\\ &= (3\mathbf{e}_x - 4\mathbf{e}_y)\,\text{m}.\end{aligned}$$

The distance between A and B is

$$r_{\text{AB}} = \sqrt{(3)^2 + (-4)^2}\,\text{m} = 5\,\text{m}.$$

The unit vector pointing from B towards A is

$$\begin{aligned}\widehat{\mathbf{r}}_{\text{AB}} &= \frac{\mathbf{r}_{\text{AB}}}{r_{\text{AB}}}\\ &= \frac{(3\mathbf{e}_x - 4\mathbf{e}_y)\,\text{m}}{5\,\text{m}}\\ &= 0.6\mathbf{e}_x - 0.8\mathbf{e}_y,\end{aligned}$$

with no units.

**Ex 8.4** The scalar product is

$$\begin{aligned}\mathbf{a}\cdot\mathbf{b} &= (\mathbf{e}_x - \mathbf{e}_y + \mathbf{e}_z)\cdot(-\mathbf{e}_x - 3\mathbf{e}_y + 0\mathbf{e}_z)\\ &= (1\times -1) + (-1\times -3) + (1\times 0) = 2.\end{aligned}$$

**Ex 8.5** From Equation 8.6 we have

$$\mathbf{a}\cdot\mathbf{b} = ab\cos\theta.$$

In order for this to be equal to $-ab$, we must have $\cos\theta = -1$, so $\theta = \pi$ radians $= 180^\circ$. The vectors point in opposite directions, that is they are *antiparallel*.

**Ex 8.6** To test for orthogonality, we evaluate the scalar product:

$$\begin{aligned}(\mathbf{a}+\mathbf{b})\cdot(\mathbf{a}-\mathbf{b}) &= \mathbf{a}\cdot\mathbf{a} - \mathbf{a}\cdot\mathbf{b} + \mathbf{b}\cdot\mathbf{a} - \mathbf{b}\cdot\mathbf{b}\\ &= a^2 - b^2.\end{aligned}$$

This is identically equal to zero because $\mathbf{a}$ and $\mathbf{b}$ have the same magnitude. Since $\mathbf{a}$ and $\mathbf{b}$ are neither parallel nor antiparallel, neither $\mathbf{a}+\mathbf{b}$ nor $\mathbf{a}-\mathbf{b}$ is equal to the zero vector. So the vanishing scalar product shows that $\mathbf{a}+\mathbf{b}$ and $\mathbf{a}-\mathbf{b}$ are orthogonal.

**Ex 8.7** The vector product is

$$\begin{aligned}\mathbf{a}\times\mathbf{b} &= (2\mathbf{e}_x + 3\mathbf{e}_y)\times(3\mathbf{e}_x + 2\mathbf{e}_y)\\ &= (2\times 2)\mathbf{e}_x\times\mathbf{e}_y + (3\times 3)\mathbf{e}_y\times\mathbf{e}_x\\ &= 4\mathbf{e}_z - 9\mathbf{e}_z\\ &= -5\mathbf{e}_z.\end{aligned}$$

Note that we have not included terms in $(\mathbf{e}_x\times\mathbf{e}_x)$ or $(\mathbf{e}_y\times\mathbf{e}_y)$ because these vector products are equal to zero.

**Ex 8.8** For $\mathbf{a}\times\mathbf{b}$, point the your right hand horizontally to the north in such a way that its fingers can bend vertically upwards. Your outstretched right thumb then points horizontally to the east; this is the direction of $\mathbf{a}\times\mathbf{b}$.

For $\mathbf{b}\times\mathbf{a}$, point your right hand vertically upwards in such a way that its fingers can bend horizontally to the north. Your outstretched right thumb then points horizontally to the west; this is the direction of $\mathbf{b}\times\mathbf{a}$.

As expected, $\mathbf{a}\times\mathbf{b}$ and $\mathbf{b}\times\mathbf{a}$ point in opposite directions.

**Ex 8.9** Before reflection, the vector $\mathbf{c} = \mathbf{a}\times\mathbf{b}$ has components

$$\begin{aligned}c_x &= (a_y b_z - a_z b_y),\\ c_y &= (a_z b_x - a_x b_z),\\ c_z &= (a_x b_y - a_y b_x).\end{aligned}$$

The reflection converts

$$(a_x, a_y, a_z) \to (a_x, a_y, -a_z)$$

and

$$(b_x, b_y, b_z) \to (b_x, b_y, -b_z)$$

Substituting these changes into the above expressions gives

$$c_x \to -c_x, \quad c_y \to -c_y, \quad c_z \to c_z.$$

So the vector product $\mathbf{c} = \mathbf{a}\times\mathbf{b}$ behaves rather strangely under reflections — its components parallel to the plane of reflection are reversed, and its component perpendicular to the plane of reflection is unchanged.

**Ex 8.10** The rate of change of the kinetic energy is

$$\begin{aligned}\frac{\mathrm{d}}{\mathrm{d}t}\left(\tfrac{1}{2}mv^2\right) &= \tfrac{1}{2}m\frac{\mathrm{d}}{\mathrm{d}t}(\mathbf{v}\cdot\mathbf{v}) \\ &= \tfrac{1}{2}m\left(\mathbf{v}\cdot\frac{\mathrm{d}\mathbf{v}}{\mathrm{d}t}+\frac{\mathrm{d}\mathbf{v}}{\mathrm{d}t}\cdot\mathbf{v}\right) \\ &= \left(m\frac{\mathrm{d}\mathbf{v}}{\mathrm{d}t}\right)\cdot\mathbf{v}.\end{aligned}$$

Alternatively, the same result can be established using components:

$$\begin{aligned}\frac{\mathrm{d}}{\mathrm{d}t}\left(\tfrac{1}{2}mv^2\right) &= \tfrac{1}{2}m\frac{\mathrm{d}}{\mathrm{d}t}\left(v_x^2+v_y^2+v_z^2\right) \\ &= m\left(v_x\frac{\mathrm{d}v_x}{\mathrm{d}t}+v_y\frac{\mathrm{d}v_y}{\mathrm{d}t}+v_z\frac{\mathrm{d}v_z}{\mathrm{d}t}\right) \\ &= \left(m\frac{\mathrm{d}\mathbf{v}}{\mathrm{d}t}\right)\cdot\mathbf{v}.\end{aligned}$$

Newton's second law, $\mathbf{F} = m\mathrm{d}\mathbf{v}/\mathrm{d}t$, then shows that the rate of change of the kinetic energy is $\mathbf{F}\cdot\mathbf{v}$. If $\mathbf{F}$ is always perpendicular to $\mathbf{v}$, the scalar product $\mathbf{F}\cdot\mathbf{v} = 0$ and the kinetic energy remains constant.

**Ex 8.11** Velocity is a vector quantity, so the velocity of water in a river is a vector field. Speed, energy density and concentration are all scalar quantities so the remaining fields are all scalar fields.

**Ex 8.12** (a) We could use Equations 8.17 to make replacements for $x$, $y$ and $z$ in the scalar field, and then simplify the result. However, it is much simpler to note that the square of the radial spherical coordinate is $r^2 = x^2 + y^2 + z^2$. Substituting the right-hand side of this equation into the scalar field immediately gives $V(r) = A/r^2$.

(b) The radial coordinate in cylindrical coordinates has a different meaning from that in spherical coordinates. In cylindrical coordinates, $r^2 = x^2 + y^2$. Substituting the right-hand side of this equation into the scalar field gives $V(r, z) = A/(r^2 + z^2)$. The transformation to cylindrical coordinates is complete because $z$ is already one of the cylindrical coordinates.

*Comment*: The same symbol $V$ is used in $V(r)$, $V(r, z)$ and $V(x, y, z)$. This is natural because $V$ represents the same field in each case. From a mathematical point of view, however, $V(r)$, $V(r, z)$ and $V(x, y, z)$ are different *functions* with different arguments. Avoid writing down an expression like $V(2\,\mathrm{m}, 30°)$, without describing the meaning of the arguments, or at least the coordinate system being used.

**Ex 8.13** At any point P, the radial unit vector $\mathbf{e}_r$ in spherical coordinates is in the direction of the position vector $\mathbf{r}$. Expressing this position vector in Cartesian coordinates,

$$\mathbf{r} = x\mathbf{e}_x + y\mathbf{e}_y + z\mathbf{e}_z,$$

where $(x, y, z)$ are the Cartesian coordinates of P. The corresponding unit vector is

$$\mathbf{e}_r = \frac{\mathbf{r}}{r} = \frac{x\mathbf{e}_x + y\mathbf{e}_y + z\mathbf{e}_z}{\sqrt{x^2+y^2+z^2}}.$$

Since $r^2 = x^2 + y^2 + z^2$, the vector field $\mathbf{F}(r)$ takes the form

$$\begin{aligned}\mathbf{F}(x,y,z) &= \frac{A}{x^2+y^2+z^2}\times\frac{x\mathbf{e}_x + y\mathbf{e}_y + z\mathbf{e}_z}{\sqrt{x^2+y^2+z^2}} \\ &= \frac{A(x\mathbf{e}_x + y\mathbf{e}_y + z\mathbf{e}_z)}{(x^2+y^2+z^2)^{3/2}}.\end{aligned}$$

**Ex 8.14**

$$\frac{\partial f}{\partial x} = \frac{\mathrm{d}}{\mathrm{d}x}(\mathrm{e}^{2x})\cos(3y) = 2\mathrm{e}^{2x}\cos(3y)$$

and

$$\frac{\partial f}{\partial y} = \mathrm{e}^{2x}\frac{\mathrm{d}}{\mathrm{d}y}(\cos(3y)) = -3\mathrm{e}^{2x}\sin(3y).$$

**Ex 8.15** Taking the first partial derivatives,

$$\frac{\partial f}{\partial x} = k\cos(k(x-ct)), \quad \text{and}$$

$$\frac{\partial f}{\partial t} = -kc\cos(k(x-ct)).$$

The second partial derivatives are then

$$\frac{\partial^2 f}{\partial x^2} = -k^2\sin(k(x-ct)), \quad \text{and}$$

$$\frac{\partial^2 f}{\partial t^2} = -k^2c^2\sin(k(x-ct)).$$

So

$$\frac{\partial^2 f}{\partial x^2} = \frac{1}{c^2}\frac{\partial^2 f}{\partial t^2} \quad \text{as required.}$$

**Ex 8.16** We divide the volume of the cylinder into a set of nested tubes, each centred on the $z$-axis (Figure S8.1).

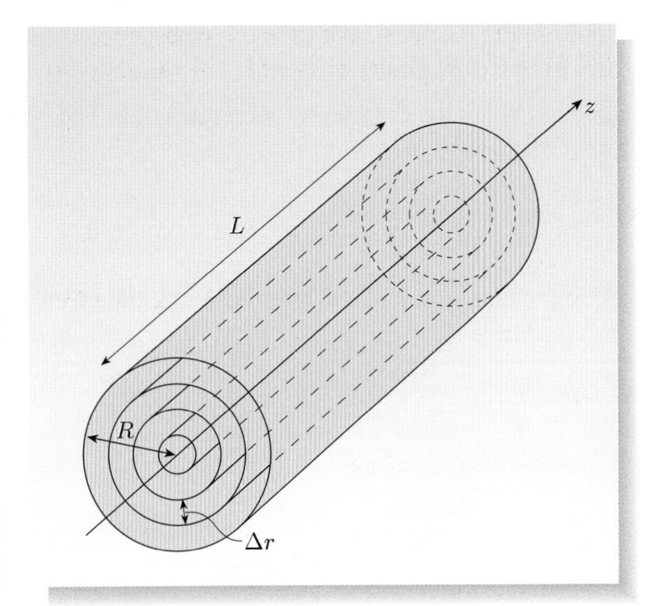


**Figure S8.1** A cylinder can be subdivided into a set of nested tubes each of thickness $\Delta r$.

We concentrate on one of these tubes of radius $r$, length $L$, and thickness $\Delta r$. The volume $\Delta V$ of this tube is its surface area, $2\pi r L$, times its thickness $\Delta r$. That is,

$$\Delta V = 2\pi r L\,\Delta r.$$

If the tube is thin enough, we can neglect any variation of $f$ in the tube. The contribution to the integral from this tube is therefore

$$Ar \times 2\pi r L\,\Delta r = 2\pi A r^2 L\,\Delta r.$$

Taking the limiting case of infinitely many tubes, each of infinitesimal thickness, and integrating outwards from the centre of the cylinder, $r = 0$, to its surface, $r = R$, we obtain

$$I = \int_0^R 2\pi A r^2 L\,\mathrm{d}r = 2\pi AL\left[\frac{r^3}{3}\right]_0^R = \tfrac{2}{3}\pi ALR^3.$$

**Ex 8.17** The function $f(r) = \exp(-r^3)$ is spherically symmetric about the origin, so we carry out the volume integral in spherical coordinates.

$$\begin{aligned} I &= \int_{\text{all space}} \exp(-r^3)\,\mathrm{d}V \\ &= \int_0^\infty \exp(-r^3)\,4\pi r^2\,\mathrm{d}r \\ &= 4\pi\int_0^\infty r^2\exp(-r^3)\,\mathrm{d}r. \end{aligned}$$

Using the standard integral given in the question, we obtain

$$I = 4\pi\left[-\frac{\exp(-r^3)}{3}\right]_0^\infty = \tfrac{4}{3}\pi.$$

**Ex 8.18** At all points on the curved surface of the cylinder, the vector field $\mathbf{F}$ points outwards, is perpendicular to the surface, and has magnitude $A/R$. The vector field $\mathbf{F}$ is parallel to the planar end-faces of the cylinder, so has no flux over these faces. The flux over the whole closed cylinder is therefore

$$\text{flux} = \frac{A}{R} \times 2\pi RL = 2\pi AL.$$

**Ex 8.19** Using Equation 8.35 for the divergence,

$$\operatorname{div}\mathbf{F} = \frac{\partial}{\partial x}(\mathbf{a}\cdot\mathbf{r}) + \frac{\partial}{\partial y}(\mathbf{b}\cdot\mathbf{r}) + \frac{\partial}{\partial z}(\mathbf{c}\cdot\mathbf{r}).$$

Since $\mathbf{a}\cdot\mathbf{r} = a_x x + a_y y + a_z z$,

$$\frac{\partial}{\partial x}(\mathbf{a}\cdot\mathbf{r}) = \frac{\partial}{\partial x}(a_x x + a_y y + a_z z) = a_x,$$

with similar results for the other two partial derivatives in the divergence, and so

$$\operatorname{div}\mathbf{F} = a_x + b_y + c_z.$$

**Ex 8.20** If the vector field $\mathbf{F}$ is a constant vector, its divergence is zero. For any closed surface $S$, enclosing a volume $V$, the divergence theorem then gives

$$\int_S \mathbf{F}\cdot\mathrm{d}\mathbf{S} = \int_V 0\,\mathrm{d}V = 0.$$

**Ex 8.21** Using the divergence theorem,

$$\int_S \mathbf{F} \cdot \mathrm{d}\mathbf{S} = \int_V \operatorname{div} \mathbf{F} \, \mathrm{d}V,$$

where $S$ is the surface of the region and $V$ is its volume. Worked Example 8.4 showed that $\operatorname{div} \mathbf{F} = 3A$, so

$$\int_S \mathbf{F} \cdot \mathrm{d}\mathbf{S} = \int_V 3A \, \mathrm{d}V = 3AV.$$

In the special case of a sphere of radius $R$ the flux can be calculated directly as a surface integral using the argument of Worked Example 8.2. We find

$$\text{flux} = \int_S \mathbf{F} \cdot \mathrm{d}\mathbf{S} = AR \times 4\pi R^2 = 4\pi A R^3.$$

Since the volume of the sphere is $V = 4\pi R^3/3$, this agrees with our previous, more general, answer.

**Ex 8.22** Evaluating $\operatorname{div} \mathbf{E}$ in spherical coordinates gives

$$\operatorname{div} \mathbf{E} = \frac{1}{r^2} \frac{\partial \left(r^2 f(r)\right)}{\partial r}.$$

(Because of spherical symmetry, terms involving partial derivatives of $\theta$ and $\phi$ all vanish.)

Setting this divergence equal to zero at any point with $r \neq 0$ gives

$$\frac{\mathrm{d}}{\mathrm{d}r}(r^2 f(r)) = 0,$$

so $r^2 f(r) =$ constant, and $f(r)$ is proportional to $1/r^2$.

*Comment*: This result is relevant to the electric field of an isolated point charge at the origin.

**Ex 8.23** Evaluating $\operatorname{div} \mathbf{E}$ in cylindrical coordinates gives

$$\operatorname{div} \mathbf{E} = \frac{1}{r} \frac{\partial}{\partial r} \left(r f(r)\right).$$

(Because of cylindrical symmetry, terms involving partial derivatives of $\phi$ and $z$ all vanish.)

Setting this divergence equal to zero at any point with $r \neq 0$ gives

$$\frac{\mathrm{d}}{\mathrm{d}r}(r f(r)) = 0,$$

so $r f(r) =$ constant, and $f(r)$ is proportional to $1/r$.

*Comment*: This result is relevant to the electric field of an infinite uniform line of charge along the $z$-axis.

**Ex 8.24** Referring to Figure 8.35 we see that the $xz$-plane is perpendicular to the plane of the page while the vector field $\mathbf{F}$ is in the plane of the page. The vector field $\mathbf{F}$ is therefore perpendicular to the circle $C_2$, which lies in the $xz$-plane. For each directed line segment $\delta\mathbf{l}$ in $C_2$, the scalar product $\mathbf{F} \cdot \delta\mathbf{l}$ vanishes, so

$$\int_{C_2} \mathbf{F} \cdot \mathrm{d}\mathbf{l} = 0.$$

**Ex 8.25** Taking the scalar product of the vector field $\mathbf{F} = x\mathbf{e}_y$ with a small directed line element $\delta\mathbf{l} = \delta x \mathbf{e}_x + \delta y \mathbf{e}_y$ gives $\mathbf{F} \cdot \delta\mathbf{l} = x\,\delta y$. Along the given curve $C_3$ we have $\delta y/\delta x = b/a$ so

$$\mathbf{F} \cdot \delta\mathbf{l} = \frac{b}{a} x \, \delta x.$$

The line integral is therefore

$$\int_{C_3} \mathbf{F} \cdot \mathrm{d}\mathbf{l} = \int_0^a \frac{b}{a} x \, \mathrm{d}x = \frac{b}{a} \left[\frac{x^2}{2}\right]_0^a = \frac{ab}{2}.$$

**Ex 8.26** Anticlockwise (see Figure 8.37).

**Ex 8.27** Using Equation 8.45 for the curl,

$$\operatorname{curl} \mathbf{V} = \begin{vmatrix} \mathbf{e}_x & \mathbf{e}_y & \mathbf{e}_z \\ \dfrac{\partial}{\partial x} & \dfrac{\partial}{\partial y} & \dfrac{\partial}{\partial z} \\ 0 & kx & 0 \end{vmatrix}$$

$$= \frac{\partial}{\partial x}(kx) \, \mathbf{e}_z$$

$$= k\mathbf{e}_z.$$

*Comment*: The curl is non-zero, even though the vector field $\mathbf{V}$ points in a constant direction. If $\mathbf{V}$ were the velocity field of a fluid, small objects placed in the fluid would tend to rotate in response to different flow rates along opposite edges parallel to the $y$-axis, so a non-zero curl is reasonable.

**Ex 8.28** First we calculate the circulation of $\mathbf{V}$ around the square ABCD shown in Figure S8.2. Because the vector field points along the $y$-axis, only the sides parallel to the $y$-axis contribute to the circulation. Side BC contributes $kL \times L$ but side DA contributes nothing (because $\mathbf{V}$ vanishes for $x = 0$). So the total circulation around the square is $kL^2$.

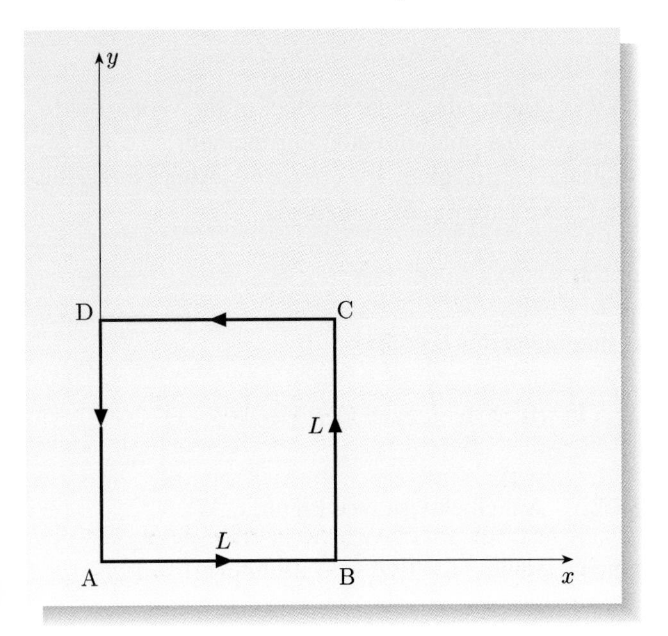


**Figure S8.2** A square path used in Exercise 8.28. The $z$-axis points out of the page, towards you.

According to the curl theorem, this circulation should be equal to the integral of $\operatorname{curl}\mathbf{V}$ over the surface of the square. Exercise 8.27 showed that $\operatorname{curl}\mathbf{V} = k\mathbf{e}_z$. Because the square ABCD is traversed anticlockwise, the right-hand rule requires us to take the unit normal of the square to be $\mathbf{e}_z$ (rather than $-\mathbf{e}_z$). The appropriate surface integral is therefore

$$\int_{y=0}^{y=L}\int_{x=0}^{x=L} (k\mathbf{e}_z)\cdot\mathbf{e}_z\,\mathrm{d}x\,\mathrm{d}y = kL^2,$$

as before.

**Ex 8.29** Evaluating $\operatorname{curl}\mathbf{B}$ in cylindrical coordinates gives

$$\operatorname{curl}\mathbf{B} = \frac{1}{r}\begin{vmatrix} \mathbf{e}_r & r\,\mathbf{e}_\phi & \mathbf{e}_z \\ \dfrac{\partial}{\partial r} & \dfrac{\partial}{\partial \phi} & \dfrac{\partial}{\partial z} \\ 0 & rf(r) & 0 \end{vmatrix}$$

$$= \frac{1}{r}\frac{\partial}{\partial r}(rf(r))\,\mathbf{e}_z.$$

Setting this equal to the zero vector at any point with $r \neq 0$ gives

$$\frac{\mathrm{d}}{\mathrm{d}r}(rf(r)) = 0,$$

so $rf(r) =$ constant, and $f(r)$ is proportional to $1/r$.

*Comment*: This result is relevant to the magnetic field produced by a uniform current flowing along the $z$-axis.

**Ex 8.30** $\mathbf{B}$ is not conservative. This can be seen by taking the line integral of $\mathbf{B}$ around a circle of radius $R$, centred on the $z$-axis and in a plane perpendicular to the $z$-axis. The circle is traversed in the direction of the unit vector $\mathbf{e}_\phi$. The vector field $\mathbf{B}$ is parallel to this path and has a constant magnitude $f(R)$ along it, so the line integral of $\mathbf{B}$ around the circular path is $f(R) \times 2\pi R \neq 0$. The existence of a closed loop with a non-zero circulation shows that the vector field $\mathbf{B}$ is not conservative.

*Comment*: This calculation is relevant to the magnetic field produced by a steady current flowing in an infinite wire centred on the $z$-axis.

**Ex 8.31** The vector field $\mathbf{F}$ is conservative, as shown in Worked Example 8.9. To find the corresponding scalar potential field $f$, we take minus the line integral of $\mathbf{F}$ along any path leading from a reference point at infinity to a point $\mathbf{r}$. The simplest choice is a radial path with line element $\delta\mathbf{l} = \delta r\,\mathbf{e}_r$. Then Equation 8.48 gives

$$f(\mathbf{r}) = -\int_\infty^r \frac{A}{s^2}\,\mathrm{d}s = -\left[-\frac{A}{s}\right]_\infty^r = \frac{A}{r},$$

where the variable of integration has been changed from $r$ to $s$ to avoid confusion with the upper limit of integration.

*Comment*: Care is needed with minus signs in calculations of this type. One minus sign arises from our definition of the scalar potential and a second appears when we integrate $A/s^2$. The *lower* limit of integration is $\infty$, which may seem strange, but is correct because the lower limit refers to the reference point, which is taken to be at infinity.

**Ex 8.32** Using

$$\mathbf{F} = -\operatorname{grad} f = -\left(\frac{\partial f}{\partial x}\,\mathbf{e}_x + \frac{\partial f}{\partial y}\,\mathbf{e}_y + \frac{\partial f}{\partial z}\,\mathbf{e}_z\right),$$

we have

$$\frac{\partial f}{\partial x} = -(x^2 + y^2), \quad \frac{\partial f}{\partial y} = -2xy \quad \text{and} \quad \frac{\partial f}{\partial z} = 0.$$

These equations can be solved by taking

$$f = -\frac{x^3}{3} - xy^2 + C, \quad \text{where } C \text{ is any constant.}$$

**Ex 8.33** Taking partial derivatives of $f$ and forming the gradient we have

$$\text{grad}\, f = yz\,\mathbf{e}_x + xz\,\mathbf{e}_y + xy\,\mathbf{e}_z.$$

At the point $\text{P} = (1, 1, 0)$, $\text{grad}\, f = \mathbf{e}_z$. At this point, $f$ increases most rapidly in the $z$-dirdction.

**Ex 8.34** The symmetry of the situation prompts the use of spherical coordinates. Using Equation 8.55, the corresponding vector field is

$$\mathbf{F} = -\,\text{grad}\, f = -\frac{\partial}{\partial r}\left(\frac{K}{r^6}\right)\mathbf{e}_r = \frac{6K}{r^7}\,\mathbf{e}_r.$$

The line integral of $\mathbf{F}$ need not be evaluated explicitly because it is related to a difference in the values of $f$. Using Equation 8.49, we have

$$\int_{\text{A}}^{\text{B}} \mathbf{F} \cdot \text{d}\mathbf{l} = -\left(f(b) - f(a)\right) = \frac{K}{a^6} - \frac{K}{b^6}.$$

**Ex 8.35** The whole of space is simply-connected, so we can use the curl test.

$$\text{curl}\,\mathbf{F} = \begin{vmatrix} \mathbf{e}_x & \mathbf{e}_y & \mathbf{e}_z \\ \dfrac{\partial}{\partial x} & \dfrac{\partial}{\partial y} & \dfrac{\partial}{\partial z} \\ x^2 + y^2 & 2xy & 0 \end{vmatrix}$$

$$= 0\,\mathbf{e}_x + 0\,\mathbf{e}_y + (2y - 2y)\,\mathbf{e}_z$$

$$= \mathbf{0}$$

and

$$\text{curl}\,\mathbf{G} = \begin{vmatrix} \mathbf{e}_x & \mathbf{e}_y & \mathbf{e}_z \\ \dfrac{\partial}{\partial x} & \dfrac{\partial}{\partial y} & \dfrac{\partial}{\partial z} \\ x^2 - y^2 & 2xy & 0 \end{vmatrix}$$

$$= 0\,\mathbf{e}_x + 0\,\mathbf{e}_y + (2y + 2y)\,\mathbf{e}_z$$

$$\neq \mathbf{0},$$

so $\mathbf{F}$ is conservative and $\mathbf{G}$ is not conservative. The gradient of any scalar field is conservative, so $\mathbf{H}$ is conservative.

# Acknowledgements

Grateful acknowledgement is made to the following sources:

*Figure 1:* Science Photo Library; *Figure 2:* Science Photo Library; *Figure 4.a:* Per-Magnus Heden/pixonnet.com/Alamy; *Figure 4.b:* Felix Stensson/Alamy; *Figure 5:* "This photograph has been provided by Railway Technical Research Institute in Japan"; *Figure 1.1:* Charles D Winters/Science Photo Library; *Figure 1.2:* Goronwy Tudor Jones, University Of Birmingham / Science Photo Library; *Figure 1.4:* Image courtesy of Carl Zeiss SMT Ltd, Cambridge, UK www.smt.zeiss.com/nts

*Figure 1.6:* Science Photo Library; *Figure 1.7:* Science Photo Library; *Figure 1.18:* Adam Hart-Davies/Science Photo Library *Figure 1.19:* Warren Faidley/OSF; *Figure 3.18:* Professor Gerald Gabrielse, CERN; *Figure 3.19:* Tyler, R. etal. (2003) 'Satellite Observations of magnetic fields due to ocean tidal flow'. Science Vol 299, 10 January 2003. Copyright ©2003. American Association for the Advancement of Science. *Figure 4.17:* St Bartholomews Hospital, London/Science Photo Library; *Figure 5.6:* Peter Menzel/Science Photo Library; *Figure 5.11:* Andrew Syred/Science Photo Library; *Figure 5.16:* Steve Gschmeissner/Science Photo Library; *Figure 6.1:* Adam Hart-Davis/Science Photo Library; *Figure 6.4:* Martin Bond/Science Photo Library; *Figure 6.5a:* David Parker/Science Photo Library; *Figure 6.5b:* Science Museum; *Figure 6.5c:* University of Durham/Simon Fraser/Science Photo Library; *Figure 7.1a:* Neil Borden/Science Photo Library; *Figure 7.1b:* NOAA/Science Photo Library; *Figure 7.1c:* Max-Planck-Institute for Radio Astronomy/Science Photo Library; *Figure 7.11:* Science Photo Library; *Figure 7.14:* Science Museum; *Figure 8.32:* Science Photo Library; *Figure 8.40:* Courtesy of Smithsonian Institution Libraries, Washington, DC.

# Index

Items that appear in the Glossary have page numbers in **bold type**. Ordinary index items have page numbers in Roman type.


addition of force, **20**, **71**
additivity of charge, **13**, 14, 37, 45
additivity of circulation, 110, **232**, 234
additivity of flux, 56, 90, **223**
alternator, **153**
amber, 12
Ampère's law, 87, 91–95, **94**, 188
  differential version, **111**
  examples of use, 97–100, 106–109, 111
  integral version, **95**
  limitations, 96, 166, 168–169, 172
Ampère, André-Marie 16, 94–95
Ampère-Maxwell law, 166, **170**
  and electromagnetic waves, 181
  differential version, 171
  examples of use, 171–176
  integral version, 171
ampere **62**, **69**
amplitude **182**
angular frequency, 81, **182**
areal charge density, **53**, 54
arrow maps, **204**
  for electric fields, 28, 117
  for magnetic fields, 74
aurora, 10, 79
axial coordinate, **210**
axial symmetry, **32**, 97, 100, 103, 148, 155, 173
azimuthal coordinate, **205**, **210**

bar magnet, 61, 88, 138
battery, 144, 146
binomial theorem, 131
Biot-Savart field law, **71**, 188
  examples of use, 72, 89, 95
Biot-Savart force law, **66**, 84
  examples of use 68–69
  limitations, 69–70
body-scanner, 77, 106
breakdown field, 33, **34**, 50

capacitance, **133**–134
  of capacitor, 133
  of isolated conducting sphere, 133, 135
  of isolated conductor, 133
  of parallel plate capacitor, 134

capacitor, **54**–55, **133**–134
  and Ampère-Maxwell law, 172–176
Cartesian components, 26, **195**
Cartesian coordinate system, **194**
Cartesian coordinates, 26, 58, **197**, 203, 249
Cartesian unit vectors, **194**, 198, 200, 208
chain rule of partial differentiation, **214**, 242
CHAMP satellite, 83
charge, see electric charge
charge density, **38**, 57, 59, 168
checking answers, 49, 58, 124, 130–131
circulation of a vector field, 119, **229**
  additivity of, 110, **232**
  of an electric field, 116–117, 141
  of a magnetic field, **92**–94, 174
Clerk Maxwell, James, see Maxwell
closed loop, **229**, 246
closed surface, **40**, **222**
coil, 16, 61, 65, 106, 108, 153–154, 176
components of a vector, **195**, 198
computer keyboards, 83
conduction electrons, **64**–65
conductors,
  electric field inside, 54, 131
  electrostatic potential of, 131
conservation of angular momentum, 85
conservation of charge, **13**, **167**
conservation of energy, 124–125
conservation of momentum, 85
conservative electric field, **115**, 116–126, 141, 144, 157
conservative vector field, **117**–118, **238**–247
contour lines **204**, 213
contour map, 213
contour surfaces, **204**
convex surface, **41**
cornea, 9
cosine rule, 127
coulomb, **19**, 62, **69**
Coulomb, Charles de, 8, 23
Coulomb's law, 17–25, **18**, 46–47, 116
  and instantaneous action at a distance, 25, 27
  evidence for, 23–24
  examples of use, 21–22
  limitations, 24–25, 32, 33
cross product, *see* vector product

curl of a vector field, **110**, 231–238, **233**
in Cartesian coordinates, 111, 119, 236
in cylindrical coordinates, 237, 246
in del notation, 249
in orthogonal coordinates, 237
in spherical coordinates, 118, 237
curl test, **119**, **247**
curl theorem, **110**, 155, 233–235, **234**, 245–247
current density, **62**–66, 94, 111, 167–168, 171, 188
current element, **65**–68, 71, 89–90, 188
current flow in a circuit 115, 140–141, 145, 158
cyclotron frequency, 82
cyclotron motion, 82
cyclotron period, 82
cylindrical coordinates, **210**–212
displacement vector, 212
scale factors, 212
unit vectors, 211
volume element, 212
cylindrical symmetry, **32**, 51–52
cylindrical unit vectors, **211**

defibrillator, 54
del operator, **248**–249
determinant, **200**, 236–237
differential version
of Ampère-Maxwell law, 171
of Ampère's law, **111**
of Faraday's law, **155**
of no-monopole law, **89**
of Gauss's law, **56**
differentiation
ordinary, 212
partial, 154, 168, 213
dipolar electric field, **29**, 127–129
dipolar magnetic field, **75**–78
dipole moment
electric, **128**–129
magnetic, **75**, 78
dipole potential, **128**
directed curve, **229**
displacement current density, 171, **187**
displacement vector, 18, **193**, **197**
divergence of a vector field, **56**, 169, **224**–228
in Cartesian coordinates, 226
in cylindrical coordinates, 58, 227
in del notation, 248
in orthogonal coordinates, 227
in spherical coordinates, 58, 227
divergence theorem, **56** 63, 89, 167, **224**, 247

divergence-free fields, **58**, 64, 89
dot product, *see* scalar product
drift speed, **64**–65
drift velocity, **64**
dummy variable, 124

Earth's electric field, **34**, 50, 134
Earth's magnetic field, 71, 78, 153
magnetic dipole moment, 78
magnetic poles, 78
Einstein, Albert, 9, 17, 82, 110, 163, 177
electric charge, **12**–14, 188
additive nature, 13, 14, 37, 45
as a scalar, 13, 46, 67
as the source of electric field, 25–26
conservation, 13, 167
invariance, 13, 32
negative, 12
of elementary particles, 14
positive, 12
quantization, 14, 26
electric current, 15–16, **62**–65
electric dipole, **29**, **127**–129
electric dipole moment, **128**–129
of elementary particles, 129
electric field, 25–35, **26**, 136
circulation of, 116–117, 141, 147, 152
conservative, **115**–121, 141
energy density, 135–136, 186
flux of, **39**, 47
inside conducting shell, 50, 120–121
inside conductor in equilibrium, 54–54, 120, 131
non-conservative, **115**, 117, 141, 149–151
of Earth, 34, 50, 134
of uniformly-charged cylinder, 52–53
of uniformly-charged plane, 53–54
of uniformly-charged sphere, 48–49
of uniformly-moving charge, 32, 117
safety guidelines, 33
typical values, 33
electric field lines, **28**–30, 126
electric field strength, **26**
electric flux, **39**, 47
electric force, **16**–17, 27
electric guitar, 139, 147, 153
electric shock, 145–146
electromagnet, 70
electromagnetic force, 12–13
velocity dependence, 14–16
electromagnetic induction, **138**–163

electromagnetic radiation, 124, **165**
electromagnetic spectrum, 184–185
electromagnetic wave, 8, **179**–187
electromotance, **143**
electromotive force, **142**
electron microscope, 15, 79, 132
electron-positron pair, 13, 35
electronic ignition system, 83, 153
electrostatic field, 27, 116–121, 125–126, 127–129
electrostatic field line, 28–30, 120, 126, 128
electrostatic force, **17**–25, 126
electrostatic potential, **122**–134
  of a conducting sphere, 132
  of a conductor, 131
  of an electric dipole, 127–129
electrostatic potential energy, 123, 125–126
  of conducting sphere, 135
electrostatic potential field, **122**
electrostatics, 17, 157
elementary particles, 14, 75, 129
emf, **142**, 160
  induced, **143**, 146, **159**
  of a battery, 144
energy density,
  in an electromagnetic wave, 186
  of an electric field, **135**, 186
  of a magnetic field, 186
energy flux, **186**–187
equation of continuity, 166–**168**, 178
equipotential surface, **126**, 128
ether, 163, 178, 188

farad, **133**
Faraday cage, **121**
Faraday's law, **146**, 156–157
  differential version, 154–156, **155**
  generalized, **162**
  integral version, 146–**154**
  sign, 151–152
Faraday, Michael, 7–8, 25, 138, 146, 179
field, 8, **26**, **202**–204
field line, **204**
  electric, 28
  magnetic 73
field line pattern, **204**
  electric, 28–30
  magnetic 73–75
flux freezing, 163
flux of a vector field, **221**–222
  additivity, 56, **223**
  of current density, 63
  of electric field, 39, 47
  of magnetic field, **88**–90, 146–147, 152
frequency, 33, 82, **182**
fundamental forces, 8
fundamental theorem of calculus, 248

Gauss's law, **41**–47
  differential version, **56**–57
  examples of use, 47–55, 57–59, 120–121
  integral version, 41–**47**
Gauss's theorem, 225
Gauss, Carl Friedrich, 41, 57, 225
Gaussian surface, **48**
  cylindrical, 52-53
  pillbox, 53–55
  spherical, 48–50
generalized Faraday law, **162**
Gilbert, William, 61
gradient of a scalar field, 125–126, 131, **241**–244
  in Cartesian coordinates, 241
  in cylindrical coordinates, 244
  in del notation, 248
  in orthogonal coordinates, 244
  in spherical coordinates, 244
gradient theorem, **244**, 247
gravimagnetic force, 9
gravitational force, 12–13
Gulf stream, 83

Hall effect, **82**–84
Heaviside, Oliver, 80
Hertz, Heinrich, 183–184
hydroelectric power station, 139

induced current, 140, 150, 152
induced emf, **143**, 146, 159
induction
  in a moving circuit, 157–163
  in a stationary circuit, 146–154
inertial frame of reference, **163**, **178**
instantaneous action at a distance, 25, 27, 57, 69, 85, 177
integral version
  of Ampère-Maxwell law, 171
  of Ampère's law, **95**
  of Faraday's law **154**
  of no-monopole law, **89**
  of Gauss's law, **47**
integration,

ordinary, 216–217
line, 228–231, **229**
surface, 220–223, **222**
volume, **217**–220
internal resistance, 146
inverse square law, 18, 25, 67
irrotational vector field, 118–119, 157, **245**–247

Kelvin, Lord, 41, 91, 234
kinetic energy, 123, 125, 202

Laplacian operator, **250**
latitude, 206
Lenz's law, 151–**152**
lightning, 34, 121
line integral, 228–231, **229**
linearly polarized wave, **180**
liquid crystal, 129
longitude, 206
Lorentz force law, **80**–81, 162
examples of use, 81–84
Lorentz, Henrick, 80, 188

magnetar, **78**–79
magnetic compass, 61
magnetic dipole, **75**–76
magnetic dipole moment, **75**, 78
magnetic field, **70**, **79**
circulation of, **92**–94
due to tidal flow, 83
energy density, 186
flux of, **88**–89, 146–147, 152
of a current loop, 72–76
of Earth, 78
of a long solenoid, 106–108
of a long straight wire, 74
of a toroidal solenoid, 108–109
of cylinders and tubes, 97–100
safety guidelines, 77
typical values, 77
magnetic field lines, **73**–75
magnetic field strength, **79**
magnetic flux, **88**
through a coil, 147
magnetic force, 16, 65–68, 71, 79, 158
magnetic force law, **71**, **79**
magnetic monopole, **88**, 178
magnetic pole, 78, 88
magnetic storm, **153**
magnetically-levitated train, 10
magnetically silent source, **106**, 171–172
magnetization, 96
magnetoencephalography, **77**
magnetostatic field, 114, 247
magnetostatic force, **65**–70
magnetostatics, 70, 96, 168
magnitude,
of a scalar, **191**
of a vector, **191**, 198
mass spectrometer, 79
mass spectroscopy, 92
Maxwell term, **170**–175, 187–188
Maxwell's equations, 8, 46, 91, 156, 165–166, 177–178
Maxwell, James Clerk, 7, 8, 46, 94–95, 146, 157, 166, 183, 188
MEG *see* magnetoencephalography,
metal detector, 139, **154**
microphone, 153
microwave oven, 129
mixed partial derivatives, **215**
mobile phone, 33–34
monochromatic wave, **182**
moving circuit, 157–163
myelin sheath, **134**

nerve cell, 9, 54, 134
nerve impulse, 9
Newton's first law, 163
Newton's second law, 14, 202
Newton's third law, 20, 68, 85–86
no-monopole law, **89**
differential version, 89–90
examples of use, 91
integral version, 87–90
status, 88, 91
non-conservative field, 141
electric, **115**, 117, 140–142, 149, 156
magnetic, 238, 246–247
non-conservative force, 144
normal, 199
nuclear fusion, 108
number density, **64**–65, 84

Oersted, Hans, 61
ohm, **145**
Ohm's law, **145**–146, 150, 159
open surface, **222**
operator, **248**
oriented area, **39**, **220**
orthogonal, **198**

orthogonal coordinate system, **227**
outer core, **78**

parallel plate capacitor, **54**–55, 133–134, 172–176
partial derivative, **213**
  first, 213–214
  higher, 214–215
  inside an integral, 154, 168
  mixed, **215**
partial differential equation, 177
partial differentiation, 212–215
particle, 14
Penning trap, **82**
perimeter, 94, 146, 171, 232
period, 82, **182**
permeability of free space, **67**
permittivity of free space, **19**
photon, 23, 47
photonic circuit, 10
planar symmetry, 53–5
plane wave, **180**
point charge, **14**
polar coordinate, **205**
polarization, 25
position vector, **193**, **197**
potential, *see* electrostatic potential
potential difference, **122**–123, 133–134, **141**
potential drop, **141**
power conversion, 153
primary coil, 153
principle of superposition, **27**, 45, **71**, 116, **127**
Pythagoras's theorem, 195

quantum electrodynamic critical field, **35**
quantum electrodynamics, 8, 35
quantum field theory, 23
quantum mechanics, 144

radial coordinate, **205**, **210**
radio wave, 184
reference frame,
  inertial, 163, 178
  rotating, 178
reflection rules, 101–106, **103**
residual current device, 153
resistance, **145**
right-hand grip rule, **74**, **75**, 94, 146, 175, **205**, **232**
right-hand rule, 67, 76, 102, **194**, 199
right-handed coordinate system, **194**
rotating frame of reference, 178

safety guidelines, 33, 77
scalar field, 56, 118, 122, **203**–204
scalar potential, **240**–244
scalar product, **197**–199
scalar quantity, 13, **191**
scale factors, **209**
  in Cartesian coordinates, 227
  in cylindrical coordinates, 212
  in spherical coordinates, 209
scaling, **192**, 196
screening, **24**
screening length, 24
secondary coil, 153
seismometer, 153
shielding in a cavity, 50, 120–121
simply-connected region, 157, **246**
solar storm, 153
solar wind, 78
solenoid, **106**–109, 148–151, 155–156
source terms, 178, 188
special relativity, 110, 163, 188
spectral lines, 129
speed of electromagnetic waves, 183
speed of light, 110, 183
spherical coordinates, **205**–209
  displacement vector, 208
  scale factors, 209
  unit vectors, 206
  volume element, 209
spherical symmetry, **30**–31, 48–50
spherical unit vectors, **206**
spin, **14**, **75**
Stokes's theorem, **234**
Stokes, George, 234
strong nuclear force, 12
sunspots, **78**
surface charge density, **54**
surface integral, 220–223, **222**
symmetry,
  axial, **32**, 97, 100, 103, 148, 155, 173
  cylindrical, **32**, 51–52
  spherical, **30**–31, 48–50
  translational, 32, 97, 103, 148, 155
symmetry principle, **30**, **101**

tesla, **71**
test charge, **26**, 114, 123
time-reversal symmetry, **32**, 76–77, 178
toroidal solenoid, **108**–109, 176
total current density, 188

transcranial magnetic stimulation, 139, **154**
transformer, 139, **153**
transistor, 145
translational symmetry, 32, 97, 148, 155
transverse wave, **180**, 184
triangle rule, **193**

unit normal, **220**, 222
unit vector, 19, **193**, 195
unit vectors,
  Cartesian, 198, 200
  cylindrical, 211
  spherical, 206

vector,
  addition, 193, 196
  components, 198
  differentiation, 201
  division, 201
  multiplication by a scalar, 196
  subtraction, 193, 196
vector calculus identity, **249**
vector field, **203**
  conservative, 245–246
  irrotational, 245–246
  non-conservative,
vector identity, **202**
vector product, 67, 103, 197, **199**, 200
vector quantity, **191**
vector sum, **193**
virtual pair, 35
virtual particle, 35
volt, **123**, 142
voltage drop, 141, **142**, 151, **159**
voltmeter, 150
volume element, 217
  in cylindrical coordinates, 212
  in spherical coordinates, 209
volume integral, **217**

wave,
  monochromatic, 182
  plane, 180
  transverse, 180, 184
wavelength, **182**
wavenumber, **182**
weak nuclear force, 12
work, 114, 122, 125, 126, 140, 228, 238
work-energy theorem, **125**

zero of potential, 240
zero vector, **192**, **196**

## Theorems

Gradient theorem: $$\int_{\mathbf{r}_1}^{\mathbf{r}_2} \operatorname{grad} f \cdot \mathrm{d}\mathbf{l} = f(\mathbf{r}_2) - f(\mathbf{r}_1)$$

Divergence theorem: $$\int_V \operatorname{div} \mathbf{F} \, \mathrm{d}V = \int_S \mathbf{F} \cdot \mathrm{d}\mathbf{S}$$

Curl theorem: $$\int_S \operatorname{curl} \mathbf{F} \cdot \mathrm{d}\mathbf{S} = \oint_C \mathbf{F} \cdot \mathrm{d}\mathbf{l}$$

## Vector and vector calculus identities

$$\mathbf{a} \times (\mathbf{b} \times \mathbf{c}) = (\mathbf{a} \cdot \mathbf{c})\mathbf{b} - (\mathbf{a} \cdot \mathbf{b})\mathbf{c}$$

$$\mathbf{a} \cdot (\mathbf{b} \times \mathbf{c}) = (\mathbf{a} \times \mathbf{b}) \cdot \mathbf{c}$$

$$\operatorname{div}(f\mathbf{F}) = f \operatorname{div} \mathbf{F} + \mathbf{F} \cdot \operatorname{grad} f$$

$$\operatorname{div}(\operatorname{grad} f) = \nabla^2 f$$

$$\operatorname{div}(\operatorname{curl} \mathbf{F}) = 0$$

$$\operatorname{curl}(\operatorname{grad} f) = \mathbf{0}$$

$$\operatorname{curl}(\operatorname{curl} \mathbf{F}) = \operatorname{grad}(\operatorname{div} \mathbf{F}) - \nabla^2 \mathbf{F}$$

$$\operatorname{div}(\mathbf{F} \times \mathbf{G}) = (\operatorname{curl} \mathbf{F}) \cdot \mathbf{G} - \mathbf{F} \cdot (\operatorname{curl} \mathbf{G})$$

## Various integrals

$$\int x \, \mathrm{e}^{-ax} \, \mathrm{d}x = -\frac{1}{a^2}(1 + ax) \, \mathrm{e}^{-ax}$$

$$\int x^2 \, \mathrm{e}^{-ax} \, \mathrm{d}x = -\frac{1}{a^3}(2 + 2ax + a^2x^2) \, \mathrm{e}^{-ax}$$

$$\int \frac{1}{(a^2 + x^2)^{1/2}} \, \mathrm{d}x = \ln((a^2 + x^2)^{1/2} + x)$$

$$\int \frac{1}{(a^2 + x^2)^{3/2}} \, \mathrm{d}x = \frac{x}{a^2\sqrt{a^2 + x^2}}$$

$$\int_{-\infty}^{\infty} \frac{1}{(1 + x^2)^{3/2}} \, \mathrm{d}x = 2$$

$$\int_0^{2\pi} \sin^2\theta \, \mathrm{d}\theta = \int_0^{2\pi} \cos^2\theta \, \mathrm{d}\theta = \pi$$

$$\langle \sin^2\theta \rangle \equiv \frac{1}{2\pi} \int_0^{2\pi} \sin^2\theta \, \mathrm{d}\theta = \frac{1}{2}$$

$$\langle \cos^2\theta \rangle \equiv \frac{1}{2\pi} \int_0^{2\pi} \cos^2\theta \, \mathrm{d}\theta = \frac{1}{2}$$

$$\int \cos^n\theta \sin\theta \, \mathrm{d}\theta = -\frac{\cos^{n+1}(\theta)}{n+1}$$

$$\int_0^{2\pi} \cos\theta \sin\theta \, \mathrm{d}\theta = 0$$